This is a "keeper"
because they've getting
harder to find AND
because I found this
one and I can't spot
them like you can!
I love you dearly,
Nat
Christmas 2010

THE KEYS OF THE KINGDOM

NOVELS BY

A. J. CRONIN

HATTER'S CASTLE
THREE LOVES
GRAND CANARY
THE STARS LOOK DOWN
THE CITADEL
THE KEYS OF THE KINGDOM

THE
KEYS OF THE
KINGDOM

By

A. J. CRONIN

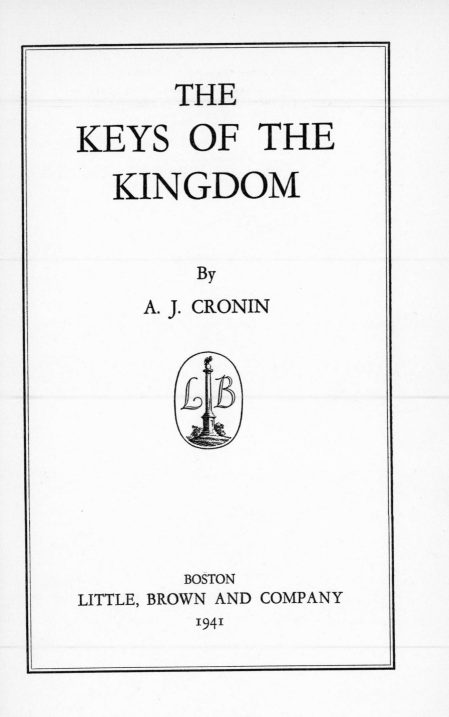

BOSTON
LITTLE, BROWN AND COMPANY
1941

Published July 1941
Reprinted July 1941 (five times)

TO MY FRIEND F. M.,
FOR TWENTY YEARS A MISSIONARY IN CHINA

"And I will give to thee the keys of the kingdom of heaven."
— CHRIST TO PETER

CONTENTS

I

BEGINNING OF THE END

LATE one afternoon in September 1938 old Father Francis Chisholm limped up the steep path from the church of St. Columba to his house upon the hill. He preferred this way, despite his infirmities, to the less arduous ascent of Mercat Wynd; and, having reached the narrow door of his walled-in garden, he paused with a kind of naïve triumph — recovering his breath, contemplating the view he had always loved.

Beneath him was the River Tweed, a great wide sweep of placid silver, tinted by the low saffron smudge of autumn sunset. Down the slope of the northern Scottish bank tumbled the town of Tweed-side, its tiled roofs a crazy quilt of pink and yellow, masking the maze of cobbled streets. High stone ramparts still ringed this Border burgh, with captured Crimean cannon making perches for the gulls as they pecked at partan crabs. At the river's mouth a wraith lay upon the sand bar, misting the lines of drying nets, the masts of smacks inside the harbour pointing upwards, brittle and motionless. Inland, dusk was already creeping upon the still bronze woods of Derham, towards which, as he gazed, a lonely heron made laboured flight. The air was thin and clear, stringent with wood smoke and the tang of fallen apples, sharp with the hint of early frost.

With a contented sigh, Father Chisholm turned into his garden: a patch beside his pleasance upon the Hill of Brilliant Green Jade, but a pretty one, and, like all Scots gardens, productive, with a few fine fruit trees splayed on the mellow wall. The jargonelle espalier in the south corner was at its best. Since there was no sign of the tyrant Dougal, with a cautious glance towards the kitchen window he stole the finest pear from his own tree, slid it under his soutane.

His yellow, wrinkled cheek was ripe with triumph as he hobbled — dot and carry — down the gravelled drive, leaning on his one indulgence, the new umbrella of Chisholm tartan which replaced his battered favourite of Pai-tan. And there, standing at the front porch, was the car.

His face puckered slowly. Though his memory was bad and his fits of absent-mindedness a perpetual embarrassment, he now recollected the vexation of the Bishop's letter, proposing, or rather announcing, this visit of his secretary Monsignor Sleeth. He hastened forward to welcome his guest.

Monsignor Sleeth was in the parlour, standing, dark, thin, distinguished, and not quite at ease, with his back to the empty fireplace — his youthful impatience heightened, his clerical dignity repelled, by the mean surroundings in which he found himself. He had looked for a note of individuality: some piece of porcelain perhaps, or lacquer, a souvenir from the East. But the apartment was bare and nondescript, with poor linoleum, horsehair chairs and a chipped mantelpiece on which, out of the corner of a disapproving eye, he had already noted a spinning top beside an uncounted litter of collection pennies. Yet he was resolved to be pleasant. Smoothing his frown, he stifled Father Chisholm's apology with a gracious gesture.

"Your housekeeper has already shown me my room. I trust it will not disturb you to have me here for a few days. What a superb afternoon it has been. The colourings! — as I drove up from Tynecastle I almost fancied myself in dear San Morales." He gazed away, through the darkening window, with a studied air.

The old man nearly smiled at the imprint of Father Tarrant and the Seminary — Sleeth's elegance, that bladelike look, even the hint of hardness in the nostril, made him a perfect replica.

"I hope you'll be comfortable," he murmured. "We'll have our bite presently. I'm sorry I can't offer you dinner. Somehow we've just fallen to the habit of a Scots high tea!"

Sleeth, head half-averted, nodded noncommittally. Indeed, at that moment, Miss Moffat entered and, having drawn the drab chenille curtains, stealthily began to set the table. He could not but reflect, ironically, how the neutral creature, darting him one frightened glance, matched the room. Though it caused him a passing asperity to observe her lay places for three, her presence enabled him to lead the conversation safely into generalities.

As the two priests sat down at table he was eulogizing the special marble which the Bishop had brought from Carrara for the transept of the new Tynecastle pro-cathedral. Helping himself with good appetite from the ashet of ham, eggs and kidneys before him, he accepted a cup of tea poured from the Britannia metal teapot. Then, busy buttering brown toast, he heard his host remark mildly: —

"You won't mind if Andrew sups his porridge with us. Andrew — this is Monsignor Sleeth!"

Sleeth raised his head abruptly. A boy about nine years of age had come silently into the room and now, after an instant's indecision, when he stood tugging at his blue jersey, his long pale face intense with nervousness, slipped into his place, reaching mechanically for the milk jug. As he bent over his plate a lock of dank brown hair — tribute to Miss Moffat's sponge — fell over his ugly bony forehead. His eyes, of a remarkable blue, held a childish prescience of crisis — they were so uneasy he dared not lift them up.

The Bishop's secretary relaxed his attitude, slowly resumed his meal. After all, the moment was not opportune. Yet from time to time his stare travelled covertly towards the boy.

"So you are Andrew!" Decency demanded speech, even a hint of benignness. "And you go to school here?"

"Yes . . ."

"Come then! Let us see how much you know." Amiably enough, he propounded a few simple questions. The boy, flushed and inarticulate, too confused to think, betrayed humiliating ignorance.

Monsignor Sleeth's eyebrows lifted. "Dreadful," he thought. "Quite a gutter brat!"

He helped himself to another kidney — then suddenly became aware that while he trifled with the rich meats of the table the other two kept soberly to porridge. He flushed: this show of asceticism on the old man's part was insufferable affectation.

Perhaps Father Chisholm had a wry perception of that thought. He shook his head: "I went without good Scots oatmeal so many years I never miss it now I have the chance."

Sleeth received the remark in silence. Presently, with a hurried glance, out of his downcast muteness, Andrew begged permission to depart. Rising to say his grace, he knocked a spoon spinning with his elbow. His stiff boots made an uncouth scuffling towards the door.

Another pause. Then, having concluded his meal, Monsignor Sleeth rose easily and repossessed, without apparent purpose, the fleshless hearth-rug. With feet apart and hands clasped behind his back he considered, without seeming to do so, his aged colleague, who, still seated, had the curious air of waiting. Dear God, thought Sleeth, what a pitiable presentation of the priesthood — this shabby old man, with the stained soutane, soiled collar and sallow, desiccated skin! On one cheek was an ugly weal, a kind of cicatrix, which everted the lower eyelid, seemed to tug the head down and sideways. The impression was that of a permanent wry neck, counterpoising the lame and shortened leg. His eyes, usually lowered, took thus — on the rare occasions that he raised them — a penetrating obliqueness which was strangely disconcerting.

Sleeth cleared his throat. He judged it time for him to speak and, forcing a note of cordiality, he inquired: "How long have you been here, Father Chisholm?"

"Twelve months."

"Ah, yes. It was a kindly gesture of His Grace to send you — on your return — to your native parish."

"And his!"

Sleeth inclined his head suavely. "I was aware that His Grace shared with you the distinction of having been born here. Let me see . . . what age are you, Father? Nearly seventy is it not?"

Father Chisholm nodded, adding with gentle senile pride: "I am no older than Anselm Mealey."

Sleeth's frown at the familiarity melted into a half-pitying smile. "No doubt — but life has treated you rather differently. To be brief, —" he gathered himself up, firm, but not unkind, — "the Bishop and I both have the feeling that your long and faithful years should now be recompensed; that you should, in short, retire!"

There was a moment of strange quiet.

"But I have no wish to retire."

"It is a painful duty for me to come here" — Sleeth kept his gaze discreetly on the ceiling — "to investigate . . . and report to His Grace. But there are certain things which cannot be overlooked."

"What things?"

Sleeth moved irritably. "Six — ten — a dozen things! It isn't my place to enumerate your — your Oriental eccentricities!"

"I'm sorry." A slow spark kindled in the old man's eyes. "You must remember that I spent thirty-five years in China."

"Your parish affairs are in a hopeless muddle."

"Am I in debt?"

"How are we to know? No returns on your quarterly collections for six months." Sleeth's voice rose, he spoke a little faster. "Everything so . . . so unbusinesslike. . . . For instance when Bland's traveller presented his bill last month — three pounds for candles, and so forth — you paid him entirely in coppers!"

"That's how it comes to me." Father Chisholm viewed his visitor thoughtfully, as though he looked straight through him. "I've always been stupid about money. I've never had any, you see. . . . But after all . . . Do you think money so dreadfully important?"

To his annoyance Monsignor Sleeth found himself reddening. "It makes talk, Father." He rushed on. "And there is other talk. Some of your sermons . . . the advice you give . . . certain points of doctrine." He consulted a Morocco-covered notebook already in his palm. "They seem dangerously peculiar."

"Impossible!"

"On Whitsunday you told your congregation, 'Don't think heaven is in the sky . . . it's in the hollow of your hand . . . it's everywhere and anywhere.'" Sleeth frowned censoriously as he turned the pages. "And again . . . here is an incredible remark you made during Holy Week. 'Atheists may not all go to hell. I knew one who didn't. Hell is only for those who spit in the face of God!' And, good gracious, this atrocity: 'Christ was a perfect man, but Confucius had a better sense of humour!'" Another page was turned indignantly. "And this incredible incident . . . when one of your best parishioners, Mrs. Glendenning, who cannot of course help her extreme stoutness, came to you for spiritual guidance you looked at her and replied, 'Eat less. The gates of Paradise are narrow.' But why should I continue?" Decisively, Monsignor Sleeth closed the gilt-edged book. "To say the least, you seem to have lost your command of souls."

"But . . ." Calmly: "I don't want to command anyone's soul."

Sleeth's colour heightened disagreeably. He did not see himself in theological discussion with this shambling dotard.

"There remains the matter of this boy whom you have so misguidedly adopted."

"Who is to look after him — if I don't?"

"Our own Sisters at Ralstone. It is the finest orphanage in the diocese."

Again Father Chisholm raised his disconcerting eyes. "Would you have wished to spend your own childhood at that orphanage?"

"Need we be personal, Father? I've told you . . . even conceding the circumstances . . . the situation is highly irregular and must be ended. Besides . . ." He threw out his hands. "If you are going away — we must find some place for him."

"You seem determined to be rid of us. Am I to be entrusted to the Sisters too?"

"Of course not. You can go to the Aged Priests' Home at Clinton. It is a perfect haven of rest."

The old man actually laughed — a dry short laugh. "I'll have enough perfect rest when I'm dead. While I'm alive I don't want to be mixed up with a lot of aged priests. You may think it strange — but I never have been able to stand the clergy in bulk."

Sleeth's smile was pained and flustered. "I think nothing strange from you, Father. Forgive me, but to say the least of it . . . your reputation, even before you went to China . . . your whole life has been peculiar!"

There was a pause. Father Chisholm said in a quiet voice: "I shall render an account of my life to God."

The younger man dropped his eyelids with an unhappy sense of indiscretion. He had gone too far. Though his nature was cold he strove always to be just, even considerate. He had the grace to look uncomfortable. "Naturally I don't presume to be your judge — or your inquisitor. Nothing is decided yet. That is why I am here. We must see what the next few days bring forth." He stepped towards the door. "I am going to the church now. Please don't trouble. I know my way." His mouth creased into an unwilling smile. He went out.

Father Chisholm remained seated, motionless, at the table, his hand shading his eyes, as though thinking deeply. He felt crushed by this threat which had gathered, so suddenly, above the quiet of his hard-won retreat. His sense of resignation, long overtaxed, refused acceptance of it. All at once he felt empty and used-up, unwanted by God or man. A burning desolation filled his breast. Such a little thing; and yet so much. He wanted to cry out: My God, my God, why hast thou forsaken me? He rose heavily, and went upstairs.

In his attic above the spare room the boy Andrew was already in bed and asleep. He lay upon his side, one skinny arm crooked before him on the pillow, defensively. Watching him, Father Chisholm took the pear from his pocket and placed it on the clothes folded upon the cane-bottomed chair beside the bed. There seemed nothing more for him to do.

A faint breeze swayed the muslin curtains. He moved to the window and parted them. Stars were quivering in the frosty sky. Under these stars the span of his years reached out in all its ineptitude, built of his puny strivings, without form or nobility. It seemed such a short time since he had been a boy himself, running and laughing in this same town of Tweedside. His thoughts flew back. If there were any pattern in his life at all the first fateful stroke was surely drawn on that April Saturday sixty years ago when, out of untroubled happiness, so deep it passed unrecognized . . .

II

STRANGE VOCATION

THAT spring morning, at early breakfast in the snug dark kitchen, with the fire warm to his stockinged feet and the smell of kindling wood and hot oat-cakes making him hungry, he was happy, despite the rain, because it was Saturday and the tide was right for salmon.

His mother finished her brisk stirring with the wooden spurtle, and placed the blue-ringed bowl of pease brose on the scrubbed table between his father and himself. He reached for his horn spoon, dipped in the bowl, then in the cup of buttermilk before him. He rolled his tongue over the smooth golden brose, made perfectly, without lumps or gritty unmixed meal.

His father, in worn blue jersey and darned fishing stockings, sat opposite, his big frame bowed, supping in silence, with quiet slow movements of his red hands. His mother shook the last batch of oat-cakes from the griddle, set them on their ends against the bowl, and sat down to her cup of tea. The yellow butter melted on the broken oat-cake which she took. There was silence and comradeship in the little kitchen, with the flames leaping across the bright fender and the pipe-clayed hearth. He was nine years of age and he was going to the bothy with his father.

There, he was known — he was Alex Chisholm's laddie, accepted by the men in their woollen jerseys and leather hip-boots with a quiet nod or, better still, a friendly silence. He had a dark secret glow of pride as he went out with them, the big flat cobble sweeping wide round the butt, the rowlocks creaking, the seine skilfully payed out by his father in the stern. Back on the butt, their tackets rasping the wet stones, the men huddled themselves low against the wind, some squatting with a yellowed sailcloth across their shoulders, others sucking warmth from a blackened inch-long clay. He stood with his father, apart. Alex Chisholm was the head man, the watcher of Tweed Fisheries Station No. 3. Together, not speaking, cut by the wind, they stood watching the far circle of corks dancing in the choppy back-lash where the river met the sea. Often the glare of sun upon the ripples made his head swim. But he would not, he could not blink. Missing even a single second might mean the missing of a dozen fish — so hard to come by, these days, that in distant Billingsgate they brought the Fisheries Company a good half-crown a pound. His father's tall figure, the head sunk a little on the shoulders, the profile keen beneath the old peaked cap, a fine blood whipped into the high cheekbones, had the same still unswerving tensity. At times, mingled exquisitely in his consciousness with the smell of wrack, the distant strike of the Burgess Clock, the cawing of the Derham rooks, the sense of this unspeaking comradeship drew moisture to the boy's already smarting eyes.

Suddenly his father shouted. Try as he might Francis could never win first sight of the dipping cork: not that tidal bobbing which sometimes caused him foolishly to start, but the slow downward tug which to long experience denoted the thrusting of a fish. At the quick high shout there was an instant clatter as the crew jumped to the windlass which hauled the net. Usage never staled that moment: though the men drew a poundage bonus on their catch, the thought of money did not stir them; this deep excitement sprang from far primeval roots. In came the net, slowly, dripping, flaked with kelp, the guide ropes squeaking on the wooden drum. A final heave, then, in the purse of the billowing seine, a molten flash, powerful, exquisite — salmon.

One memorable Saturday they had taken forty at a cast. The great shining things arched and fought, bursting through the net, slithering back to the river from the slippery butt. Francis flung himself forward with the others, desperately clutching at the precious escaping fish. They had picked him up, sequined with scales and soaked to the bone, a perfect monster locked in his embrace. Going home that evening, his hand inside his father's, their footfalls echoing in the smoky twilight, they had stopped, without comment, at Burley's in the High Street, to buy a pennyworth of cockles, the peppermint ones that were his special choice.

Their fellowship went further still. On Sundays, after mass, they took their rods and slipped secretly — lest they shock finer sensibilities — through the back ways of the Sabbath-stricken town, out into the verdant valley of the Whitadder. In his tin, packed with sawdust, were luscious maggots, picked the night before from Mealey's boneyard. Thereafter the day was heady with the sound of the stream, the scent of meadowsweet, — his father showing him the likely eddies, — the crimson-speckled trout wriggling on bleached shingle, — his father bent over a twig fire, — the crisp sweet goodness of the frizzled fish . . .

At other seasons they would go to gather blueberries, wood strawberries, or the wild yellow rasps which made good jam. It was a gala day when his mother accompanied them. His father knew all the best places and would take them deep into devious woods, to untouched cane-brakes of the juicy fruit.

When snow came and the ground was clamped by winter, they stalked between the frozen trees of Derham "policies," his breath a rime before him, his skin pricking for the keeper's whistle. He could hear his own heart beating as they cleared their snares, under the windows, almost, of the great house itself — then home, home with the heavy gamebag, his eyes smiling, his marrow melting to the thought of rabbit pie. His mother was a grand cook, a woman who earned — with her thrift, her knack of management and homely skill — the grudging panegyric of a Scots community: "Elizabeth Chisholm is a well-doing woman!"

Now, as he finished his brose, he became conscious that she was speaking, with a look across the breakfast table towards his father.

"You'll mind to be home early tonight, Alex, for the Burgess."

There was a pause. He could see that his father, preoccupied, — perhaps by the flooded river and the indifferent salmon season, — was caught unawares, recalled to the annual formality of the Burgess Concert which they must sustain that evening.

"You're set on going, woman?" With a faint smile.

She flushed slightly; Francis wondered why she should seem so queer. "It's one of the few things I look forward to in the year. After all, you are a Burgess of the town. It's . . . it's right for you to take your seat on the platform with your family and your friends."

His smile deepened, setting lines of kindness about his eyes — it was a smile Francis would have died to win. "Then it looks like we maun gang, Lisbeth." He had always disliked "the Burgess," as he disliked teacups, stiff collars, and his squeaky Sunday boots. But he did not dislike this woman who wanted him to go.

"I'm relying on you, Alex. You see," her voice, striving to be casual, sounded an odd note of relief, "I have asked Polly and Nora up from Tynecastle — unfortunately it seems Ned cannot get away." She paused. "You'll have to send someone else to Ettal with the tallies."

He straightened with a quick look which seemed to see through her, right to the bottom of her tender subterfuge. At first, in his delight, Francis noticed nothing. His father's sister, now dead, had married Ned Bannon, proprietor of the Union Tavern in Tynecastle, a bustling city some sixty miles due South. Polly, Ned's sister, and Nora, his ten-year-old orphan niece, were not exactly close relations. Yet their visits could always be counted occasions of joy.

Suddenly he heard his father say in a quiet voice: "I'll have to go to Ettal all the same."

A sharp and throbbing silence. Francis saw that his mother had turned white.

"It isn't as if you had to. . . . Sam Mirlees, any of the men, would be glad to row up for you."

He did not answer, still gazing at her quietly, touched on his pride, his proud exclusiveness of race. Her agitation increased. She dropped all pretence of concealment, bent forward, placed nervous fingers upon his sleeve.

"To please me, Alex. You know what happened last time. Things are bad again there — awful bad, I hear."

He put his big hand over hers, warmly, reassuringly.

"You wouldn't have me run away, would you, woman?" He smiled and rose abruptly. "I'll go early and be back early . . . in plenty time for you, our daft friends, and your precious concert to the bargain."

Defeated, that strained look fixed upon her face, she watched him pull on his hip-boots. Francis, chilled and downcast, had a dreadful premonition of what must come. And indeed, when his father straightened it was towards him he turned, mildly, and with rare compunction.

"Come to think of it, boy, you'd better bide home today. Your mother could do with you about the house. There'll be plenty to see to before our visitors arrive."

Blind with disappointment, Francis made no protest. He felt his mother's arm tensely, detainingly about his shoulders.

His father stood a moment at the door, with that deep contained affection in his eyes, then he silently went out.

Though the rain ceased at noon the hours dragged dismally for Francis. While pretending not to see his mother's worried frown, he was racked by the full awareness of their situation. Here in this quiet burgh they were known for what they were — unmolested, even warily esteemed. But in Ettal, the market town four miles away where, at the Fisheries Head Office, his father, every month, was obliged to check the record of the catches, a different attitude prevailed. A hundred years before the Ettal moors had blossomed with the blood of Covenanters; and now the pendulum of oppression had relentlessly swung back. Under the leadership of the new Provost a furious religious persecution had recently arisen. Conventicles were formed, mass gatherings held in the Square, popular feelings whipped to frenzy. When the violence of the mob broke loose, the few Catholics in the town were hounded from their homes, while all others in the district received solemn warning not to show themselves upon the Ettal streets. His father's calm disregard of this threat had singled him for special execration. Last month there had been a fight in which the sturdy salmon-watcher had given good account of himself. Now, despite renewed menaces, and the careful plan to stay him, he was going again. . . . Francis flinched at his own thoughts and his small fists clenched violently. Why could not people let each other be? His father and his mother had not the same belief; yet they lived together, respecting each other, in perfect peace. His father was a good man, the best in the world . . . why should they want to do him harm? Like a blade thrust into the warmth of his life came a dread, a shrinking from that word "religion," a chill bewilderment that men could hate each other for worshipping the same God with different words.

Returning from the station at four o'clock, sombrely leaping the puddles to which Nora, his half-cousin, gaily dared him, — his mother walking with Aunt Polly, who came, dressed up and sedate, behind, — he felt the day oppressive with disaster. Nora's friskiness, the neatness of her new brown braided dress, her manifest delight in seeing him, proved but a wan diversion.

Stoically, he approached his home, the low neat greystone cottage, fronting the Cannelgate, behind a trim little green where in summer his father grew asters and begonias. There was evidence of his mother's passionate cleanliness in the shining brass knocker and the spotless doorstep. Behind the immaculately curtained windows three potted geraniums made a scarlet splash.

By this time, Nora was flushed, out of breath, her blue eyes sparkling with fun, in one of her moods of daring, impish gaiety. As they went round the side of the house to the back garden where, through his mother's arrangement, they were to play with Anselm Mealey until teatime, she bent close to Francis' ear so that her hair fell across her thin laughing face, and whispered in his ear. The puddles they had barely missed, the sappy moisture of the earth, prompted her ingenuity.

At first Francis would not listen — strangely, for Nora's presence stirred him usually to a shy swift eagerness. Standing small and reticent, he viewed her doubtfully.

"I know he will," she urged. "He always wants to play at being holy. Come on, Francis. Let's do it. Let's!"

A slow smile barely touched his sombre lips. Half-unwilling, he fetched a spade, a watering can, an old news sheet from the little toolshed at the garden end. Led by Nora, he dug a two-foot hole between the laurel bushes, watered it, then spread the paper over it. Nora artistically sprinkled the sheet with a coating of dry soil. They had barely replaced the spade when Anselm Mealey arrived, wearing a beautiful white sailor suit. Nora threw Francis a look of terrible joy.

"Hello, Anselm!" she welcomed brilliantly. "What a lovely new suit. We were waiting on you. What shall we play at?"

Anselm Mealey considered the question with agreeable condescension. He was a large boy for eleven, well-padded, with pink and white cheeks. His hair was fair and curly, his eyes were soulful. The only child of rich and devoted parents, — his father owned the profitable bone-meal works across the river, — he was already destined, by his own election and that of his pious mother, to enter Holywell, the famous Catholic college in Northern Scotland, to study for the priesthood. With Francis he served the altar at St. Columba's. Frequently he was to be found kneeling in church, his big eyes fervent with tears. Visiting nuns patted him on the head. He was acknowledged, with good reason, as a truly saintly boy.

"We'll have a procession," he said. "In honour of St. Julia. This is her feast day."

Nora clapped her hands. "Let's pretend her shrine is by the laurel bushes. Shall we dress up?"

"No." Anselm shook his head. "We're praying more than playing. But imagine I'm wearing a cope and bearing a jewelled monstrance. You're a white Carthusian Sister. And Francis, you're my acolyte. Now, are we all ready?"

A sudden qualm swept over Francis. He was not of the age to analyze his relationships; he only knew that, though Anselm claimed him fervently as his best friend, the other's gushing piety evoked in him a curious painful shame. Towards God he had a desperate reserve. It was a feeling he protected without knowing why, or what it was, like a tender nerve, deep within his body. When Anselm burningly declared in the Christian Doctrine class "I love and adore our Saviour from the bottom of my heart," Francis, fingering the marbles in his pocket, flushed a deep dark red, went home sullenly from school and broke a window.

Next morning when Anselm, already a seasoned sick-visitor, arrived at school with a cooked chicken, loftily proclaiming the object of his charity as Mother Paxton, — the old fishwife, sere with hypocrisy and cirrhosis of the liver, whose Saturday-night brawls made the Cannelgate a bedlam, — Francis, possessed, visited the cloakroom during class and opened the package, substituting for the delicious bird — which he consumed with his companions — the decayed head of a cod. Anselm's tears, and the curses of Meg Paxton, had later stirred in him a deep dark satisfaction.

Now, however, he hesitated, as if to offer the other boy an opportunity of escape. He said slowly: "Who'll go first?"

"Me, of course," Anselm gushed. He took up his position as leader. "Sing, Nora: Tantum Ergo."

In single file, at Nora's shrill pipe, the procession moved off. As they neared the laurel bushes Anselm raised his clasped hands to heaven. The next instant he stepped through the paper and squelched full-length in the mud.

For ten seconds no one moved. It was Anselm's howl as he struggled to get up that set Nora off. While Mealey blubbered clammily, "It's a sin, it's a sin!" she hopped about laughing, taunting wildly, "Fight, Anselm, fight. Why don't you hit Francis?"

"I won't, I won't," Anselm bawled. "I'll turn the other cheek."

He started to run home. Nora clung deliriously to Francis — helpless, choking, tears of laughter running down her cheeks. But Francis did not laugh. He stared in moody silence at the ground. Why had he stooped to such inanity while his father walked those hostile Ettal causeways? He was still silent as they went in to tea.

In the cosy front room, where the table was already set for the supreme rite of Scots hospitality, with the best china and all the electroplate the little household could muster, Francis' mother sat with Aunt Polly, her open rather earnest face a trifle flushed from the fire, her stocky figure showing an occasional stiffening towards the clock.

Now, after an uneasy day, shot equally with doubt and reassurance, — when she told herself how stupid were her fears, — her ears were tuned acutely for her husband's step: she was conscious of an overwhelming longing for him. The daughter of Daniel Glennie, a small and unsuccessful baker by profession, and by election an open-air preacher, leader of his own singular Christian brotherhood in Darrow, that shipbuilding town of incomparable drabness which lies some twenty miles from the city of Tynecastle, she had, at eighteen, during a week's holiday from the parental cake counter, fallen wildly in love with the young Tweedside fisher, Alexander Chisholm, and promptly married him.

In theory, the utter incompatibility of such a union foredoomed it. Reality had proved it a rare success. Chisholm was no fanatic: a quiet, easy-going type, he had no desire to influence his wife's belief. And she, on her side, sated with early piety, grounded by her peculiar father in a strange doctrine of universal tolerance, was not contentious.

Even when the first transports had subsided she knew a glowing happiness. He was, in her phrase, such a comfort about the place; neat, willing, never at a loss when it came to mending her wringer, drawing a fowl, clearing the bee-skeps of their honey. His asters were the best in Tweedside, his bantams never failed to take prizes at the show, the dovecot he had finished recently for Francis was a wonder of patient craftsmanship. There were moments, in the winter evenings when she sat knitting by the hearth, with Francis snug in bed, the wind whistling cosily around the little house, the kettle hissing on the hob, while her long raw-boned Alex padded the kitchen in his stocking feet, silently intent upon some handiwork, when she would turn to him with an odd, tender smile: "Man, I'm fond of you."

Nervously she glanced at the clock: yes, it was late, well past his usual time of homecoming. Outside a gathering of clouds was precipitating the darkness and again heavy raindrops splashed against the window-panes. Almost immediately Nora and Francis came in. She found herself avoiding her son's troubled eye.

"Well, children!" Aunt Polly summoned them to her chair and wisely apostrophized the air above their heads. "Did you have a good play? That's right. Have you washed your hands, Nora? You'll be looking forward to the concert tonight, Francis. I love a tune myself. God save us, girl, stand still. And don't forget your company manners, either, my lady — we're going to get our tea."

There was no disregarding this suggestion. With a hollow sensation of distress, intensified because she concealed it, Elizabeth rose.

"We won't wait on Alex any longer. We'll just begin." She forced a justifying smile. "He'll be in any moment now."

The tea was delicious, the scones and bannocks home-made, the preserves jelled by Elizabeth's own hands. But an air of strain lay heavily about the table. Aunt Polly made none of those dry remarks which usually gave Francis such secret joy, but sat erect, elbows drawn in, one finger crooked for her cup. A spinster, under forty, with a long, worn, agreeable face, somewhat odd in her attire, stately, composed, abstracted in her manner, she looked a model of conscious gentility, her lace handkerchief upon her lap, her nose humanly red from the hot tea, the bird in her hat brooding warmly over all.

"Come to think, Elizabeth — " She tactfully filled a pause. "They might have brought in the Mealey boy — Ned knows his father. A wonderful vocation, Anselm has." Without moving her head she touched Francis with her kindly omniscient eye. "We'll need to send you to Holywell too, young man. Elizabeth, you'd like to see your boy wag his head in a pulpit?"

"Not my only one."

"The Almighty likes the only ones." Aunt Polly spoke profoundly. Elizabeth did not smile. Her son would be a great man, she was resolved, a famous lawyer, perhaps a surgeon; she could not bear to think of him as suffering the obscurity, the sorry hardships of the clerical life. Torn by her growing agitation she exclaimed: "I do wish Alex would come. It's . . . it's most inconsiderate. He'll keep us all late if he doesn't look sharp."

"Maybe he's not through with the tallies," Aunt Polly reflected considerately.

Elizabeth flushed painfully, out of all control. "He must be back at the bothy by now . . . he always goes there after Ettal." Desperately she tried to stem her fears. "I wouldn't wonder if he'd forgotten all about us. He's the most heedless man." She paused. "We'll give him five minutes. Another cup, Aunt Polly?"

But tea was over and could not be prolonged. There was an unhappy silence. What had happened to him? . . . Would he never, never come? Sick with anxiety, Elizabeth could restrain herself no longer. With a last glance, charged with open foreboding, towards the marble timepiece, she rose. "You'll excuse me, Aunt Polly, I'll have to run down, and see what's keeping him. I'll not be long."

Francis had suffered through these moments of suspense — haunted by the terror of a narrow wynd, heavy with darkness and surging faces and confusion, his father penned . . . fighting . . . falling under the crowd . . . the sickening crunch of his head upon the cobblestones. Unaccountably he found himself trembling. "Let me go, Mother," he said.

"Nonsense, boy." She smiled palely. "You stay and entertain our visitors."

Surprisingly, Aunt Polly shook her head. Hitherto she had betrayed no perception of the growing stress. Nor did she now. But with a penetrating staidness she remarked: "Take the boy with you, Elizabeth. Nora and I can manage fine."

There was a pause during which Francis pleaded with his eyes.

"All right . . . you can come."

His mother wrapped him in his thick coat; then, bundling into her plaid cape, she took his hand and stepped out of the warm bright room.

It was a streaming, pitch-dark night. The rain lathered the cobblestones, foamed down the gutters of the deserted streets. As they struggled up the Mercat Wynd past the distant Square and the blurred illumination of the Burgess Hall, new fear reached at Francis from the gusty blackness. He tried to combat it, setting his lips, matching his mother's increased pace with quivering determination.

Ten minutes later they crossed the river by the Border Bridge and picked their way along the waterlogged quay to Bothy No. 3. Here his mother halted, dismayed. The bothy was locked, deserted. She turned indecisively, then suddenly observed a faint beacon, vaporous in the rainy darkness, a mile up-river: Bothy No. 5, where Sam Mirlees, the underwatcher, made his lodging. Though Mirlees was an aimless, tippling fellow, he could surely give them news. She started off again, firmly, plodding across the sodden meadows, stumbling over unseen tussocks, fences, ditches. Francis, close at her side, could sense her apprehension, mounting with every step.

At last they reached the other bothy, a wooden shanty of tarred boards, stoutly planted on the riverbank, behind the high stone butt and a swathe of hanging nets. Francis could bear it no longer. Darting forward with throbbing breast, he threw open the door. Then, at the consummation of his day-long fear, he cried aloud in choking anguish, his pupils wide with shock. His father was there with Sam Mirlees, stretched on a bench, his face pale and bloodied, one arm bound up roughly in a sling, a great purple weal across his brow. Both men were in their jerseys and hip-boots, glasses and a mutchkin jar on the near-by table, a dirty crimsoned sponge beside the turbid water dipper, the hurricane swing lamp throwing a haggard yellow beam upon them, while beyond the indigo shadows crept, wavered in the mysterious corners and under the drumming roof.

His mother rushed forward, flung herself on her knees beside the bench. "Alex . . . Alex . . . are ye hurt?"

Though his eyes were muddled he smiled, or tried to, with his blenched and battered lips.

"No worse nor some that tried to hurt me, woman."

Tears sprang to her eyes, born of his wilfulness and her love for him, tears of rage against those who had brought him to this pass.

"When he came in he was near done," Mirlees interposed with a hazy gesture. "But I've stiffened him up with a dram or two."

She threw a blazing look at the other man: fuddled, as usual on Saturday night. She felt weak with anger that this sottish fool should have filled Alex up with drink on top of the dreadful hurt he had sustained. She saw that he had lost a great quantity of blood . . . she had nothing here to treat him with . . . she must get him away at once . . . at once. She murmured, tensely: —

"Could you manage home with me, Alex?"

"I think so, woman . . . if we take it slow."

She thought feverishly, battling her panic, her confusion. All her instinct was to move him to warmth, light and safety. She saw that his worst wound, a gash to the temple bone, had ceased to bleed. She swung round towards her son.

"Run back quick, Francis. Tell Polly to get ready for us. Then fetch the doctor to the house at once."

Francis, shivering as with ague, made a blind, convulsive gesture of understanding. With a last glance at his father he bent his head and set off frantically along the quay.

"Try, then, Alex . . . let me give you a hand." Bitterly dismissing Mirlees' offer of assistance which she knew to be worse than none, she helped her husband up. He swayed slowly, obediently to his feet. He was dreadfully shaky, hardly knew what he was doing. "I'll away then, Sam," he muttered, dizzily. "Good night to ye."

She bit her lip in a torment of uncertainty, yet persisted, led him out, met by the stinging sheets of rain. As the door shut behind them and he stood, unsteady, heedless of the weather, she was daunted by the prospect of that devious return, back through the mire of the fields with a helpless man in tow. But suddenly, as she hesitated, a thought illuminated her. Why had it not occurred to her before? If she took the short cut by the Tileworks Bridge she could save a mile at least, have him home and safe in bed within half an hour. She took his arm with fresh resolution. Pressing into the downpour, supporting him, she pointed their course up-river towards the bridge.

At first he did not apparently suspect her purpose, but suddenly, as the sound of rushing water struck his ear, he halted.

"Whatna way's this to come, Lisbeth? We cannot cross by the Tileworks with Tweed in such a spate."

"Hush, Alex . . . don't waste your strength by talking." She soothed him, helped him forward.

They came to the bridge, a narrow hanging span, fashioned of planks with a wire rope handrail, crossing the river at its narrowest, quite sound, though rarely used, since the Tileworks which it served had long ago shut down. As Elizabeth placed her foot upon the bridge, the blackness, the deafening nearness of the water, caused a vague doubt, perhaps a premonition, to cross her mind. She paused, since there was not room for them to go abreast, peering back at his subdued and sodden figure, swept by a rush of strange maternal tenderness.

"Have ye got the handrail?"

"Ay, I have the handrail."

She saw plainly that the thick wire rope was in his big fist. Distracted, breathless and obsessed, she could not reason further. "Keep close to me, then." She turned and led on.

They began to cross the bridge. Halfway across his foot slid off a rain-slimed board. It would have mattered little another night. Tonight it mattered more, for the Tweed, in flood, had risen to the planking of the bridge. At once the racing current filled his thighboot. He struggled against the pull, the overpowering weight. But they had beaten the strength from him at Ettal. His other leg slipped, both boots were waterlogged, loaded as with lead.

At his cry she spun round with a scream and caught at him. As the river tore the handrail from his grip her arms enfolded him; she fought closely, desperately, for a deathless instant to sustain him. Then the sound and the darkness of the waters sucked them down.

All that night Francis waited for them. But they did not come.

Next morning they were found, clasped together, at low tide, in the quiet water near the sand bar.

II

One Thursday evening in September four years later, when Francis Chisholm ended his nightly tramp from Darrow Shipyard by veering wearily towards the blistered double headboard of Glennie's Bakery, he had reached a great decision. As he trudged down the floury passage dividing the bakehouse from the shop — his smallish figure oddly suppressed by an outsize suit of dungarees, his face grimy, beneath a man's cloth cap worn back to front — and went through the back door, placing his empty lunch pail on the scullery sink, his dark young eyes were smouldering with this purpose.

In the kitchen Malcom Glennie occupied the table — its soiled cover now, as always, littered with crockery — lolling on his elbow over *Locke's Conveyancing,* a lumpish pallid youth of seventeen, one hand massaging his oily black hair, sending showers of dandruff to his collar, the other attacking the sweetbread cooked for him by his mother on his return from the Armstrong College. As Francis took his supper from the oven — a twopenny pie and potatoes cremated there since noon — and cleared a place for himself, aware, through the torn opaque paper on the half-glazed partition door, of Mrs. Glennie serving a customer in the front shop, the son of the house threw him a glance of peevish disapproval. "Can't you make less noise when I'm studying? And God! What hands! Don't you ever wash before you eat?"

In stolid silence — his best defence — Francis picked up a knife and fork in his calloused, rivet-burned fingers.

The partition door clicked open and Mrs. Glennie solicitously scuffled in. "Are you done yet, Malcom dear? I have the nicest baked custard — just fresh eggs and milk — it won't do your indigestion a mite of harm."

He grumbled: "I've been gastric all day." Swallowing a deep

bellyful of wind, he brought it back with an air of virtuous injury. "Listen to that!"

"It's the study, son, that does it." She hurried to the range. "But this'll keep your strength up . . . just try it . . . to please me."

He suffered her to remove his empty plate and to place a large dish of custard before him. As he slobbered it down she watched him tenderly, enjoying every mouthful he took, her raddled figure, in broken corsets and dowdy, gaping skirt, inclined towards him, her shrewish face with its long thin nose and pinched-in lips doting with maternal fondness.

She murmured, presently: "I'm glad you're back early tonight, son. Your father has a meeting."

"Oh, no!" Malcom reared himself, in startled annoyance. "At the Mission Hall?"

She shook her narrow head. "Open air. On the Green."

"We're not going?"

She answered with a strange, embittered vanity: "It's the only position your father ever gave us, Malcom. Until he fails at the preaching too, we'd better take it."

He protested heatedly. "You may like it, Mother. But it's damned awful for me, standing there, with Father Bible-banging, and the kids yelling 'Holy Dan.' It wasn't so bad when I was young, but now when I'm coming out for a solicitor!" He stopped short, sulkily, as the outer door opened and his father, Daniel Glennie, came gently into the room.

Holy Dan advanced to the table, absently cut himself a slice of cheese, poured a glass of milk and, still standing, began his simple meal. Changed from his working singlet, slacks and burst carpet slippers, he was still an insignificant and drooping figure in shiny black trousers, an old cut-away coat too tight and short for him, a celluloid dickey and a stringy black tie. His cuffs were of celluloid too, to save the washing; they were cracked; and his boots might have done with mending. He stooped slightly. His gaze, usually harassed, often ecstatically remote, was now thoughtful, kind, behind his steel-rimmed spectacles. As he chewed, he let it dwell in quiet consideration on Francis.

"You look tired, grandson. Have you had your dinner?"

Francis nodded. The room was brighter since the baker's entry. The eyes upon him now were like his mother's.

"There's a batch of cherry cakes I've just drawn. You can have one, if you've a mind to — on the oven rack."

At the senseless prodigality Mrs. Glennie sniffed: casting his goods about like this had made him twice a bankrupt, a failure. Her head inclined in greater resignation.

"When do you want to start? If we're going now I'll shut the shop."

He consulted his big silver watch with the yellow bone guard. "Ay, close up now, Mother, the Lord's work comes first. And besides — " sadly — "we'll have no more customers tonight."

While she pulled down the blinds on the fly-blown pastries he stood, detached, considering his address for tonight. Then he stirred. "Come, Malcom!" And to Francis: "Take care of yourself, grandson. Don't be late out your bed!"

Malcom, muttering beneath his breath, shut his book and picked up his hat. He sulkily followed his father out. Mrs. Glennie, pulling on tight black kid gloves, assumed her martyred "meeting" face. "Don't forget the dishes, now." She threw a meaning sickly smile at Francis. "It's a pity you're not coming with us!"

When they had gone he fought the inclination to lay his head upon the table. His new heroic resolution inflamed him, the thought of Willie Tulloch galvanized his tired limbs. Piling the greasy dishes into the scullery he began to wash them, rapidly probing his position, his brows tense, resentful.

The blight of enforced benefactions had lain upon him since that moment, before the funeral, when Daniel had raptly told Polly Bannon: "I'll take Elizabeth's boy. We are his only blood relations. He must come to us!"

Such rash benevolence alone would not have uprooted him. It

took that later hateful scene when Mrs. Glennie, grasping at the small estate, money from his father's insurance and the sale of the furniture, had beaten down Polly's offer of guardianship, with intimidating invocations of the law.

This final acrimony had severed all contact with the Bannons — abruptly, painfully, as though he, indirectly, had been to blame: Polly, hurt and offended, yet with the air of having done her best, had undoubtedly erased him from her memory.

On his arrival at the baker's household, with all the attraction of a novelty, he was sent, a new satchel on his back, to the Darrow Academy: escorted by Malcom; straightened and brushed by Mrs. Glennie, who watched the departing scholars from the shop door with a vague proprietary air.

Alas! The philanthropic flush soon faded. Daniel Glennie was a saint, a gentle noble derided soul who passed out tracts of his own composition with his pies and every Saturday night paraded his van horse through the town with a big printed text on the beast's rump: "*Love thy neighbour as thyself.*" But he lived in a heavenly dream, from which he periodically emerged, careworn, damp with sweat, to meet his creditors. Working unsparingly, with his head on Abraham's bosom and his feet in a tub of dough, he could not but forget his grandson's presence. When he remembered he would take the small boy by the hand to the back yard, with a bag of crumbs, to feed the sparrows.

Mean, shiftless yet avaricious, viewing with a self-commiserating eye her husband's progressive failure, — the sacking of the van man, of the shopgirl, the closing of one oven after another, the gradual decline to a meagre output of twopenny pies and farthing pastries, — Mrs. Glennie soon discovered in Francis an insufferable incubus. The attraction of the sum of seventy pounds she had acquired with him quickly faded, seemed dearly bought. Already wrung by a desperate economy, to her the cost of his clothing, his food, his schooling became a perpetual Calvary. She counted his mouthfuls resignedly. When his trousers wore out she "made down" an old green suit of Daniel's, a relic of her husband's youth, of such outlandish pattern and colour it provided derisive outcry in the streets, shrouded the boy's life in misery. Though Malcom's fees at the Academy were paid upon the nail she usually succeeded in forgetting Francis' until, trembling, pale with humiliation, having publicly been called as a defaulter before the class, he was forced to approach her. Then she would gasp, feign a heart attack by fumbling at her withered bosom, count out the shillings as though he drew away her very blood.

Though he bore it with stoic endurance the sense of being alone . . . alone . . . was terrible for the little boy. Demented with sorrow, he took long solitary walks, combing the sick country vainly for a stream in which to guddle trout. He would scan the outgoing ships, consumed with longing, stuffing his cap between his teeth to stifle his despair. Caught between conflicting creeds, he knew not where he stood; his bright and eager mind was dulled, his face turned sullen. His only happiness came on the nights that Malcom and Mrs. Glennie were from home, when he sat opposite Daniel by the kitchen fire watching the little baker turning the pages of his Bible, in perfect silence, with a look of ineffable joy.

Daniel's quiet but inflexible resolve not to interfere with the boy's religion — how could he, when he preached universal tolerance! — was an added, ever-present goad to Mrs. Glennie. To a "Christian" like herself, who was saved, this reminder of her daughter's folly was anathema. It made the neighbours talk.

The climax came at the end of eighteen months when Francis, with ungrateful cleverness, had the bad taste to beat Malcom in an essay competition open to the school. It was not to be endured. Weeks of nagging wore the baker down. He was on the verge of another failure. It was agreed that Francis' education was complete. Smiling archly for the first time in months, Mrs. Glennie assured him that now he was a little man, fit to contribute to the household, to take his coat off and prove the nobility of toil. He went to work in Darrow Shipyard as a rivet-boy, twelve years old, at three and six a week.

By quarter-past seven he had finished the dishes. With greater alacrity, he spruced himself before the inch of mirror and went out.

It was still light, but the night air made him cough and turn up his jacket as he hurried into High Street, past the livery stable and the Darrow Spirit Vaults, reaching at length the doctor's shop on the corner, with its two bulbous red and green vials and its square brass plate: DR. SUTHERLAND TULLOCH: PHYSICIAN AND SURGEON. Francis' lips were parted, faintly, as he entered.

The shop was dim and aromatic with the smell of aloes, assafœtida and liquorice root. Shelves of dark green bottles filled one side and at the end three wooden steps gave access to the small back surgery where Dr. Tulloch held his consultations. Behind the long counter, wrapping physic on a marble slab spattered with red sealing wax, stood the doctor's eldest son, a sturdy freckled boy of sixteen with big hands, sandy colouring and a slow taciturn smile.

He smiled now, staunchly, as he greeted Francis. Then the two boys looked away, avoiding one other, each reluctant to view the affection in the other's eyes.

"I'm late, Willie!" Francis kept his gaze intently on the skirting of the counter.

"I was late myself . . . and I've to deliver these medicines for Father, bless him." Now that Willie had begun his medical curriculum at the Armstrong College, Dr. Tulloch had, with solemn facetiousness, accredited him his assistant.

There was a pause. Then the older boy threw a secret glance towards his friend.

"Have you decided?"

Francis' gaze was still downcast. He nodded broodingly, his lips set. "Yes."

"You're right, Francis." Approval flooded Willie's plain and stolid features. "I wouldn't have stood it so long."

"I wouldn't . . . either . . ." Francis mumbled, "except for . . . well . . . my grandfather and you." His thin young face, concealed and sombre, reddened deeply as the last words came out with a rush.

Flushing in sympathy, Willie muttered: "I found out the train for you. There's a through leaves Alstead every Saturday at six-thirty-five . . . Quiet. Here's Dad." He broke off, with a warning glance, when the surgery door opened and Dr. Tulloch appeared, showing his last patient out. As the doctor returned toward the boys, a brusque, bristling dark-skinned figure in pepper-and-salt tweeds, his bushy hair and glossy whiskers seemed to spark with sheer vitality. For one who bore the awful reputation of the town's professed free-thinker, open adherent of Robert Ingersoll and Professor Darwin, he had a most disarming charm, and the look of one who would be useful in a sick-room. Because the hollows in Francis' cheeks made him grave, he cracked a frightful joke. "Well, my lad—that's another one killed off! Oh, he's not dead yet! Soon will be! Such a nice man too, leaves a large family." The boy's smile was too drawn to please him. He cocked his clear, challenging eye, mindful of his own troubled boyhood: "Cheer up, young housemaid's knee—it'll all be the same in a hundred years." Before Francis could reply the doctor laughed briefly, thrust his hard square hat on the back of his head and began pulling on his driving gloves. On his way out to his gig he called back: "Don't fail to bring him for supper, Will. Hot prussic acid served at nine!"

An hour later, with the physic delivered, the two boys made their way in unspeaking comradeship towards Willie's house, a large dilapidated villa facing the Green. As they talked in low voices of the daring promise of the day beyond tomorrow, Francis' spirits lifted. Life never seemed so hostile in Willie Tulloch's company. And yet, perversely, their friendship had begun in strife. After school, one day, larking down Castle Street with a dozen classmates, Willie's gaze had strayed to the Catholic church, ugly but inoffensive, beside the gasworks. "Come on," he shouted, in animal spirits. "I've got sixpence. Let's go in and get our sins forgiven!" Then, glancing round, he saw Francis in the group. He reddened with healthy shame. He had not meant the stupid jibe, which would have passed unheeded if Malcom Glennie had not pounced on it and fanned it skilfully into the occasion for a fight.

Incited by the rest, Francis and Willie fought a bloody indecisive battle on the Green. It was a good fight, rich in uncomplaining courage, and when the darkness stopped it, though neither was the victor, each had clearly had enough. But the spectators, with the cruelty of youth, refused to let the quarrel rest. On the next night, after school, the contestants were brought together, whetted with the taunt of cowardice and set to batter each other's already battered head. Again, bloody, spent, yet dogged, neither would concede the victory. Thus for a dreadful week they were matched, like gamecocks, to make sport for their baser fellows. The inhuman conflict, motiveless and endless, became, for each, a nightmare. Then, on the Saturday, the two met unexpectedly, face to face, alone. An agonizing moment followed, then the earth opened, the sky melted and each had an arm round the other's neck, Willie blubbering: "I don't want to fight you, I like ye, man!" — while Francis, knuckling his purple eyes, wept back: "Willie, I like you best in the whole of Darrow!"

They were halfway across the Green, a public open space carpeted by dingy grass, with a forlorn bandstand in the centre, a rusty iron urinal at the far end and a few benches, mostly without backs, where pale-faced children played and loafers smoked and argued noisily, when suddenly Francis saw, with a tightening of his skin, that they must pass his grandfather's meeting. At the end farthest from the urinal a small red banner had been planted bearing the words in tarnished gilt: *"Peace on Earth to Men of Goodwill."* Opposite the banner stood a portable harmonium furnished with a camp-stool on which Mrs. Glennie sat, wearing her victim's air, with Malcom, glumly clasping a hymn-book, beside her. Between the banner and the harmonium on a low wooden stand, surrounded by some thirty persons, was Holy Dan.

As the boys drew up on the fringe of the gathering Daniel had finished his opening prayer and, with his uncovered head thrown back, was beginning his address. It was a gentle and beautiful plea. It expressed Daniel's burning conviction, bared his simple soul. His doctrine was based on brotherhood, the love of one another and of God. Man should help his fellow man, bring peace and goodwill to earth. If only he could lead humanity to that ideal! He had no quarrel with the churches but chastised them mildly: it was not the form which mattered but the fundamentals, humility and charity. Yes, and tolerance! It was worthless to voice these sentiments if one did not practise them.

Francis had heard his grandfather speak before, and felt a throb of dogged sympathy for these views which made Holy Dan the laughing-stock of half the town. Now, edged by his wild intention, his heart swelled in understanding and affection, in longing for a world free of cruelty and hate. Suddenly, as he stood listening, he saw Joe Moir, the skip of his riveting squad at the Shipyard, sidle up the outskirts of the meeting. Accompanying Joe was the gang that hung about the Darrow Vaults, with an armament of bricks, decayed fruit, and oily waste thrown out from the boiler works. Moir was a ribald likeable giant, who, when drunk, gleefully pursued salvation rallies and other outdoor conclaves. He fingered a fistful of dripping waste and shouted: "Hey! Dan! Give us a song and dance!"

Francis' eyes dilated in his pale face. They were going to break up the meeting! He had a vision of Mrs. Glennie, clawing a ripe tomato from her splattered hair, of Malcom, with a greasy rag plastering his hateful face. His being exulted with a wild ecstatic joy.

Then he saw Daniel's face: still unconscious of the danger, lit by a strange intensity, every word throbbing, born of unquenchable sincerity, from the depths of his soul.

He started forward. Without knowing how, or why, he found himself at Moir's side, restraining his elbow, pleading breathlessly: "Don't Joe! Please don't! We're friends, aren't we?"

"Hell!" Moir glanced down, his boozy scowl melting to friendly recognition. "For Christ's sake, Francis!" Then, slowly, "I forgot he was your grandpa." A desperate pause. Then, commandingly, to his followers: "Come on lads, we'll go up to the Square and take it out on the Hallelujas!"

As they moved off the harmonium wheezed with life. No one but Willie Tulloch knew why the thunderbolt had not fallen.

A minute later, entering his house, he asked, baffled yet impressed: "Why did you, Francis?"

Francis answered shakily: "I don't know . . . There's something in what he says . . . I've had enough hating these last four years. My father and mother wouldn't have got drowned if people hadn't hated him . . ." He broke off, inarticulate, ashamed.

Silently, Willie led the way to the living room, which, after the outer dusk, glowed with light and sound and a prodigal untidy comfort. It was a long high maroon-papered chamber, asprawl with broken red plush furniture, the chairs castorless, the vases cracked and glued together, the bell pull tugged out, a litter of vials, labels, pillboxes on the mantelpiece and of toys, books and children upon the worn ink-stained Axminster. Though it was shockingly near nine o'clock none of the Tulloch family was abed. Willie's seven young brothers and sisters, Jean, Tom, Richard, — a list so complex even their father admitted to forgetting it, — were diversely occupied in reading, writing, drawing, scuffling and swallowing their supper of hot bread and milk while their mother Agnes Tulloch, a dreamy voluptuous woman with her hair half down and her bosom open, had picked the baby from his crib upon the hearth and, having removed its steaming napkin, now placidly refreshed the nuzzling bare-bottomed infant at her creamy, fire-lit breast.

She smiled her welcome, unperturbed, to Francis. "Here you are then, boys. Jean, set out more plates and spoons. Richard, leave Sophia alone. And Jean, dear, a fresh diaper for Sutherland from the line! Also see that the kettle's boiling for your father's toddy. What lovely weather we are having. Dr. Tulloch says there is much inflammation about though. Be seated, Francis. Thomas, didn't your father tell you to keep away from the others!" The doctor was always bringing home some disorder: measles one month, chicken-pox the next. Now Thomas, aged six, was the victim. His poll shorn and smelling of carbolic, he was happily disseminating ringworm through the tribe.

Squeezed on the crowded twanging sofa beside Jean, at fourteen the image of her mother, with the same creamy skin, the same placid smile, Francis supped his bread and milk flavoured with cinnamon.

He was still upset from his recent outburst; there was an enormous lump inside his chest, his mind was a maze of confusion. Here was another problem for his aching brain. Why were these people so kind, happy, and contented? Reared by an impious rationalist to deny, or rather to ignore, the existence of their God, they were damned, hell fire already licked their feet.

At quarter-past nine the crunch of the dogcart's wheels was heard on the gravel. Dr. Tulloch strode in, a shout went up, he was at once the centre of an attacking mob. When the tumult stilled the doctor had bussed his wife heartily, was in his chair, a glass of toddy in his hand, slippers on his feet, the infant Sutherland goggling on his knee.

Catching Francis' eye, he raised his steaming tumbler in friendly satire.

"Didn't I tell you there was poison going! Strong drink is raging — eh, Francis?"

Seeing his father in high humour, Willie was tempted to relate the story of the prayer meeting. The doctor slapped his thigh, smiling at Francis. "Good for you, my wee Roman Voltaire. I will disagree to the death with what you say and defend with my life your right to say it! Jean, stop making sheep's eyes at the poor laddie. I thought ye wanted to be a nurse! Ye'll have me a grandfather before I'm forty. Eh, well — " He sighed suddenly, toasting his wife. "We'll never get to heaven, woman — but at least we get our meat and drink."

Later, at the front door, Willie gripped Francis by the hand.

"Good luck . . . Write to me when you're there."

At five next morning, while all was still dark, the Shipyard hooter sounded, long and dolorous, over the cowering dreariness of Darrow. Half senseless with sleep, Francis tumbled out of bed and into his dungarees, stumbled downstairs. The frigid morning, pale yet murky, met him like a blow as he joined the march of silent shivering figures, hurrying with bent head and huddled shoulders towards the Shipyard gates.

Over the weighbridge, past the checker's window, inside the

gates . . . Gaunt spectres of ships rose dimly in their stocks around him. Beside the half-formed skeleton of a new ironclad Joe Moir's squad was mustering: Joe and the assistant plater, the holders-on, the two other rivet-boys and himself.

He lit the charcoal fire, blew the bellows beneath the forge. Silently, unwillingly, as in a dream, the squad set itself to work. Moir lifted his sledge, the hammers rang, swelled and strengthened, throughout the Shipyard.

Holding the rivets, white-hot from the brazier, Francis shinned up the ladder and thrust them quickly through the bolt-holes in the frame, where they were hammered flat and tight, annealing the great sheets of metal which formed the ship's hull. The work was fierce: blistering by the brazier, freezing on the ladders. The men were paid by piece work. They wanted rivets fast, faster than the boys could give them. And the rivets must be heated to the proper incandescence. If they were not malleable the men threw them back at the boys. Up and down the ladder, to and from the fires, scorched, smoky, with inflamed eyes, panting, perspiring, Francis fed the platers all day long.

In afternoon the work went faster: the men seemed careless, straining every nerve, unsparing of their bodies. The closing hour passed in a swimming daze with ear drums tense for the final hooter.

At last, at last it sounded. What blessed relief! Francis stood still, moistening his cracked lips, deafened by the cessation of all sound. On the way home, grimed and sweaty, through his tiredness, he thought: Tomorrow . . . tomorrow. That strange glitter returned to his eye, he squared his shoulders.

That night he took the wooden box down from its hiding place in the disused oven and changed his hoard of silver and coppers, saved with agonizing slowness, into half a sovereign. The golden coin, clutched deep in his trouser pocket, fevered him. With a queer, exalted flush he asked Mrs. Glennie for a needle and thread. She snubbed him, then threw him suddenly a veiled appraising glance.

"Wait! There's a reel in the top drawer — by that card of needles. You can take it." She watched him go out.

In the privacy of his bare and wretched room above the bakehouse he folded the coin in a square of paper, sewed it firm and tight inside the lining of his coat. He had a sense of glad security as he came down to give her back the thread.

The following day, Saturday, the Shipyard closed at twelve. The thought that he would never enter these gates again so elated him that at dinner he could scarcely eat; he felt his flushed restlessness more than enough to raise some sharp inquiry from Mrs. Glennie. To his relief she made no comment. As soon as he left the table, he edged out of the house, slipped down East Street, then fairly took to his heels.

Outside the town, he slipped into a brisk walk. His heart was singing within him. It was pathetic commonplace: the timeworn flight of all unhappy childhood. Yet for him it was the road to freedom. Once he was in Manchester he could find work at the cotton-mills, he was sure, doubly sure. He covered the fifteen miles to the railway Junction in four hours. It was striking six o'clock as he entered Alstead Station.

Seated under an oil lamp on the draughty deserted platform, he opened his penknife, cut the sewing on his jacket, removed the folded paper, took the shining coin from within. A porter appeared on the platform, some other passengers, then the booking office opened.

He took his place at the grille, demanded his ticket.

"Nine and six," the clerk said, punching the green cardboard slip into the machine.

Francis gasped with relief: he had not, after all, miscalculated the fare. He pushed his money through the grille.

There was a pause. "What's the game? I said nine and six."

"I gave you half a sovereign."

"Oh, you did! Try that again young feller and I'll have you run in!" The clerk indignantly flung the coin back at him.

It was not a half-sovereign but a bright new farthing.

In anguished stupor, Francis saw the train tear in, take up its freight, and go whistling into the night. Then his mind, groping dully, struck the heart of the enigma. The sewing, when he ripped it open, was not his own clumsy stitching but a close firm seam. In a withering flash he knew who had taken his money: Mrs. Glennie.

At half-past nine, outside the colliery village of Sanderston, in the dank wet mist which blurred his gig-lamps, a man in a dogcart almost ran down the solitary figure keeping the middle of the road. Only one person was likely to be driving in such a place on such a night. Dr. Tulloch, holding in his startled beast, peered downwards through the fog, his masterly invective suddenly cut short.

"Great Lord Hippocrates! It's you. Get in. Quick, will you — before the mare pulls my arms from their sockets." Tulloch wrapped the rug about his passenger; proceeded without questions; he knew the virtue of a healing silence.

By half-past ten Francis was drinking hot broth before the fire in the doctor's living room, now bereft of its occupants and so unnaturally still the cat slept peacefully on the hearth-rug. A moment later Mrs. Tulloch came in, her hair in plaits, her quilted dressing gown open above her nightgown. She stood with her husband studying the dead-beat boy, who seemed unconscious of their presence, their murmured converse, wrapped in a curious apathy. Though he tried to smile, he could not when the doctor came forward, producing his stethoscope with a jocular air: "I'll bet my boots that cough of yours is a put-up job." But he submitted, opening his shirt, letting the doctor tap, and listen to, his chest.

Tulloch's saturnine face wore a queer expression as he straightened himself. His fund of humour had surprisingly dried up. He darted a look at his wife, bit his full lip, and suddenly kicked the cat.

"Damn it to hell!" he cried. "We use our children to build our battleships. We sweat them in our coal mines and our cotton-mills. We're a Christian country. Well! I'm proud to be a pagan." He turned brusquely, quite fiercely, to Francis. "Look here, boy, who are these folks you knew in Tynecastle? What's that — Bannon, eh? The Union Tavern. Get away home now and into bed unless you want treble pneumonia."

Francis went home, resistance crushed in him. All the next week Mrs. Glennie wore a martyred frown and Malcom a new checked waistcoat: price half a sovereign at the stores.

It was a dire week for Francis. His left side hurt him, especially when he coughed; he had to drag himself to work. He was aware, dimly, that his grandfather fought a battle for him. But Daniel was beaten down, defeated. All the little baker could do was to offer, humbly, some cherry cakes that Francis could not eat.

When Saturday afternoon came round he had not the strength to go out. He lay upstairs in his bedroom gazing in hopeless lethargy through the window.

Suddenly he started, his heart gave a great and unbelieving bound. In the street below, slowly approaching, like a barque navigating strange and dangerous waters, was a hat, a thing of memory, unique, unmistakable. Yes, yes: and the gold-handled umbrella, tightly rolled, the short sealskin jacket with the braided buttons. He cried out weakly, with pale lips: "Aunt Polly."

The shop door pinged below. Dithering to his feet, he crept downstairs, poised himself, trembling, behind the half-glazed door.

Polly was standing, very erect, in the centre of the floor, her lips pursed, her gaze sweeping the shop, as though amusedly inspecting it. Mrs. Glennie had half-risen, to confront her. Lounging against the counter, his mouth half-open, gaping from one to the other, was Malcom.

Aunt Polly's vision came to rest above the baker's wife. "Mrs. Glennie, if I remember right!"

Mrs. Glennie was at her worst: still unchanged, wearing her dirty forenoon wrapper, her blouse open at the neck, a loose tape hanging from her waist.

"What do you want?"

Aunt Polly raised her eyebrows. "I have come to see Francis Chisholm."

"He's out."

"Indeed! Then I'll wait till he comes in." Polly arranged herself on the chair by the counter as though prepared to remain all day.

There was a pause. Mrs. Glennie's face had turned a dirty red. She remarked, aside: "Malcom! Run round to the bakehouse and fetch your father."

Malcom answered shortly: "He went to the Hall five minutes ago. He won't be back till tea."

Polly removed her gaze from the ceiling, brought it critically to bear on Malcom. She smiled slightly when he flushed, then, entertained, she glanced away.

For the first time Mrs. Glennie showed signs of uneasiness. She burst out angrily: "We're busy people here, we can't sit about all day. I've told you the boy is out. Like enough he won't be back till all hours — with the company he keeps. He's a regular worry with his late hours and bad habits. Isn't that so, Malcom?"

Malcom nodded sulkily.

"You see!" Mrs. Glennie rushed on. "If I was to tell you everything you'd be amazed. But it makes no difference, we're Christian people here, we look after him. You have my word for it — he's perfectly well and happy."

"I'm glad to hear it," Polly spoke primly, politely stifling a slight yawn with her glove, "for I've come to take him away."

"What!" Taken aback, Mrs. Glennie fumbled at the neck of her blouse, the colour flooding, then fading from, her face.

"I have a doctor's certificate," Aunt Polly enunciated, almost masticated, the formidable phrase with a deadly relish, "that the boy is underfed, overworked and threatened with a pleurisy."

"It's not true."

Polly pulled a letter from her muff and tapped it significantly with the head of her umbrella. "Can you read the Queen's English?"

"It's a lie, a wicked lie. He's as fat and well fed as my own son!"

There was an interruption. Francis, flat against the door, following the scene in an agony of suspense, leaned too heavily against the ricketty catch. The door flew open, he shot into the middle of the shop. There was a silence.

Aunt Polly's preternatural calm had deepened. "Come over, boy. And stop shaking. Do you want to stay here?"

"No, I don't."

Polly threw a look of justification towards the ceiling. "Then go and pack your things."

"I haven't anything to pack."

Polly stood up slowly, pulling on her gloves. "There's nothing to keep us."

Mrs. Glennie took a step forward, white with fury. "You can't walk over me. I'll have the law on you."

"Go ahead, my woman." Polly meaningly restored the letter to her muff. "Then maybe we'll find out how much of the money that came from the sale of poor Elizabeth's furniture has been spent on her son and how much on yours."

Again there was a shattered silence. The baker's wife stood, pale, malignant and defeated, one hand clutching at her bosom.

"Oh, let him go, Mother," Malcom whined. "It'll be good riddance."

Aunt Polly, cradling her umbrella, examined him from top to toe. "Young man, you're a fool!" She swung round towards Mrs. Glennie. "As for you, woman," looking straight over her head, "you're another!"

Taking Francis triumphantly by the shoulder, she propelled him, bare-headed, from the shop.

They proceeded in this fashion towards the station, her glove grasping the fabric of his jacket firmly, as though he were some rare and captive creature who might at any moment escape. Outside the station she bought him, without comment, a bag of Abernethy biscuits, some cough drops, and a brand-new bowler hat. Seated opposite him in the train, serene, singular, erect, observing him moisten the dry biscuits with tears of thankfulness, extinguished almost by his new hat which enveloped him to the ears, she remarked with half-closed, judicial eyes: —

"I always knew that creature was no lady, I could see it in her face. You made an awful mistake letting her get hold of you, Francis dear. The next thing we'll do is get your hair cut!"

III

IT WAS wonderful these frosty mornings to lie warm in bed until Aunt Polly brought his breakfast, a great plate of bacon and eggs still sizzling, boiling black tea and a pile of hot toast, all on an oval metal tray stamped *Allgood's Old Ale*. Sometimes he woke early, in an agony of apprehension; then came the blessed knowledge that he need no longer fear the hooter. With a sob of relief he burrowed more deeply into his thick yellow blankets, in his cosy bedroom with its paper of climbing sweet peas, its stained boards and woolwork rug, a lithograph of Allgood's Prize Brewery Dray Horse on one wall, of Pope Gregory on another, and a little china holy-water font with a sprig of Easter palm stuck sideways in it by the door. The pain in his side was gone, he seldom coughed, his cheeks were filling out. The novelty of leisure was like a strange caress and, though the uncertainty of his future still troubled him, he received it gratefully.

On this fine morning of the last day of October, Aunt Polly sat on the edge of his bed exhorting him to eat. "Lay in, boy! That'll stick to your ribs!" There were three eggs on the plate, the bacon was crisp and streaky, he had forgotten that food could taste so good.

As he balanced the tray on his knees, he sensed an unusual festivity in her manner. And soon she gave him one of her profound nods.

"I've news for you today, young man — if you can stand it."

"News, Aunt Polly?"

"A little excitement to cheer you up — after your dull month with Ned and me." She smiled dryly at the quick protest in his warm brown eyes. "Can't you guess what it is?"

He studied her with the deep affection which her unceasing kind-

ness had awakened in him. The homely angular face — poor-com-
plexioned, the long upper lip downed with hair, a tufted blemish
at the angle of the cheek — was now familiar and beautiful.

"I can't think, Aunt Polly."

She was moved to her short rare laugh, a little snort of satisfaction at her success in provoking his curiosity.

"What's happened to your wits, boy? I believe too much sleep
has addled them."

He smiled happily in sympathy. It was true that the routine of
his convalescence had hitherto been tranquil. Encouraged by Polly,
who had feared for his lungs, — she had a dread of "consumption,"
which "ran" in her family, — he had usually lain abed until ten.
Dressed, he accompanied her on her shopping, a stately progress
through the main streets of Tynecastle which, since Ned ate largely
and nothing but the best, demanded great prodding of poultry and
sniffing of steak. These excursions were revealing. He could see
that it pleased Aunt Polly to be "known," deferred to, in the best
stores. She would wait, aloof and prim, until her favourite shopman
was free to serve her. Above all, she was ladylike. That word was
her touchstone, the criterion of her actions, even of her dresses,
made by the local milliner in such dreadful taste they sometimes
evoked a covert snigger from the vulgar. In the street she had a
graduated series of bows. To be recognized, greeted by some local
personage — the surveyor, the sanitary inspector or the chief con-
stable — afforded her a joy which, though sternly concealed, was
very great. Erect, the bird in her hat atwitter, she would murmur
to Francis: "That was Mr. Austin, the tramway manager . . .
a friend of your uncle's . . . a fine man." The height of her gratification was reached when Father Gerald Fitzgerald, the handsome
portly priest of St. Dominic's, gave her in passing his gracious and
slightly condescending smile. Every forenoon they would stop in
at the church and, kneeling, Francis would be conscious of Polly's
intent profile, the lips moving silently, above her rough chapped
reverent hands. Afterwards she bought him something for himself,
a stout pair of shoes, a book, a bag of aniseed drops. When he pro-

tested, often with tears in his eyes, as she opened her worn purse, she would simply press his arm and shake her head. "Your uncle won't take 'no.'" She was touchingly proud of her relationship with Ned, her association with the Union Tavern.

The Union stood near the docks at the corner of Canal and Dyke Streets, with an excellent view of the adjacent tenements, of coal barges, and the terminus of the new horse tramway. The brown painted stucco building was of two stories, and the Bannons lived above the tavern. Every morning at half-past seven Maggie Magoon, the scrubwoman, opened the saloon and began, talking to herself, to clean it. At eight precisely Ned Bannon came down, in his braces, but closely shaved, with his forelock oiled, and strewed the floor with fresh sawdust from the box behind the bar. It was unnecessary: a kind of ritual. Next, he inspected the morning, took in the milk and crossed the back yard to feed his whippets. He kept thirteen — to prove that he was not superstitious.

Soon the first of the regulars began to drop in, Scanty Magoon always in the van, hobbling on his leather padded stumps to his favourite corner, followed by a few dockers, a tram driver or two, returning from the night shift. These workmen did not stop: only long enough to down their half of spirits and chase it with a glass, a schooner, or a pint of beer. But Scanty was a permanent, a kind of faithful watchdog, gazing propitiatingly at Ned as he stood bland, unconscious, behind the bar with its sombre woodwork and the framed notice: GENTLEMEN BEHAVE OTHERS MUST.

Ned, at fifty, was a big thick figure of a man. His face was full and yellowish, with prominent eyes, very solemn in repose, match-ing his dark clothes. He was neither genial nor flashy, the qualities popularly attributed to a publican. He had a kind of solemn, bilious dignity. He was proud of his reputation, his establishment. His parents had been driven out of Ireland by the potato famine, he had known poverty and starvation as a boy, but he had succeeded against inconceivable odds. He had a "free" house, stood well with the licencing authorities and the brewers, had many influential friends. He said, in effect, The drink trade is respectable and I prove it. He set his face against young men drinking and refused rudely to serve any woman under forty: there was no *Family Department* in the Union Tavern. He hated disorder, at the first sound of it he would rap crossly with an old shoe — maintained handy for that purpose — on the bar, and keep rapping till the discord ceased. Though a heavy drinker himself he was never seen the worse for it. Perhaps his grin was loose, his eye inclined to wander on those rare evenings which he deemed "an occasion," such as St. Patrick's night, Halloween, Hogmanay, or after a day's dog racing when one of his whippets had added another medal to the galaxy on the heavy watchchain that spanned his stomach. At any rate, on the following day he would wear a sheepish air and send Scanty up for Father Clancy, the curate at St. Dominic's. When he had made his confession he rose heavily, dusting his knees, from the boards of the back room and pressed a sovereign for the poor-box into the young priest's hand. He had a healthy respect for the clergy. For Father Fitzgerald, the parish priest, he had, indeed, considerable awe.

Ned was reputed "comfortable," he ate well, gave freely and, distrusting stocks and shares, had money invested in "bricks and mortar." Since Polly had a competence of her own, inherited from Michael, the dead brother, he had no anxiety on her account.

Though slow to form an affection, Ned was, in his own cautious word, "taken" with Francis. He liked the boy's unobtrusiveness, the sparseness of his speech, the quiet way he held himself, his silent gratitude. The sombreness of the young face, caught unguarded, in repose, made him frown dumbly, and scratch his head.

In the afternoon Francis would sit with him in the half-empty bar, drowsy with food, the sunlight slanting churchwise through the musty air, listening with Scanty to Ned's genial talk. Scanty Magoon, husband and encumbrance of the worthy witless Maggie, was so named because there was not enough of him, only in fact a torso. He had lost his legs from gangrene caused by some obscure disorder of the circulation. Capitalizing on his complaint, he had promptly "sold himself to the doctors," signing a document which would deliver his body to the dissecting slab on his demise. Once the purchase price was drunk, a sinister aura settled on the bleary, loquacious, wily, unfortunate old scamp. An object now of popular awe, in his cups he indignantly declared himself defrauded. "I never got enough for myself. Them bloody scalpers! But they'll never get ahold of me poor old Adam! God damn the fear! I'll enlist for a sailor and drown myself."

Occasionally Ned would let Francis draw a beer for Scanty, partly for charity, partly to give the boy the thrill of the "engine." As the ivory-handled pull came back, filling the mug — Scanty prompting anxiously, "Get a head on her, boy!" — the foamy brew smelled so nutty and good Francis wanted to taste it. Ned nodded permission, then smiled in slow delight at the wryness of his nephew's face. "It's a acquired taste," he gravely asserted. He had a number of such clichés, from "Women and beer don't mix," to "A man's best friend is his own pound note," which, through frequency and profundity of utterance, had been hallowed into epigrams.

Ned's gravest, most tender affection was reserved for Nora, daughter of Michael Bannon. He was devoted to his niece who when three had lost her brother from tuberculosis, and her father through that same murderous malady, so fatal to the Celtic race, two years later. Ned had brought her up, sent her off at the age of thirteen to St. Elizabeth's, the best convent boarding school in Northumberland. It was a genuine pleasure for him to pay the heavy fees. He watched her progress with a fond indulgent eye. When she came home for the holidays he was a new man: spryer, never seen in braces, ponderously devising excursions and amusements and, lest anything should offend her, much stricter in the bar.

"Well — " Aunt Polly was gazing half-reproachfully across the breakfast tray at Francis. "I see I'll have to tell you what it's all about. In the first place your uncle's decided to give a party tonight to celebrate Halloween . . . and" — momentarily she dropped her eyes — "for another reason. We'll have a goose, a four-pound black bun, raisins for the snapdragon, and of course the apples —

your uncle gets special ones at Lang's market garden in Gosforth. Maybe you'll go over for them this afternoon. It's a nice walk."

"Certainly, Aunt Polly. Only, I'm not quite sure of where it is."

"Someone'll show you the way." Polly composedly produced her main surprise. "Someone who's coming home from her school to spend a long week-end with us."

"Nora!" he exclaimed abruptly.

"The same." She nodded, took up his tray and rose. "Your uncle's pleased as punch she's got leave. Hurry up and dress now, like a good boy. We're all going to the station to meet the little monkey at eleven."

When she had gone Francis lay staring in front of him with a queer perplexity. This unexpected announcement of Nora's arrival had taken him aback, and strangely thrilled him. He had always liked her, of course. But now he faced the prospect of meeting her again with an odd new feeling, between diffidence and eagerness. To his surprise and confusion he suddenly found himself reddening to the roots of his hair. He jumped up hurriedly and began to pull on his clothes.

Francis and Nora started off, at two o'clock, on their excursion, taking the tram across the city to the suburb of Clermont, then walking across country toward Gosforth, each with a hand on the big wicker basket, swinging it between them.

It was four years since Francis had seen Nora and, stupidly tongue-tied all through lunch, when Ned had surpassed himself in massive playfulness, he was still painfully shy of her. He remembered her as a child. Now she was nearly fifteen and, in her modestly long navy-blue skirt and bodice, she seemed quite grown-up, more elusive and unreadable than ever before. She had small hands and feet and a small, alert provoking face, which could be brave or suddenly timid. Though she was tall and awkward from her growth her bones were fine and slender. Her eyes were teasing, darkly blue against her pale skin. The cold made them sparkle, made her little nostrils pink.

Occasionally, across the basket handle, his fingers touched Nora's. The sensation was remarkable: sweet and warmly confusing. Her hands were the nicest things to touch that he had ever known. He could not speak, did not dare look at her, though from time to time he felt her looking at him and smiling. Though the golden blaze of the autumn was past, the woods still glowed with bright red embers. To Francis the colours of the trees, of the fields and sky, had never appeared more vivid. They were like a singing in his ears.

Suddenly she laughed outright and, tossing back her hair, began to run. Attached to her by the basket he raced like the wind alongside until she drew up, gasping, her eyes sparkling like frost on a sunny morning.

"Don't mind me, Francis. I get wild sometimes. I can't help it. It's being out of school, perhaps."

"Don't you like it there?"

"I do and I don't. It's funny and strict. Could you believe it?" She laughed, with a little rush of disconcerting innocence. "They make us wear our nightgowns when we take a bath! Tell me, did you ever think of me all the time you were away?"

"Yes." He stumbled out the answer.

"I'm glad . . . I thought of you." She threw him a swift glance, made as though to speak, and was silent.

Presently they reached the Gosforth market garden. Geordie Lang, Ned's good friend and the owner of the garden, was in the orchard, among the half-denuded trees, burning leaves. He gave them a friendly nod, an invitation to join him. They raked the crackling brown and yellow leaves towards the great smouldering cone he had already built, until the smell of the leaf smoke impregnated their clothing. It was not work but glorious sport. They forgot their earlier embarrassment, competed as to who should rake the most. When he had raked a great pile for himself Nora mischievously despoiled it. Their laughter rang in the high clear air. Geordie Lang grinned in broad sympathy. "That's women, lad. Take your pile and laugh at ye."

At last Lang waved them towards the apple shed, a wooden erection at the end of the orchard.

"You've earned your keep. Go and help yourself!" he called after them. "And give my best respects to Mr. Bannon. Tell him I'll look in for my drop spirits sometime this week."

The apple shed was soft with crepuscular twilight. They climbed the ladder to the loft where, spaced out on straw, not touching, were rows and rows of the Ribston Pippins for which the garden was renowned. While Francis filled the basket, crouching under the low roof, Nora sat crosslegged on the straw, picked an apple, shone it on her bony hip and began to eat.

"Oh, my, it's good," she said. "Have one, Francis?"

He sat down opposite, took the apple she held out to him. The taste was delicious. They watched each other eating. When her small teeth bit through the amber skin into the crisp white flesh, little spurts of juice ran down her chin. He did not feel so shy in the dark little loft, but dreamy and warm, suffused with the joy of living. He had never liked anything so much as being here, in the garden, eating the apple she had given him. Their eyes, meeting frequently, smiled; but she had a half-smile, strange and inward, that seemed entirely for herself.

"I dare you to eat the seeds," she teased suddenly; then added quickly: "No, don't, Francis! Sister Margaret Mary says they give you colic. Besides a new apple tree will grow from each of those seeds. Isn't it funny! Listen, Francis . . . you're fond of Polly and Ned?"

"Very." He stared. "Aren't you?"

"Of course . . . except when Polly coddles me every time I get a cough . . . and when Ned pets me on his knee — I hate that."

She hesitated, lowered her gaze for the first time. "Oh, it's nothing, I shouldn't, Sister Margaret Mary thinks I'm impudent, do you?"

He glanced away awkwardly, his passionate repudiation of the charge condensed in a clumsy: "No!"

She smiled almost timidly. "We're friends, Francis, so I will say it, and spite old Margaret Mary. When you're a man what are you going to be?"

Startled, he stared at her. "I don't know. Why?"

She picked with sudden nervousness at the serge of her dress. "Oh, nothing . . . only, well . . . I like you. I've always liked you. All those years I've thought of you a lot and it wouldn't be nice if you . . . sort of disappeared again."

"Why should I disappear?" He laughed.

"You'd be surprised!" Her eyes, still childish, were wide and wise. "I know Aunt Polly . . . I heard her again today. She'd give anything to see you made a priest. Then you'd have to give up everything, even me." Before he could reply she jumped up, shaking herself, with a great show of animation. "Come on, don't be silly, sitting here all day. It's ridiculous with the sun shining outside, and the party tonight." He made to rise. "No, wait a minute. Shut your eyes and you might get a present."

Even before he thought of complying she darted over and gave him a hurried little kiss on the cheek. The quick warm contact, the touch of her breath, the closeness of her thin face with the tiny brown mole on the cheekbone, stunned him. Blushing deeply, unexpectedly she slipped down the ladder and ran out of the shed. He followed slowly, darkly red, rubbing the small moist spot upon his cheek as though it were a wound. His heart was pounding.

That night the Halloween party began at seven o'clock. Ned, with a sultan's privilege, closed the bar at five minutes to the hour. All but a few favoured patrons were politely asked to leave. The guests assembled upstairs, in the parlour, with its glass cases of wax fruit, the picture of Parnell above the blue-glass lustres, the velvet-framed photograph of Ned and Polly at the Giant's Causeway, the bog oak jaunting car, — a present from Killarney, — the aspidistra, the varnished shillelagh hung on the wall with green ribbon, the heavy padded furniture which emitted a puff of dust when heavily sat upon. The mahogany table was fully extended, with legs like a dropsical woman, and set for twenty. The coal fire, banked halfway up the chimney, would have prostrated an African explorer. The smell, off, was of rich basting birds. Maggie Magoon, in cap and apron, ran about like a maniac. In the crowded room were the young curate, Father Clancy, Thaddeus Gilfoyle, several of the neighbouring tradesmen, Mr. Austin the manager of the tramways, his wife and three children, and, of course, Ned, Polly, Nora and Francis.

Amidst the din, with beaming benevolence and a sixpenny cigar, Ned stood laying down the law to his friend Gilfoyle. A pale, prosaic and slightly catarrhal young man of thirty was Thaddeus Gilfoyle, clerk at the gasworks, — who in his spare time collected the rents of Ned's property in Varrell Street, was a sidesman at St. Dominic's, a steady-going chap who could always be relied on to do an odd job, to fill the breach, to "come forward," as Ned phrased it, — who never had two words to rub against one another nor a single idea that might be called his own, yet who somehow managed to be there, hanging around, on the spot when he was wanted, dull and dependable, nodding in agreement, blowing his nose, fingering his confraternity badge, fish-eyed, flat-footed, solemn, safe.

"You'll be for making a speech tonight?" he now inquired of Ned, in a tone which implied that if Ned did not make a speech the world would be desolate.

"Ah, I don't know now." Modestly yet profoundly, Ned considered the end of his cigar.

"Ah, you will now, Ned!"

"They'll not expect it."

"Pardon me, Ned, if I beg to differ."

"Ye think I should?"

With solemnity, "Ned, ye both should and would!"

"Ye mean . . . I ought to?"

"You must, Ned, and you will."

Delighted, Ned rolled the cigar across his mouth. "As a matter of fact, Thad," he cocked his eye, significantly, "I have a announcement . . . a important announcement I want to make. I'll say a few words later, since you press me."

Led by Polly as a kind of overture to the main event, the children began to play Halloween games — first snapdragon, scrambling for the flat blue raisins, ablaze with spirit, on a big china dish, then duck-apple, dropping a fork from between the teeth over the back of a chair into a tub of swimming apples.

At seven o'clock the "gowks" came in: working lads from the neighbourhood, with soot-blackened faces and grotesque attire, mumming their way around the district, singing for sixpences, in the strange tradition of All Hallows Eve. They knew how to please Ned. They sang "Dear Little Shamrock," "Kathleen Mavourneen," and "Maggie Murphy's Home." Largesse was distributed. They clattered out. "Thank you, Mr. Bannon! Up the Union! Good night, Ned!"

"Good lads. Good lads all of them!" Ned rubbed his hands, his eye still moist with Celtic sentiment. "Now, Polly, our friends' stomachs will be thinking their throats is cut."

The company sat down at table, Father Clancy said grace, and Maggie Magoon staggered in with the largest goose in Tynecastle. Francis had never tasted such a goose — it dissolved, in rich flavours, upon the tongue. His body glowed from the long excursion in the keen air and from a strange interior joy. Now and then his eyes met Nora's across the table, shyly, with exquisite understanding. Though he was so quiet her gaiety thrilled him. The wonder of this happy day, of the secret bond which lay between them, was like a pain.

When the repast was over Ned got up slowly, amidst applause. He struck an oratorical attitude, one thumb in his armpit. He was absurdly nervous.

"Your Reverence, Ladies and Gentlemen, I thank you one and all. I'm a man of a few words," — a cry of "No, No" from Thaddeus Gilfoyle, — "I say what I mean, and I mean what I say!" A short pause while Ned struggled for more confidence. "I like to see my friends happy and contented round about me — good company and good beer never hurt any man." Interruption at the doorway from Scanty Magoon, who had sneaked in with the gowks and contrived to remain. "God save you, Mr. Bannon!" — brandishing a drumstick of the goose. "You're a fine man!" Ned remained unperturbable —

every great man has his sycophants. "As I was remarkin' when Mrs. Magoon's husband flung a brick at me . . ." Laughter. ". . . I favour the social occasion. I'm sure we're proud and pleased, every mother's son of us, — and daughter, — to welcome into our midst my poor wife's brother's boy!" Loud applause and Polly's voice: "Take a bow, Francis." "I'm not going into recent history. Let the past bury its dead, I say. But I say and say it I will, Look at him now, I say, and when he came!" Applause and Scanty's voice in the corridor: "Maggie, for the love of God, will ye bring some more of the goose!" "Now, I'm not one to blow my own trumpet! I try to do fair between God and man and beast. Look at my whippets if ye don't believe me." Gilfoyle's voice: "The best dogs in Tyne-castle!" A longer pause, during which Ned lost the thread of his speech. "Where am I?" "Francis!" Polly prompted quickly. "Ah, yes." Ned raised his voice. "When Francis came, I said to myself, says I, Here's a boy that might be useful. Shove him behind the bar and let him earn his keep? No, by God — Saving your presence, Father Clancy — that's not us. We talk it over, Polly and me. The boy's young, the boy's been ill-treated, the boy has a future before him, the boy's my poor dead wife's brother's boy. Let's send him to col-lege, we say; we can manage it between us." Ned paused. "Your Reverence, Ladies and Gentlemen, I'm pleased and proud to an-nounce that next month Francis starts off for Holywell!" Making the name the triumphant keystone of his peroration, Ned sat down, perspiring, amidst loud applause.

IV

THOUGH the elm shadows were long upon the cropped lawns of Holywell, the northern June evening was still light as noon. The darkness would come late, so close to dawn the aurora borealis would but briefly glitter across the high pale heavens. As Francis sat at the open window of the high little study which he shared, since his election to the "Philosophers," with Laurence Hudson and

Anselm Mealey, he felt his attention wander from the notebook, drawn, almost sadly, with a sense of the transience of beauty, to the lovely scene before him.

From the steep angle of his vision he could see the school, a noble grey granite baronial mansion, built for Sir Archibald Frazer in 1609, and endowed, this century, as a Catholic College. The chapel, styled in the same severity, lay at right angles, linked by a cloister, to the library, enclosing a quadrangle of historic turf. Beyond were the fives and handball courts, the playing fields, the end of a game still in progress, wide reaches of pasture threaded by the Stinchar River with stumpy black Polled Angus cattle grazing stolidly, woods of beech and oak and rowan clustering the lodge, and in the ultimate distance the backdrop, blue, faintly serrated, of the Aberdeenshire Grampians.

Without knowing, Francis sighed. It seemed only yesterday that he had landed at Doune, the draughty northern junction, a new boy, scared out of his wits, facing the unknown and that first frightful interview with the Headmaster, Father Hamish MacNabb. He remembered how "Rusty Mac," great little Highland gentleman, blood cousin to MacNabb of the Isles, had crouched at his desk beneath his tartan cape, peering from bushy red eyebrows, dreadfully formidable.

"Well, boy, what can you do?"

"Please, sir . . . nothing."

"Nothing! Can't you dance the Highland Fling?"

"No, sir."

"What! With a grand name like Chisholm?"

"I'm sorry, sir."

"Humph! There's not much profit in you, is there boy?"

"No, sir, except sir . . ." Trembling: ". . . Maybe I can fish."

"Maybe, eh?" A slow dry smile. "Then maybe we'll be friends." The smile deepened. "The clans of Chisholm and MacNabb fished together, ay, and fought together, before you or I were thought of. Run now, before I cane ye."

And now, in one more term, he would be leaving Holywell. Again his gaze slanted down to the little groups promenading to and fro on the gravelled terraces beside the fountain. A seminary custom! Well, what of it? Most of them would go from here to the Seminary of San Morales in Spain. He discerned his room-mates walking together: Anselm, as usual, extrovert in his affections, one arm tenderly linking his companion's, the other gesticulating, but nicely, as befitted the outright winner of the Frazer Good Fellowship Prize! Behind the two, surrounded by his coterie, paced Father Tarrant — tall, dark, thin . . . intense yet sardonic . . . classically remote.

At the sight of the youngish priest Francis' expression tightened oddly. He viewed the open notebook before him on the window ledge with distaste, picked up his pen and began, after a moment, his imposition. His frown of resolution did not mar the clean brown moulding of his cheek or the sombre clearness of his hazel eyes. Now, at eighteen, his body had a wiry grace. The chaste light heightened absurdly his physical attractiveness, that air, unspoiled and touching, which — inescapable — so often humiliated him.

"*June 14th, 1887.* Today there occurred an incident of such phenomenal and thrilling impropriety I must revenge myself on this beastly diary, and Father Tarrant, by recording it. I oughtn't really to waste this hour before vespers — afterwards I shall be dutifully cornered by Anselm to play handball — I should jot down *Ascension Thursday: Fine day; memorable adventure with Rusty Mac,* and leave it. But even our incisive Administrator of Studies admitted the virtue of my breed — conscientiousness — when he said to me, after his lecture: 'Chisholm! I suggest you keep a diary. Not of course for publication,' — his confounded satire flashed out, — 'as a form of examen. You suffer, Chisholm, inordinately, from a kind of spiritual obstinacy. By writing your inmost heart out . . . if you could . . . you might possibly reduce it.'

"I blushed, of course, like a fool, as my wretched temper flared. 'Do you mean I don't do what I'm told, Father Tarrant?'

"He barely looked at me, hands tucked away in the sleeves of his habit, thin, dark, pinched in at the nostrils and oh, so unanswerably

clever. As he tried to conceal his dislike of me, I had a sharp awareness of his hard shirt, of the iron discipline I know he uses unsparingly upon himself. He said vaguely: 'There is a mental disobedience . . .' and walked away.

"Is it conceit to imagine he has his knife in me because I do not
model myself upon him? Most of us do. Since he came here two
years ago he has led quite a cult of which Anselm is deacon. Perhaps
he cannot forget the occasion when, at his instruction to us upon the
'one, true, and apostolic religion' I suddenly remarked: 'Surely, sir,
creed is such an accident of birth God can't set an exclusive value
on it.' In the shocked hush which followed he stood nonplussed, but
icy cold. 'What an admirable heretic you would have made, my
good Chisholm.'

"At least we have one point in common: agreement that I shall
never have a vocation.

"I'm writing ridiculously pompously for a callow youth of eighteen. Perhaps it is what is named the affectation of my age. But I'm
worried . . . about several things. Firstly, I'm terribly, probably
absurdly, worried about Tynecastle. I suppose it's inevitable that
one should lose touch, when one's 'home-leave' is limited to four
short summer weeks. This brief annual vacation, Holywell's only
rigour, may serve its purpose of keeping vocations firm, but it also
strains the imagination. Ned never writes. His correspondence during my three years at Holywell has been effected through the
medium of sudden and fantastic gifts of food: that colossal sack of
walnuts for instance, from the docks, in my first winter, and last
spring, the crate of bananas, three quarters of which were over-ripe
and created an undignified epidemic amongst the 'clergy and laity'
here.

"But even in Ned's silence there's something queer. And Aunt
Polly's letters make me more apprehensive. Her dear inimitable
gossip about parochial events has been replaced by a meagre
catalogue of, mainly, meteorological facts. And this change in tone
arrived so suddenly. Naturally Nora hasn't helped me. She is the
original postcard girl, who scribbles off her obligations in five min-

utes, once a year, at the seaside. It seems, however, centuries since
her last brilliant 'Sunset from Scarborough Pier' and two letters of
mine have failed even to produce a 'Moon over Whitley Bay.' Dear
Nora! I shall never forget your Eve-like gesture in the apple loft.
It's because of you that I anticipate these coming holidays so eagerly.
Shall we walk again, I wonder, to Gosforth? I have watched you
grow, holding my breath — seen your character — by which I mean
your contradictions — develop. I know you as someone quick, shy,
bold, sensitive and gay, a little spoiled by flattery, full of innocence
and fun. Even now, I see your impudent sharp little face, lit up from
within, as you indulge your amazing gift of mimicry — 'taking off'
Aunt Polly . . . or me — your skinny arms akimbo, blue eyes provoking, reckless, ending by flinging yourself into a dance of gleeful
malice. Everything about you is so — human and alive, and — even
those flashes of petulance and fits of temper which shake your
delicate physique and end in such tremendous weepings. And I
know, despite your faults, how warm and impulsive is your nature,
making you run, with a quick and shamefaced blush, towards someone you have hurt . . . unconsciously. I lie awake thinking of you,
of the look in your eyes, the tender pathos of your collar bones above
your small round breasts . . ."

Francis broke off here, and with a sudden flush scored out the
last line he had written. Then, conscientiously, he resumed.

"Secondly, I am selfishly concerned about my future. I'm now
educated above — here again Fr. Tarrant would agree — my station.
I've only another term at Holywell. Am I to return gracefully to
the beer-pulls of the Union? I can't continue to be a charge on
Ned — or more justly Polly, since I recently ascertained quite by
accident that my fees have been discharged, out of her modest in-
come, by that wonderful woman! My ambitions are so muddled.
My fondness for Aunt Polly, my overbrimming gratitude, make me
long to repay her. And it is her dearest wish to see me ordained.
Again, in a place like this, where three quarters of the students and

most of one's friends are predestined for the priesthood, it is hard to escape the inevitable pull of sympathy. One wants to line up in the ranks. Tarrant apart, Father MacNabb thinks I should make a good priest — I can feel it in his shrewd, friendly provocativeness, his almost Godlike sense of waiting. And as Principal of this College he should know something about vocations.

"Naturally I'm impetuous and hot-tempered; and my mixed up-bringing has left me with a schismatic quirk. I can't pretend to be one of these consecrated youths — our college library teems with them — who lisp prayers throughout their infancy, make boyish shrines in the woods and sweetly rebuke the little girls who jostle them at the village fair. 'Keep away, Thérèse and Annabelle, I am not for thee.'

"Yet who can describe those moments that come to one suddenly: alone upon the back road to Doune, waking in the darkness in one's silent room, remaining behind, quite solitary, when the scraping, coughing, whispering mob has gone in the empty yet breathing church. Moments of strange apprehension, of intuition. Not that sentimental ecstasy which is as loathsome to me as ever — Query: why do I want to vomit when I see rapture on the Master of Novices' face? — but a sense of consolation, of hope.

"I'm distressed to find myself writing like this — though it is for no other eye than mine. One's private ardours make chilling stuff on paper. Yet I must record this inescapable sense of belonging to God which strikes at me through the darkness, the deep conviction, under the measured, arranged, implacable movement of the universe, that man does not emerge from, or vanish into, nothing. And here — is it not strange? — I feel the influence of Daniel Glennie, dear, cracked Holy Dan, feel his warm unearthly gaze upon me. . . .

"Confound it! And Tarrant! I *am* literally pouring out my heart. If I am such a Holy Willie why don't I set out and do something for God, attack the great mass of indifference, of sneering material-ism in the world today . . . in short, become a priest? Well . . . I must be honest. I think it is because of Nora. The beauty and tenderness of my feeling for her overfills my heart. The vision of her face, with its light and sweetness, is before me even when I am praying to Our Lady in church. Dear, dear Nora. You are the real reason why I don't take my ticket on the celestial express for San Morales!"

He stopped writing and let his gaze travel into the distance, a faint frown on his brow, but his lips smiling. With an effort, he again collected himself.

"I must, I must get back to this morning and Rusty Mac. This being a holiday of obligation, I had the forenoon on my hands. On my way down to post a letter at the lodge I ran into the Headmaster coming up from the Stinchar with his rod and without fish. He stopped, supporting his short burly form on the gaff, his ruddy face screwed up, rather put out, beneath his blaze of red hair. I do love Rusty Mac. I think he has some fondness for me and perhaps the simplest explanation is that we are so dourly Scottish and both of us fishers . . . the only two in the school. When Lady Frazer endowed the College from her Stinchar properties, Rusty claimed the river as his own. The jingo in the *Holywell Monitor* beginning,

> I'll not have my pools
> Whipped to ribbons by fools . . .

neatly takes off his attitude — for he's a mad fisher. There's a story of him, in the middle of mass at Frazer Castle, which Holywell serves, when his staunch friend, the Presbyterian Gillie, stuck his head through the window of the oratory, bursting with suppressed excitement. 'Your reverence! They're rising like fury in Lochaber Pool!' Never was a mass more quickly completed. The stupefied congregation, including Her Ladyship, was pattered over, blessed at breakneck speed; then a dark streak, not unlike the local concept of the Devil, was seen flying from the sacristy. 'Jock! Jock! What flee are they taking?'

"Now, he looked at me disgustedly. 'Not a fish in sight. Just when

I wanted one for the notables!' The Bishop of the diocese and the retiring principal of our English Seminary at San Morales were coming to lunch at Holywell that day.

"I said, 'There's a fish in the Glebe Pool, sir.'

" 'There's no fish in the river at all, not even a grilse . . . I've been out since six.'

" 'It's a big one.'

" 'Imaginary!'

" 'I saw it there yesterday, under the weir, but of course I didn't dare try for it.'

"From beneath his sandy brows he gave me his dour smile. 'You're a perverse demon, Chisholm. If you want to waste your time — you've my dispensation.' He handed me his rod and walked off.

"I went down to the Glebe Pool, my heart leaping as it always does at the sound of running water. The fly on the leader was a Silver Doctor, perfect for the size and colour of the river. I began to fish the pool. I fished it for an hour. Salmon are painfully scarce this season. Once I thought I saw the movement of a dark fin in the shadows of the opposite bank. But I touched nothing. Suddenly I heard a discreet cough. I swung round. Rusty Mac, dressed in his best blacks, wearing gloves and his ceremonial top hat, had stopped, on his way to meet his guests at Doune Station, to condole with me.

" 'It's these large ones, Chisholm — ' he said with a sepulchral grin — 'they're always the hardest!'

"As he spoke, I made a final cast thirty yards across the pool. The fly fell exactly on the spume eddying beneath the far edge of the weir. The next instant I felt the fish, struck, and was fast in it.

" 'Ye have one!' Rusty cried. Then the salmon jumped — four feet in the air. Though for my own part I nearly dropped, the effect on Rusty was stupendous. I could feel him stiffen beside me. 'In the name of God!' he muttered in stricken awe. The salmon was the biggest I had ever seen, here, in the Stinchar, or in my father's Tweedside bothy. 'Keep his head up!' Rusty suddenly shouted. 'Man, man — give him the butt!'

"I was doing my best. But now the fish was in control. It set off, downstream, in a mad tearing rush. I followed. And Rusty followed me.

"The Stinchar, at Holywell, is not like the Tweed. It runs in a brown torrent through pines and gorges, making not inconsiderable somersaults over slippery boulders and high shaley ledges. At the end of ten minutes, Rusty Mac and I were half a mile downstream, somewhat the worse for wear. But we still stayed with the fish.

"'Hold him, hold him!' Mac was hoarse from shouting. 'You fool, you fool, don't let him get in that slack!' The brute, of course, was already in the slack, sulking in a deep hole, with the leader ensnared in a mess of sunken roots.

"'Ease him, ease him!' Mac hopped in anguish. 'Just ease him while I give him a stone.'

"Gingerly, breathlessly, he began flipping stones, trying to start out the fish without snapping the cast. The game continued for an agony of time. Then *whirr!* — off went the fish, to the scream of the reel. And off again went Rusty and I.

"An hour later, or thereabouts, in the slow wide flats opposite Doune village, the salmon at last showed signs of defeat. Exhausted, panting, torn by a hundred agonizing and entrancing hazards, Rusty gave a final command.

"'Now, now! On this sand!' He croaked: 'We've no gaff. If he takes you down farther, he's gone for good.'

"My mouth was gulpy and dry. Nervously, I stood the fish close. It came, quiet, then suddenly made a last frantic scuttle. Rusty let out a hollow groan. 'Lightly . . . lightly! If you lose him now I'll never forgive you!'

"In the shallows the fish seemed incredible. I could see the frayed gut of the leader. If I lost him! — an icy lump came under my shirt. I slid him gently to the little flat of sand. In an absolute tense silence Mac bent over, whipped his hand in the gills and heaved the fish, monstrous, onto the grass.

"It made a noble sight on the green meadow, a fish of over forty pounds, run so freshly the sea lice still were on its arching back.

"'A record, a record!' Mac chanted, swept, as was I, by a wave of heavenly joy. We had joined hands and were dancing the fandango. 'Forty-two pounds if it's an ounce . . . we'll put it in the book.' He actually embraced me. 'Man, man — You're a bonny, bonny fisher.'

"At that moment, from the single railway line across the river, came the faint whistle of an engine. Rusty paused, gazed in bewildered fashion at the plume of smoke, at the toylike red-and-white signal which had suddenly dipped over Doune village station. Recollection flooded him. He dug in consternation for his watch. 'Good Heavens, Chisholm!' His tone was that of the Holywell Headmaster. 'That's the Bishop's train.'

"His dilemma was apparent: he had five minutes to meet his distinguished visitors and five miles of roundabout road to reach the station — visible, only two fields away, across the Stinchar.

"I could see him slowly make up his mind. 'Take the fish back, Chisholm, and have them boil it whole for luncheon. Go quickly now. And remember Lot's wife and the pillar of salt. Whatever you do, *don't look back!*'

"I couldn't help it. Once I reached the first bend of the stream, from behind a bush, I risked a salty ending. Father Mac had already stripped to the buff and tied his clothing in a bundle. Wearing his top hat firmly on his head, with the bundle uplifted like a crozier, he stepped stark naked into the river. Wading and swimming, he reached the other side, scrambled into his suit and sprinted manfully towards the approaching train.

"I lay on the grass, rolling, in a kind of ecstasy. It was not the vision — which would live with me forever — of the top hat planted dauntlessly upon the nubile brow, but the moral pluck which lay behind the escapade. I thought: He too must hate our pious prudery, which shudders at the sight of human flesh, and cloaks the female form as though it were an infamy."

A sound outside made Francis pause and he ceased writing as the door opened. Hudson and Anselm Mealey came into the room. Hudson, a dark quiet youth, sat down and began to change his shoes. Anselm had the evening mail in his hand.

"Letter for you, Francis," he said effusively.

Mealey had grown into a fine pink-and-white young man. His cheek had the smoothness of perfect health. His eye was soft and limpid, his smile ready. Always eager, busy, smiling: without question he was the most popular student in the school. Though his work was never brilliant, the masters liked him — his name was usually on the prize list. He was good at fives and racquets and all the less rough games. And he had a genius for procedure. He ran half a dozen clubs — from the Philatelists to the Philosophers. He knew, and glibly employed, such words as "quorum," "minutes" and "Mr. Chair." Whenever a new society was proposed, Anselm's advice was sure to be invoked — automatically he became its president. In praise of the clerical life he was lyrical. His only cross was this singular paradox: the Headmaster and a few odd lonely souls cordially disliked him. To the rest he was a hero, and he bore his successes with open smiling modesty.

Now, as he handed Francis the letter, he gave him that warm disarming smile. "Hope it's full of good news, dear fellow."

Francis opened the letter. Undated, it was written in pencil upon an invoice headed:

Dr. to Edward Bannon
Union Tavern,
Corner Dyke and Canal Streets,
Tynecastle.

Dear Francis,

I hope this finds you well as it leaves me. Also please excuse pencil. We are all upset. It grieves me to tell you Francis you won't be able to come home this holiday. No one is more sick and sorry than me about it not having seen you since last summer and all. But believe me it is impossible and we must bow to the will of God. I know you are not one to take no for an answer but this time you must the B.V.M. be my witness. I won't disguise we have trouble as you must guess but it is nothing you can help or hinder. It is not money nor sickness so do not worry. And it will all pass by the help of God and be forgotten. You can easy arrange to stay the holidays at the college. Ned will pay all extras. You'll have your books and your nice surroundings and all. Maybe we'll fix for you to come down at Christmas, so don't fret. Ned has sold his whippets but not for the money. Mr. Gilfoyle is a comfort to all. You are not missing much in the weather, it has been terrible wet. Now don't forget Francis we have people in the house, there isn't no room, you are not [underlined twice] to come.

Bless you my dear boy and excuse haste.

Yours affectionately,

POLLY BANNON

At the window, Francis read the letter several times: though its purpose was plain, its meaning remained troubling and inscrutable. With a strained look he folded the sheet and placed it in his pocket.

"Nothing wrong I hope?" Mealey had been studying his face solicitously.

Francis, uncomfortably silent, hardly knew what to say.

"My dear fellow, I am sorry." Anselm took a step forward, placed his arm lightly, comfortingly, around the other's shoulders. "If there's anything I can do for mercy's sake let me know. Perhaps," — he paused earnestly, — "perhaps you don't feel like handball tonight?"

"No," Francis mumbled. "I believe I'd rather not."

"Quite all right, my dear Francis!" The vespers bell rang. "I can see there is something bothering you. I'll remember you tonight in my prayers."

All through vespers Francis worried about Polly's incomprehensible letter. When the service was over he had a sudden impulse to take his trouble to Rusty Mac. He went slowly up the wide staircase.

As he entered the study he became aware that the Headmaster was not alone, Father Tarrant sat with him, behind a pile of papers; and from the odd sudden silence his appearance provoked, Francis had the extraordinary feeling that the two had been discussing him.

"I'm sorry, sir." He cast an embarrassed glance towards Rusty Mac. "I didn't know you were engaged."

"That's all right, Chisholm. Sit down."

The quick warmth of the tone compelled Francis, already half-turned towards the door, into the wicker chair beside the desk. With slow movements of his stubby fingers Rusty went on stuffing shag into his corroded briar pipe. "Well! What can we do for you, my good man?"

Francis coloured. "I . . . I rather thought you'd be alone."

For some queer reason the Headmaster avoided his appealing gaze. "You don't mind Father Tarrant? What is it?"

There was no escape. Without guile to invent further excuse Francis stumbled out: "It's a letter I've had . . . from home." He had meant to show Polly's note to Rusty Mac but, in Tarrant's presence, his pride restrained him. "For some obscure reason they don't seem to want me back for the vacation."

"Oh!" Was he mistaken: was there again swift interchange between the two? "That must be something of a disappointment."

"It is, sir. And I feel worried. I was wondering . . . in fact I came to ask you what I should do."

Silence. Father MacNabb himself sank more deeply into his old cape, still fumbling at his pipe. He had known many boys, known them inside-out; yet there was about this youth who sat beside him a fineness, beauty, and dogged honesty which lit a fire in his heart. "We all have our disappointments, Francis." His meditative voice was sad, more than unusually mild. "Father Tarrant and I have suffered one today. Retirements are the order of the day at our Seminary in Spain." He paused. "We are appointed there, I as Rector, Father Tarrant as my Administrator of Studies."

Francis stammered a reply. San Morales was, indeed, a coveted advancement, next step to a bishopric; but whatever Tarrant's reaction — Francis shot a quick glance at the expressionless profile — MacNabb would not so regard it. The dry Aragon plains would be alien for a man who loved the green woods and rushing waters of Holywell with all his soul. Rusty Mac smiled gently. "I had my heart set on staying here. You had set yours on going away. What d'you say? Shall we both agree to take a beating from Almighty God?"

Francis strove to pluck the proper phrase from his confusion. "It's just . . . being anxious . . . I wondered if I shouldn't find out what's wrong and try to help?"

"I question if I should." Father MacNabb answered quickly. "What would you say, Father Tarrant?"

In the shadow, the younger master stirred. "Troubles resolve themselves best, in my experience, without outside interference."

There appeared nothing more to be said. The Headmaster turned up his desk lamp which, while it brightened the dark study, seemed to terminate the interview. Francis got up. Though he faced them both, haltingly, from his heart, he spoke to Rusty Mac.

"I can't say how sorry I am that you are leaving for Spain. The school . . . I . . . I shall miss you."

"Perhaps we shall see you there?" There was hope, quiet affection in the voice.

Francis did not answer. As he stood there, indecisively, hardly knowing what to say, torn by conflicting difficulties, his downcast gaze struck suddenly upon a letter, lying open on the desk. It was not so much the letter — illegible at that distance — as the letter's bright blue-stamped heading which caught his eye. Quickly he glanced away. But not before he had read *St. Dominic's Presbytery, Tynecastle.*

A shiver went through him. Something was wrong at home. Now he was sure. His face revealed nothing, remained impassive. Neither of the two masters was aware of his discovery. But as he moved towards the door he knew, despite all persuasion to the contrary, that one course at least was clear before him.

v

THE train arrived at two o'clock that sultry June afternoon. Carrying his handbag, Francis walked rapidly from the station, his heart beating faster as he approached the familiar quarter of the city.

A queer air of quiet hung outside the tavern. Thinking to take Aunt Polly by surprise, he ran lightly up the side stairs and entered the house. Here, too, it was quiet and oddly dim after the glare of the dusty pavements; no one in the lobby or the kitchen, no sound but the thunderous ticking of a clock. He went into the parlour.

Ned was seated at the table, both elbows on the red drugget cover, gazing endlessly at the opposite blank wall. Not the attitude alone, but the alteration in the man himself, drew from Francis a stifled exclamation. Ned had lost three stones in weight, his clothes hung upon him, the rotund beaming face had turned dreary and cadaverous.

"Ned!" Francis held out his hand.

There was a pause, then Ned sluggishly slewed round, perception slowly dawning through his settled wretchedness.

"It's you, Francis." His smile was bewitching, evasive. "I'd no idea you were expected."

"I'm not really, Ned." Through his anxiety Francis essayed a laugh. "But the minute we broke up I simply couldn't wait. Where's Aunt Polly?"

"She's away. . . . Yes . . . Polly's away for a couple of days to Whitley Bay."

"When'll she be back?"

"Like enough . . . tomorrow."

"And where's Nora?"

"Nora!" Ned's tone was flat. "She's away with Aunt Polly."

"I see." Francis was conscious of a throb of relief. "That's why she didn't answer my wire. But Ned . . . you . . . you're well yourself, I hope?"

"I'm all right, Francie. A trifle under the weather maybe . . . but the like of me'll come to no harm." His chest took a sudden grotesque heave. Francis was horrified to see tears run down the egg-shaped face. "Away now and get yourself a bite. There'll be plenty in the cupboard. Thad'll get you anything you want. He's below in the bar. A great help he's been to us, has Thad." Ned's gaze wavered, then wandered back to the opposite wall.

In a daze, Francis turned, put his bag in his own small room. As he came along the passage the door of Nora's room was open: the neat white privacy caused him to withdraw his eyes in sudden confusion. He hastened downstairs.

The saloon was empty, even Scanty vanished, his vacant corner arresting, unbelievable, like a gap blown through the solid structure of the wall. But behind the bar, in his shirt sleeves, smugly drying glasses, was Thaddeus Gilfoyle.

Thad stopped his silent whistle as Francis entered. Slightly taken aback, an instant elapsed before he offered a welcome with his limp and dampish hand.

"Well, well!" he exclaimed. "Here's a sight for sore eyes."

Gilfoyle's air of proprietorship was hateful. But Francis, now thoroughly alarmed, succeeded in affecting indifference. He said lightly: "I'm surprised to see you here, Thad? What's happened to the gasworks?"

"I've give up the office," Thad answered composedly.

"What for?"

"To be here. Permanent." He picked up a glass and eyed it professionally, breathed on it softly, and began to polish. "When they asked me to come forward . . . I couldn't do more!"

Francis felt his nerves tighten beyond endurance. "In the name of heaven, what's all this about, Gilfoyle?"

"*Mister* Gilfoyle, if you don't mind, Francis!" Thad rolled his tongue smugly around the reproach. "It heartbreaks Ned not to see me get my place. He's not the same man, Francis. I doubt he'll ever be himself again."

"What's happened to him? You talk as if he were out of his mind!"

"He was, Francis, he was . . ." Gilfoyle groaned, "but he's come to senses now, poor man." His eye watchful, he stopped Francis' angry interruption with a whine. "Now don't take on that way with me. I'm the one that's doin' right. Ask Father Fitzgerald if you disbelieve me. I know you've never liked me much. I've seen ye on vacations making sport of me as you growed up. I've the best intentions towards you, Francis. We ought to pull together . . . now, especially."

"Why now especially?" Francis gritted his teeth.

"Oh, yes, yes . . . you wouldn't know . . . to be sure." Thad darted a fearful smirk. "The banns was only put up for the first time last Sunday. You see, Francis, me and Nora's going to be wed!"

Aunt Polly and Nora returned late the following evening. Francis, sick with apprehension, with his failure to penetrate Gilfoyle's fish-like secrecy, had awaited their arrival in an agony of impatience. He tried immediately to corner Polly.

But Polly, after her first start, her wail of recognition,—"Francis, I told you not to come,"—had fled upstairs with Nora, her ears closed to his importunities, reiterating the formula, "Nora's not well . . . she's sick I tell you . . . get out of my road . . . I've got to tend to her."

Rebuffed, he climbed sombrely to his room, chilled by the mounting premonitions of this unknown dread. Nora, having scarcely given him a look, had gone immediately to bed. And for an hour he heard Polly, scurrying with trays and hot-water bottles, entreating Nora in a low voice, persecuting her with agitated attentions. Nora, thin as a wand, and pale, somehow had the air of sick-rooms. Polly, worn and harassed, even more negligent in her dress, had acquired a new gesture—a quick pressing of her hand against her brow. Late into the night, from her adjoining room, he heard the mutter of her prayers. Torn by the enigma, Francis bit his lip, turning restlessly between his sheets.

Next morning dawned clear. He rose and, according to his habit, went out to early mass. When he returned he found Nora seated outside on the back-yard steps warming herself in a patch of sunshine while at her feet some chickens cheeped and scuttled. She made no move to let him pass, but when he had stood a moment, she raised her head contemplatively.

"It's the holy man . . . been out already, saving his soul!"

He reddened at her tone, so unexpected, so quietly bitter.

"Did the Very Reverend Fitzgerald officiate?"

"No. It was the curate."

"The dumb ox in the stall! Ah, well, at least he's harmless."

Her head drooped, she stared at the chickens, propping her thin chin upon a thinner wrist. Though she had always been slight he was startled to discover this almost childish fragility which matched so ill the sullen maturity in her eyes, and the new grey dress, womanly and costly, which stiffly adorned her. His heart melted, his breast was filled with a white fire, an unsupportable pain. Her hurt plucked at the chords of his soul. He hesitated, his gaze averted. His voice was low.

"Have you had breakfast?"

She nodded. "Polly shoved it down my throat. God! If she'd only leave me be!"

"What are you doing today?"

"Nothing."

He paused again, then blurted out, all his feeling for her flooding through the anxiety in his eyes, "Why don't we go for a walk, Nora? Like we used to. It's so glorious a day!"

She did not move. Yet a faint tinge of animation seemed to penetrate her hollow, shadowed cheek.

"I can't be bothered," she said heavily. "I'm tired!"

"Oh, come on, Nora . . . please."

A dull pause. "All right."

His heart gave another great painful thud. He hurried into the kitchen and cut, with nervous haste, some sandwiches and cake, wrapped them clumsily into a packet. There was no sign of Polly and now, indeed, he was eager to avoid her. In ten minutes Nora and he sat in the red tram, clanging across the city. Within the hour, they tramped side by side, unspeaking, towards the Gosforth Hills.

He wondered at the impulse which had sent him to this familiar stretch. Today the burgeoning countryside was lovely; but its very loveliness was tremulous, unbearable. As they came upon Lang's orchard, now foamy with blossom, he paused, tried to break the steely silence which lay between them.

"Look, Nora! Let's take a stroll round. And have a word with Lang."

She threw one glance at the orchard, the trees standing spaced and stiff, like chessmen, around the apple shed. She said rudely, bitterly: "I don't want to. I hate that place!"

He did not answer. Dimly he knew her bitterness was not towards him.

By one o'clock they reached the summit of Gosforth Beacon. He could see that she was tired and, without consulting her, stopped under a tall beech, for lunch. The day was unusually warm and clear. In the flat distance beneath them, sparkling with golden light, lay the city, domed and spired, and from afar, ineffably beautiful.

She scarcely touched the sandwiches he produced and, remembering Polly's demonstrative tyranny, he did not press her. The shade was soothing. Overhead the new green flickering leaves sent quiet patterns chasing across the moss, carpeted with dry beechnuts, on which they sat. There was a smell of flowing sap; the throaty call of a thrush came from a high twig overhead.

After a few moments she leaned back against the bole of the tree, tilted her head, and closed her eyes.

Her relaxation seemed somehow the greatest tribute she could pay him. He considered her with a deeper surge of tenderness, stirred to undreamed-of compassion by the arch of her neck, so thin and unprotected. The welling tenderness within him made him strangely protective. When her head slipped a little from the tree he scarcely dared touch her. Yet, fancying her asleep, he moved his arm instinctively to support her. The next instant she wrenched herself free, struck him repeatedly on the face and chest with her clenched knuckles, hysterically breathless.

"Leave me alone! You brute! You beast!"

"Nora, Nora! What's the matter?"

Panting, she drew back, her face quivering, distorted. "Don't try to get round me that way. You're all the same. Every one of you!"

"Nora!" He pleaded with her desperately. "For pity's sake . . . let's get this straight."

"Get what straight?"

"Everything . . . why you're going on like this . . . why you're marrying Gilfoyle."

"Why shouldn't I marry him?" She threw the question at him, with a bitter defensiveness.

His lips were dry, he could scarcely speak. "But Nora, he's such a poor creature . . . He's not your sort."

"He's as good as anybody. Haven't I said you're all the same? At least I'll keep him in his place."

Confounded, he stared at her with a pale and stricken face. And there was that in his unbelieving eyes which cut her so cruelly, she more cruelly cut back.

"Perhaps you think I should be marrying you . . . the bright-eyed altar boy . . . the half-baked carpet priest!" Her lip twitched with the bitterness of her sneer. "Let me tell you this. I think you're a joke . . . a sanctimonious scream. Go on, turn up your blessed eyes. You don't know how funny you are . . . you holy pater noster. Why if you were the last man in the world I wouldn't . . ." She choked and shuddered violently, tried, painfully, uselessly, to check her tears with the back of her hand and then, sobbing, flung her head upon his breast. "Oh, Francis, Francis, dear, I'm sorry! You know I've always loved you. Kill me if you want to . . . I don't care."

While he quieted her, clumsily, stroking her brow, he felt himself trembling as much as she. The racking violence of her sobs diminished gradually. She was like a wounded bird in his arms. She lay, spent and passive, her face hidden against his coat. Then slowly she straightened herself. With averted eyes, she took her handkerchief, rubbed her ravaged, tear-stained face, straightened her hat, then said, in an exhausted neutral tone: "We'd better get home."

"Look at me, Nora?"

But she would not, only remarking in that same odd monotone: "Say what you want to say."

"I will then, Nora." His youthful vehemence overcame him. "I'm not going to stand this! I can see there's something behind it. But

I'll get to the bottom of it. You're not going to marry that fool Gilfoyle. I love you, Nora. I'll stand by you."

There was a pitiful stillness.

"Dear Francis," she said, with an oddly hollow smile. "You make me feel as though I'd lived a million years." And rising, she bent and kissed him, as she had kissed him once before, upon the cheek. As they went down the hill the thrush had ceased its singing in the high tree.

That evening, with fixed intention, Francis set out for the dockside tenement inhabited by the Magoons. He found the banished Scanty alone, since Maggie was still out charring, squatting by a spark of fire in the single "back to back" apartment, glumly working a wool-rug shuttle by the light of a tallow dip. As he recognized his visitor there was no mistaking the pleasure in the exile's bleary eye, a gleam that heightened when Francis uncovered the gill bottle of spirits he had privily removed from the bar. Quickly, Scanty produced a chipped delft cup, solemnly toasted his benefactor.

"Ah, that's the stuff!" he muttered, across the back of his ragged sleeve. "Devil the sup have I had since that skinflint Gilfoyle took over the bar."

Francis drew up the backless wooden chair. He spoke with dark intensity, the shadows heavy beneath his eyes.

"Scanty! What's happened at the Union — to Nora, Polly, Ned? I've been back three days and I'm still no wiser. You've got to tell me!"

A look of alarm invaded Scanty's expression. He glanced from Francis to the bottle — from the bottle to Francis.

"Ah! How would I know?"

"You do know! I can see it in your face."

"Didn't Ned say nothing?"

"Ned! He's like a deaf-mute these days!"

"Poor ould Ned!" Scanty groaned, blessed himself, and poured out more whiskey. "God save us! Who would ever have dreamed it. Sure there's bad in the best of us." With a sudden hoarse emphasis: "I couldn't tell ye, Francis, it's a shame to remember, it don't do no good."

"It will do good, Scanty," Francis urged. "If I know, I can do something."

"Ye mean, Gilfoyle . . ." With head cocked, Scanty considered, then he nodded slowly. He took another tot to stiffen himself, his battered face oddly sober, his tone subdued. "I'll tell you then, Francis, if you swear to keep it dark. The truth of it is . . . God pity us . . . that Nora's had a baby."

Silence: long enough for Scanty to take another drink. Francis said: "When?"

"Six weeks ago. She went down to Whitley Bay. The woman there has the child . . . a daughter. . . . Nora can't bear the sight of it."

Cold, rigid, Francis struggled with the tumult in his breast. He made himself ask: "Then Gilfoyle is the father?"

"That gutless fish!" Hatred overcame Scanty's caution. "No, no, he's the one that came forward, as he's pleased to call it, to give the little one a name, and get his foot in the Union to the bargain, the bla'g'ard! Father Fitzgerald's behind him, Francis. It's all settin' pretty as a pictur', the way they've pulled it. Marriage lines in the drawer, not a soul the wiser, and the daughter brought here later on, as it were, at the end of a long vaycation. God strike me down dead, if it don't turn the stomach of a pig!"

A band, an insupportable constriction, girded Francis' heart. He fought to keep his voice from breaking.

"I never knew Nora was in love with anyone? Scanty . . . Do you know who it was . . . I mean . . . the father of her child?"

"Before God I don't!" The blood rushed to Scanty's forehead as he thumped the floor boards in vociferous denial. "I don't know nothing about that at all. How should a poor creature like me! And Ned don't either, that's gospel truth! Ned always treated me right, a fine generous upstanding man, except for occasions, like when Polly was away, and the drink took hold of him. No, no. Francis, take it from me, there's not a hope of findin' the man!"

Again a silence, frozen, prolonged. A film clouded Francis' eyes. He felt deathly sick. At last, with a great effort he got up.

"Thank you, Scanty, for telling me."

He quitted the room, went giddily down the bare flights of tenement stairs. His brow, the palms of his hands, were bedewed with icy sweat. A vision haunted, tormented him: the trim neatness of Nora's bedroom, white and undisturbed. He had no hatred, only a searing pity, a dreadful convulsion of his soul. Outside in the squalid courtyard he leaned, suddenly overcome, against the single lamp-post and retched his heart out, into the gutter.

Now he felt cold, but firmer in his intention. He set out resolutely in the direction of St. Dominic's.

The housekeeper at St. Dominic's admitted him with that noise-less discretion which typified the Presbytery. In a minute, she glided back to the half-lit hall, where she had left him, and for the first time faintly smiled at him. "You're fortunate, Francis. His Reverence is free to see you."

Snuff-box in hand, Father Gerald Fitzgerald rose as Francis entered, his manner a mixture of cordiality and inquiry, his fine handsome presence matching the French furniture, the antique prie-dieu, the choice copies of Italian primitives upon the walls, the vase of lilies on the escritoire, scenting the tasteful room.

"Well young man, I thought you were up North? Sit down! How are all my good friends in Holywell?" As he paused to take snuff, his eye touched upon the College tie, which Francis wore, with affectionate approval. "I was there myself, you know, before I went to the Holy City . . . a grand gentlemanly place. Dear old MacNabb. And Father Tarrant. A classmate of mine at the English College in Rome. There's a fine, a coming man! Well now, Francis." He paused, his needled glance sheathed by a courtier's suavity. "What can we do for you?"

Painfully distressed, breathing quickly, Francis kept his eyes down. "I came to see you about Nora."

The stammered remark rent the room's serenity, its note of mannered ease.

"And what about Nora, pray?"

"Her marriage with Gilfoyle . . . She doesn't want to go through with it . . . she's miserable . . . it seems so stupid and unjust . . . such a needless and horrible affair."

"What do you know about the horrible affair?"

"Well . . . everything . . . that she wasn't to blame."

There was a pause. Fitzgerald's fine brow expressed annoyance, yet he gazed at the distraught youth before him with a kind of stately pity.

"My dear young man, if you enter the priesthood, as I trust you will, and gain even half the experience which unhappily is mine, you will comprehend that certain social disorders demand equally specific remedies. You are staggered by this —" He returned the phrase with an inclination of his head — "horrible affair. I am not. I even anticipated it. I know and abominate the whiskey trade for its effect upon the brute mentality of the clods who constitute this parish. You and I may sit down and quietly enjoy our Lachryma Christi, like gentlemen. Not so Mr. Edward Bannon. Enough! I make no allegations. I merely say, we have a problem, unhappily not unique to those of us who spend drab hours in the confessional." Fitzgerald paused to take snuff, with a distinguished wrist. "What are we to do with it? I will tell you. First, legitimize and baptize the offspring. Secondly, marry the mother if we can, to as decent a man as will have her. We must regularize, regularize. Make a good Catholic home out of the mess. Weave the loose ends into our sound social fabric. Believe me, Nora Bannon is highly fortunate to get Gilfoyle. He's not so bright, but he's steady. In a couple of years you'll see her at mass with her husband and family . . . perfectly happy."

"No, no." The interruption was wrenched from Francis' shut lips. "She'll never be happy — only broken and miserable."

Fitzgerald's head was a trifle higher. "And is happiness the ultimate objective of our earthly life?"

"She'll do something desperate. You can't compel Nora. I know her better than you."

"You seem to know her intimately." Fitzgerald smiled with

withering suavity. "I hope you have no physical interest in the lady yourself."

A dark red spot burned on Francis' pale cheek. He muttered: "I am very fond of Nora. But if I love her — it's nothing that would make your confessional more drab. I beg you — " His voice held a low, desperate entreaty. "Don't force her into this marriage. She's not common clay . . . she's a bright sweet spirit. You can't thrust a child upon her bosom and a husband into her arms — because — in her innocence, she's been . . ."

Stung to the quick, Fitzgerald banged his snuff-box on the table. "Don't preach at me, sir!"

"I'm sorry. You can see I don't know what I'm saying. I'm trying to beg you to use your power." Francis mustered his flagging forces in a final effort. "At least give her a little time."

"That is enough, Francis!"

The parish priest, too much master of himself, and of others, to lose his temper or his countenance for long, rose abruptly from his chair and looked at his flat gold watch. "I have a confraternity meeting at eight. You must excuse me." As Francis got up, he patted him reproachfully on the back. "My dear boy, you are very immature. Might I even say a little foolish? But thank God you have a wise old mother in Holy Church. Don't run your head against the walls, Francis. They've stood for generations — against stronger batterings than yours. But there now — I know you're a good lad. Come up and have a chat about Holywell when the wedding's over. And meanwhile — as a little act of reparation for your rudeness will you say the Salve Regina for my intention?"

A pause. It was useless, quite useless. "Yes, Father."

"Good night then, my son . . . and God bless you!"

The night air was raw and chill. Defeated, crushed by the impotence of his youth, Francis dragged himself away from the Presbytery. His footsteps echoed dully on the paved pathway. As he passed the chapel steps, the sacristan was closing the side doors. When the last chink of light was gone, Francis stood, hatless, in the darkness, his eyes fixed on the wraith-like windows of the clerestory.

He blurted out, in a kind of final desperation: "Oh, God! Do what's best for all of us."

As the wedding day approached, consuming Francis with a deadly, sleepless fever, the atmosphere of the tavern seemed insensibly to settle, like a stagnant pool. Nora was quiet, Polly vaguely hopeful; and though Ned still cringed in solitude, the muddled terror in his eyes was less. The ceremony would, of course, be private. But no restraint need operate upon the trousseau, the dowry, the elaborate honeymoon to Killarney. The house was littered with robes and rich materials. Polly, beseeching another "try-on," with a mouthful of pins, waded through bales of cloth and linen, enveloped in merciful fog.

Gilfoyle, smugly observant, smoking the Union's best cigars, would occasionally hold conference, upon matters of finance, with Ned. There was a deed of partnership, duly signed, and great talk of building, to accommodate the new ménage. Already Thad's numerous poor relatives hung about the house, sycophantic yet assertive. His married sister, Mrs. Neily, and her daughter Charlotte, were perhaps the worst.

Nora had little enough to say. Once, meeting Francis in the passage, she stopped.

"You know . . . don't you?"

His heart was breaking, he dared not meet her eye. "Yes, I know."

There was a suffocating pause. He could not sustain the torture in his breast. Incoherently he burst out, boyish tears starting in his eyes: "Nora . . . We can't let this happen. If you knew how I've felt for you . . . I could look after you — work for you. Nora . . . let me take you away."

She considered him with that strange and pitying tenderness. "Where would we go?"

"Anywhere." He spoke wildly, his cheek wet and shining.

She did not answer. She pressed his hand without speaking, then went on, quickly, to be fitted for a dress.

On the day before the wedding, she unbent a little, losing something of her marble acquiescence. Suddenly, over one of those cups of tea which Polly inflicted upon her, she declared: "I believe I'd like to go to Whitley Bay today."

Astounded, Polly echoed: "Whitley Bay?" — then added in a flutter, "I'll come with you."

"There's no need." Nora paused, gently stirring her cup. "But of course if you want to . . ."

"I do indeed, my dear!"

Reassured by that lightness in Nora's manner, — as though a bar of that old mischievous gaiety re-echoed, like distant music, in her being, — Polly came to view the excursion without disfavour. She had a gratified, bewildered idea that Nora was "coming round." As she finished her tea she discoursed upon the beautiful Lake of Killarney, which she had once visited as a girl. The boatmen there had been most amusing.

The two women, dressed for the expedition, left for the station after the dinner hour. As she turned the corner, Nora looked up towards the window where Francis stood. She seemed to linger for a second, smiled gravely, and waved her hand. Then she was gone.

News of the accident reached the district even before Aunt Polly was brought home, in a state of collapse, in a cab. The sensation throughout the city was impressive. Popular interest could never have been so stirred by the mere stupidity of a young woman stumbling between a platform and a moving train. It was the prenuptial timing which made the thing so exquisite. Around the docks women ran out of their doorways, gathering in groups, beshawled, arms akimbo. Blame for the tragedy was finally pinned upon the victim's new shoes. There was enormous sympathy for Thaddeus Gilfoyle, for the family, for all young women about to be married and under the necessity of travelling by train. There was talk of a public funeral — with the confraternity band — for the mangled remains.

Late that night, how he knew not, Francis found himself in St. Dominic's church. It was quite deserted. The flickering wick of the sanctuary lamp drew his haggard eyes, a feeble beacon. Kneeling, stiff and pale, he felt, like an embrace, the remorseless foreclosure of his destiny. Never had he known such a moment of desolation, of abandonment. He could not weep. His lips, cold and stricken, could not move in prayer. But from his tortured mind there soared an offering of anguished thought. First his parents; and now Nora. He could no longer ignore these testaments from above. He would go away . . . he must go . . . to Father MacNabb . . . to San Morales. He would give himself entirely to God. He must become a priest.

VI

DURING Easter, in the year 1892, an event occurred in the English Seminary of San Morales which set the place humming with a note of consternation. One of the students, in the subdiaconate, disappeared completely for the space of four entire days.

Naturally the Seminary had witnessed other seditions since its foundation in these Aragon uplands fifty years before. Students had mutinied for an hour or so, skulking to the *posada* outside the walls, hurriedly deranging conscience and digestion with long *cigarros* and the local *aguardiente*. Once or twice it had been necessary to drag some tottering recusant by the ears from the dingy parlours of the Via Amorosa in the town. But this — for a student to march out through the open gates in broad daylight and, half a week later, by the same gates, in even brighter light of day, to limp in again, dusty, unshaven, dishevelled, offering every evidence of horrible dissipation, and then, with no other excuse than "I've been for a walk!" to fling himself upon his bed and sleep the clock round — it was apostasy.

At the recreation the students discussed it in awed tones — little groups of dark figures on the sunny slopes, between the bright green copperas-sprayed vineyards, with the Seminary, white and gleaming against the pale pink earth, beneath them.

It was agreed that Chisholm would undoubtedly be expelled.

The Committee of Examination had immediately been constituted. According to precedent, as in all grave breaches of discipline it was composed of the Rector, the Administrator, the Director of Novices and the Head Seminarian. After some preliminary discussion, the tribunal opened its proceedings, in the theological atrium, on the day following the runagate's return.

Outside the *solano* was blowing. The ripe black olives fell from the blade-leafed trees and burst beneath the sun. A scent of orange flowers swept across from the grove above the infirmary. The baked earth crackled with the heat. As Francis entered the white and lofty-pillared room, its polished empty benches cool and dark, he had a quiet air. The black alpaca soutane stressed the thinness of his figure. His hair, cropped and tonsured, gave tautness to his face-bones, intensified the darkness of his eyes, his dark contained reserve. There was an odd tranquillity about his hands.

Before him, on the platform reserved for protagonists in debate, were four desks, already occupied by Father Tarrant, Monsignor MacNabb, Father Gomez and Deacon Mealey. Conscious of a mingling of displeasure and concern in the united gaze now upon him, Francis hung his head, while in a rapid voice Gomez, Director of Novices, read out the accusation.

There was a silence. Then Father Tarrant spoke.

"What is your explanation?"

Despite the quietness which enclosed him Francis suddenly began to flush. He kept his head down.

"I went for a walk!" The words resounded lamely.

"That is sufficiently apparent. We use our legs whether our intentions are good or bad. Apart from the obvious sin of leaving the Seminary without permission, were your intentions bad?"

"No."

"During your absence did you indulge in alcoholic liquor?"

"No."

"Did you visit the bullfight, the fair, the casino?"

"No."

"Did you consort with women of ill fame?"

"No."

"Then what did you do?"

Silence again, then the muttered inarticulate reply. "I've told you. You wouldn't understand. I . . . I went for a walk!"

Father Tarrant smiled thinly. "Do you wish us to believe that you spent these entire four days ceaselessly perambulating the countryside?"

"Well . . . practically."

"What destination did you reach eventually?"

"I — I got to Cossa!"

"Cossa! But that is fifty miles away!"

"Yes, I suppose so."

"You were there for some specific purpose?"

"No."

Father Tarrant bit his thin lip. He could not brook obstruction. He had a sudden wild longing for the rack, the boot, the wheel. Small wonder the mediævalists had recourse to such instruments! There were circumstances which fully justified them.

"I believe you are lying, Chisholm."

"Why should I lie — to you?"

A muffled exclamation came from Deacon Mealey. His presence was purely formal. As the chief prefect he sat there as a symbol, perhaps a cipher, expressive of the student body. Yet he could not restrain his earnest pleading.

"Please, Francis! For the sake of all of the students . . . all of us who love you . . . I . . . I implore you to own up."

As Francis remained silent, Father Gomez, the young Spanish novice master, inclined his head and murmured to Tarrant: "I've had no evidence . . . none whatever, from the town. But we might write to the priest at Cossa."

Tarrant shot a swift glance at the Spaniard's subtle face.

"Yes. That is decidedly an idea."

Meanwhile the Rector had taken advantage of the lull. Older, slower than at Holywell, he leaned forward. He spoke slowly and kindly.

"Of course, you must realize, Francis, that in the circumstances, so general an explanation is barely adequate. After all, it is a serious matter to play truant — not merely the breaking of the Seminary rule — the disobedience — but rather the underlying motive which prompted you. Tell me! Are you not happy here?"

"Yes, I am happy."

"Good! And you've no reason to doubt your vocation?"

"No! I want more than ever to try to do some good in the world."

"That pleases me greatly. You don't wish to be sent away?"

"No!"

"Then tell us in your own words how you came to — to take your remarkable adventure."

At the quiet encouragement, Francis raised his head. He made a great effort, his eyes remote, his face troubled.

"I . . . I had just been to the chapel. But I couldn't pray, I couldn't seem to settle. I was restless. The *solano* was blowing — the hot wind seemed to make me more restless, the routine of the Seminary suddenly seemed petty and vexatious. Suddenly, I saw the road outside the gates, white and soft with dust. I couldn't help myself. I was on the road, walking. I walked all night, miles and miles. I walked — "

"All the next day." Father Tarrant bit out the satiric interruption. "And the next!"

"That's what I did."

"I never heard such a pack of rubbish in my life! It is an insult to the intelligence of the Committee."

The Rector, with frowning resolution, suddenly straightened himself in his chair.

"I propose that we temporarily adjourn." While the two priests stared at him in surprise, he said decisively to Francis: "You may go for the present. If we think it necessary we will recall you."

Francis left the room in a dead silence. Only then did the Rector turn to the others. He declared coldly: "I assure you that bullying will do no good. We must go carefully. There is more in this than meets the eye."

Smarting under the interference, Father Tarrant moved fretfully.

"It is the culmination of an unruly career."

"Not at all." The Rector demurred. "He's been eager and persevering ever since he came here. There is nothing damaging in his record, Father Gomez?"

Gomez turned the pages, on the desk, before him.

"No." He spoke slowly, reading from the record. "A few practical jokes. Last winter he set fire to the English newspaper when Father Despard was perusing it in the common room. Asked why . . . he laughed and answered, 'The Devil finds work for idle hands!' "

"Never mind that." The Rector spoke sharply. "We all know Father Despard corners every paper that comes into this Seminary."

"Then," Gomez resumed, "when deputed to read aloud in the refectory he smuggled in and substituted for *The Life of St. Peter of Alcantara* a C. R. S. tract entitled *When Eva Stole the Sugar* which — until he was stopped — induced much unseemly hilarity."

"Harmless mischief."

"Again . . ." Gomez turned another page. "In the comical procession the students got up, representing the Sacraments — you may remember, one dressed up as a baby representing Baptism, two others were got up as Matrimony, and so on — it was all done with permission of course. But," Gomez shot a dubious glance at Tarrant, "on the back of the corpse carried in for Extreme Unction, Chisholm pinned a card:

> "Here lies Father Tarrant
> I've gladly signed his warrant.
> If ever — "

"That's enough." Tarrant broke in sharply. "We've more to concern us than these absurd lampoons."

The Rector nodded. "Absurd, yes. But not malicious. I like a young man who can knock some fun out of life. We cannot ignore the fact that Chisholm is an unusual character — most unusual. He has great depth and fire. He's sensitive, inclined to fits of melancholy. He conceals it behind these high spirits. You see, he's a fighter, he'll never give in. He's a queer mixture of childlike simplicity and logical directness. And, above all, he's a complete individualist!"

"Individualism is rather a dangerous quality in a theologian," Tarrant interposed acidly. "It gave us the Reformation."

"And the Reformation gave us a better-behaved Catholic Church." The Rector smiled mildly at the ceiling. "But we're getting from the point. I don't deny there's been a gross breach of discipline. It must be punished. But the punishment cannot be rushed. I can't expel a student of Chisholm's quality without first knowing positively that he deserves expulsion. Therefore, let us wait a few days." He rose, innocently. "I'm sure you all agree."

As the three priests left the platform, Gomez and Tarrant went off together.

During the next two days an air of suspended doom overhung the unhappy Francis. He was not restrained. No apparent ban was placed upon his studies. But wherever he went — to the library, refectory or common room — an unnatural silence struck his fellows, followed swiftly by an exaggerated casualness which deceived no one. The knowledge that he was the universal topic gave him a guilty look. His Holywell companion, Hudson, also in the subdiaconate, pursued him with affectionate attentions and a worried frown. Anselm Mealey led another faction which clearly felt itself outraged. At recreation they consulted, approached the solitary figure. Mealey was the spokesman.

"We don't want to hit you when you're down, Francis. But this touches all of us. It's a slur upon the student body as a whole. We feel that it would be so much finer and manlier if you would make a clean breast and own up to it."

"Own up to what?"

Mealey shrugged his shoulders. There was a silence. What more could he do? As he turned away with the others he said: —

"We've decided to make a novena for you. I feel it worse than the others. I hoped you were my best friend."

Francis found it harder to maintain his pretence of normality. He would start off to walk in the Seminary grounds, then stop, sharply, recollecting that walking had been his ruin. He drifted about, aware that for Tarrant and the other professors he had ceased to exist. At the lectures he found he was not listening. The summons to the Rector he half hoped for did not come.

His sense of personal stress increased. He failed to understand himself. He was a purposeless enigma. He brooded over the justification of those who had predicted that he had no vocation. He had wild conceptions of setting out as a lay brother to some dangerous and distant mission. He began to haunt the church — but secretly. Above all there existed the necessity of putting on a face to meet his little world.

It was on the morning of the third day, Wednesday, that Father Gomez received the letter. Shocked but deeply gratified, his resourcefulness confirmed, he ran with it to the Administrator's office. He stood, while Father Tarrant read the note, like an intelligent dog awaiting its reward, a kind word or a bone.

Mi Amigo,

In reply to your honoured communication of Whit-Sunday, I deeply regret to inform you that inquiries have elicited the fact that a Seminarian, of such bearing, height and colour as you define, was observed in Cossa on April 14th. He was seen to enter the house of one Rosa Oyarzabal late that evening and to leave early the following morning. The woman in question lives alone, is of a known character, and has not frequented the altar rails for seven years.

I have the honour to remain, dear Padre,
Your devoted brother in Jesus Christus,

SALVADOR BOLAS
P. P. Cossa

Gomez murmured: "Don't you agree it was good strategy?"

"Yes, yes!" With a brow of thunder Tarrant brushed the Spaniard aside. Bearing the letter like something obscene, he strode into the Rector's room at the end of the corridor. But the Rector was saying his mass. He would be occupied for half an hour.

Father Tarrant could not wait. He crossed the courtyard like a whirlwind and, without knocking, burst into Francis' room. It was empty.

Checked, realizing that Francis must also be at mass, he struggled with his fury as an ungovernable horse might fight its bit. He sat down, abruptly, forcing himself to wait, his dark thin figure charged with lightning.

The cell was barer even than others of its kind, its inventory a bed, a chest, a table, the chair he occupied. Upon the chest stood one faded photograph, an angular woman in a frightful hat holding the hand of a white-clad little girl: *Love from Aunt Polly and Nora.*

Tarrant repressed his sneer. But his lip curled at the single picture on the whitewashed walls, a tiny replica of the Sistine Madonna, Our Lady of Chastity.

Suddenly, upon the table, he saw an open notebook: a diary. Again he started, like a nervous horse, his nostrils dilated, a dark red fire in his eye. For a moment he sat, battling his scruples, then rose and went slowly towards the book. He was a gentleman. It was repugnant to pry like a vulgar chambermaid, into another's privacy. But it was his duty. Who could guess what further iniquities this scroll contained? With relentless austerity upon his face, he picked up the written page.

". . . was it Saint Anthony who spoke of his 'ill-judged, obstinate and perverse behaviour'? I must console myself in the greatest despondency I have ever known, with that single thought! If they send me away from here my life will be broken. I'm a miserable crooked character, I don't think straight like the others, I cannot train myself to run with the pack. But with my whole soul I desire passionately to work for God. In our Father's house there are many mansions! There was room for such diversities as Joan of Arc and . . . well, Blessed Benedict Labre who let even the lice run over him. Surely there is room for me!

"They ask me to explain to them. How can one explain nothing —or what is so obvious as to be shameful? Francis de Sales said: 'I will be ground to powder rather than break a rule.' But when I walked out of the Seminary I did not think of rules, or of breaking them. Certain impulses are unconscious.

"It helps me to write this down: it gives my transgression the semblance of reason.

"For weeks I had been sleeping badly, tossing through these hot nights in a fever of unrest. Perhaps it is harder for me here than for the others — judged at least by the voluminous literature on the subject, wherein the steps to the priesthood are represented as sweet untroubled joys, piled one upon another. If our beloved laity knew how one has to fight!

"Here my greatest difficulty has been the sense of confinement, of physical inaction — what a bad mystic I should make! — always aggravated by echoes, stray sounds, penetrating inwards from the outer world. Then I realize that I am twenty-three, that I have done nothing yet to help a single living soul, and I am fevered with unrest.

"Willie Tulloch's letters provide — in Father Gomez' phrase — the most pernicious stimuli. Now that Willie is a qualified doctor and his sister Jean a certified nurse, both working for the Tynecastle Poor Law Board and enjoying many thrilling, if verminous adventures, in the slums, I feel that I should be out and fighting too.

"Of course I shall, one day. . . . I must be patient. But my present ferment seems heightened by the news of Ned and Polly. I was happy when they decided to remove from above the tavern and have Judy, the child, to live with them in the little flat which Polly had taken at Clermont, on the outskirts of the city. But Ned has been ill, Judy troublesome, and Gilfoyle — left to manage Union Tavern — a most unsatisfactory business partner. Ned, in fact, has gone to pieces, refuses to go out, sees no one. That one impulse of blind unthinkable stupidity has finished him. A baser man would have survived it.

"The pattern of life sometimes demands great faith. Dear Nora! That tender platitude conceals a thousand avenues of thought and feeling. When Father Tarrant gave us that practical talk — *agendo contra* — he said most truly: 'Some temptations cannot be fought — one must close one's mind and fly from them!' My excursion to Cossa must have been that kind of flight.

"At first, though walking fast, I did not mean to go far when I passed through the Seminary gates. But the relief, the sense of escape from myself which the violent exercise afforded, drove me on. I sweated gloriously, like a peasant in the fields — that salty running sweat which seems to purge one of human dross. My mind lifted, my heart began to sing. I wanted to go on and on until I dropped!

"I walked all day without food or drink. I covered a great distance, for, when evening drew near, I could smell the sea. And as the stars broke out in the pale sky, I came over the hill and found Cossa at my feet. The village, harboured on a sheltered creek where the sea barely lapped, with blossoming acacia trees lining its single street, had an almost heavenly beauty. I was dead with tiredness. There was an enormous blister on my heel. But as I came down the hill the place welcomed me with its quiet pulse of life.

"In the little square the villagers were enjoying the cool air, scented with acacia flowers, the dusk made dimmer by the lamps of the little inn, where at an open doorway stood two pine benches. Before the benches in the soft dust some old men were playing bowls with wooden balls. From the creek came the booming of frogs. Children laughed and ran. It was simple and beautiful. Though I now realized that I had not a peseta in my pocket, I seated myself on one of the benches outside the door. How good it was to rest. I was stupid with fatigue. Suddenly, in the quiet darkness beneath the trees, the sound of Catalan pipes rang out. Not loud — low, attuned to the night. If one has not heard these reeds, or the shrill, sweet native tunes, one cannot fully estimate the gladness of that moment. I was enchanted. I suppose, as a Scot, I've the lilt of the pipes in my blood. I sat as though drugged by the music, the darkness, the beauty of the night, my utter weakness.

"I had resolved to sleep out on the beach. But presently, as I thought to move there, a mist rolled in from the sea. It fell like a mystery upon the village. In five minutes the square was choked with twisting vapour, the trees dripping, and everybody going home. I had reached the conclusion, unwillingly, that I must go to the local priest, 'give myself up,' and get a bed, when a woman seated on the other bench suddenly spoke to me. For some time I had felt her gazing at me with that mixture of pity and contempt which the mere sight of a religious seems to provoke in Christian countries. Now, as if she read my thoughts, she said: 'They are tight people there. They will not take you in.'

"She was about thirty years of age, dressed quietly in black, with a pale face, dark eyes and a thickened figure. She continued indifferently:

" 'There is a bed in my house if you wish to sleep in it.'

" 'I have no money to pay for a lodging.'

"She laughed scornfully. 'You can pay me with your prayers.'

"It had now begun to rain. They had closed the *fonda*. We both sat on the wet benches under the dripping acacia trees in the deserted square. The absurdity of this seemed to strike her. She rose.

" 'I am going home. If you are not a fool you will accept my hospitality.'

"My thin soutane was soaked. I had begun to shiver. I reflected that I could send her money for my room on my return to the Seminary. I got up and walked with her down the narrow street.

"Her house was halfway down the row. We descended two steps into the kitchen. When she had lit the lamp, she threw off the black shawl, put a pot of chocolate on the fire and took a new loaf from the oven. She spread a red-checked tablecloth. Bubbling chocolate and hot bread made a good smell in the small clean room.

"As she poured the chocolate into thick cups she looked at me across the table. 'You had better say grace. That improves the flavour!' Though now there was no mistaking the irony in her voice, I said grace. We began to eat and drink. The flavour needed no improvement.

"She kept watching me. She had once been a very pretty woman, but the remnants of her beauty made her dark-eyed olive face seem hard. Her small ears were close to her head and pierced with heavy gold rings. Her hands were plump like the hands of a Rubens Madonna.

" 'Well, little padre, you are lucky to be here. I have no liking for the priests. In Barcelona, when I pass them I break into open laughter!'

"I couldn't help smiling. 'You don't surprise me. It's the first thing we learn — to be laughed at. The best man I ever knew used to preach in the open air. The whole town turned out to laugh at him. They named him, in mockery, Holy Daniel. You see, there's so little doubt nowadays that anyone who believes in God is a hypocrite or a fool!'

"She took a slow drink of chocolate, watching me over her cup. 'You are no fool. Tell me, do I please you?'

" 'I think you are charming and kind.'

" 'It is my nature to be kind. I've had a sad life. My father was a Castilian noble who was dispossessed by the Madrid Government. My husband commanded a great ship in the Navy. He was lost at sea. I myself am an actress — living quietly here at present until my father's estate is recovered. Of course you understand that I am lying.'

" 'Perfectly!'

"She didn't take this as a joke as I had hoped. She reddened slightly. 'You are too clever. But I know why you are here, my runaway priestling; you are all the same.' She got over her fit of pique, and mocked: 'You forsake Mother Church for Mother Eve.'

"I was puzzled, then her meaning dawned on me. It was so absurd I wanted to laugh. But it was annoying too — I supposed I'd have to clear out. I had finished my bread and chocolate. I rose and took my hat. 'Thank you exceedingly for my supper. It was excellent.'

"Her expression changed, all the malice driven out of it by surprise. 'So you are a hypocrite then.' She bit her lip sulkily. As I went to the door she said suddenly: 'Don't go!'

"A silence. She said defiantly: —

" 'Don't look at me like that. I'm entitled to do as I choose. I enjoy myself. You should see me Saturday evenings, sitting in the Cava at Barcelona — more fun than ever you'll have in your miserable little life. Go upstairs and sleep.'

"There was a pause. Her attitude now seemed reasonable; and I could hear the rain outside. I hesitated, then moved towards the narrow stairs. My feet were swollen and smarting. I must have limped badly, for she exclaimed suddenly, coldly: 'What is the matter with your precious foot?'

" 'It's nothing . . . only blistered.'

"She studied me with those strange unfathomable eyes.

" 'I will bathe it for you.'

"In spite of all my protests she made me sit down. When she had filled a basin with warm water she knelt and took off my boot. My sock was sticking to the raw flesh. She softened it with water and drew it off. Her unexpected kindness embarrassed me. She bathed both my feet and put some ointment on them. Then she stood up.

" 'That should feel better. Your socks will be ready for you in the morning.'

" 'How can I thank you?'

"She said unexpectedly in an odd dull tone: 'What does one do with a life like mine!' Before I could answer she raised the pitcher in her right hand. 'Do not preach at me or I will break your head. Your bed is on the second landing. Good night.'

"She turned away towards the fire. I went upstairs, found a small room beneath the skylight. I slept as though stunned.

"Next morning when I came down, she was moving about the kitchen, making coffee. She gave me breakfast. As I took my leave I tried to express my gratitude. But she cut me short. She gave me her sad peculiar smile. 'You are too innocent to be a priest. You will be a great failure.'

"I started back for San Morales. I was lame and rather scared of my reception. I was afraid. I took my time."

Father Tarrant remained motionless at the window for a long moment, then quietly replaced the diary upon the table, reminded by a glint of recollection that it was he who had first asked Francis to keep it. Methodically he tore the Spanish priest's letter into fragments. The expression on his face was quite remarkable. For once it lacked its bleakness, that iron austerity seared into every feature by pitiless self-mortification. It became a young face, flooded with generosity and thoughtfulness. With his clenched hand still holding the pieces of the letter, slowly, almost unconsciously, he struck his breast three times. Then he spun round and left the room.

As he descended the broad staircase Anselm Mealey's solid head came up and around the spiral balustrade. Observing Father Tarrant, the model seminarian dared to pause. He admired the Administrator to excess. To be noticed by him was a heavenly joy. He ventured modestly: —

"Excuse me, sir. We are all very anxious. I am wondering if there is any more news . . . concerning Chisholm?"

"What news?"

"Well . . . of his leaving."

Tarrant contemplated his creature with remote distaste. "Chisholm is not leaving." He added, with sudden violence, "You fool!"

That evening as Francis sat in his study, dizzy and unbelieving under the miracle of his redemption, one of the college servants silently handed in a packet. It contained a superb figure of the Virgin of Montserrat carved in ebony, a tiny masterpiece of fifteenth-century Spanish craftsmanship. No message accompanied the exquisite thing. Not a word of explanation. Suddenly, with a wild consuming thought, Francis remembered he had seen it above the prie-dieu in Father Tarrant's room.

It was the Rector, meeting Francis at the end of the week, who put his finger on the manifest inconsistency. "It strikes me, young sir, that you have escaped gey lightly, through a sinister screen of sanctity. In my young days playing truant — 'plunking' we called it — was a punishable crime." He fixed on Francis his shrewd and twinkling gaze. "As a penance you might write me an essay — two thousand words — on 'The Virtue of Walking.'"

In the small universe of a seminary the very walls have ears, the keyholes diabolic vision. The story of Francis' escapade came gradually to light, was fitted, piece by piece, together. It grew, gained indeed, as it passed from lip to ear. Assuming the facets of the finished gem, it seemed likely to descend — a classic in the Seminary's history. When Father Gomez had the final details, he wrote fully to his friend the parish priest of Cossa. Father Bolas was much impressed. He wrote back, a glowing five-page letter, of which, perhaps, the final paragraph merits quotation: —

Naturally, the pinnacle of achievement would have been the conversion of the woman, Rosa Oyarzabal. How wonderful it would have been had she come to me and wept, on her knees, in true contrition, as the result of our young apostle's visitation! But alas! She has gone into partnership with another madam and opened a brothel in Barcelona, which I grieve to report is flourishing.

III

AN UNSUCCESSFUL CURATE

I

It was raining steadily, early that Saturday evening in January when Francis arrived at Shalesley, on the branch line, some forty miles from Tynecastle. But nothing could damp the eagerness, the burning of his spirit. While the train disappeared into the mist, he stood expectantly on the wet open platform, his alert eyes sweeping its dreary vacancy. No one had come to meet him. Undismayed, he picked up his bag and swung into the main street of the colliery village. The Church of the Redeemer should not be hard to find.

It was his first appointment, his first curacy. He could scarcely believe it. His heart sang . . . at last, at last, newly ordained, he had his chance to get into the battle and fight for human souls.

Though he had been forewarned, Francis had never seen greater ugliness than that which now surrounded him. Shalesley consisted of long grey rows of houses and poor cheap shops, interspaced with plots of waste land, slag heaps, — smoking even in the rain, — a refuse dump, several taverns and chapels, all dominated by the high black headstocks of the Renshaw Colliery. But he told himself gaily that his interest lay in the people, not the place.

The Catholic church stood on the east side of the village, adjacent to the colliery, harmonizing with the scene. It was a big erection of raw red brick with Gothic blue-stained windows, a dark red corrugated iron roof, and a sawed-off rusty spire. The school lay on one side; the Presbytery, fronted by a weedy plot and girded by a broken-toothed fence, upon the other.

With a deep, excited breath, Francis approached the small, ramshackle house and pulled the bell. After some delay, when he was about to ring again, the door was opened by a stout woman in a blue striped apron. Inspecting him, she nodded.

"It'll be yourself, Father! His Reverence is expecting you. In there!" She pointed with privileged good nature to the parlour door. "What weather to be sure. I'll away and put on the kippers."

Francis sturdily entered the room. Already seated at a table covered with a white cloth and laid for a repast, a thickset priest of about fifty stopped his impatient knife-tapping to greet his new curate.

"You're here at last. Come in."

Francis extended his hand. "Father Kezer, I imagine?"

"That's right. Who did you expect? King William of Orange? Well, you're just in time for supper. Trust you!" Tilting back, he called to the adjoining kitchen. "Miss Cafferty! Are you going to be all night?" Then, to Francis: "Sit down and stop looking like the lost chord. I hope you play cribbage. I like a game of an evening."

Francis took a chair at the table and soon Miss Cafferty hurried in with a large covered dish of kippers and poached eggs. As Father Kezer helped himself to two eggs and a brace of kippers she laid another place for Francis. Then Father Kezer passed over the dish, his mouth full.

"Go ahead and help yourself. Don't stint. You'll have to work hard here so you'd better eat."

He himself ate rapidly, his strong crunching jaws and capable hands, felted with black hairs, never at rest. He was burly, with a round cropped head, and a tight mouth. His nose was flat, with wide nostrils out of which sprouted two dark snuff-stained tufts. He conveyed the impression of strength, of authority. Every movement was a masterpiece of unconscious self-assertion. As he cut an egg in two and slipped one half into his mouth his little eyes watched, formed an opinion of Francis, as a butcher might weigh the merits of a steer.

"You don't look too hardy. Under eleven stone, eh? I don't know what you curates are coming to. My last was a weak-kneed effort! Should have called himself flea — not Lee — he hadn't the guts of one. It's this Continental la-de-da that ruins you. In my time — well, the fellows that came out of Maynooth with me were men."

"I think you'll find me sound in wind and limb." Francis smiled.

"We'll soon see." Father Kezer grunted. "Go in and hear confessions when you've finished. I'll be in later. There won't be many tonight though . . . seeing it's wet. Give them an excuse! They're bone lazy — my beautiful lot!"

Upstairs, in his thin-walled room, massively furnished with a heavy bed and an enormous Victorian wardrobe, Francis washed his hands and face at the stained washstand. Then he hastened down towards the church. The impression Father Kezer had given him was not favourable, but he told himself he must be fair: immediate judgements were so often unjust. He sat for a long time in the cold confessional box, — still marked with the name of his predecessor, Fr. Lee, — hearing the drumming of the rain on the tin roof. At last he came out and wandered round the empty church. It was a depressing spectacle — bare as a barn and not very clean. An unhappy attempt had been made to marble the nave with dark green paint. The statue of Saint Joseph had lost a hand and been clumsily repaired. The stations of the cross were sad little daubs. On the altar some gaudy paper flowers, in vases of tarnished brass, hit the eye like an affront. But these little shortcomings only made his opportunity the greater. The tabernacle was there. And Francis knelt before it, with throbbing fervour, dedicating his life anew.

Habituated to the cultured atmosphere of San Morales, a halfway house for scholars and preachers, men of breeding and distinction moving between London, Madrid and Rome, Francis found the next few days increasingly difficult. Father Kezer was not an easy man. Naturally irascible and inclined to surliness, age, experience, and failure to win affection from his flock had made him hard as nails.

At one time he had held an excellent parish in the seaside resort of Eastcliffe. He had proved himself so disagreeable that important people in the town had petitioned the Bishop to remove him. The incident, at first bitterly resented, had been hallowed by time into an act of personal sacrifice. He would remark, soulfully: "Of my own free will I stepped from the throne to the footstool . . . but, ah! . . . those were the days."

Miss Cafferty, his cook and housekeeper combined, alone stood by him. She had been with him for years. She understood him, she was of his own kidney, she could take his slangings and heartily slang him back. The two respected each other. When he departed on his annual six weeks' holiday to Harrogate he allowed her to go home for her own vacation.

In his personal habits he had scant refinement. He stamped around his bedroom, opened and slammed the single bathroom door. The matchboard house reverberated with his wind.

Unwittingly, he had reduced his religion to a formula — with no conception of interior meanings, of the unsubstantial, no elasticity of outlook. "Do this or be damned" was imprinted on his heart. There were certain things to be accomplished with words, water, oil and salt. Without them, hell was ready, hot and gaping. He was deeply prejudiced, loudly voicing his detestation of every other denomination in the village — an attitude which did little to gain him friends.

Even in his relations with his own congregation he was not at peace. The parish was a poor one with a heavy debt upon the church and despite a stringent economy he was often desperately pressed to make ends meet. He had a legitimate case to place before his people. But his natural ire was a poor substitute for tact. In his sermons, planted solidly on his feet, head thrust aggressively forward, he lashed the sparse congregation for its neglect.

"How do you expect me to pay the rent, and the taxes, and the insurance? And keep the church roof over your heads? You're not giving it to me, you're giving it to Almighty God. Now listen to me, every man and woman of ye. It's silver I want to see in the plate, not your miserable brass farthings. You're most of you in work you men, thanks to the generosity of Sir George Renshaw. You've no excuse! As for the wimmen of the parish — if they'd put more in the offertory and less on their backs it would fit them better." He thundered on, then took up the collection himself, glaring accusingly at each of his parishioners as he shoved the plate beneath their noses.

His demands had provoked a feud, a bitter vendetta between himself and his parishioners. The more he berated them the less they gave. Enraged, he devised schemes, took to distributing little buff envelopes. When they left the empty envelopes behind he went round the church after the service, gathering up the litter and muttering furiously: "That's how they treat Almighty God!"

In this gloomy financial sky there was one bright sun.

Sir George Renshaw, who owned the Shalesley colliery, with, indeed, fifteen other coal mines in the county, was not only a man of immense resources and a Catholic but an inveterate philanthropist. Though his country seat, Renshaw Hall, was seventy miles away, on the other side of the shire, the Church of the Redeemer had somehow gained a place upon his list. Every Christmas, with the utmost regularity, a cheque for one hundred guineas reached the parish priest. "Guineas, mind ye!" Father Kezer anointed the word. "Not just measly pounds. Ah! There's a gentleman for ye!" He had seen Sir George only twice, at public gatherings in Tynecastle many years before, but he spoke of him with reverence and awe. He had a lurking fear that, through no fault of his, the magnate might discontinue the charity.

By the end of his first month at Shalesley, close association with Father Kezer began to take effect on Francis. He was continually on edge. No wonder young Father Lee had had such a bad nervous breakdown. His spiritual life became overcast, his sense of values confused. He found himself regarding Father Kezer with growing hostility. Then he would recollect himself with an inward groan, and strive wildly for obedience, for humility.

His parochial work was desperately hard, particularly in this wintry weather. Three times a week he had to bicycle to Broughton and Glenburn, two distant wretched hamlets, to say mass, hear confessions, and take the catechism class in the local town hall. The lack of response amongst his people increased his difficulties. The very children were lethargic, shuffling. There was much poverty, heartrending destitution; the whole parish seemed steeped in apathy, savourless and stale. Passionately he told himself he would not surrender to routine. Conscious of his clumsiness and inefficiency, he had a burning desire to reach these poor hearts, to succour and revive them. He would kindle a spark, blaze the dead ashes into life, if it were the last thing he did.

What made it worse was the fact that the parish priest, astute and watchful, seemed to sense, with a kind of grim humour, the difficulties his curate was experiencing, and to anticipate slyly a readjustment of the other's idealism to his own practical common sense. Once when Francis came in, tired and wet, having bicycled ten miles through wind and rain to an outlying sick call at Broughton, Father Kezer compressed his attitude into a single gibe. "Handing out halos isn't what you thought it was — eh?" He added, naturally: "A good-for-nothing lot."

Francis flushed hotly. "Christ died for a good-for-nothing lot."

Deeply upset, Francis began to mortify himself. At meals he ate sparingly, often only a cup of tea and some toast. Frequently, when he woke up in the middle of the night, tortured by misgivings, he would steal down to the church. Shadowed and silent, washed in pale moonlight, the bare edifice lost its distracting crudity. He flung himself down on his knees, begging for courage to embrace the tribulations of this beginning, praying with impetuous violence. At last, as he gazed at the wounded figure on the cross, patient, gentle, suffering, peace would fill his soul.

One night, shortly after midnight, when he had made a visit of this nature and was tiptoeing upstairs, he found Father Kezer waiting on him. Wearing his nightshirt and an overcoat, a candle in his hand, the parish priest planted his thick hairy legs on the top landing, angrily barred the way.

"What d'you think you're doing?"

"Going to my room."

"Where have you been?"

"To the church."

"What! At this time of night!"

"Why not?" Francis forced a smile. "Do you think I might wake our Lord up?"

"No, but you might wake me up." Father Kezer lost his temper. "I won't have it. I never heard such nonsense in my life. I'm running a parish, not a religious order. You can pray all you want in the day, but while you're under my orders you'll sleep at night."

Francis suppressed the hot answer on his tongue. He walked to his bedroom in silence. He must curb himself, make a great effort to get on with his superior, if he were to do any good in the parish at all. He tried to concentrate on Father Kezer's good points: his frankness and courage, his odd jocularity, his adamantine chastity.

A few days later, choosing a moment which he thought propitious, he diplomatically approached the older priest.

"I've been wondering, Father . . . we've such a scattered district, so out of the way, with no proper places of amusement . . . wondering if we couldn't have a club for the youngsters of the parish."

"Aha!" Father Kezer was in his jocular mood. "So you're out for popularity, my lad!"

"Good gracious, no." Francis took up an equal heartiness, so intent was he on winning his point. "I don't want to presume. But a club might take the young people off the streets — and the older ones out of the pubs. Develop them physically and socially." He smiled. "Even make them want to come to church."

"Ho, ho!" Father Kezer guffawed. "It's well you're young. I believe you're worse than Lee. Well, go ahead if you want to. But you'll get all your thanks in one basket from the good-for-nothing crowd that hangs out here."

"Thank you, thank you. I only wanted your permission."

With thrilling eagerness Francis immediately began to carry out his plan. Donald Kyle, the manager at Renshaw Colliery, was a Scot and a steady Catholic who had showed signs of good will. Two other officials at the pit, Morrison the check-weigher, whose wife occasionally came in to help at the Presbytery, and Creeden, the head shot-firer, were also members of the church. Through the manager, Francis received permission to use the Colliery first-aid hall three nights a week. With the help of the other two he set out to stir up interest in the proposed club. His own money, added up, made less than two pounds, and he would have died sooner than ask assistance from the parish. But he wrote to Willie Tulloch — whose work brought him into touch with the Tynecastle Corporation Recreation Centres — begging him to send along some old and cast-off athletic gear.

Puzzling how he might best launch the venture, he decided that nothing could draw the young people better than a dance. There was a piano in the room and Creeden was a first-rate performer on the fiddle. He posted up a notice on the Red Cross door, and when Thursday arrived, he expended his capital on a buffet of cakes, fruit and lemonade.

The success of the evening, after a stiff start, surpassed his wildest expectations: so many turned out they managed eight sets of lancers. Most of the lads had no shoes, they danced in their pit boots. Between the dances they sat on the benches round the room, red-faced and happy, while the girls went to the buffet to find them refreshment. When they waltzed they all sang the words of the refrain. A little group of pitmen going off shift gathered at the entrance, the gaslight showing their teeth white against their grimed faces. Towards the end they joined in the singing, and one or two of the brighter sparks amongst them nipped in and stole a dance. It was a merry evening.

As he stood at the door, with their good-nights ringing in his ears, Francis thought with a surge of trembling joy: "They've begun to come alive. Dear God, I've made a start."

Next morning Father Kezer came in to breakfast in a towering rage.

"What's this I hear? A fine to-do! A right royal example. You ought to be ashamed of yourself."

Francis looked up in amazement. "What on earth do you mean?"

"You know what I mean! That infernal stew you put on last night."

"You gave me permission — only a week ago."

Father Kezer snarled: "I didn't give you permission to start a promiscuous rigadoon on the very doorstep of my church. I've had trouble enough to keep my young girls pure without your introducin' your immodest pawing and prancing!"

"The entire evening was perfectly innocent."

"Innocent! — As God is above us!" Father Kezer was dark red with anger. "Don't you know what that sort of gallantry leads to — you poor dolt — clutching and clasping and bodies and legs together? It starts bad thoughts working in these young folks' minds. It leads to concupiscence, carnality and lusts of the flesh."

Francis was very pale, his eyes were blazing with indignation.

"Aren't you confusing lust with sex?"

"Holy St. Joseph! What's the difference?"

"As much as there is between disease and health."

Father Kezer's hands made a convulsive gesture. "What in the foul fiend's name are you talking about?"

The pent-up bitterness of the past two months broke over Francis in a tempestuous wave. "You can't suppress nature. If you do it'll turn on you and rend you. It's perfectly natural and good for young men and women to mix together, to dance together. It's a natural prelude to courtship and marriage. You can't keep sex under a dirty sheet like a stinking corpse. That's what starts the sly laugh, the prurient sneer. We must learn to educate and transmute sex, not choke it as though it were an adder. If you try that you'll fail, besides making something filthy out of what is clean and fine!"

A horrible silence. The veins in Father Kezer's neck were swollen, purple. "You blasphemous pup! I'll not have my young folks couplin' in your dance halls!"

"Then you'll drive them to couple — as you call it — in the dark lanes and fields."

"You lie," Father Kezer stuttered. "I'll keep the maidenhood of this parish undeflowered. I know what I'm about."

"No doubt," Francis answered bitterly. "But the fact remains that statistics show the Shalesley illegitimacy rate to be the highest in the diocese."

For a moment it seemed as though the parish priest must have a fit. His hands clenched and unclenched, as though seeking something to strangle. Rocking slightly on his feet, he raised his finger and levelled it at Francis.

"Statistics'll show another thing. And that is there's no club within five miles of this spot I'm standing on. Your fine plan is finished, smashed, done for. I say that! And in this case *my* word is final!" He flung himself down at the table and furiously began his breakfast.

Francis finished quickly and went upstairs to his room, pale and shaken. Through the dusty panes he could see the first-aid room, with the packing case of boxing gloves and Indian clubs outside, which had arrived yesterday from Tulloch, all useless now, forbidden. A terrible emotion rose up in him. He thought rigidly: I cannot continue to submit, God cannot demand such subservience, I must fight, fight, on Father Kezer's level, fight, not for myself, but for this pitiful, broken-winded parish. He was rent by an overflowing love, an undreamed-of longing to help these poor people, his first charge from God.

During the next few days, as he went through the routine of the parish, he sought feverishly for some means of lifting the ban upon his club. Somehow the club had become the symbol of the parish's emancipation. But the more he dwelt upon it the more unassailable Father Kezer's position appeared.

Drawing his own conclusions from Francis' quietness the older priest showed an ill-concealed jubilation. He was the one to tame them, to bring these young pups to heel. The Bishop must know how good he was to send him so many, one after the other. His sour grin broadened.

Quite suddenly, Francis had an idea. It struck him with overwhelming force, a slender chance, perhaps, yet one which might succeed. His pale face coloured slightly, he almost cried out loud.

With a great effort, he calmed himself. He thought: I'll try, I must try . . . whenever Aunt Polly's visit is over.

He had arranged for Aunt Polly and Judy to come to Shalesley for a holiday during the last week in June. Shalesley, it is true, was not a health resort. But it stood high, the air was good. The fresh green of spring had touched its bleakness with a transient beauty. And Francis was particularly anxious that Polly should have the rest she so richly deserved.

The winter had been hard for her, physically and financially. Thaddeus Gilfoyle was, in her own phrase, "ruining" the Union, drinking more than he sold, failing to show receipts, trying to get the remnants of the business into his own hands. Ned's chronic illness had taken a peculiar turn, for twelve months now he had lost the power of his legs and was quite beyond business. Confined to a wheeled chair, he had lately become irresponsible and irrational. He had absurd delusions, spoke to the smirking, toadying Thaddeus of his steam yacht, his private brewery in Dublin. One day he had escaped her care and attended by Scanty — a grotesque spectacle of motion — had propelled himself to the Clermont shops and ordered himself two dozen hats. Dr. Tulloch, called in at Francis' request, had pronounced Ned's condition no stroke, but a tumour of the brain. It was he who had procured the male nurse who was now relieving Polly.

Francis would have greatly preferred Judy and Aunt Polly to occupy the guest room at the Presbytery — indeed, one of his dreams was a parish of his own where Polly would be his housekeeper and Judy his particular charge. But Father Kezer's attitude made a request for hospitality out of the question. Francis found a comfortable lodging for them at Mrs. Morrison's. And on June 21st, Aunt Polly and Judy arrived.

Welcoming them at the station, he felt a sudden pain in his heart. Polly, a stiff valiant figure, advanced from the train, leading by the hand, as she had led Nora, the small, dark, glossy-haired child.

"Polly. Dear Polly." He spoke as to himself. She was little

changed, a trifle shabbier perhaps, her gaunt cheeks more drawn. She had the same short coat, gloves, and hat. She never spent a penny on herself, always on others. She had cared for Nora and himself, for Ned and now for Judy. She was so utterly selfless, his breast filled. He stepped forward and hugged her.

"Polly, I'm so glad to see you . . . you're . . . you're eternal."

"Oh, dear." She fumbled in her bag for her handkerchief. "It's windy here. And there's something in my eye."

He took her arm and Judy's, and escorted them to their rooms.

He did his utmost to give them a happy time. In the evenings he had long talks with Polly. Her pride in him, in what he had become, was touching. She made light of her troubles.

But she admitted one anxiety — Judy was a problem.

The child, now ten years of age and attending the day school at Clermont, was a queer mixture. Superficially she had an engaging frankness, but beneath she was suspicious and secretive. She hoarded all sorts of odds and ends in her bedroom, and would shake with temper if they were disturbed. She had wild enthusiasms which quickly faded. In other moods she was timid and uncertain. She could not bear to admit a fault and would wander glibly from the truth to hide it. The hint that she was lying brought floods of indignant tears.

With this before him Francis made every effort to win her confidence. He had her frequently to the Presbytery where, with the complete unconsciousness of the young, she made herself at home, often wandering off into Father Kezer's room, climbing on his sofa, fingering his pipes and paperweights. It was embarrassing, but since the parish priest made no protest, Francis did not restrain the child.

On the last day of their short holiday, when Aunt Polly had gone for a final walk and Judy had at length come to rest with a picture book in the corner of Francis' room, a knock sounded on the door. It was Miss Cafferty. She addressed Francis.

"His Reverence wants to see you immediately."

Francis' brows lifted at the unexpected request. There was something ominous in the housekeeper's words. He rose, slowly.

Father Kezer stood waiting in his own room. For the first time in weeks he looked straight at Francis.

"That child is a thief."

Francis said nothing. But he felt a sudden hollow in his stomach.

"I trusted her. I let her play about the place. I thought she was a nice little thing even though — " Kezer broke off angrily.

"What has she taken?" Francis said. His lips were stiff.

"What do thieves usually take?" Father Kezer swung round to the mantelpiece where a row of little pillars stood, each made up of twelve pennies, wrapped in white paper by his own careful hands. He picked one up. "She's stolen from the collection money. It's worse than thievery. It's simony. Look at this."

Francis examined the packet. It had been opened and clumsily retwisted at the top. Three of the pennies were missing.

"What makes you think Judy did this?"

"I'm not a fool," Father Kezer snapped. "I've been missing pennies all week. Every copper in these packets is marked."

Without a word Francis turned towards his own room. The parish priest followed him.

"Judy. Show me your purse."

Judy looked as though she had been struck. But she recovered quickly. She smiled innocently.

"I left it at Mrs. Morrison's."

"No, here it is." Francis bent forward and took the purse from the outside patch pocket of her dress. It was a new little strap purse which Aunt Polly had given her before the holiday. Francis opened it with a sinking heart. There were three pennies inside. Each had a cross scratched on the back.

Father Kezer's scowl was both outraged and triumphant. "What did I tell you? Ah! You wicked little brat, stealing from God!" He glared at Francis. "She ought to be prosecuted for this. If she were my responsibility I'd march her straight down to the police."

"No, no." Judy burst into tears. "I meant to put it back, truly, I did."

Francis was very pale. The situation was horrible for him. He took his courage in both hands.

"Very well," he said quietly. "We'll go down to the police station and charge her before Sergeant Hamilton straightaway."

Judy's grief became hysterical. Father Kezer, taken aback, sneered: "I'd like to see you."

Francis picked up his hat and took Judy's hand.

"Come along, Judy. You must be brave. We're going down to Sergeant Hamilton to tell him Father Kezer charges you with stealing three pennies."

As Francis led the child towards the door, confusion, then positive apprehension, flared up in Father Kezer's eyes. He had let his tongue run away with him. Sergeant Hamilton, an Orangeman, was no friend of his: they had often clashed bitterly in the past. And now . . . this trivial charge . . . he saw himself jeered at all over the village. He mumbled suddenly:—

"Ye needn't go!"

Francis did not seem to hear.

"Stop!" Father Kezer shouted. He fought down his temper, choked out: "We'll . . . we'll forget about it. Talk to her yourself."

He walked out of the room seething with rage.

When Aunt Polly and Judy returned to Tynecastle, Francis had a quick revulsion: he wanted to explain, to express his regret for Judy's petty pilfering. But Father Kezer froze him. A sense of being balked had further embittered the older man. Besides, he was shortly leaving on his vacation. He wanted to put the curate thoroughly in his place before he left.

He ignored Francis with tight-mouthed surliness. By arrangement with Miss Cafferty he took his meals alone, before the junior priest was served. On the Sunday before his departure, he preached a violent sermon, every word aimed at Francis, on the seventh commandment: "Thou shalt not steal."

The sermon decided Francis. Immediately the service was over he went direct to Donald Kyle's house, took the manager aside, and talked to him with restrained intensity. Gradually a light broke over Kyle's face, still dubious perhaps, but hopeful, aroused. He muttered, finally: "I doubt if we can do it! But I'm with ye all the way." The two men shook hands.

On Monday morning Father Kezer left for Harrogate where, for the next six weeks, he would drink the waters. That evening Miss Cafferty went off to her native Rosslare. And on Tuesday, early, Francis met Donald Kyle by appointment at the station. Kyle carried a portfolio of papers and a glossy new brochure recently issued by a large rival coal combine in Nottingham. He wore his best clothes and an air only slightly less resolved than Francis'. They took the eleven o'clock train from Shalesley.

The long day passed slowly, they did not return until late evening. They came up the road together in silence; each looked straight ahead. Francis seemed tired, his expression revealed nothing. It was perhaps significant that the colliery manager smiled with grim solemnity as they said "Good night."

The next four days passed normally. Then, without warning, there began a period of strange activity.

The activity seemed centred upon the colliery, not unnaturally, since the colliery was the centre of the district. Francis was there a good deal between the works of the parish, consulting with Donald Kyle, studying the architect's blue prints, watching the squads of men at work. It was remarkable how quickly the new building grew. In a fortnight it had risen above the adjoining aid-room, in a month the structure was complete. Then the carpenters and plasterers came in. The sound of hammering fell exquisitely on Francis' ears. He sniffed the aroma of fresh wood shavings. Occasionally he set to and did a job with the men. They liked him. He had inherited from his father a fondness for working with his hands.

Alone in the Presbytery, except for the unobtrusive daily visits of Mrs. Morrison, his temporary housekeeper, free of the nagging of his superior, his fervour knew no limits, a pure white glow pervaded him. He felt himself getting close to the people, breaking down suspicion, gradually entering their dulled lives, bringing to hidden stolid eyes a sudden startled gleam. It was a glorious sensation, a mingling of purpose and achievement, as though, embracing the poverty and wretchedness about him, he drew near in pity and soaring tenderness to the threshold of the unseen God.

Five days before Father Kezer's return, Francis sat down and wrote a letter. It ran as follows: —

Shalesley,
September 15th, 1897.

Dear Sir George,

The new recreation centre which you have so generously donated to Shalesley Village is now practically complete. It should prove a tremendous boon, not only to your own colliery workers and their families, but to everyone else in this scattered industrial district, irrespective of class or creed. A non-partisan committee has already been formed and a syllabus drawn up on the lines we discussed. From the copy I enclose you will see how comprehensive is our winter programme: boxing and singlestick classes, physical culture, first-aid instruction and a weekly dance every Thursday.

When I consider the unhesitating liberality with which you met the diffident and perhaps unwarranted approach of Mr. Kyle and myself I am quite overwhelmed. Any words of gratitude which I might use would be hopelessly inadequate. Your real thanks will come from the happiness which you bring to the working people of Shalesley and from the good which must undoubtedly result from their increased social unity.

We propose holding a gala opening night on September 21st. If you would consent to honour us with your presence our gratification would be complete.

Believe me,
Yours most sincerely,
FRANCIS CHISHOLM
Curate of the Church of the Redeemer

He posted the letter with a strange taut smile. His words were heartfelt, burningly sincere. But his legs were trembling.

At midday on the nineteenth, one day after his housekeeper's return, Father Kezer reappeared. Fortified by the saline waters, he was bursting with energy — in his own phrase: fair itching to get his fingers on the reins. Reinfusing the Presbytery with his loud, black, hairy essence, with his shouted greeting to Miss Cafferty, his demand for substantial food, he ran through his correspondence. Then he bustled into lunch, rubbing his hands. On his plate lay an envelope. He ripped it open, drew out the printed card.

"What's this?"

Francis moistened his dry lips, mustered all his courage. "It appears to be an invitation to the opening night of the new Shalesley Athletic and Recreation Club. I've had one too."

"Recreation Club. What's that to us!" Holding it at arm's length, he glared redly at the card. "What is it?"

"A fine new centre. You can see it from the window." Francis added, with a tremor: "The gift of Sir George Renshaw."

"Sir George . . ." Kezer broke off, stupefied, then stamped to the window. He gazed through the window, a long time, at the impressive proportions of the new erection. Then he returned, sat down and slowly began his lunch. His appetite was scarcely that of a man with a purified liver. He kept darting glances at Francis out of his small, lowering eyes. His silence blasted the room.

At length Francis spoke — awkwardly, with tense simplicity. "You must decide, Father. You've put a ban on dancing and all mixed recreation. On the other hand if our people don't co-operate, ostracize the club, and stop away from the dances, Sir George will feel himself mortally insulted." Francis kept his eyes on his plate. "He's coming down, in person, on Thursday, for the opening."

Father Kezer could eat no more. The thick and juicy beefsteak on his plate might have been dishcloth. He rose abruptly, crushing the card in his hairy fist with sudden, dreadful violence. "We'll not go to the foul fiends' opening! We'll not. Do you hear me? Once and for all, I've said it!" He rampaged out of the room.

On the Thursday evening, freshly shaved, in clean linen and his best black, his face a dreadful compromise of gaiety and gloom, Father Kezer stalked over to the ceremony. Francis followed behind him.

The new hall was warm with lights and excitement, filled to capacity with the working people of the community. On the raised platform a number of the local notables were seated, Donald Kyle and his wife, the colliery doctor, the council schoolmaster, and two other ministers of religion. As Francis and Father Kezer took their seats there was prolonged cheering, then a few catcalls and loud laughter. Father Kezer's jaws snapped sourly together.

The sound of a car arriving outside heightened the expectation and a minute later, amidst a great ovation, Sir George appeared on the platform. He was a medium-sized man of about sixty with a shining bald head fringed with white hair. His moustache was silvery also, and his cheeks were brightly coloured. He had that remarkably fresh pink-and-whiteness achieved by some fair-haired persons in their declining years. It seemed preposterous that one so quiet in his dress and manner should command such enormous power.

He listened agreeably while the ceremony proceeded, sustained the address of welcome from Mr. Kyle, then delivered a few remarks himself. He concluded amiably: —

"I should like in fairness to state that the first suggestion of this very worthy project came directly from the vision and broadmindedness of Father Francis Chisholm."

The applause was deafening and Francis flushed, his eyes, pleading and remorseful, bent on his superior.

Father Kezer raised his hands automatically, brought them soundlessly together twice, with a grin of sickly martyrdom. Later, when the impromptu dance started, he stood watching Sir George swing round the hall with young Nancy Kyle. Then he faded into the night. The music of the fiddlers followed him.

When Francis returned, late, he found the parish priest sitting up in the parlour, with no fire, his hands on his knees.

Father Kezer seemed oddly inert. All the fight had gone out of him. In the last ten years he had knocked out more curates than Henry VIII had wives. And now a curate had knocked him out. He said tonelessly: —

"I'll have to report you to the Bishop!"

Francis felt his heart turn over in his breast. But he did not flinch. No matter what happened to him, Father Kezer's authority was shaken. The older priest continued glumly: "Perhaps you'd be the better of a change. The Bishop can decide. Dean Fitzgerald needs another curate in Tynecastle . . . your friend Mealey's there, isn't he?"

Francis was silent. He did not wish to leave this now faintly stirring parish. Yet even if he were forced to do so things would be easier for his successor. The club would continue. It was a beginning. Other changes would come. He had no personal exultation, but a quiet, almost visionary, hope. He said in a low voice: "I'm sorry if I have upset you, Father. Believe me, I was only trying to help . . . our good-for-nothing lot."

The eyes of the two priests met. Father Kezer's fell first.

II

ONE Friday towards the end of Lent, in the dining room of St. Dominic's Presbytery, Francis and Father Slukas were already seated at the meagre midday repast of boiled stock-fish and butterless brown toast served on Victorian silver and fine blue Worcester china, when Father Mealey returned from an early sick call. From the suppression of his manner, his indifferent mode of helping himself, Francis was immediately aware that Anselm had something on his mind. Dean Fitzgerald dined upstairs at this season of the Church and the three junior priests were alone. But Father Mealey, munching without taste, a faint colour beneath his skin, kept silence till the end of the meal. Only when the Lithuanian had brushed the crumbs from his beard, risen, bowed, and departed, did his tension relax. He drew a long pressing breath.

"Francis! I want you to come with me this afternoon. You've no engagements?"

"No . . . I'm free till four o'clock."

"Then you must come. I'd like you as my friend, as my fellow priest, to be the first . . ." He broke off, would say no more to lift the heavy mystery of his words.

For two years Francis had been the second curate at St. Dominic's, where Gerald Fitzgerald, now Dean Fitzgerald, still remained, with Anselm his senior assistant and Slukas, the Lithuanian Father, a necessary encumbrance on account of the many Polish immigrants who kept crowding into Tynecastle.

The change from the backwoods of Shalesley to this familiar city parish where the services went like clockwork and the church was elegantly perfect had left a curious mark on Francis. He was happy to be near Aunt Polly, to maintain an eye on Ned and Judy, to see the Tullochs, Willie and his sister, once or twice a week. He had a queer consolation, a sense of indefinable support, in the recent elevation of Monsignor MacNabb from San Morales to be Bishop of the diocese. Yet his new air of maturity, the lines about his steady eyes, the spareness of his frame, gave silent indications that the transition had not been easy.

Dean Fitzgerald, refined and fastidious, priding himself on being a gentleman, stood at the opposite pole from Father Kezer. Yet, though he strove to be impartial, the Dean was not without a certain lofty prejudice. While he warmly approved Anselm — now his prime favourite — and blankly ignored Father Slukas, — whose broken English and table habits, a napkin tucked beneath the beard at every meal, coupled with a strange predilection for wearing a derby hat with his soutane, placed him far beyond the pale, — towards his other curate he had a strange wariness. Francis soon realized that his humble birth, his association with the Union Tavern, with, indeed, the whole stark Bannon tragedy, must prove a handicap he could not lightly overcome.

And he had made such a bad beginning! Tired of the shopworn platitudes, the same old parrot sermons that came, almost by rote, on the appointed Sundays of the year, Francis had ventured, soon after his arrival, to preach a simple homily, fresh and original, his own thoughts, on the subject of personal integrity. Alas, Dean Fitzgerald had cuttingly condemned the dangerous innovation. Next Sunday, at his behest, Anselm had mounted the pulpit and given forth the antidote: a magnificent peroration on The Star of the Sea, in which harts panted for the water and barques came safe across the bar; ending dramatically with arms outstretched, a handsome suppliant for Love, on the admonition: "Come!" All the women of the congregation were in tears, and afterwards, as Anselm ate a hearty breakfast of mutton chops, the Dean pointedly congratulated him. "That! — Father Mealey — was eloquent. I heard our late Bishop deliver practically the same sermon twenty years ago."

Perhaps these opposite orations set their courses: as the months passed Francis could not but dejectedly compare his own indifferent showing with Anselm's remarkable success. Father Mealey was a figure in the parish, always cheerful, even gay, with a ready laugh and a comforting pat on the back for anyone in trouble. He worked hard and with great earnestness, carrying a little book full of his engagements in his waistcoat pocket, never refusing an invitation to address a meeting or make an after-dinner speech. He edited the *St. Dominic's Gazette:* a newsy and often humorous little sheet. He went out a good deal and, though no one could call him a snob, took tea at all the best houses. Whenever an eminent cleric came to preach in the city, Anselm was sure to meet him and to sit admiringly at his feet. Later he would send a letter, beautifully composed, expressing ardently the spiritual benefit he had derived from the encounter. He had made many influential friends through this sincerity.

Naturally there were limits to his capacity for work. While he vigorously assumed the post of secretary to the new Diocesan Foreign Missionary Centre in Tynecastle — a cherished project of the Bishop — and worked unremittingly to please His Grace, he had been obliged reluctantly to decline, and depute to Francis, the management of the Working Boy's Club in Shand Street.

The property round Shand Street was the worst in the city, tall tenements and lodging houses, a network of slums, and this, properly enough, had come to be regarded as Francis' district. Here, though his results seemed trivial and meaningless, he found plenty to do. He had to train himself to look destitution in the eye, to view without shrinking the sorrow and the shame of life, the eternal irony of poverty. It was not a communion of saints that grew about him but a communion of sinners, rousing such pity in him it brought him sometimes to the brink of tears.

"Don't say you're taking forty winks," said Anselm reproachfully.

Almost with a start Francis came out of his reverie to find Father Mealey, waiting on him, hat and stick in hand, beside the lunch table. He smiled and rose in acquiescence.

Outside, the afternoon was fresh and fine, with a rousing, bustling breeze, and Anselm strode along with a brisk swing, clean, honest and healthy, greeting his parishioners bluffly. His popularity at St. Dominic's had not spoiled him. To his many admirers his most engaging characteristic was the way in which he deprecated his achievements.

Soon Francis saw that they were making for the new suburb recently added to the parish. Beyond the city boundary, a housing development was in progress, on the parklands of an old country property. Workmen were moving with hods and barrows. Francis subconsciously noted a big white board: *Hollis Estate, Apply Malcom Glennie, Solicitor.* But Anselm was pushing on, over the hill, past some green fields, then down a wooded pathway to the left. It was a pleasant rural stretch to be so near the chimney-pots.

Suddenly Father Mealey halted, with the still excitement of a pointing hound.

"You know where we are, Francis? You've heard of this place?"

"Of course."

Francis had often passed it: a little hollow of lichened rocks, screened with yellow broom and enclosed by an oval copse of copper beeches. It was the prettiest spot for miles around. He had often wondered why it was known as "The Well" and sometimes, indeed, as "Marywell." The basin had been dry for fifty years.

"Look!" Clutching his arm, Father Mealey led him forward. From the dry rocks gushed a crystal spring. There was an odd silence, then, stooping with cupped hands, Mealey took an almost sacramental drink.

"Taste it, Francis. We ought to be grateful for the privilege of being among the first."

Francis bent and drank. The water was sweet and cold. He smiled. "It tastes good."

Mealey regarded him with wise indulgence, not without its tinge of patronage. "My dear fellow, I could call it a heavenly taste."

"Has it been flowing long?"

"It began yesterday afternoon at sundown."

Francis laughed. "Really, Anselm, you're a Delphic oracle today — full of signs and portents. Come on, give me the whole story. Who told you about this?"

Father Mealey shook his head. "I can't . . . yet."

"But you've made me so confoundedly curious."

Pleased, Anselm smiled. Then his expression regained its solemnity. "I can't break the seal yet, Francis. I must go to Dean Fitzgerald. He's the one who must deal with this. Meantime, of course, I trust you . . . I know you will respect my confidence."

Francis knew his companion too well to press him further.

On their return to Tynecastle, Francis parted from his fellow curate and went on to Glanville Street to make a sick call. One of his club members, a boy named Owen Warren, had been kicked on the leg in a football game some weeks before. The youngster was poor and undernourished and heedless of the injury. When the Poor Law doctor was eventually called in, the condition had developed into an ugly ulcer of the shin.

The affair had upset Francis — the more so since Dr. Tulloch seemed dubious of the prognosis. And this evening, in his endeavour to bring some comfort to Owen and his worried mother, the peculiar and inconclusive excursion of the afternoon was driven completely from his mind.

Next morning, however, loud and minatory sounds emerging from Dean Gerald Fitzgerald's room brought it back before him.

Lent was a deadly penance for the Dean. He was a just man, and he fasted. But fasting did not suit his full elegant body, well habituated to the stimuli of rich and nourishing juices. Sorely tried in health and temper, he kept to himself, walked the Presbytery with no recognition in his hooded eye, and each night marked another cross upon the calendar.

Although Father Mealey stood so high in Fitzgerald's favour it demanded considerable resourcefulness to approach him at such a time, and Francis heard Anselm's voice fall, persuasive and pleading, across the Dean's irascible abruptness. In the end the softer voice triumphed — like drops of water, Francis reflected, wearing out granite through sheer persistence.

An hour later, with a very bad grace, the Dean came out of his room. Father Mealey was waiting on him in the vestibule. They departed together in a cab in the direction of the centre of the town. They were absent three hours. It was lunchtime when they returned and for once the Dean broke his rule. He sat down at the curate's table. Though he would eat nothing he ordered a large pot of French coffee, his one luxury in a desert of self-denial. Sitting sideways, his legs crossed, a handsome elegant figure, sipping the black and aromatic brew, he diffused an air of warmth, almost of comradeship, as though a little taken out of himself by an inner, thrilling exaltation. He said, meditatively, to Francis and the Polish priest — it was notable that he included Slukas in his friendly glance: —

"Well, we may thank Father Mealey for his persistence . . . in the face of my somewhat violent disbelief. Naturally it is my duty to maintain the utmost scepticism towards certain . . . phenomena. But I have never seen, I had never hoped to see, such a manifestation, in my own parish — " He broke off and, taking up his coffee cup, made a generous gesture of renunciation towards the senior curate. "Let it be your privilege to tell them, Father."

That faint excited colour persisted in Father Mealey's cheek. He cleared his throat and began, readily and earnestly, as though the incident he related demanded his most formal eloquence: —

"One of our parishioners, a young woman, who has been delicate for a considerable time, was out walking on Monday of this week. The date, since we wish above everything to be precise, was March fifteenth, and the time, half-past three in the afternoon. The reason for her excursion was no idle one — this girl is a devout and fervent soul not given to giddiness or loitering. She was walking in accordance with her doctor's instructions — to get some fresh air — the medical man being Dr. William Brine of 42 Boyle Crescent, whom we all know as a physician of unimpeachable, I might say, of the highest, integrity. Well!" Father Mealey took a tense gulp of water and went on. "As she was returning from her walk, murmuring a prayer, she chanced to pass the place which we know as Mary's Well. It was twilight, the last rays of the sun lingering in pure radiance upon the lovely scene. This young girl stopped to gaze and admire when suddenly to her wonder and surprise she saw standing before her a lady in a white robe and a blue cape with a diadem of stars upon her forehead. Guided by holy instinct our Catholic girl immediately fell upon her knees. The lady smiled to her with ineffable tenderness and said: 'My child, sickly though you are, you are the one to be chosen!' Then, half-turning, still addressing the awestruck yet comprehending girl: 'Is it not sad that this Well which bears my name is dry? Remember! It is for you and those like you that this shall happen.' With a last beautiful smile she disappeared. At that instant a fount of exquisite water sprang from the barren rock."

There was a silence when Father Mealey concluded.

Then the Dean resumed: "As I have said, our approach to this delicate matter was made in the frankest incredulity. We don't expect miracles to grow on every gooseberry bush. Young girls are notoriously romantic. And the starting of the spring might have been a sheer coincidence. However — " His tone took on a deeper gratification. "I've just completed a long interrogation of the girl in question with Father Mealey and Dr. Brine. As you may imagine, the solemn experience of her vision was a great shock to her. She went to bed immediately after it and has remained there ever since." The voice became slower, fraught with immense significance. "Though she is happy, normal and physically well-nourished, in these five days she has touched neither food nor drink." He gave the amazing fact its due weight in silence. "Moreover . . . moreover, I say, she shows plainly, unmistakably and irrefutably, the blessed stigmata!" He went on triumphantly: "While it is too early to speak yet, while final evidence must be collected, I have the strongest premonition, amounting almost to conviction, that we in this parish have been privileged by Almighty God to participate in a miracle comparable to, and perhaps far-reaching as, those which gave our holy religion the new-found Grotto at Digby and the older and more historic Shrine at Lourdes."

It was impossible not to be affected by the nobility of his peroration.

"Who is the girl?" Francis asked.

"She is Charlotte Neily!"

Francis stared at the Dean. He opened his lips and closed them again. The silence remained impressive.

The next few days brought a growing excitement to the Presbytery. No one could have been better equipped to deal with the crisis than Dean Gerald Fitzgerald. A man of sincere devotion, he was wise also in worldly ways. Long and hard-won experience on the local school board and urban councils gave him an astute approach to temporal affairs. No news of the event was permitted to escape, not a whisper, even, in the parochial halls. The Dean had everything under his own hand. He would raise his hand only when he was ready.

The incident, so miraculously unexpected, was a breath of new life to him. Not for many years had he known such inner satisfaction: both spiritual and material. He was a strange mixture of piety and ambition. His exceptional attributes of mind and body had seemed to destine him, automatically, for advancement in the Church. And he longed passionately for that advancement as much, perhaps, as he longed for the advancement of Holy Church herself. A keen student of contemporary history, he likened himself often in his own mind to Newman. He merited equal eminence. Yet he remained, becalmed, at St. Dominic's. The only preferment they had given him, the reward of twenty distinguished years, was this petty elevation to the rank of Dean, an infrequent title in the Catholic Church and one which often embarrassed him on his journeying beyond the city, causing him to be mistaken for an Anglican clergyman, an inference he most cordially resented.

Perhaps he realized that while he was admired he was not liked. With the passage of each day he was growing more and more a disappointed man. He strove for resignation. Yet when he bent his head and said "O Lord, Thy will be done!" deep down beneath his humility was the burning thought: "By this time they should have given me my mozzetta."

Now everything was changed. Let them keep him at St. Dominic's. He would make St. Dominic's a shrine of light. Lourdes was his exemplar and, nearer in time and space, the recent striking instance of Digby in the Midlands, where the foundation of a miraculous grotto, with many authenticated cures, had transformed the dreary hamlet into a thriving town, and elevated, at the same time, an unknown but resourceful parish priest to the status of a national figure.

The Dean sank into a splendid vision of a new city, a great basilica, a solemn triduum, himself enthroned in stiff vestments . . . then sharply took himself in hand and scrutinized the draft contracts. His first action had been to place immediately a Dominican nun, Sister Teresa, trustworthy and discreet, in Charlotte Neily's home. Reassured by her impeccable reports he had taken to the law.

It was fortunate that Marywell and all the land adjacent formed the estate of the old and wealthy Hollis family. Though not a Catholic, Captain Hollis had married one, Sir George Renshaw's sister. He was friendly and well-disposed. He and his solicitor, Malcom Glennie, were closeted with the Dean upon successive days, holding long conferences over sherry and biscuits. A fair and amicable arrangement was at length worked out. The Dean had no personal interest in money. He regarded it contemptuously as so much dross. But the things that money could purchase were important and he must ensure the future of his shining project. No one but a fool could fail to realize that the value of the land would rocket to the sky.

On the last day of the negotiations Francis ran into Glennie in the upper corridor. Frankly, he was surprised to find Malcom dealing with the Hollis affairs. But the solicitor, when articled, had shrewdly bought himself into an old established firm with his wife's money, and quietly succeeded to some first-rate practice.

"Well, Malcom!" Francis held out his hand. "Glad to see you again."

Glennie shook hands with damp effusiveness.

"But I'm amazed," Francis smiled, "to find you in the house of the Scarlet Woman!"

The solicitor's answering smile was thin. He mumbled: "I'm a liberal man, Francis . . . besides being obliged to chase the pennies."

There was a silence. Francis had often thought to restore his relationship with the Glennies. But news of the death of Daniel had dissuaded him — and a chance encounter with Mrs. Glennie in Tynecastle when, as he crossed the street to greet her, she had sighted him from the corner of her eye, and shied away, as though she spied the Devil.

He said: "It made me very sad to hear of your father's death."

"Ay, ay! We miss him of course. But the old man was such a failure."

"It's no great failure to get into heaven," Francis joked.

"Well, yes, I suppose he's there." Glennie vaguely twisted the emblem on his watchchain. He was already tending towards an early middle age, his figure slack, shoulders and stomach pendulous, his thin hair plastered in streaks over his bare scalp. But his eye, though palely evasive, was gimlet sharp. As he moved towards the stairs he threw off a tepid invitation.

"Look us up when you have time. I'm married, as you know — two of a family — but Mother still lives with us."

Malcom Glennie had his own peculiar interest in the beatific vision of Charlotte Neily. Since his early youth he had been patiently seeking an opportunity to acquire wealth. He inherited from his mother a burning avarice and something of her long-nosed cunning. He smelled money in this ridiculous Romish scheme. Its very uniqueness convinced him of its possibilities. His opportunity was here, dangling like a ripe fruit. It would never occur again, never in a lifetime.

Working disingenuously for his client, Malcom remembered what everyone else had forgotten. Secretly, and at considerable expense, he had a geological survey carried out. Then he was sure of what he had already suspected. The flow of water to the property came exclusively through an upper tract of heath land, above and remote from the estate.

Malcom was not rich. Not yet. But by taking all his savings, by mortgaging his house and business, he had just enough to execute a three months' option on this land. He knew what an artesian bore would do. That bore would never be driven. But a bargain would be driven, later, on the threat of that bore, which would make Malcom Glennie a landed gentleman.

Meanwhile the water still gushed clear and sweet. Charlotte Neily still maintained her rapture and her stigmata, still existed without sustenance. And Francis still prayed, broodingly, for the gift of faith.

If only he could believe like Anselm who, without a struggle, blandly, smilingly, accepted everything from Adam's rib to the less probable details of Jonah's sojourn in the whale! He did believe, he did, he did . . . but not in the shallows, only in the depths . . . only by an effort of love, by keeping his nose to the grindstone in the slums, when shaking the fleas from his clothing into the empty bath . . . never, never easily . . . except when he sat with the sick, the crippled, those of stricken, ashen countenance. The cruelty of this present test, its unfairness, was wrecking his nerves, withering in him the joy of prayer.

It was the girl herself who disturbed him. Doubtless he was prejudiced: he could not overlook the fact that Charlotte's mother was Thaddeus Gilfoyle's sister. And her father was a vague and windy character, pious yet lazy, who stole away from his small chandler's premises every day, to light candles before the side altar for success in his neglected business. Charlotte had all her father's fondness for the Church. But Francis had a worried suspicion that the incidentals drew her, the smell of incense and of candle grease, that the darkness of the confessional struck overtures upon her nerves. He did not deny her unblemished goodness, the regularity with which she carried out her duties. As against that, she washed sketchily, and her breath was rancid.

On the following Saturday as Francis walked down Glanville Street, feeling absurdly depressed, he observed Dr. Tulloch come out of Number 143, the house of Owen Warren. He called, the doctor turned, stopped, then fell into step beside his friend.

Willie had broadened with the years, but had otherwise changed little. Slow, tenacious and canny, loyal to his friends, hostile to his enemies, he had, in manhood, all his father's honesty, but little of his charm and nothing of his looks. His blunt-nosed face was red and stolid, topped by a shock of unmanageable hair. He had an air of plodding decency. His medical career had not been brilliant, but he was sound and enjoyed his work. He was quite contemptuous of all orthodox ambitions. Though he spoke occasionally of "seeing the world," of pursuing adventure in far-off romantic lands, he remained in his Poor Law appointment — which demanded no hateful bedside falsities and enabled him at most times to speak his mind — anchored by the humdrum, by his matter-of-fact capacity of living from day to day. Besides, he never could save money. His salary was not large; and much of it was spent on whiskey.

Always careless of his appearance, this morning he had not shaved. And his deepset eyes were sombre, his expression unusually put out: as though today he had a grudge against the world. He indicated briefly that the Warren boy was worse. He had been in to take a shred of tissue for pathological examination.

They continued along the street, linked by one of their peculiar silences. Suddenly, on an unaccountable impulse, Francis divulged the story of Charlotte Neily.

Tulloch's face did not change, he trudged along, fists in his deep coat pockets, collar up, head down.

"Yes," he said at last. "A little bird told me."

"What do you think of it?"

"Why ask me?"

"At least you're honest."

Tulloch looked oddly at Francis. For one so modest, so conscious of his mental limitations, the doctor's rejection of the myth of God was strangely positive. "Religion isn't my province, I inherited a most satisfying atheism . . . which the anatomy room confirmed. But if you want it straight — in my old dad's words, I have my doubts. See here, though! Why don't we take a look at her? We're not far from the house. We'll go in together."

"Won't that get you into trouble with Dr. Brine?"

"No. I can square it with Salty tomorrow. In dealing with my colleagues I find it pays to act first and apologize afterwards." He threw Francis a singular smile. "Unless you're afraid of the hierarchy?"

Francis flushed but controlled his answer. He said a minute later: "Yes, I'm afraid, but we'll go in."

It proved surprisingly easy to effect an entrance. Mrs. Neily, worn-out by a night of watching, was asleep. Neily, for once, was at his business. Sister Teresa, short, quiet and amiable, opened the door. Since she came from a distant section of Tynecastle she had no knowledge of Tulloch, but she knew and recognized Francis, at once. She admitted them to the polished, immaculately tidy room where Charlotte lay on spotless pillows, washed and clothed in a high white nightgown, the brasses of the bedstead shining. Sister Teresa bent over the girl, not a little proud of her stainless handiwork.

"Charlotte, dear. Father Chisholm has come to see you. And brought a doctor who is a great friend of Dr. Brine."

Charlotte Neily smiled. The smile was conscious, vaguely languid, yet charged with curious rapture. It lit up the pale, already luminous face, motionless upon the pillow. It was deeply impressive. Francis felt a stir of genuine compunction. There was no doubt that something existed, here, in this still white room, outside the bonds of natural experience.

"You don't mind if I examine you, Charlotte?" Tulloch spoke kindly.

At his tone, her smile lingered. She did not move. She had the cushioned repose of one who is watched, who knows that she is watched, yet is undisturbed, rather exalted, by such watching: a consciousness of inner power, a mollification, a dreamy and elevated awareness of the deference and reverence evoked amongst the watchers. Her pale eyelids fluttered. Her voice was untroubled, remote.

"Why should I mind, doctor? I'm only too glad. I'm not worthy to be chosen as God's vessel . . . but since I am chosen I can only joyfully submit."

She allowed the respectful Tulloch to examine her.

"You don't eat anything, Charlotte?"

"No, doctor."

"You've no appetite?"

"I never think of food. I just seem sustained by an inner grace."

Sister Teresa said quietly: "I can assure you she hasn't put a bite in her mouth since I came into this house."

A silence fell in the hushed white room. Dr. Tulloch straightened himself, pushing back his unruly hair. He said simply: —

"Thank you, Charlotte. Thank you, Sister Teresa. I'm much indebted to you for your kindness." He went towards the bedroom door.

As Francis made to follow the doctor a shadow fluttered over Charlotte's face.

"Don't you want to see too, Father? Look . . . my hands! My feet are just the same."

She extended both her arms, gently, sacrificially. Upon both her pale palms, unmistakably, were the blood-stained marks of nails.

Outside, Dr. Tulloch maintained his attitude of reserve. He kept his lips shut until they reached the end of the street. Then, at the point where their ways diverged, he spoke rapidly. "You want my opinion I suppose. Here it is. A borderline case — or just over: manic depressive in the exalted stage. Certainly a hysteric bleeder. If she steers clear of the asylum, she'll probably be canonized!" His composure, his perfect manner left him. His red plain face became congested. His words choked him. "Damn it to hell! When I think of her trigged up there in her simpering holiness, like an anæmic angel in a flour bag — and little Owney Warren, stuck in a dirty garret, with worse pain than your hellfire in his gangrenous leg, and the threat of malignant sarcoma over him, I could just about explode. Bite on that when you say your prayers. You're probably going back to say them now. Well, I'm going home to have a drink." He walked rapidly away before Francis could reply.

That same evening when Francis returned from tenebrae an urgent summons awaited him, written on the slate which hung in the Presbytery vestibule. With a premonition of misfortune, he went upstairs to the study. The Dean was wearing out his temper and his carpet with short exasperated paces.

"Father Chisholm! I am both amazed and indignant. Really, I expected better of you than this. To think that you should bring in — from the streets — an atheistic doctor — I resent it violently!"

"I'm sorry." Francis answered heavily. "It's just — oh, well, he happens to be my friend."

"That in itself is highly reprehensible. I find it wildly improper that one of my curates should associate with a character like Dr. Tulloch."

"We . . . we were boys together."

"That is no excuse. I'm hurt and disappointed. I'm thoroughly and justifiably incensed. From the very beginning your attitude towards this great event has been cold and unsympathetic. I daresay you are jealous that the honour of the discovery should have fallen to the senior curate. Or is there some deeper motive behind your manifest antagonism?"

A sense of wretchedness flowed over Francis. He felt that the Dean was right. He mumbled: —

"I'm terribly sorry. I'm not disloyal. That's the last in the world I'd want to be. But I admit I've been lukewarm. It's because I've been troubled. That's why I took Tulloch in today. I have such doubts — "

"Doubts! Do you deny the miracles of Lourdes?"

"No, no. They're unimpeachable. Authenticated by doctors of all creeds."

"Then why deny us the opportunity to create another monument of faith — here — in our very midst?" The Dean's brow darkened. "If you disregard the spiritual implications, at least respect the physical." He sneered. "Do you fondly imagine that a young girl can go nine days without food or drink — and remain well and perfectly nourished — unless she is receiving other sustenance?"

"What sustenance?"

"Spiritual sustenance." The Dean fumed. "Didn't Saint Catherine of Siena receive a spiritual mystic drink which supplanted all earthly food? Such insufferable doubting! Can you wonder that I lose my temper?"

Francis hung his head. "Saint Thomas doubted. In the presence of all the disciples. Even to putting his fingers in our Lord's side. But no one lost their temper."

There was a sudden shocked pause. The Dean paled, then recovered himself. He bent over his desk, fumbling at some papers, not looking at Francis. He said in a restrained tone: —

"This is not the first time you have proved obstructive. You are getting yourself into very bad odour in the diocese. You may go."

Francis left the room with a dreadful sense of his own deficiencies. He had a sudden overwhelming impulse to take his troubles to Bishop MacNabb. But he suppressed it. Rusty Mac seemed no longer approachable. He would be too fully occupied by his new high office to concern himself with the worries of a wretched curate.

Next day, Sunday, at the eleven o'clock high mass, Dean Fitzgerald broke the news in the finest sermon he had ever preached.

The sensation was immediate and tremendous. The entire congregation stood outside the church talking in hushed voices, unwilling to go home. A spontaneous procession formed up and departed, under the leadership of Father Mealey, for Marywell. In the afternoon crowds collected outside the Neily home. A band of young women of the confraternity, to which Charlotte belonged, knelt in the street reciting the rosary.

In the evening the Dean consented to be interviewed by a highly curious press. He conducted himself with dignity and restraint. Already esteemed in the city, rated as a public-spirited clergyman, he produced a most favourable impression. Next morning the newspapers gave him generously of their space. He was on the front page of the *Tribune,* had a eulogistic double spread inside the *Globe.* "Another Digby," proclaimed the *Northumberland Herald.* Said the *Yorkshire Echo,* "Miraculous Grotto Brings Hope to Thousands." The *Weekly High Anglican* hedged, rather cattily, "We await further evidence." But the London *Times* was superb with a scholarly article from its theological correspondent tracing the history of the Well back to Aidan and Saint Ethelwulf. The Dean flushed with gratification. Father Mealey could eat no breakfast, and Malcom Glennie was beside himself with joy.

Eight days later Francis paid an evening visit to Polly's little flat in Clermont, at the north end of the city. He was tired, after a long day's visiting in the dingy tenements of his district, and most desperately depressed. That afternoon a note had come round from Dr. Tulloch which curtly signed young Warren's death warrant. The condition had been revealed as malignant sarcoma of the leg. There was no hope whatsoever for the boy: he was dying and might not last the month.

At Clermont, Polly was her indomitable self, Ned, perhaps, a trifle more trying than usual. Hunched in his wheeled chair, a blanket wrapped about his knees, he talked much and rather foolishly. Some sort of final settlement had at last been squeezed out of Gilfoyle on account of the remnants of Ned's interest in the Union Tavern. A pitiful sum. But Ned had boasted as though it were a fortune. As the result of his complaint his tongue seemed too large for his mouth, he was distressingly inarticulate.

Judy was already asleep when Francis arrived, and although Polly said nothing there was a hint in her manner that the child had misbehaved and been sent off early. The thought saddened him further.

Eleven o'clock was striking when he left the flat. The last tram to Tynecastle had gone. Tramping home, his shoulders drooping slightly under this final discomfiture, he entered Glanville Street. As he drew opposite the Neily home he observed that the double window on the ground floor, which marked Charlotte's room, was still illuminated. He made out the movements of figures, vague shadows on the yellow blind.

A rush of contrition overcame him. Oppressed by the realization of his obduracy, he had a sudden desire to see the Neilys and make amends. The instinct of reparation was strong within him as he crossed the street and went up the three front steps. He raised his hand towards the knocker, altered his mind and turned the old-fashioned handle of the door. He had acquired that facility, common to priests and physicians, of making his sick visits unannounced.

The bedroom, opening off the small lobby, projected a wide slant of gaslight. He tapped gently on the lintel and entered the room. Then he stood, suddenly transformed to stone.

Charlotte, propped up in bed, with an oval tray before her laden with breast of chicken and a custard, was stuffing herself with food. Mrs. Neily, wrapped in a faded blue dressing gown, bent with solicitude, was noiselessly decanting stout.

It was the mother who saw Francis first. Arrested, she gave a neighing cry of terror. Her hand flew to her throat, dropping the glass, spilling the stout upon the bed.

Charlotte raised her gaze from the tray. Her pale eyes dilated. She gazed at her mother, her mouth opened, she began to whimper. She slid down on the bed, shielding her face. The tray crashed on to the floor. No one had spoken. Mrs. Neily's throat worked convulsively. She made a stupid, feeble effort to secrete the bottle in her dressing gown. At last she gasped: "I've got to keep her strength up somehow . . . all she's been through . . . it's invalid's stout!"

Her look of frightened guilt revealed everything. It sickened him. He felt debased and humiliated. He had difficulty in finding words.

"I suppose you've given her food every night . . . when Sister left her, thinking she was asleep?"

"No, Father! As God is my witness!" She made a last desperate attempt at denial, then broke down, lost her head completely. "What if I did? I couldn't see my poor child starve, not for nobody. But dear Saint Joseph . . . I'd never have let her do it if I'd known it would mean so much . . . with the crowds . . . and the papers . . . I'm glad to be through with it. . . . Don't . . . don't be hard on us, Father."

He said in a low voice: "I'm not going to judge you, Mrs. Neily."

She wept.

He waited patiently until her sobs subsided, seated on a chair at the door, gazing at his hat, between his hands. The folly of what she had done, the folly, at that moment, of all human life, appalled him. When the two were quieter he said: "Tell me about it."

The story came, gulped out, mostly by Charlotte.

She had read such a nice book, from the church library, about Blessed Bernardette. One day when she was passing Marywell, it was her favourite walk, she noticed the water running. That's funny, she thought. Then the coincidence struck her, between the water, Bernardette and herself. It was a shock. She had almost, in a sort of way, fancied she saw the Blessed Virgin. When she got home, the more she thought of it the surer she became. It gave her quite a turn. She was all white and trembling, she had to take to her bed and send for Father Mealey. And before she knew where she was, she was telling him the whole story.

All that night she'd lain in a kind of ecstasy, her body seemed to go rigid, stiff as a board. Next morning, when she woke up, the marks were there. She'd always bruised terrible but these were different.

Well, that convinced her. All that day, when food came, she

refused it, just waved it away. She was too happy, too excited to eat. Besides, lots of Saints had lived without food. That idea fixed itself on her, too. When Father Mealey and the Dean heard she was living on Grace — and perhaps she was too — it was a glorious feeling. The attention she had, it was like she was a bride. But of course, after a bit, she got dreadfully hungry. She couldn't disappoint Father Mealey and the Dean: the way she was looked up to by Father Mealey especially. She just told her mother. And things had gone so far her mother had to help her. She had a big meal, sometimes two, every night.

But then, oh, dear, things had gone even further. "At first, as I told you, Father, it was wonderful. The best of all was the confraternity girls praying to me outside the window!" But when the newspapers started and all that, she got really frightened. She wished to God she had never done it. Sister Teresa was harder to pull the wool over. The marks on her hands were getting faint, instead of being all lifted up and excited she was turning low, depressed . . .

A fresh burst of sobbing terminated the pitiful revelation — tawdry as an illiterate scrawl upon a wall. Yet tragic, somehow, with the idiocy of all humanity.

The mother interposed.

"You won't tell Dean Fitzgerald on us, will you, Father?"

Francis was no longer angry, only sad and strangely merciful. If only the wretched business had not gone so far. He sighed.

"I won't tell him, Mrs. Neily, I won't say a word. But — " He paused. "I'm afraid you must."

Terror leaped again in her eyes. "No, no . . . for pity's sake no, Father."

He began, quietly, to explain why they must confess, how the scheme which the Dean contemplated could not be built upon a lie, especially one which must soon be palpable. He comforted them with the thought that the nine days' wonder would soon subside and be forgotten.

He left them an hour later, somewhat appeased, and with their faithful promise that they would follow out his advice. But as he directed his echoing footsteps homewards through the empty streets his heart ached for Dean Gerald Fitzgerald.

The next day passed. He was out visiting most of the time, and did not see the Dean. But a curious hollowness, a kind of suspended animation, seemed to float within the Presbytery. He was sensitive to atmosphere. He felt this strongly.

At eleven o'clock on the following forenoon, Malcom Glennie broke into his room.

"Francis! You've got to help me. He's not going on with it. For God's sake, come in and talk to him."

Glennie was painfully distressed. He was pale, his lips worked, there was a wildness in his eye. He stuttered: —

"I don't know what's taken him. He must be out of his mind. It's such a beautiful scheme. It'll do so much good — "

"I have no influence with him."

"But you have — he thinks the world of you. And you're a priest. You owe it to your flock. It'll be good for the Catholics — "

"That hardly interests you, Malcom."

"But it does," Glennie babbled. "I'm a liberal man. I admire the Catholics. It's a beautiful religion. I often wish — Oh, for God's sake, Francis, come in, quick, before it's too late."

"I'm sorry, Malcom. It's disappointing for all of us." He turned away towards the window.

At that Glennie lost all control of himself. He caught hold of Francis' arm. He snivelled abjectly.

"Don't turn me down, Francis. You owe everything to us. I've bought a little bit of land, put all my savings in it, it's worthless if the scheme falls through. Don't see my poor family ruined. My poor old mother! Think of how she brought you up, Francis. Please, please persuade him. I'd do anything in the world. I'll even turn a Catholic for you!"

Francis kept staring out of the window, his hand gripping the curtain, his eyes fixed on the church gable, pointed with a grey stone cross. A dull thought crossed his mind. What would mankind do for money? Everything. Even to selling its immortal soul.

Glennie exhausted himself at last. Convinced, finally, that nothing could be gained from Francis, he struggled for the remnants of his dignity. His manner altered.

"So you won't help me. Well, I'll remember you for this." He moved towards the door. "I'll get even with you all. If it's the last thing I do."

He paused on his way out, his pallid face contorted with malice. "I should have known you'd bite the hand that fed you. What else could you expect from a lot of dirty papists!"

He slammed the door behind him.

The hollowness continued within the Presbytery: that kind of vacuum in which people lose their clear outlines, become unsubstantial, transitory. The servants moved on tiptoe, as though it were a house of death. The Lithuanian Father wore a look of sheer bewilderment. Father Mealey went about with his eyes cast down. He had received a grave hurt. But he kept silence, which in one so naturally effusive was a singular grace. When he spoke it was of other matters. He distracted himself, passionately, with his work at the Foreign Missions office.

For more than a week after Glennie's outburst Francis had no encounter with Fitzgerald. Then, one morning, as he entered the sacristy, he found the Dean unvesting. The altar boys had gone; the two were alone.

Whatever his personal humiliation, the Dean's control of the disaster had been consummate. Indeed, in his hands it ceased to be disaster. Captain Hollis had willingly torn up the contracts. An occupation had been found for Neily in a distant town: the first step towards discreet withdrawal of the family. The clangour in the journals was tactfully stilled. Then, on Sunday, the Dean climbed again into the pulpit. Facing the hushed congregation, he gave the text: "O Ye of Little Faith!"

Quietly, with still intensity, he developed his thesis: What need had the Church of additional miracles? Had she not fully justified herself, miraculously, already? Her foundations were planted deep, foursquare, upon the miracles of Christ. It was pleasant, no doubt exciting, to meet a manifestation like that of Marywell. They had all, himself included, been carried away with it. But on sober reflection, why all this outcry about a single blossom, when the very flower of heaven bloomed here in the church, before their eyes? Were they so weak, so pusillanimous in their faith they needed further material evidence? Had they forgotten the solemn words: "Blessed are they that have not seen, and have believed"? It was a superb feat of oratory. It surpassed his triumph of the previous Sunday. Gerald Fitzgerald, still a Dean, alone knew what it cost him.

At first, in the sacristy, the Dean seemed about to maintain his inflexible reserve. But, when ready to leave, with his black coat cast about his shoulders, he suddenly swung round. In the clear light of the sacristy Francis was shocked to see the deep lines on the handsome face, the weariness in the full grey eyes.

"Not one lie, Father, but a tissue of lies. Well! God's will be done!" He paused. "You're a good fellow, Chisholm. It's a pity you and I are incompatible." He went out of the sacristy, erect.

By the end of Easter the event had almost been forgotten. The neat white railing which had been erected round the Well in the Dean's first ardour still stood; but the little entrance gate remained unlocked, swinging, rather pathetically, in the light spring air. A few good souls went occasionally to pray and bless themselves with the sparkling, ever-gushing water.

Francis, caught by a spurt of parish work, rejoiced in his own forgetfulness. The smear of the experience was gradually wearing off. What remained was only a faint ugliness at the back of his mind, which he quickly suppressed and would soon bury completely. His idea of a new playing field for the boys and young men of the parish had taken tangible form. He had been offered the use of a strip of the Public Park by the local council. Dean Fitzgerald had given his consent. He was now immersed in a pile of catalogues.

On the eve of Ascension Day he received an urgent call to visit Owen Warren. His face clouded. He rose immediately, the cricket folder falling from his knee. Though he had expected this summons for many weeks, he dreaded it. He went quickly to the church and, with the viaticum upon his person, hurried through the crowded town to Glanville Street.

His expression was fixed and sad as he saw Dr. Tulloch pacing restlessly outside the Warren home. Tulloch was attached to Owen too. He looked deeply upset as Francis approached.

"Has it come at last?" Francis said.

"Yes, it's come!" As an afterthought: "Yesterday the main artery thrombosed. It wasn't any use — even to amputate."

"Am I too late?"

"No." Tulloch's manner held a subdued violence. He shouldered roughly past Francis. "But I've been in three times at the boy while you've been strolling along. Come in, damn it . . . if you're coming in at all."

Francis followed the other up the steps. Mrs. Warren opened the door. She was a spare woman of fifty, worn out by the weeks of anxiety, plainly dressed in grey. He saw that her face was wet with tears. He pressed her hand in sympathy.

"I'm so sorry, Mrs. Warren."

She laughed — weakly, chokingly.

"Go into the room, Father!"

He was shocked. He thought that grief had momentarily turned her mind. He went into the room.

Owen was lying on the counterpane of his bed. His lower limbs were unbandaged, bare. They were rather thin, showing the wasting of disease. Both were sound, unblemished.

Dazed, Francis watched Dr. Tulloch lift up the right leg and run his hand firmly down the sound straight shin which yesterday had been a festering malignant mass. Finding no answer in the doctor's challenging eyes, he turned giddily to Mrs. Warren, saw that her tears were tears of joy. She nodded blindly, through these tears.

"I bundled him up warm in the old gocar' this morning before anybody was about. We wouldn't give up, Owney and me. He had

always believed . . . if he could only get up there to the Well . . .
We prayed and dipped his leg in the water. . . . When we got
back . . . Owney . . . took the bandage off himself!"

The stillness in the room was absolute. It was Owen who
finally broke it.

"Don't forget to put me down for your new cricket team, Father."

In the street, outside, Willie Tulloch stared doggedly at his
friend.

"There's bound to be a scientific explanation beyond the scope
of our present knowledge. An intense desire for recovery — psychological regeneration of the cells." He stopped short, his big
hand trembling on Francis' arm. "Oh, God! — if there is a God! —
let's all keep our bloody mouths shut about it!"

That night Francis could not rest. He stared with sleepless eyes
into the blackness above his head. The miracle of faith. Yes, faith
itself was the miracle. The waters of Jordan, Lourdes, or Marywell — they mattered not a jot. Any muddy pool would answer, if
it were the mirror of God's face.

Momentarily, the seismograph of his mind faintly registered the
shock: a glimmering of the knowledge of the incomprehensibility of
God. He prayed fervently. O dear God, we don't even know the
beginning. We are like tiny ants in a bottomless abyss, covered with
a million layers of cotton wool, striving . . . striving to see the sky.
O God . . . dear God, give me humility . . . and give me faith!

III

It was three months later when the Bishop's summons arrived.
Francis had expected it for some time now, yet its actual arrival
somewhat dismayed him. Heavy rain began as he walked up the
hill towards the palace; only by racing the intervening distance did
he avoid a thorough drenching. Out of breath, wet and splashed
with mud, he felt his arrival somewhat lacking in dignity. Insensibly
his anxiety increased as he sat, slightly shivering, in the formal

parlour, gazing at his mired boots, so incongruous upon the red pile carpet.

At last the Bishop's secretary appeared, ushered him up a shallow flight of marble stairs, and silently indicated a dark mahogany door. Francis knocked and went in.

His Lordship was at his desk, not bent at work but resting, his cheek against his hand, elbow on the arm of his leather chair. The fading light, striking sideways through the velvet pelmets of the tall window, enriched the violet of his biretta but found his face in shadow.

Francis paused uncertainly, disconcerted by the impassive figure, asking himself if this were really his old friend of Holywell and San Morales. There was no sound but the faint ticking of the Buhl clock on the mantelpiece. Then a severe voice said: —

"Well, Father, any miracles to report tonight? And by the by, before I forget, how is the dance-hall business doing now?"

Francis felt a thickness in his throat, he could have cried for sheer relief. His Lordship continued his scrutiny of the figure marooned on the wide rug. "I must confess it affords some relief to my old eyes to see a priest so manifestly unprosperous as you. Usually they come in here looking like successful undertakers. That's an abominable suit you're wearing — and dreadful boots!" He rose slowly, and advanced towards Francis. "My dear boy, I am delighted to see you. But you're horribly thin." He placed his hand on the other's shoulder. "And good gracious, horribly wet, too!"

"I got caught in the rain, your Grace."

"What! No umbrella! Come over to the fire. We must get you something warm." Leaving Francis, he went to a small escritoire and produced a decanter and two liqueur glasses. "I am not yet properly acclimatized to my new dignity. I ought to ring and command some of these fine vintages used by all the Bishops one reads about. This is only Glenlivet, but it's fit tipple for two Scots." He handed Francis a tiny glassful of the neat spirit, watched him drink it, then drank his own. He sat down on the other side of the fireplace. "Speaking of dignity, do not look so scared of me. I'm bedizened now — I admit. But underneath is the same clumsy anatomy you saw wading through the Stinchar!"

Francis reddened. "Yes, your Grace."

There was a pause, then His Lordship said, directly and quietly: "You've had a pretty thin time, I imagine, since you left San Morales."

Francis answered in a low voice. "I've been a pretty good failure."

"Indeed?"

"Yes, I felt this coming . . . this disciplinary interview. I knew I wasn't pleasing Dean Fitzgerald lately."

"Just pleasing Almighty God, eh?"

"No, no. I'm really ashamed, dissatisfied with myself. It's my incorrigibly rebellious nature." A pause.

"Your culminating iniquity seems to be that you failed to attend a banquet in honour of Alderman Shand . . . who has just made a magnificent donation of five hundred pounds to the new high altar fund. Can it be that you disapprove of the good Alderman — who, I am told, is slightly less pious in his dealings with the tenants of his slum property in Shand Street?"

"Well . . ." Francis halted in confusion. "I don't know. I was wrong not to go. Dean Fitzgerald specially advised us we must attend . . . he attached great importance to it. But something else cropped up . . ."

"Oh?" The Bishop waited.

"I was called to see someone that afternoon." Francis spoke with great reluctance. "You may remember . . . Edward Bannon . . . though he's unrecognizable now, in his illness, paralyzed, drooling, a caricature of God-made man. When it was time for me to go he clutched my hand, implored me not to leave him. I couldn't help myself . . . or restrain a terrible sick pity for this . . . grotesque, dying outcast. He fell asleep mumbling, 'John the Father, John the Son, John the Holy Ghost,' saliva running down his grey unshaven chin, holding my hand. . . . I remained with him till morning."

A longer pause. "No wonder the Dean was annoyed that you preferred the sinner to the saint."

Francis hung his head. "I am annoyed with myself. I keep trying to do better. It's strange — when I was a boy I had the conviction that priests were all quite infallibly good . . ."

"And now you are discovering how terribly human we are. Yes, it's unholy that your 'rebellious nature' should fill me with joy, but I find it a wonderful antidote to the monotonous piety I am subjected to. You are the stray cat, Francis, who comes stalking up the aisle when everyone is yawning their head off at a dull sermon. That's not a bad metaphor — for you *are* in the church even if you don't match up with those who find it all by the well-known rule. I am not flattering myself, when I say that I am probably the only cleric in this diocese who really understands you. It's fortunate I am now your Bishop."

"I know that, your Grace."

"To me," His Lordship meditated, "you are not a failure, but a howling success. You can do with a little cheering up — so I'll risk giving you a swelled head. You've got inquisitiveness and tenderness. You're sensible of the distinction between thinking and doubting. You're not one of our ecclesiastical milliners who must have everything stitched up in neat little packets — convenient for handing out. And quite the nicest thing about you, my dear boy, is this — you haven't got that bumptious security which springs from dogma rather than from faith."

There was a silence. Francis felt his heart melt towards the old man. He kept his eyes cast down. The quiet voice went on.

"Of course, unless we do something about it you're going to get hurt. If we go on with cudgels there'll be too many bloody heads — including your own! Oh, yes, I know — you're not afraid. But I am. You're too valuable to be fed to the lions. That's why I have something to put before you."

Francis raised his head quickly, met His Lordship's wise and affectionate gaze. The Bishop smiled.

"You don't imagine I'd be treating you as a boon companion if I didn't want you to do something for me!"

"Anything . . ." Francis stumbled on the words.

There was a long pause. The Bishop's face was gravely chiselled. "It's a big thing to ask . . . a great change to suggest . . . if it is too much . . . you must tell me. But I think it is the very life for you." Again a pause. "Our Foreign Missions Society has at last been promised a vicariate in China. When all the formalities are completed, and you've had some preparation, will you go there as our first unprincipled adventurer?"

Francis remained completely still, numb with surprise. The walls seemed to crumble about him. The request was so unexpected, so tremendous, it took his breath away. To leave home, his friends, and move into a great unknown void . . . He could not think. But slowly, mysteriously, a strange animation filled his being. He answered haltingly: "Yes . . . I will go."

Rusty Mac leaned over and took Francis' hand in his. His eyes were moist and had a poignant fixity. "I thought you would, dear boy. And I know you'll do me credit. But you'll get no salmon fishing there, I warn you."

IV

THE CHINA INCIDENT

I

EARLY in the year 1902 a lopsided junk making dilatory passage up the endless yellow reaches of the Ta-Hwang River in the province of Chek-kow, not less than one thousand miles inland from Tientsin, bore a somewhat unusual figurehead in the shape of a medium-sized Catholic priest wearing list slippers and an already wilted topee. With his legs astride the stubby bowsprit and his breviary balanced on one knee, Francis ceased momentarily his vocal combat with the Chinese tongue, in which every syllable seemed to his exhausted larynx to have as many inflections as a chromatic scale, and let his gaze rest on the drifting brown-and-ochre landscape. Fatigued after his tenth night in the three-foot den between-decks which was his cabin, he had, in the hope of a breath of air, forced himself forward into the bows through the packed welter of his fellow passengers: farm labourers, basket and leather workers from Sen-siang, bandits and fishermen, soldiers and merchants on their way to Pai-tan, squatting elbow to elbow, smoking, talking and tending their cooking pots amongst the crates of ducks, the pigpens and the heaving net which held the solitary but fractious goat.

Although Francis had vowed not to be fastidious the sounds, sights and smells of this final yet interminable stage of his journey had tried him severely. He thanked God and Saint Andrew that tonight, short of further delay, he would at last reach Pai-tan.

Even yet he could not believe himself a part of this new fantastic world, so remote and alien, so incredibly divorced from all that he had known, or hoped to know. He felt as if his life had suddenly been bent, grotesquely, away from its natural form. He checked his sigh. Others lived to a smooth and normal pattern. He was the oddity, the misfit, the little crooked man.

It had been hard to say good-bye to those at home. Ned, mercifully, had passed away three months ago, a blessed ending to that grotesque and pitiful epilogue of life. But Polly . . . he hoped, he prayed he might see Polly in the future. There was consolation in the fact that Judy had been accepted as a shorthand-typist in the Tynecastle Council offices — a post which offered security and good chances of promotion.

As if to steel himself anew he pulled from his inside pocket the final letter relating to his appointment. It was from Father Mealey, now relieved of his parish duties at St. Dominic's to devote himself exclusively to the F.M.S. Administration.

Addressed to him at Liverpool University, where for the past twelve months he had hammered out his language course, the letter ran: —

My dear Francis,

I am overjoyed to be the bearer of glad tidings! We have just received news that Pai-tan, in the Vicariate of Chek-kow, which, as you well know, was presented to us by the A.F.M.S. in December, has now been ratified by the Congregation of Propaganda. It was decided at our meeting held at the F. M. S. in Tynecastle tonight that nothing need delay your departure. At last, at last, I am able to speed you on your glorious mission to the Orient.

So far as I can ascertain Pai-tan is a delightful spot, some miles inland, but on a pleasant river, a thriving city specializing in the manufacture of baskets, with an abundance of cereal, meat, poultry, and tropical fruits. But the supremely important, the blessed fact is that the mission itself, while somewhat remote and for the past twelve months unfortunately without a priest, is in a highly flourishing condition. I'm sorry we have no photographs but I can assure you the layout is most satisfactory: comprising chapel, priest's house and compound. (What an exciting sound that word "compound" has! Don't you remember as boys when we played Indians? Forgive my enthusiasms.)

But la crème de la crème lies in our proved statistics. Enclosed you will find the annual report of the late incumbent, Father Lawler, who, a year ago, returned to San Francisco. I don't propose to analyze this for you since you will indubitably con it over, nay, digest it in the wee small hours. Nevertheless I may stress these figures: that although established only three years ago the Pai-tan mission can boast of four hundred communicants and over one thousand baptisms, only a third of which were in articulo mortis. Is it not gratifying, Francis? An example of how the dear old grace of God leavens even heathen hearts amidst pagan temple bells.

My dear fellow, I rejoice that this prize is to be yours. And I have no doubt that by your labours in the field you will materially increase the vineyard's crop. I look forward to your first report. I feel that you have at last found your métier and that the little eccentricities of tongue and temper which have been your trouble in the past will no longer be part and parcel of your daily life. Humility, Francis, is the life blood of God's Saints. I pray for you every night.

I will be writing you later. Meanwhile don't neglect your outfit. Get good strong durable soutanes. Short drawers are the best and I advise a body belt. Go to Hanson & Son; they are sound people; and cousins of the organist at the Cathedral.

It is just possible I may be seeing you sooner than you imagine. My new post may make me quite a globe trotter. Wouldn't it be grand if we met in the shady compound of Pai-tan?

Again my congratulations and with every good wish,

I remain, your devoted brother in J. C.

ANSELM MEALEY
Secretary to the Foreign Missions Society,
Diocese of Tynecastle.

Towards sundown a heightening of the commotion in the junk indicated the imminence of their arrival. As the vessel yawed round a bend into a great bight of dirty water, mobbed by a pack of sampans, Francis eagerly scanned the low tiered reaches of the town. It seemed like a great low hive, humming with sound and yellow light, fronted by the reedy mud flats with their flotsam of rafts and boats, backed distantly by mountains, pink and of a pearly translucency.

He had hoped the mission might send a boat for him but the only private wherry was for Mr. Chia, merchant and wealthy resident of Pai-tan, who now emerged for the first time, silent and satin-clad, from the recesses of the junk.

This personage was about thirty-five, but of such composure he looked older, with a supple golden skin and hair so black it seemed moist. He stood with leisurely indifference while the kapong fussed around him. Though his lashes did not once flicker in the direction of the priest, Francis had the odd conviction he was being taken in minutely.

Owing to the preoccupation of the purser, some time elapsed before the new missioner secured passage for himself and his japanned tin trunk. As he stepped down to the sampan he clutched his large silk umbrella, a glorious thing covered in Chisholm tartan which Bishop MacNabb had pressed upon him as a parting gift.

His excitement rose when, nearing the bank, he saw a great press of people on the landing steps. Was it a welcome from his congregation? What a splendid thought for the end of his long, long journey! His heart began to beat almost painfully, with happy expectation. But alas, when he landed he saw he was mistaken. No one greeted him. He had to push his way through the staring yet incurious throng.

At the end of the steps, however, he stopped short. Before him, smiling happily, dressed in neat blue and bearing, as a symbol of their credentials, a brightly coloured picture of the Holy Family, were a Chinese man and woman. As he stood, the two small figures approached him, their smile deepening, overjoyed to see him, bowing and zealously blessing themselves.

Introductions began — less difficult than he had supposed. He asked warmly: —

"Who are you?"

"We are Hosannah and Philomena Wang — your beloved catechists, Father."

"From the mission?"

"Yes, yes, Father Lawler made a most excellent mission, Father."

"You will conduct me to the mission?"

"By all means, let us go. But perhaps Father will honour us and come first to our humble abode."

"Thank you. But I am eager to reach the mission."

"Of course. We will go to the mission. We have bearers and a chair for Father."

"You are very kind, but I would prefer to walk."

Still smiling, though less perceptibly, Hosannah turned and in a rapid unintelligible exchange, which had some semblance of an argument, dismissed the sedan chair and the string of porters which he had in tow. Two coolies remained: one shouldered the trunk, the other the umbrella, and the party set off on foot.

Even in the tortuous and dirty streets it was agreeable for Francis to stretch his legs, cramped from confinement in the junk. A quick fervour stirred his blood. Amidst the strangeness he could feel the pulse of humanity. Here were hearts to be won, souls to be saved!

He became aware of one of the Wangs, pausing, to address him.

"There is an agreeable dwelling in the Street of the Netmakers ... only five taels by the month ... where Father might wish to spend the night."

Francis looked down in amused surprise. "No, no, Hosannah. Onwards to the mission!"

There was a pause. Philomena coughed. Francis realized that they were standing still. Hosannah politely smiled.

"Here, Father, is the mission."

At first he did not fully understand.

Before them on the riverbank was an acre of deserted earth, sun-scorched, gullied by the rains, encircled by a tramped-down piece of kaolin. At one end stood the remnants of a mud-brick chapel, the roof blown off, one wall collapsed, the others crumbling. Alongside lay a mass of caved-in rubble which might once have been a house. Tall feathery weeds were sprouting there. A single meagre shell remained, amidst the ruins, leaning yet still straw-roofed — the stable.

For three minutes Francis stood in a kind of stupor, then he slowly turned to the Wangs, who were close together, watching him, neat, unfathomable, similar as Siamese twins.

"Why has this taken place?"

"It was a beautiful mission, Father. It cost much — and we made many financial arrangements for its building. But alas, the good Father Lawler placed it near the river. And the Devil sent much wicked rain."

"Then where are the people of the congregation?"

"They are wicked people without belief in the Lord of Heaven." The two spoke more rapidly now, helping each other, gesticulating.

"Father must understand how much depends upon his catechists. Alas! Since the good Father Lawler has gone away we have not been paid our lawful stipend of fifteen taels each month. It has been impossible to keep these wicked people properly instructed."

Crushed and devastated, Father Chisholm removed his gaze. This was his mission, these two his sole parishioners. The recollection of the letter within his pocket sent a sudden upsurge of passion over him. He clenched his hands, stood thinking, rigidly.

The Wangs were still talking fluently, trying to persuade him to return to the town. With an effort he rid himself of their importunities, their unctuous presence. It was, at least, a relief to be alone.

Determinedly, he carried his box into the stable. At one time a stable had been good enough for Christ. Gazing round he saw that some straw still littered the earthen floor. Though he had neither food nor water, at least he had a bed. He unpacked his blankets, began to make the place as habitable as he could. Suddenly a gong sounded. He ran out of the stable. Across the decapitated fence, outside the nearest of the temples which stippled the adjacent hill, stood an aged bonze wearing thick stockings and a quilted yellow robe, beating his metal plaque into the short unheeding twilight with measured boredom. The two priests — of Buddha and of Christ — inspected each other in silence; then the old man turned, expressionless, mounted the steps and vanished.

Night fell with the swiftness of a blow. Francis knelt down in the darkness of the devastated compound and lifted his eyes to the dawning constellations. He prayed with fierce, with terrible intensity. Dear God, you wish me to begin from nothing. This is the answer to my vanity, my stubborn human arrogance. It's better so! I'll work, I'll fight for you. I'll never give up . . . never . . . never!

Back in the stable, trying to rest, while the shrill ping of mosquitoes and the crack of flying beetles split the sweltering air, he forced himself to smile. He did not feel heroic, but a dreadful fool. Saint Teresa had likened life to a night in a hotel. This one they had sent him to was not the Ritz!

Morning came at last. He rose. Taking his chalice from its cedar box, he made an altar of his trunk and offered up his mass, kneeling on the stable floor. He felt refreshed, happy and strong. The arrival of Hosannah Wang failed to discompose him.

"Father should have let me serve his mass. That is always included in our pay. And now — shall we find a room in the Street of the Netmakers?"

Francis reflected. Though he had stubbornly made up his mind to live here till the situation cleared, it was true that he must find a more fitting center for his ministrations. He said: "Let us go there now."

The streets were already thronged. Dogs raced between their legs, pigs were rooting for garbage in the gutter. Children followed them, jeering and shouting. Beggars wailed with importunate palms. An old man setting out his wares, in the Street of the Lanternmakers, spat sullenly across the foreign devil's feet. Outside the yamen of justice, a peripatetic barber stood twanging his long tongs. There were many poor, many crippled, and some, blinded by smallpox, who tapped their way forward with a long bamboo and a queer high whistle.

It was an upper room Wang brought him to, clumsily partitioned with paper and bamboo, but sufficient for any service he would conduct. From his small store of money he paid a month's rent to the shopkeeper, named Hung, and began to set out his crucifix and solitary altar cloth. His lack of vestments, of altar furnishings, fretted him. Led to expect a full equipment at the "flourishing" mission, he had brought little. But his standard, at least, was planted.

Wang had preceded him to the shop below and as he turned to descend he observed Hung take two of the silver taels which he had given him and pass them, with a bow, to Wang. Though he had early guessed the worth of Father Lawler's legacy Francis was conscious of a sudden mounting of his blood. Outside, in the street, he turned quietly to Wang.

"I regret, Hosannah, I cannot pay your stipend of fifteen taels a month."

"Father Lawler could pay. Why cannot the Father pay?"

"I am poor, Hosannah. Just as poor as was my Master."

"How much will the Father pay?"

"Nothing, Hosannah! Even as I am paid nothing. It is the good Lord of Heaven who will reward us!"

Wang's smile did not falter. "Perhaps Hosannah and Philomena must go where they are appreciated. At Sen-siang the Methodys pay sixteen taels for highly respected catechists. But doubtless the good Father will change his mind. There is much animosity in Pai-tan. The people consider the *feng shua* of the city — the Laws of Wind and Order — destroyed by the intrusion of the missionary."

He waited for the priest's reply. But Francis did not speak. There was a strained pause. Then Wang bowed politely and departed.

A coldness settled upon Francis as he watched the other disappear. Had he done right in alienating the friendly Wangs? The answer was that the Wangs were not his friends, but lick-spittle opportunists who believed in the Christian God because of Christian money. And yet . . . his one contact with the community was severed. He had a sudden, frightening sense of being alone.

As the days passed this horrible loneliness increased, coupled with a paralyzing impotence. Lawler, his predecessor, had built upon sand. Incompetent, credulous, and supplied with ample funds, he had rushed about, giving money and taking names, baptizing promiscuously, acquiring a string of "rice-Christians," filling long reports, unconsciously the victim of a hundred subtle squeezes, sanguine, bombastic, gloriously triumphant. He had not even scratched the surface. Of his work nothing remained except perhaps — in the city's official circles — a lingering contempt for such lamentable foreign folly.

Beyond a small sum set for his living expenses, and a five-pound note pressed into his hand by Polly on his departure, Francis had no money whatsoever. He had been warned, too, on the futility of requesting grants from the new society at home. Sickened by

Lawler's example, he rejoiced in his poverty. He swore, with a feverish intensity, that he would not hire his congregation. What must be done would be done with God's help and his own two hands.

Yet so far he had done nothing. He hung a sign outside his makeshift chapel; it made no difference: none appeared to hear his mass. The Wangs had spread a wide report that he was destitute, with nothing to distribute but bitter words.

He attempted an open-air meeting outside the courts of justice. He was laughed at, then ignored. His failure humiliated him. A Chinese laundryman preaching Confucianism in pigeon-English in the streets of Liverpool would have met with more success. Wildly he fought that insidious demon, the inner whisper of his own incompetence.

He prayed, he prayed most desperately. He ardently believed in the efficacy of prayer. "Oh God, you've helped me in the past. Help me now, for God's sake, please."

He had hours of raging fury. Why had they sent him, with plausible assurances, to this outlandish hole? The task was beyond any man, beyond God Himself! Cut from all communications, buried in the hinterland, with the nearest missioner, Father Thibodeau, at Sen-siang, four hundred miles away, the place was quite untenable.

Fostered by the Wangs, the popular hostility towards him increased. He was used to the jeers of the children. Now, on his passage through the town, a crowd of young coolies followed, throwing out insults. When he stopped a member of the gang would advance and perform his natural functions in the vicinity. One night, as he returned to the stable, a stone sailed out of the darkness and struck him on the brow.

All Francis' combativeness rose hotly in response. As he bandaged his broken head, his own wound gave him a wild idea, making him pause, rigid and intent. Yes . . . he must . . . he must get closer to the people . . . and this . . . no matter how primitive . . . this new endeavour might help him to that end.

Next morning, for two extra taels a month, he rented the lower back room of the shop from Hung and opened a public dispensary. He was no expert — God knew. But he had his St. John's certificate, and his long acquaintance with Dr. Tulloch had grounded him soundly in hygiene.

At first no one ventured near him; and he sweated with despair. But gradually, drawn by curiosity, one or two came in. There was always sickness in the city and the methods of the native doctors were barbaric. He had some success. He exacted nothing in money or devotion. Slowly his clientèle grew. He wrote urgently to Dr. Tulloch, enclosing Polly's five pounds, clamouring for an additional supply of dressings, bandages, and simple drugs. While the chapel remained empty the dispensary was often full.

At night, he brooded frantically amongst the ruins of the mission. He could never rebuild on that eroded site. And he gazed across the way in fierce desire at the pleasant Hill of Brilliant Green Jade where, above the scattered temples, a lovely slope extended, sheltered by a grove of cedars. What a noble situation for a monument to God!

The owner of this property, a civil judge named Pao, member of that inner intermarried community of merchants and magistrates who controlled the city's affairs, was rarely to be seen. But on most afternoons, his cousin, a tall dignified mandarin of forty, who managed the estate for Mr. Pao, came to inspect and to pay the labourers who worked the clay-pits in the cedar grove.

Worn by weeks of solitude, desolate and persecuted, Francis was undoubtedly a little mad. He had nothing; he was nothing. Yet one day, on an impulse, he stopped the tall mandarin as he crossed the road towards his chair. He did not understand the impropriety of this direct approach. In fact he knew little of what he did: he had not been eating properly, and was lightheaded from a touch of fever.

"I have often admired this beautiful property which you so wisely administer."

Taken wholly by surprise, Mr. Pao's cousin formally viewed the short alien figure with its burning eyes, and the soiled bandage on its forehead. In frigid politeness he bore with the priest's continued assaults upon the syntax, briefly deprecated himself, his family, his miserable possessions, remarked on the weather, the crops, and the difficulty the city had experienced last year in buying off the Wai-Chu bandits; then pointedly opened the door of his chair. When Francis, with swimming head, strove to return the conversation to the Green Jade land, he smiled coldly.

"The Green Jade property is a pearl without price, in extent more than sixty mous . . . shade, water, pasture . . . in addition a rich and extraordinary clay-pit for the purpose of tiles, pottery and bricks. Mr. Pao has no desire to sell. Already, for the estate, he has refused . . . fifteen thousand silver dollars."

At the price, ten times greater than his most fearful estimate, Francis' legs shook. The fever left him, he suddenly felt weak and giddy, ashamed at the absurdity into which his dreams had led him. With splitting head, he thanked Mr. Pao's cousin, muttered a confused apology.

Observing the priest's disappointed sadness, the lean, middle-aged, cultured Chinese allowed a flicker of disdain to escape his watchful secrecy.

"Why does the Shang-Foo come here? Are there no wicked men to regenerate in his own land? For we are not wicked people. We have our own religion. Our own gods are older than his. The other Shang-Foo made many Christians by pouring water from a little bottle upon dying men and singing 'Ya . . . ya!' Also, by giving food and clothing, to many more who would sing any tune to have their skins covered and their bellies full. Does the Shang-Foo wish to do this also?"

Francis gazed at the other in silence. His thin face had a worn pallor, there were deep shadows beneath his eyes. He said quietly: "Do you think that is my wish?"

There was a strange pause. All at once, Mr. Pao's cousin dropped his eyes.

"Forgive me," he said, in a low tone. "I did not understand.

You are a good man." A vague friendliness tinctured his compunction. "I regret that my cousin's land is not available. Perhaps in
some other manner I may assist you?"

Mr. Pao's cousin waited with a new courtesy, as if anxious to
make amends. Francis thought for a moment, then asked heavily:
"Tell me, since we are being honest. . . . Are there no true Christians here?"

Mr. Pao's cousin answered slowly: "Perhaps. But I should not
seek them in Pai-tan." He paused. "I have heard, however, of a
village in the Kwang Mountains." He made a vague gesture towards
the distant peaks. "A village Christian for many years . . . but it is
far away, many many li from here."

A gleam of light shot into the haggard gloom of Francis' mind.
"That interests me deeply. Can you give me further information?"

The other shook his head regretfully. "It is a small place on the
uplands — almost unknown. My cousin only learned of it from his
trade in sheepskins."

Francis' eagerness sustained him. "Could you ask him? Could you
procure directions for me . . . perhaps a map?"

Mr. Pao's cousin reflected, then nodded gravely. "It should be
possible. I shall ask Mr. Pao. Moreover I shall be careful to inform him that you have spoken with me in a most honourable
fashion."

He bowed and went away.

Overwhelmed with this wholly unexpected hope, Francis returned
to the ruined compound where, with some blankets, a water-skin
and the few utensils purchased in the town, he had made his primitive encampment. As he prepared himself a simple meal of rice, his
hands trembled, as from shock. A Christian village! He must find
it — at all costs. It was his first sense of guidance, of divine inspiration, in all these weary, fruitless months.

As he sat tensely thinking in the dusk he was disturbed by a
hoarse barking of crows, fighting and tearing at some carrion by
the water's edge. He went over at length, to drive them off. And
there, as the great ugly birds flapped and squawked at him, he

saw their prey to be the body of a newly born female child.

Shuddering, he took up the infant's torn body from the river, saw it to be asphyxiated, thrown in and drowned. He wrapped the little thing in linen, buried it in a corner of the compound. And as he prayed he thought: yes, despite my doubts, there is need for me, in this strange land, after all.

II

Two weeks later, when the early summer burgeoned, he was ready. Placing a painted notice of temporary closure on his premises in Netmaker Street, he strapped a pack of blankets and food upon his back, took up his umbrella and set off briskly on foot.

The map given him by Mr. Pao's cousin was beautifully executed, with wind-belching dragons in the corners and a wealth of topographic detail as far as the mountains. Beyond it was sketchy, with little drawings of animals instead of place names. But from their conversations and his own sense of direction Francis had in his head a fair notion of his route. He set his face towards the Kwang Gap.

For two days his journey lay through easy country, the green wet rice-fields giving place to woods of spruce, where the fallen needles made a soft resilient carpet for his feet. Immediately below the Kwangs he traversed a sheltered valley aflame with wild rhododendrons, and later, that same dreamy afternoon, a glade of flowering apricots whose perfume pricked the nostrils like the fume of sparkling wine. Then he began the steep ascent of the ravine.

It grew colder with every step up the narrow stony track. At night he folded himself under the shelter of a rock, hearing the whistle of the wind, the thunder of snow-water in the gorge. In the daytime, the cold blazing whiteness of the higher peaks burned his eyes. The thin iced air was painful to his lungs.

On the fifth day he crossed the summit of the ridge, a frozen wilderness of glacier and rock, and thankfully descended the other side. The pass led him to a wide plateau, beneath the snowline, green with verdure, melting into softly rounded hills. These were the grasslands of which Mr. Pao's cousin had spoken.

Thus far the sheer mountains had defined his twisted course. Now he must rely on Providence, a compass and his good Scot's sense. He struck out directly towards the west. The country was like the uplands of his home. He came on great herds of stoic grazing goats and mountain sheep that streamed off wildly at his approach. He caught the fleeting image of a gazelle. From the bunch-grass of a vast dun marsh thousands of nesting ducks rose screaming, darkening the sky. Since his food was running low, he filled his satchel gratefully with the warm eggs.

It was trackless, treeless plain: he began to despair of stumbling on the village. But early on the ninth day when he felt he must soon turn back, he sighted a shepherd's hut, the first sign of habitation since he'd left the southern slopes. He hastened eagerly towards it. The door was sealed with mud, there was no one inside. But as he swung round, his eyes sharp with disappointment, he saw a boy approaching over the hill behind his flock.

The young shepherd was about seventeen, small and wiry, like his sheep, with a cheerful and intelligent face now caught between wonderment and laughter. He wore short sheepskin trousers and a woollen cape. Round his neck was a small bronze Yuan cross, wafer-thin with age, and roughly scratched with the symbol of a dove. Father Chisholm gazed from the boy's open face to the antique cross in silence. At last he found his voice and greeted him, asking if he were from the Liu village.

The lad smiled. "I am from the Christian village. I am Liu-Ta. My father is the village priest." He added, not to be thought boasting, "One of the village priests!"

Again, there was a silence. Father Chisholm thought better of questioning the boy further. He said: "I have come a long distance, and I too am a priest. I should be grateful if you would take me to your home."

The village lay in an undulating valley five li farther to the westward, a cluster of some thirty houses, tucked away in this fold of the uplands, surrounded by little stone-walled fields of grain. Prominent, upon a central hillock, behind a queer conical mound of stones shaded by a ginkgo tree, was a small stone church.

As he entered the village the entire community immediately surrounded him, men, women, children and dogs, all crowding round in curiosity and excited welcome, pulling at his sleeves, touching his boots, examining his umbrella with cries of admiration, while Ta threw off a rapid explanation in a dialect he could not understand. There were perhaps sixty persons in the throng, primitive and healthy, with naïve, friendly eyes and features that bore the imprint of their common family. Presently, with a proprietary smile, Ta brought forward his father Liu-Chi, a short and sturdy man of fifty with a small grey beard, simple and dignified in his manner.

Speaking slowly, to make himself understood, Liu-Chi said: "We welcome you with joy, Father. Come to my house and rest a little before prayer."

He led the way to the largest house, built on a stone foundation next the church, and showed Father Chisholm, with courteous urbanity, into a low cool room. At the end of the room stood a mahogany spinet and a Portuguese wheel clock. Bewildered, lost in wonder, Francis stared at the clock. The brass dial was engraved: *Lisbon 1632.*

He had no time for closer inspection, Liu-Chi was addressing him again. "Is it your wish to offer mass, Father? Or shall I?"

As in a dream Father Chisholm nodded his head towards the other. Something within him answered: "You . . . please!" He was groping in a great confusion. He knew he could not rudely break this mystery with speech. He must penetrate it graciously, in patience, with his eyes.

Half an hour later they were all within the church. Though small it had been built with taste in a style that showed the Moorish influence on the Renaissance. There were three simple arcades, beautifully fluted. The doorway and the windows were supported by flat pilasters. On the walls, partly incomplete, free mosaics had been traced.

He sat in the front row of an attentive congregation. Every one had ceremonially washed his hands before entering. Most of the men and a few of the women wore praying caps upon their heads. Suddenly a tongueless bell was struck and Liu-Chi approached the altar, wearing a faded yellow alb and supported by two young men. Turning, he bowed ceremoniously to Father Chisholm and the congregation. Then the service began.

Father Chisholm watched, kneeling erect, spellbound, like a man beholding the slow enactment of a dream. He saw now that the ceremony was a strange survival, a touching relic of the mass. Liu-Chi must know no Latin, for he prayed in Chinese. First came the confiteor, then the creed. When he ascended the altar and opened the parchment missal on its wooden rest, Francis clearly heard a portion of the gospel solemnly intoned in the native tongue. An original translation. . . . He drew a quick breath of awe.

The whole congregation advanced to take communion. Even children at the breast were carried to the altar steps. Liu-Chi descended, bearing a chalice of rice wine. Moistening his forefinger he placed a drop upon the lips of each.

Before leaving the church, the congregation gathered at the Statue of the Saviour, placing lighted joss-sticks on the heavy candelabrum before the feet. Then each person made three prostrations and reverently withdrew.

Father Chisholm remained behind, his eyes moist, his heart wrung by the simple childish piety — the same piety, the same simplicity he had so often witnessed in peasant Spain. Of course this ceremony was not valid — he smiled faintly, visualizing Father Tarrant's horror at the spectacle — but he had no doubt it was pleasing to God Almighty none the less.

Liu-Chi was waiting outside to conduct him to the house. There a meal awaited them. Famished, Father Chisholm did full justice to the stew of mountain mutton — little savoury balls floating in cabbage soup — and the strange dish of rice and wild honey which followed. He had never tasted such a delicious sweet in all his life.

When they had both finished, he began tactfully to question Liu-Chi. He would have bitten out his tongue rather than give offence. The gentle old man answered trustingly. His beliefs were Christian, quite childlike and curiously mingled with the traditions of *Tâo-tê*. Perhaps, thought Father Chisholm, with an inward smile, a touch of Nestorianism thrown in for value. . . .

Chi explained that the faith had been handed down from father to son through many generations. The village was not dramatically isolated from the world. But it was sufficiently remote; and so small, so integrated in its family life, that strangers rarely troubled it. They were one great family. Existence was purely pastoral and self-supporting. They had grain and mutton in plenty even through the hardest times; cheese, which they sealed in the stomach of a sheep, and two kinds of butter, red and black, both made from beans and named *chiang*. For clothing they had home-carded wool, sheepskins for extra warmth. They beat a special parchment from the skins that was much prized in Pekin. There were many wild ponies on the uplands. Rarely, a member of the family went out with a ponyload of vellum.

In the little tribe there were three Fathers, each chosen for this honoured position while still in infancy. For certain religious offices a fee of rice was paid. They had a special devotion to the Three Precious Ones — the Trinity. Within living memory they had never seen an ordained priest.

Father Chisholm had listened with rapt attention and now he put the question uppermost in his mind.

"You have not told me how it first began!"

Liu-Chi looked at his visitor with final appraisal. Then with a faint reassured smile he got up and went into the adjoining room. When he returned he bore under his arm a sheepskin-covered bundle. He handed it over silently, watched Father Chisholm open it, then, as the priest's absorption became apparent, silently withdrew.

It was the journal of Father Ribiero, written in Portuguese, brown, stained and tattered, but mostly legible. From his knowledge of Spanish, Francis was able slowly to decipher it. The fascinating interest of the document made the labour as nothing. It held him riveted. He remained motionless, except for the slow movement of his hand turning, at intervals, a heavy page. Time flew back three hundred years: the old stopped clock took up its measured tick.

Manoel Ribiero was a missioner of Lisbon who came to Pekin in 1625. Francis saw the Portuguese vividly before him: a young man of twenty-nine, spare, olive-skinned, a little fiery, his swart eyes ardent yet humble. In Pekin the young missionary had been fortunate in his friendship with Father Adam Schall, the great German Jesuit, missionary, courtier, astronomer, trusted friend and canon founder extraordinary to the Emperor Tchoun-Tchin. For several years Father Ribiero shared a little of the glory of this astounding man who moved untouched through the seething intrigues of the Courts of Heaven, advancing the Christian Faith, even in the celestial harem, confounding virulent hatreds with his accurate predictions of comets and eclipses, compiling a new calendar, winning friendship and illustrious titles for himself and all his ancestors.

Then the Portuguese had pressed to be sent on a distant mission to the Royal Court of Tartary. Adam Schall had granted his request. A caravan was sumptuously equipped and formidably armed. It started from Pekin on the Feast of the Assumption, 1629.

But the caravan had failed to reach the Tartar Royal Courts. Ambushed by a horde of barbarians on the northern slopes of the Kwang Mountains the formidable defenders dropped their arms and fled. The valuable caravan was plundered. Father Ribiero escaped, desperately wounded by flint arrows, with only his personal belongings and the least of his ecclesiastical equipment. Benighted in the snow, he thought his last hour had come and offered himself, bleeding, to God. But the cold froze his wounds. He dragged himself next morning to a shepherd's hut, where he lay for six months neither dead nor alive. Meanwhile an authentic report reached Pekin that Father Ribiero was massacred. No expedition was sent out to search for him.

When the Portuguese decided he might live, he made plans to return to Adam Schall. But time went on and he still remained. In these wide grasslands, he gained a new sense of values, a new habit of contemplation. Besides, he was three thousand li from Pekin, a forbidding distance, even to his intrepid spirit. Quietly he took his decision. He collected the handful of shepherds into one small settlement. He built a church. He became friend and pastor — not to the King of Tartary but to this humble little flock.

With a strange sigh Francis put down the journal. In the failing light he sat thinking, thinking, and seeing many things. Then he rose and went out to the great mound of stones beside the church. Kneeling, he prayed at Father Ribiero's tomb.

He remained at the Liu village for a week. Persuasively, in a manner to hurt no one, he suggested a ratification of all baptisms and marriages. He said mass. Gently he dropped a hint, now here, now there, suggesting an emendation of certain practices. It would take a long time to regularize the village to hidebound orthodoxy: months—no, years. What did that matter? He was content to go slowly. The little community was as clean and sound as a good apple.

He spoke to them of many things. In the evenings a fire would be lit outside Liu-Chi's house, and when they had all seated themselves about it, he would rest himself on the doorstep and talk to the silent, flame-lit circle. Best of all they liked to hear of the presence of their own religion in the great outside world. He drew no captious differences. It enthralled them when he spoke of the churches of Europe, the great cathedrals, the thousands of worshippers flocking to St. Peter's, great kings and princes, statesmen and nobles, all prostrating themselves before the Lord of Heaven, that same Lord of Heaven whom they worshipped here, their master too, their friend. This sense of unity, hitherto but dimly surmised, gave them a joyful pride.

As the intent faces, flickering with light and shadow, gazed up at him in happy wonderment, he felt Father Ribiero at his elbow smiling a little, darkly, not displeased with him. At such moments he had a terrible impulse to throw up Pai-tan and devote himself entirely to these simple people. How happy he could be here! How lovingly he would tend and polish this jewel he had found so unexpectedly in the wilderness! But no, the village was too small, and too remote. He could never make it a centre for true missionary work. Resolutely, he put the temptation away from him.

The boy Ta had become his constant follower. Now he no longer called him Ta but Joseph, for that was the name the youngster had demanded at his conditional baptism. Fortified by the new name, he had begged permission to serve Father Chisholm's mass; and though he naturally knew not a shred of Latin, the priest had smilingly consented. On the eve of his departure Father Chisholm was seated at the doorway of the house when Joseph appeared, his usually cheerful features set and woebegone, the first arrival for the final lecture. Studying the boy the priest had an intuition of his regret, followed by a sudden happy thought.

"Joseph! Would it please you to come with me — if your father would permit it? There are many things you might do to help me."

The boy jumped up with a cry of joy, fell before the priest and kissed his hand.

"Master, I have waited for you to ask me. My father is willing. I will serve you with all my heart."

"There may be many rough roads, Joseph."

"We shall travel them together, Master."

Father Chisholm raised the young man to his feet. He was moved and pleased. He knew he had done a wise thing.

Next morning the preparations for departure were completed.

Scrubbed and smiling, Joseph stood with the bundles, beside the two shaggy mountain ponies he had rounded up at dawn. A small group of younger boys surrounded him, already he was awing his companions with the wonders of the world. In the church Father Chisholm was finishing his thanksgiving. As he rose, Liu-Chi beckoned him to the cryptlike sanctuary. From a cedar chest he drew an embroidered cope, an exquisite thing, stiff with gold. In parts the satin had rubbed paper-thin but the vestment was intact, usable and priceless. The old man smiled at the expression on Francis' face.

"This poor thing pleases you?"

"It is beautiful."

"Take it. It is yours!"

No protestations could prevent Liu-Chi from making the superb gift. It was folded, wrapped in clean flax-cloth, and placed in Joseph's pack.

At last Francis had to bid them all farewell. He blessed them, gave repeated assurances that he would return within six months. It would be easier next time, mounted, and with Joseph as his guide. Then the two departed, together, their ponies nodding neck-to-neck, climbing to the uplands. The eyes of the little village followed them with affection.

With Joseph beside him, Father Chisholm set a good round pace. He felt his faith restored, gloriously fortified. His breast throbbed with fresh hope.

III

THE summer which followed their return to Pai-tan had passed. And now the cold season fell upon the land. With Joseph's help he made the stable snug, patching the cracks with fresh mud and kaolin. Two wooden bunks now buttressed the weakest wall and a flat iron brazier made a hearth upon the beaten earth floor. Joseph, whose appetite was healthy, had already acquired an interesting collection of cooking pots. The boy, now less angelic, improved upon acquaintance: he was a great prattler, loved to be praised and could be wilful at times, with a naïve facility for abstracting ripe musk mellons from the market garden down the way.

Francis was still determined not to quit their lowly shelter until he saw his course ahead. Gradually a few timid souls were creeping to his chapel room in Netmaker Street, the first an old woman, ragged and ashamed, furtively pulling her beads from the sacking which served her for a coat, looking as though a single word would send her scurrying. Firmly, he restrained himself, pretended not to notice her. Next morning she returned with her daughter.

The pitiful sparsity of his followers did not discourage him. His resolve neither to cajole nor to buy his converts was tempered, like fine steel.

His dispensary was going with a swing. Apparently his absence from the little clinic had been regretted. On his return he found a nondescript assembly awaiting him outside Hung's premises. With practice, his judgment, and indeed his skill, increased. All sorts of conditions came his way: skin diseases, colics and coughs, enteritis, dreadful suppurations of the eyes and ears; and most were the result of dirt and overcrowding. It was amazing what cleanliness and a simple bitter tonic did for them. A grain of potassium permanganate was worth its weight in gold.

When his meagre supplies threatened to run out, an answer came to his supplication to Dr. Tulloch — a big nailed-up box of lint, wool and gauze, iodine and antiseptics, castor oil and chlorodyne, with a scrawled torn-off prescription sheet crumpled at the foot.

"Your Holiness: I thought I was the one to go doctoring in the tropics! And where is your degree? Never mind — cure what you can and kill what you can't. Here is a little bag of tricks to help you."

It was a neatly packed first-aid case of lancet, scissors, and forceps. A postscript added: "For your information, I am reporting you to the B.M.A., the Pope and Chung-lung-soo."

Francis smiled at the irrepressible facetiousness. But his throat was tight with gratitude. With this stimulation of his own endeavour and the comfort of Joseph's companionship, he felt a new and thrilling exaltation. He had never worked harder, nor slept sounder, in his life.

But one night in November his sleep was light and troubled and after midnight he suddenly awoke. It was piercing cold. In the still darkness he could hear Joseph's deep and peaceful breathing. He lay for a moment, trying to reason away his vague distress. But he could not. He got up, cautiously, so that he might not wake the sleeping boy, and slipped out of the stable into the compound. The frozen night stabbed him: the air was razor-edged with cold, each breath a cutting pain. There were no stars, but from the frosted snow came a strange and luminous whiteness. The silence seemed to reach a hundred miles. It was terrifying.

Suddenly, through that stillness, he fancied he heard a faint and uncertain cry. He knew he was mistaken, listened, and heard no more. But as he turned to re-enter the stable the sound was repeated, like the feeble squawking of a dying bird. He stood indecisively, then slowly crunched his way across the crusted snow, towards the sound.

Outside the compound, fifty paces down the path, he stumbled on a stiff dark shadow: the prostrate form of a woman, her face sunk into the snow, starkly frozen. She was quite dead, but under her, in the garments about her bosom, he saw the feeble writhings of a child.

He stooped and lifted up the tiny thing, cold as a fish, but soft. His heart was beating like a drum. He ran back, slipping, almost falling, to the stable, calling in a loud voice to Joseph.

When the brazier was blazing with fresh wood, throwing out light and heat, the priest and his servant bent over the child. It was not more than twelve months old. Its eyes were dark and wild, unbelieving towards the warmth of the fire. From time to time it whimpered.

"It is hungry," Joseph said in a wise tone.

They warmed some milk and poured it into an altar vial. Father Chisholm then tore a strip of clean linen and coaxed it, like a wick, into the flask's narrow neck. The child sucked greedily. In five minutes the milk was finished and the child asleep. The priest wrapped it in a blanket from his own bed.

He was deeply moved. The strangeness of his premonition, the simplicity of the coming of the little thing, into the stable, out of the cold nothingness, was like a sign from God. There was nothing upon the mother's body to tell who she might be, but her features, worn by hardship and poverty, had a thin, fine Tartar cast. A band of nomads had passed through the day before: perhaps she had been overcome by cold, had fallen behind to die. He sought in his mind for a name for the child. It was the feast day of Saint Anna. Yes, he would name her Anna.

"Tomorrow, Joseph, we shall find a woman to take care of this gift from heaven."

Joseph shrugged. "Master, you cannot give away a female child."

"I shall not give the child away," Father Chisholm said sternly.

His purpose was already clear and fixed. This babe, sent to him by God, would be his first foundling — yes, the foundation of his children's home . . . that dream he had cherished since his arrival in Pai-tan. He would need help of course, the Sisters must one day come — it was all a long way off. But, seated on the earth floor, by the dark red embers, gazing upon the sleeping infant, he felt it was a pledge from heaven that he would, in the end, succeed.

It was Joseph, the prize gossip, who first told Father Chisholm that Mr. Chia's son was sick. The cold season was late in breaking, the Kwang Mountains were still deep in snow; and the cheerful Joseph blew upon his nipped fingers as he chattered away after mass, assisting the priest to put away his vestments. "*Tch!* My hand is as useless as that of the little Chia-Yu."

Chia-Yu had scratched his thumb upon no one knew what; but in consequence, his five elements had been disturbed and the lower humours had gained ascendency, flowing entirely into one arm, distending it, leaving the boy's body burning and wasted. The three highest physicians of the city were in attendance and the most costly remedies had been applied. Now a messenger had been despatched to Sen-siang for the *elixir vitae:* a priceless extract of frog's eyes, obtained only in the circle of the Dragon's moon.

"He will recover," Joseph concluded, showing his white teeth in a sanguine smile. "This *hao kao* never fails . . . which is important for Mr. Chia, since Yu is his only son."

Four days later, at the same hour, two closed chairs, one of which was empty, drew up outside the chapel shop in the Street of the Netmakers, and a moment later the tall figure of Mr. Pao's cousin, wrapped in a cotton-padded tunic, gravely confronted Father Chisholm. He apologized for his unseemly intrusion. He asked the priest to accompany him to Mr. Chia's house.

Stunned by the implication of the invitation, Francis hesitated. Close relationship, through business and marriage ties, existed between the Paos and the Chias, both were highly influential families. Since his return from the Liu village he had not infrequently encountered the lean, aloof, and pleasantly cynical cousin of Mr. Pao, who was, indeed, also first cousin to Mr. Chia. He had some evidence of the tall mandarin's regard. But this abrupt call, this sponsorship, was different. As he turned silently to get his hat and coat, he felt a sudden hollow fear.

The Chia house was very quiet, the trellised verandahs empty, the fish pond brittle with a film of ice. Their steps rang softly, but with a momentous air, upon the paved, deserted courtyards. Two flanking jasmine trees, swathed in sacking, lolled like sleeping giants, against the tented, red-gold gateway. From the women's quarters across the terraces came the strangled sound of weeping.

It was darkish in the sick-chamber, where Chia-Yu lay upon a heated *kang*, watched by the three bearded physicians in long full robes seated upon fresh rush matting. From time to time one of the physicians bent forward and placed a charcoal lump beneath the boxlike *kang*. In the corner of the room, a Taoist priest in a slate-coloured robe was mumbling, exorcising, to the accompaniment of flutes behind the bamboo partition.

Yu had been a pretty child of six, with soft cream colouring and sloe-black eyes, reared in the strictest traditions of parental respect, idolized, yet unspoiled. Now, consumed by remorseless fever and the terrible novelty of pain, he was stretched upon his back, his bones sticking through his skin, his dry lips twisting, his gaze upon the ceiling, motionless. His right arm, livid, swollen out of recognition, was encased in a horrible plaster of dirt mixed with little printed paper scraps.

When Mr. Pao's cousin entered with Father Chisholm there was a tiny stillness; then the Taoist mumbling was resumed, while the three physicians, more strictly immobilized, maintained their vigil by the *kang*.

Bent over the unconscious child, his hand upon the burning brow, Father Chisholm knew the full import of that limpid and passionless restraint. His present troubles would be as nothing to the persecution which must follow a futile intervention. But the desperate sickness of the boy and this noxious pretence of treatment whipped his blood. He began, quickly yet gently, to remove from the infected arm the *hao kao,* that filthy dressing he had so often met with in his little dispensary.

At last the arm was free, washed in warm water. It floated almost, a bladder of corruption, with a shiny greenish skin. Though now his heart was thudding in his side Francis went on steadfastly, drew from his pocket the little leather case which Tulloch had given him, took from that case the single lancet. He knew his inexperience. He knew also that if he did not incise the arm the child, already moribund, would die. He felt every unwatching eye upon him, sensed the terrible anxiety, the growing doubt gripping Mr. Pao's cousin as he stood motionless behind him. He made an ejaculation to Saint Andrew. He steeled himself to cut, to cut deep, deep and long.

A great gush of putrid matter came heaving through the wound, flowing and bubbling into the earthenware bowl beneath. The stench was dreadful, evil. In all his life Francis had never savoured anything so gratefully. As he pressed, with both his hands, on either side of the wound, encouraging the exudation, seeing the limb collapse to half its size, a great relief surged through him, leaving him weak.

When, at last, he straightened up, having packed the wound with clean wet linen, he heard himself murmur, foolishly, in

English: "I think he'll do now, with a little luck!" It was old Dr. Tulloch's famous phrase: it demonstrated the tension of his nerves. Yet on his way out he strove to maintain an attitude of cheerful unconcern, declaring to the completely silent cousin of Mr. Pao, who accompanied him to his chair: "Give him nourishing soup if he wakes up. And no more *hao kao*. I will come tomorrow."

On the next day little Yu was greatly better. His fever was almost gone, he had slept naturally and drunk several cups of chicken broth. Without the miracle of the shining lancet he would almost certainly have been dead.

"Continue to nourish him." Father Chisholm genuinely smiled as he took his departure. "I shall call again tomorrow!"

"Thank you." Mr. Pao's cousin cleared his throat. "It is not necessary." There was an awkward pause. "We are deeply grateful. Mr. Chia has been prostrate with grief. Now that his son is recovering he also is recovering. Soon he may be able to present himself in public!" The mandarin bowed, hands discreetly in his sleeves, and was gone.

Father Chisholm strode down the street — he had angrily refused the chair — fighting a dark and bitter indignation. This was gratitude. To be thrown out, without a word, when he had saved the child's life, at the risk, perhaps, of his own . . . From first to last he had not even seen the wretched Mr. Chia, who, even on the junk, that day of his arrival, had not deigned to glance at him. He clenched his fists, fighting his familiar demon: "O God, let me be calm! Don't let this cursed sin of anger master me again. Let me be meek and patient of heart. Give me humility, dear Lord. After all it was Thy merciful goodness, Thy divine providence, which saved the little boy. Do with me what Thou wilt, dear Lord. You see, I am resigned. But, O God!" — with sudden heat: "You must admit it was such damned ingratitude after all!"

During the next few days Francis rigorously shunned the merchant's quarter of the city. More than his pride had been hurt. He listened in silence while Joseph gossiped of the remarkable progress of little Yu, of the largesse distributed by Mr. Chia to the wise physicians, the donation to the Temple of Lao-tzŭ, for the exorcising of the demon which had troubled his beloved son. "Is it not truly remarkable, dear Father, how many sources have benefited by the mandarin's noble generosity?"

"Truly remarkable," said Father Chisholm dryly, but wincing.

A week later, when about to close his dispensary after a stale and profitless afternoon, he suddenly observed, across the flask of permanganate he had been mixing, the discreet apparition of Mr. Chia.

He started hotly, but said nothing. The merchant wore his finest clothes: a rich black satin robe with yellow jacket, embroidered velvet boots in one of which was thrust the ceremonial fan, a fine flat satin cap, and an expression both formal and dignified. His too-long fingernails were protected by gold metal cases. He had an air of culture and intelligence, his manners expressed perfect breeding. There was a gentle, enlightened melancholy on his brow.

"I have come," he said.

"Indeed!" Francis' tone was not encouraging. He went on stirring with his glass rod, mixing the mauve solution.

"There have been many matters to attend to, much business to settle. But now," — a resigned bow, — "I am here."

"Why?" Shortly, from Francis.

Mr. Chia's face indicated mild surprise. "Naturally . . . to become a Christian."

There was a moment of dead silence — a moment which, traditionally, should have marked the climax of these meagre toiling months, the thrilling first fruits of the missionary's achievement: here, the leading savage, bowing the head for baptism. But there was little exultation in Father Chisholm's face. He chewed his lip crossly, then he said slowly: "Do you believe?"

"No!" Sadly.

"Are you prepared to be instructed?"

"I have not time to be instructed." A subdued bow. "I am only eager to become a Christian."

"Eager? You mean you want to?"

Mr. Chia smiled wanly. "Is it not apparent — my wish to profess your faith?"

"No, it is not apparent. And you have not the slightest wish to profess my faith. Why are you doing this?" The priest's colour was high.

"To repay you," Mr. Chia said simply. "You have done the greatest good to me. I must do the greatest good for you."

Father Chisholm moved irritably. Because the temptation was so alluring, because he wished to yield and could not, his temper flared. "It is not good. It is bad. You have neither inclination nor belief. My acceptance of you would be a forgery for God. You owe me nothing. Now please go!"

At first Mr. Chia did not believe his ears.

"You mean you reject me?"

"That is putting it politely," growled Father Chisholm.

The change in the merchant was seraphic. His eyes brightened, glistened, his melancholy dropped from him like a shroud. He had to struggle to contain himself; but although he had the semblance of desiring to leap into the air he did contain himself. Formally, he made the kowtow three times. He succeeded in mastering his voice.

"I regret that I am not acceptable. I am of course most unworthy. Nevertheless, perhaps in some slight manner . . ." He broke off, again he made the kowtow three times and, moving backwards, went out.

That evening, as Father Chisholm sat by the brazier with a sternness of countenance which caused Joseph, who was cooking tasty river mussels in his rice, to gaze at him timidly, there came the sudden sound of firecrackers. Six of Mr. Chia's servants were exploding them, ceremoniously, in the road outside. Then Mr. Pao's cousin advanced, bowed, handed Father Chisholm a parchment wrapped in vermilion paper.

"Mr. Chia begs that you will honour him by accepting this most unworthy gift — the deeds of the Brilliant Green Jade property with all land and water rights and the rights to the crimson clay-pit. The property is yours, without restraint, forever. Mr. Chia further begs that you accept the help of twenty of his workmen till any building you may wish to carry out is fully accomplished."

So completely taken aback was Francis he could not speak a word. He watched the retreating figure of the cousin of Mr. Pao, and of Mr. Chia, with a strange still tensity. Then he wildly scanned the title deeds and cried out joyfully, "Joseph! Joseph!"

Joseph came hurrying, fearing another misfortune had befallen them. His master's expression reassured him. They went together to the Hill of Brilliant Green Jade and there, standing under the moon amidst the tall cedars, they sang aloud the Magnificat.

Francis remained bare-headed, seeing in a vision what he would create on this noble brow of land. He had prayed with faith, and his prayer had been answered.

Joseph, made hungry by the keen wind, waited uncomplainingly, finding his own vision in the priest's rapt face, glad he had shown the presence of mind to take his rice-pot from the fire.

IV

Eighteen months later, in the month of May, when all Chekkow province lay basking in that span of short perfection between the winter snows and the swelterings of summer, Father Chisholm crossed the paved courtyard of his new Mission of St. Andrew.

Never, perhaps, had such a sense of quiet contentment suffused him. The crystal air, where a cloud of white pigeons wheeled, was sweet and sparkling. As he reached the great banyan tree which, through his design, now shaded the forecourt of the mission, he threw a look across his shoulder, partly of pride, part in wry wonderment, as though still apprehensive of a mirage which might vanish overnight.

But it was there, shining and splendid: the slender church sentineled between the cedars, his house, vivid with scarlet lattices, adjoining the little schoolroom, the snug dispensary opening through the outer wall, and a further dwelling screened by the foliage of papaw and catalpa, which sheltered his freshly planted garden. He sighed, his lips smiling, blessing the miracle of the fruitful clay-pit which had yielded, through many blendings and experimental bakings, bricks of a lovely soft pale rose, making his mission a symphony in cinnabar. He blessed, indeed, each subsequent wonder: the implacable kindness of Mr. Chia; the skilful patience of his workers; the incorruptibility — almost complete — of his sturdy foreman; even the weather, this recent brilliant spell, which had made his opening ceremony, held last week and politely attended by the Chia and Pao families, a notable success.

For the sole purpose of viewing the empty classroom he took the long way round: peering, like a schoolboy, through the window at the brand-new pictures upon the whitewashed wall, at the shining benches which, like the blackboard, he had carpentered himself. The knowledge that his handiwork was in that particular room lay warmly round his heart. But recollection of the task he had in mind drove him to the end of the garden where, near the lower gate, and beside his private workshop, was a small brick kiln.

Happily, he jettisoned his old soutane and, in stained denim trousers, shirt sleeves and suspenders, he took a wooden spade and began to puddle-up some clay.

Tomorrow the three Sisters would arrive. Their house was ready — cool, curtained, already smelling of beeswax. But his final conceit, a secluded loggia in which they might rest and meditate, was not quite finished, demanding at least another batch of bricks from his own especial oven. As he shaped the marl he shaped the future in his mind.

Nothing was more vital than the advent of these nuns. He had seen this from the outset, he had worked and prayed for it, sending letter upon letter to Father Mealey and even to the Bishop, while the mission slowly rose before his eyes. Conversion of the Chinese adult was, he felt, a labour for archangels. Race, illiteracy, the tug of an older faith — these were formidable barriers to break down honestly, and one knew that the Almighty hated being asked to do conjuring tricks with each individual case. True, now that he was sustained in "face" by his fine new church, increasing numbers of repentant souls were adventuring to mass. He had some sixty persons in his congregation. As their pious cadences ascended at the Kyrie it sounded quite a multitude.

Nevertheless, his vision was focussed, brightly, on the children. Here, quite literally, children went two a penny. Famine, grinding poverty, and the Confucianism of masculine perpetuation made female infants, at least, a drug upon the market. In no time at all he would have a schoolful of children, fed and cared for by the Sisters, here in the mission, spinning their hoops, making the place gay with laughter, learning their letters and their catechism. The future belonged to the children: and the children . . . his children . . . would belong to God!

He smiled self-consciously at his thoughts as he shoved the moulds into the oven. He could not call himself, precisely, a ladies' man. Yet he had hungered, these long months, amidst this alien race, for the comfort of intercourse with his own kind. Mother Maria-Veronica, though Bavarian by birth, had spent the past five years with the Bon Secours in London. And the two whom she led, the French Sister Clotilde and Sister Martha, a Belgian, had equal experience in Liverpool. Coming direct from England they would bring him, at least, a friendly breath of home.

A trifle anxiously — for he had taken enormous trouble — he reviewed his preparations for their arrival on the following day: A few fireworks in the best Chinese style, but not enough to alarm the ladies, at the river landing stage, where the three best chairs in Pai-tan would await them. Tea served immediately they reached the mission. A short rest followed by benediction — he hoped they would like the flowers — and then, a special supper.

He almost chuckled as he conned, in his mind's eye, the menu of that supper. Well . . . they'd get down to hard-tack soon enough, poor things! His own appetite was scandalously meagre. During the building of the mission he had subsisted abstractedly, standing on scaffolds, or fingering a plan with Mr. Chia's foreman, upon rice and bean curd. But now he had sent Joseph scouring the city for mangos, chowchow and, rarest delicacy of all, fresh bustard from Shon-see in the North.

Suddenly, across his meditation, came the sound of footsteps. He lifted his head. As he turned, the gate was thrown open. Signed forward by their guide, a ragged riverside coolie, three nuns appeared. They were travel-stained, with a vague uneasiness in their uncertain glances. They hesitated, then advanced wearily up the garden path. The foremost, about forty years of age, had both dignity and beauty. There was high breeding in the fine bones of her face and in her wide heavy blue eyes. Pale with fatigue, impelled by a kind of inward fire, she forced herself on. Barely looking at Francis, she addressed him in fair Chinese.

"Please take us immediately to the mission Father."

Dreadfully put out at their obvious distress, he answered in the same tongue.

"You were not expected till tomorrow."

"Are we to return to that dreadful ship?" She shivered with contained indignation. "Take us to your master at once."

He said slowly, in English: "I am Father Chisholm."

Her eyes, which had been searching the mission buildings, returned incredulously to his short shirt-sleeved figure. She stared with growing dismay at his working clothes, dirty hands and caked boots, the smear of mud across his cheek. He murmured awkwardly: "I'm sorry . . . most distressed you weren't met."

For a moment her resentment mastered her. "One might have supposed some welcome at the end of six thousand miles."

"But you see . . . the letter said quite definitely — "

She cut him short with a repressed gesture.

"Perhaps you will show us to our quarters. My companions" — with a proud negation of her own exhaustion — "are completely worn-out."

He was about to make a final explanation, but the sight of the two other Sisters, staring and very frightened, restrained him. He led the way in painful silence to their house. Here he stopped.

"I hope you will be comfortable. I will send for your baggage. Perhaps . . . perhaps you will dine with me tonight."

"Thank you. It is impossible." Her tone was cold. Once again her eyes, holding back haughty tears, touched his disreputable garments. "But if we could be spared some milk and fruit . . . tomorrow we shall be fit for work."

Subdued and mortified, he returned slowly to his house, bathed and changed. From amongst his papers he found and carefully examined the letter from Tientsin. The date given was May 19th, which, as he had said, was tomorrow. He tore the letter into little pieces. He thought of that fine, that foolish bustard. He flushed. Downstairs he was confronted by Joseph, bubbling with spirits, his arms full of purchases.

"Joseph! Carry the fruit you have bought to the Sisters' house. Take everything else and distribute it to the poor."

"But, Master. . . ." Stupefied at the tone of the command, the expression on the priest's face, Joseph swallowed rapidly; then, his jubilation gone, he gulped: "Yes, Master."

Francis went towards the church, his lips compressed as though they sealed an unexpected hurt.

Next morning the three Sisters heard his mass. And he hurried, unconsciously, through his thanksgiving, hoping to find Mother Maria-Veronica awaiting him outside. She was not there. Nor did she come, for her instructions, to his house. An hour later he found her writing in the schoolroom. She rose quietly.

"Please sit down, Reverend Mother."

"Thank you." She spoke pleasantly. Yet she continued to stand, pen in hand, notepaper before her on the desk. "I have been waiting on my pupils."

"You shall have twenty by this afternoon. I've been picking them for many weeks." He strove to make his tone light and agreeable. "They seem intelligent little things."

She smiled gravely. "We shall do our utmost for them."

"Then there is the dispensary. I am hoping you will assist me there. I've very little knowledge — but it's amazing what even a little does here."

"If you will tell me the dispensary hours I shall be there."

A brief silence. Through her quiet civility, he felt her reserve deeply. His gaze, downcast, moving awkwardly, lit suddenly upon a small framed photograph which she had already established on the desk.

"What a beautiful scene!" He spoke at random, striving to break the impersonal barrier between them.

"Yes, it is beautiful." Her heavy eyes followed his to the picture of a fine old house, white and castellated against a dark wall of mountain pines, with a sweep of terraces and gardens running down towards the lake. "It is the Schloss Anheim."

"I have heard that name before. It is historic, surely. Is it near your home?"

She looked at him for the first time straight in the face. Her expression was completely colourless. "Quite near," she said.

Her tone absolutely closed the subject. She seemed to wait for him to speak, and when he did not she said, rather quickly:—

"The Sisters and I . . . we are most earnest in our desire to work for the success of the mission. You have only to mention your wishes and they will be carried out. At the same time—" Her voice chilled slightly. "I trust you will afford us a certain freedom of action."

He stared at her oddly. "What do you mean?"

"You know our rule is partly contemplative. We should like to enjoy as much privacy as possible." She gazed straight in front of her. "Take our meals alone . . . maintain our separate establishment."

He flushed. "I never dreamed of anything else. Your little house is your convent."

"Then you permit me to manage all our convent affairs."

Her meaning was quite plain to him. It settled like a weight upon his heart. He smiled, unexpectedly, rather sadly.

"By all means. Only be careful about money. We are very poor."

"My order has made itself responsible for our support."

He could not resist the question. "Does not your order enforce holy poverty?"

"Yes," she gave back swiftly, "but not meanness."

There was a pause. They remained standing side by side. She had broken off sharply, with a catch in her breath, her fingers tight upon the pen. His own face was burning; he had a strange reluctance to look at her.

"I will send Joseph with a note of the dispensary hours . . . and of church services. Good morning, Sister."

When he had gone she sat down, slowly, at the desk, her gaze still fixed ahead, her expression proudly unreadable. Then a single tear broke and rolled mysteriously down her cheek. Her worst forebodings were justified. Passionately, almost, she dipped her pen in the inkwell and resumed her letter.

". . . It has happened, already, as I feared, my dear, dear brother, and I have sinned again in my dreadful . . . my ineradicable Hohenlohe pride. Yet who could blame me? He has just been here, washed free of earth and approximately shaved — I could see the scrubby razor cuts upon his chin — and armed with such a dumb authority. I saw instantly, yesterday, what a little bourgeois it was. This morning he surpassed himself. Were you aware, dear count, that Anheim was historic? I almost laughed as his eyes fumbled at the photograph: you remember the one I took from the boathouse that day we went sailing with Mother on the lake — it's gone with me everywhere — my sole temporal treasure. He said, in effect, 'Which Cook's tour did you take to view it?' I felt like saying, 'I was born there!' My pride restrained me. Yet had I done so he would probably have kept on gazing at his boots, still creviced with mud, where he had failed to clean them — and muttered: 'Oh, indeed! Our blessed Lord was born in a stable.'

"You see, there is something about him which strikes at one. Do you recollect Herr Spinner, our first tutor . . . we were such brutes to him . . . and the way he had of looking up suddenly with such hurt, yet humble restraint? His eyes, here, are the same. Probably his father was a woodcutter like Herr Spinner's, and he too has struggled up, precariously, with dogged humility. But, dear Ernst, it is the future that I dread, shut up in this strange and isolated spot which intensifies every aspect of the situation. The danger is a lowering of one's inborn standards, yielding to a kind of mental intimacy with a person one instinctively despises. That odious familiar cheerfulness! I must drop a hint to Martha and Clotilde — who has been such a poor sick calf all the way from Liverpool. I am resolved to be pleasant and to work myself to the bone. But only complete detachment, an absolute reserve, will . . ."

She broke off, gazing again, remote and troubled, through the window.

Father Chisholm soon perceived that the two under Sisters went out of their way to avoid him.

Clotilde was not yet thirty, flat-bosomed and delicate, with bloodless lips and a nervous smile. She was very devout and when she prayed, with her head inclined to one side, tears would gush from her pale green eyes. Martha was a different person: past forty, stocky and strong, a peasant type, dark-complexioned and with a net of wrinkles round her eyes. Bustling and outspoken, a trifle coarse in manner, she looked as though she would be immediately at home in a kitchen or a farmyard.

When by chance he met them in the garden the Belgian sister would drop a quick curtsey while Clotilde's sallow face flushed nervously as she smiled and fluttered on. He knew himself to be the subject of their whisperings. He had the impulse, often, to stop them violently. "Don't be so scared of me. We've made a stupid beginning. But I'm a much better fellow than I look."

He restrained himself. He had no grounds whatsoever for complaint. Their work was executed scrupulously, with minute perfection of purpose. New altar linen, exquisitely stitched, appeared in the sacristy; and an embroidered stole which must have taken days of patient labour. Bandages and dressings, rolled, cut to all sizes, filled the store-cupboard in the surgery.

The children had come and were comfortably housed in the big ground-floor dormitory of the Sisters' house. And presently the schoolroom hummed with little voices, or with the chanted rhythm of a much-repeated lesson. He would stand outside, open breviary in hand, sheltered by the bushes, listening. It meant so much to him, this tiny school, he had so joyfully anticipated its opening. Now he rarely went in; and never without a sense of his intrusion. He withdrew into himself, accepting the situation with a sombre logic. It was very simple. Mother Maria-Veronica was a good woman, fine, fastidious, devoted to her work. Yet from the first she had conceived a natural aversion to him. Such things cannot be overcome. After all, he was not a prepossessing character, he had been right when he judged himself no squire of dames. It was a sad disappointment, nevertheless.

The dispensary brought them together on three afternoons each week when, for four hours at a stretch, Maria-Veronica worked close beside him. He could see that she was interested, often so deeply as to forget her aversion. Though they spoke little he had on such occasions a strange sense of comradeship with her.

One day, a month after her arrival, as he finished dressing a severe whitlow, she exclaimed, involuntarily: "You would have made a surgeon."

He flushed. "I've always liked working with my hands."

"That is because you are clever with them."

He was ridiculously pleased. Her manner was friendlier than it had ever been. At the end of the clinic, as he put away his simple medicines, she gazed at him questioningly. "I've been meaning to ask you . . . Sister Clotilde has had too much to do lately, preparing the children's meals with Martha in the kitchen. She isn't strong and I'm afraid it is too much for her. If you have no objection I would like to get some help."

"But of course." He agreed at once—even happier that she should have asked his permission. "Shall I find you a servant?"

"No thank you. I already have a good couple in mind!"

Next morning when crossing the compound, he observed on the convent balcony, airing and brushing the matting, the unmistakable figures of Hosannah and Philomena Wang. He stopped short, his face darkening, then he took immediate steps towards the Sisters' house.

He found Maria-Veronica in the linen room checking over the sheets. He spoke hurriedly: "I'm sorry to disturb you. But — these new servants — I'm afraid you won't find them satisfactory."

She turned slowly from the cupboard, sudden displeasure in her face. "Surely I am the best judge of that?"

"I don't want you to think I'm interfering. But I'm bound to warn you that they are far from reliable characters."

Her lip curled. "Is that your Christian charity?"

He paled. She was placing him in a horrible position. But he went on determinedly. "I am obliged to be practical. I am thinking of the mission. And of you."

"Please do not trouble about me." Her smile was icy. "I am quite capable of looking after myself."

"I tell you these Wangs are a really bad lot."

She answered with peculiar emphasis: "I know they've had a really bad time. They told me."

His temper flared. "I advise you to get rid of them."

"I won't get rid of them!" Her voice was cold as steel. She had always suspected him, and now she knew. Because she had relaxed her vigilance yesterday, for a moment, in the dispensary, he had rushed to interfere, to show his authority, on this frivolous pretext. Never, never would she be weak with him again. "You already agreed that I am not responsible to you for the administration of my house. I must ask you to keep your word."

He was silent. There was nothing more that he could say. He had meant to help her. But he had made a bad mistake. As he turned away he knew that their relationship, which he had thought to be improving, was now worse than it had been before.

The situation began to affect him seriously. It was hard to keep his expression unruffled when the Wangs passed him, with an air of muted triumph, many times a day. One morning, towards the end of July, Joseph brought him his breakfast of fruit and tea with swollen knuckles and a sheepish air — part triumphant, part subdued.

"Master, I am sorry. I have had to give that rascal Wang a beating."

Father Chisholm sat up sharply, his eye stern: "Why so, Joseph?"

Joseph hung his head. "He says many unkind words about us. That Reverend Mother is a great lady and we are simply dust."

"We all are dust, Joseph." The priest's smile was faint.

"He says harder words than that."

"We can put up with hard words."

"It is more than words, Master. He has become puffed-up beyond measure. And all the time he is making a bad squeeze on the Sisters' housekeeping."

It was quite true. Because of his opposition, the Reverend Mother was indulgent towards the Wangs. Hosannah was now the majordomo of the Sisters' house while Philomena departed, every day, with a basket on her arm, to do the shopping as if she owned the place. At the end of each month, when Martha paid the bills with the roll of notes which the Reverend Mother gave her, the precious pair would depart for the town, in their best clothes, to collect a staggering commission from the tradesmen. It was barefaced robbery, anathema to Francis' Scottish thrift.

Gazing at Joseph he said grimly: "I hope you did not hurt Wang much."

"Alas! I fear I hurt him greatly, Master."

"I am cross with you, Joseph. As a punishment you shall have a holiday tomorrow. And that new suit you have long been asking of me."

That afternoon, in the dispensary, Maria-Veronica broke her rule of silence. Before the patients were admitted she said to Francis:

"So you have chosen to victimize poor Wang again?"

He answered bluntly: "On the contrary. It is he who is victimizing you."

"I do not understand you."

"He is robbing you. The man is a born thief and you are encouraging him."

She bit her lip fiercely. "I do not believe you. I am accustomed to trust my servants."

"Very well then, we shall see." He dismissed the matter quietly.

In the next few weeks his silent face showed deeper lines of strain. It was dreadful to live in close community with a person who detested, despised, him — and to be responsible for that person's spiritual welfare. Maria-Veronica's confessions, which contained nothing, were torture to him. And he judged they were equal torture for her. When he placed the sacred wafer between her lips while her long delicate fingers upheld the altar cloth in the still and pallid dawn of each new day, her upturned pale face, with eyelids veined and tremulous, seemed still to scorn him. He began to rest badly and to walk in the garden at night. So far, their disagreement had been limited to the sphere of her authority. Constrained, more silent than ever, he waited for the moment when he must enforce his will.

It was autumn when that necessity arose, quite simply, out of her inexperience. Yet he could not pass it by. He sighed as he walked over to the Sisters' house.

"Reverend Mother . . ." To his annoyance he found himself trembling. He stood before her, his eyes upon those memorable boots. "You have been going into the city these last few afternoons with Sister Clotilde?"

She looked surprised. "Yes, that is true."

There was a pause.

On guard, she inquired with irony: "Are you curious to know what we are doing?"

"I already know." He spoke as mildly as he could. "You go to visit the sick poor of the city. As far away as the Manchu Bridge. It is commendable. But I'm afraid it must cease."

"May I ask why?" She tried to match his quietness but did not quite succeed.

"Really, I'd rather not tell you."

Her fine nostrils were tense. "If you are prohibiting my acts of charity . . . I have a right . . . I insist on knowing."

"Joseph tells me there are bandits in the city. Wai-Chu has begun fighting again. His soldiers are dangerous."

She laughed outright proudly, contemptuously.

"I am not afraid. The men in my family have always been soldiers."

"That is most interesting." He gazed at her steadily. "But you are not a man, nor is Sister Clotilde. And Wai-Chu's soldiers are not exactly the kid-gloved cavalry officers infallibly found in the best Bavarian families."

He had never used that tone with her before. She reddened, then paled. Her features, her whole figure seemed to contract. "Your outlook is common and cowardly. You forget that I have given myself to God. I came here prepared for anything — sickness, accident, disaster, if necessary death — but not to listen to a lot of cheap sensational rubbish."

His eyes remained fixed on her, so that they burned her, like points of light. He said unconditionally: "Then we will cease to be sensational. It would, as you infer, be a small matter if you were captured and carried off. But there is a stronger reason why you should restrain your charitable promenades. The position of women in China is very different from that to which you are accustomed. In China women have been rigidly excluded from society for centuries. You give grave offense by walking openly in the streets. From a religious standpoint it is highly damaging to the work of the mission. For that reason I forbid you, absolutely, to enter Pai-tan unescorted, without my permission."

She flushed, as though he had struck her in the face. There was a mortal stillness. She had nothing whatever to say.

He was about to leave her when there came a sudden scud of footsteps in the passage and Sister Martha bundled into the room. Her agitation was so great she did not observe Francis, half-hidden by the shadow of the door. Nor did she guess the tension of the moment. Her gaze, distraught beneath her rumpled wimple, was bent on Maria-Veronica. Wringing her hands, she lamented wildly: —

"They've run away . . . taken everything . . . the ninety dollars you gave me yesterday to pay the bills . . . the silver . . . even Sister Clotilde's ivory crucifix . . . they've gone, gone . . ."

"Who has gone?" The words came, with a dreadful effort, from Maria-Veronica's stiff lips.

"The Wangs, of course . . . the low, dirty thieves. I always knew they were a pair of rogues and hypocrites."

Francis did not dare to look at the Mother Superior. She stood there, motionless. He felt a strange pity for her. He made his way clumsily from the room.

V

As FATHER CHISHOLM returned to his own house he became aware, through the strained preoccupation of his mind, of Mr. Chia and his son, standing by the fish pond, watching the carp, with a quiet air of waiting. Both figures were warmly padded against the chill, — it was a "six-coat cold day," — the boy's hand was in his father's, and the slow dusk, stealing from the shadows of the banyan tree, seemed reluctant to envelop them, and to efface a charming picture.

The two were frequent visitors to the mission and perfectly at home there; they smiled, as Father Chisholm hurried over, greeted him with courteous formality. But Mr. Chia, for once, gently turned aside the priest's invitation to enter his house.

"We come instead to bid you to our house. Yes, tonight, we are leaving for our mountain retreat. It would afford me the greatest happiness if you would accompany us."

Francis stood amazed. "But we are entering upon winter!"

"It is true, my friend, that I and my unworthy family have hitherto ventured to our secluded villa in the Kwangs only during the inclement heat of summer." Mr. Chia paused blandly. "Now we make an innovation which may be even more agreeable. We have many cords of wood and much store of food. Do you not think, Father, it would be edifying to meditate, a little, amongst these snowy peaks?"

Searching the maze of circumlocution with a puzzled frown, Father Chisholm shot a swift glance of interrogation at the merchant.

"Is Wai-Chu about to loot the town?"

Mr. Chia's shoulders mildly deprecated the directness of the query but his expression did not falter. "On the contrary, I myself have paid Wai considerable tribute and billeted him comfortably. I trust he will remain in Pai-tan for many days."

A silence. Father Chisholm's brows were drawn in complete perplexity.

"However, my dear friend, there are other matters which occasionally make the wise man seek the solitudes. I beg of you to come."

The priest shook his head slowly. "I am sorry, Mr. Chia — I am too busy in the mission. . . . How could I leave this noble place which you have so generously given me?"

Mr. Chia smiled amiably. "It is most salubrious here at present. If you change your mind do not fail to inform me. Come, Yu . . . the waggons will be loaded now. Give your hand to the holy Father in the English fashion."

Father Chisholm shook hands with the little wrapped-up boy. Then he blessed them both. The air of restrained regret in Mr. Chia's manner disturbed him. His heart was strangely heavy as he watched them go.

The next two days passed in a queer atmosphere of stress. He saw little of the Sisters. The weather turned worse. Great flocks of birds were seen flying to the South. The sky darkened and lay like lead upon all living things. But except for a few flurries no snow came. Even the cheerful Joseph showed unusual signs of grievance, coming to the priest and expressing his desire to go home.

"It is a long time since I have seen my parents. It is fitting for me to visit them."

When questioned, he waved his hand around vaguely, grumbling that there were rumours in Pai-tan of evil things travelling from the North, the East, the West.

"Wait till the evil spirits come, Joseph, before you run away." Father Chisholm tried to rally his servant's spirits. And his own.

Next morning, after early mass, he went down to the town, alone, in determined quest of news. The streets were teeming, life apparently pulsed undisturbed, but a hush hung about the larger dwellings and many of the shops were closed. In the Street of the Net-makers, he found Hung boarding up his windows with unobtrusive urgency.

"There is no denying it, Shang-Foo!" The old shopkeeper paused to give the Father a calamitous glance over his small pebble spectacles. "It is sickness . . . the great coughing sickness which they name the Black Death. Already six provinces are stricken. People are fleeing with the wind. The first came last night to Pai-tan. And one of the women fell dead inside the Manchu Gate. A wise man knows what that portends. Ay, ay, when there is famine we march and when there is pestilence we march again. Life is not easy when the gods show their wrath."

Father Chisholm climbed the hill to the mission with a shadow upon his face. He seemed already to smell the sickness in the air.

Suddenly he drew up. Outside the mission wall, and directly in his path, lay three dead rats. Judging by the priest's expression there was, in this stiff trinity, a dire foreboding. He shivered unexpectedly, thinking of his children. He went himself for kerosene, and poured it on the corpses of the rats, ignited the oil, and watched their slow cremation. Hurriedly, he took up the remains with tongs and buried them.

He stood thinking deeply. He was five hundred miles from the nearest telegraph terminal. To send a messenger to Sen-siang by sampan, even by the fastest pony, might take at least six days.

And yet he must at all costs establish some contact with the outer world.

Suddenly his expression lifted. He found Joseph and led him quickly by the arm to his room. His face was set with gravity as he addressed the boy.

"Joseph! I am sending you on an errand of the first importance. You will take Mr. Chia's new launch. Tell the kapong you have Mr. Chia's permission and mine. I even command you to steal the launch if it is necessary. Do you understand?"

"Yes, Father." Joseph's eyes flashed. "It will not be a sin."

"When you have the boat, proceed with all speed to Sen-siang. There you will go to Father Thibodeau at the mission. If he is away go to the offices of the American oil company. Find someone in authority. Tell him the plague is upon us, that we need immediately medicine, supplies, and doctors. Then go to the telegraph company, send these two messages I have written for you. See . . . take the papers . . . the first to the Vicariate at Pekin, the second to the Union General Hospital at Nankin. Here is money. Do not fail me, Joseph. Now go . . . go. And the good God go with you!"

He felt better an hour later as the lad went padding down the hill, his blue bundle bobbing on his back, his intelligent features screwed to a staunch tenacity. The better to view the departure of the launch, the priest hastened to the belfry tower. But here, as he perched himself against the pediment, his eye darkened. On the vast plain before him he saw two thinly moving streams of beasts and straggling humans, reduced, alike, by distance to the size of little ants — two moving streams, the one approaching, the other departing from the city.

He could not wait; but, descending, crossed immediately to the school. In the wooden corridor Sister Martha was on her knees scrubbing the boards. He stopped.

"Where is Reverend Mother?"

She raised a damp hand to straighten her wimple. "In the classroom." She added, in a sibilant, confederate's whisper: "And lately much disarranged."

He went into the class-room, which, at his entry, fell immediately to silence. The rows of bright childish faces gave him, suddenly, a gripping pang. Quickly, quickly, he fought back that unbearable fear.

Maria-Veronica had turned towards him with a pale, unreadable brow. He approached and addressed her in an undertone.

"There are signs of an epidemic in the city. I am afraid it may be plague. If so, it is important for us to be prepared." He paused, under her silence, then went on. "At all costs we must try to keep the sickness from the children. That means isolating the school and the Sisters' house. I shall arrange at once for some kind of barrier to be put up. The children and all three Sisters should remain inside, with one Sister always on duty at the entrance." He paused again, forcing himself to be calm. "Don't you think that wise?"

She faced him, cold and undismayed. "Profoundly wise."

"Are there any details we might discuss?"

She answered bitterly: "You have already familiarized us with the principle of segregation."

He took no notice. "You know how the contagion is spread?"

"Yes."

There was a silence. He turned towards the door, sombre from her fixed refusal to make peace. "If God sends this great trouble upon us, we must work hard together. Let us try to forget our personal relations."

"They are best forgotten." She spoke in her most frigid tone, submissive upon the surface, yet charged, beneath, with high disdainful breeding.

He left the class-room. He could not but admire her courage. The news he had conveyed to her would have terrified most women. He reflected tensely that they might need all their spirit before the month was past.

Convinced of the need of haste, he recrossed the compound and despatched the gardener for Mr. Chia's foreman and six of the men who had worked on the church. Immediately, when these arrived, he set them to build a thick fence of kaolin on the boundary he had marked off. The dried stalks of maize made an excellent barricade. While it rose under his anxious eyes, girding the school and convent house, he trenched a narrow ditch around the base. This could be flooded with disinfectant if the need arose.

The work went on all day and was not completed until late at night. Even after the men had gone he could not rest, a mounting tide of dread was in his blood. He took most of his stores into the enclosure, carrying sacks of potatoes and flour on his shoulders, butter, bacon, condensed milk, and all the tinned goods of the mission. His small stock of medicines he likewise transferred. Only then did he feel some degree of relief. He looked at his watch: three o'clock in the morning. It was not worth while to go to bed. He went into the church and spent the hours remaining until dawn in prayer.

When it was light, before the mission was astir he set out for the yamen of the Chief Magistrate. At the Manchu Gate fugitives from the stricken provinces were still crowding unhindered into the city. Scores had taken up their lodging beneath the stars, in the lee of the Great Wall. As he passed the silent figures, huddled under sacking, half-frozen by the bitter wind, he heard the racking sound of coughing. His heart flowed out towards these poor exhausted creatures, many already stricken, enduring humbly, suffering without hope; and a burning, impetuous desire to help them suffused his soul. One old man lay dead and naked, stripped of the garments he no longer needed. His wrinkled toothless face was upturned towards the sky.

Spurred by the pity in his breast, Francis reached the yamen of justice. But here a blow awaited him. Mr. Pao's cousin was gone. All the Paos had departed, the closed shutters of their house stared back at him like sightless eyes.

He took a swift and painful breath and turned, chafing, into the courts. The passages were deserted, the main chamber a vault of echoing emptiness. He could see no one, except a few clerks scurrying with a furtive air. From one of these he learned that the Chief Magistrate had been called away to the obsequies of a distant relative in Tchientin, eight hundred li due south. It was plain to the harassed priest that all but the lowest court officials had been "summoned" from Pai-tan. The civil administration of the city had ceased to exist.

The furrow between Francis' eyes was deeply cut, a haggard wound. Only one course lay open to him now. And he knew that it was futile. Nevertheless, he turned and made his way rapidly to the cantonment.

With the bandit Wai-Chu complete overlord of the province, ferociously exacting voluntary gifts, the position of the regular military forces was academic. They dissolved or seceded as a matter of routine on the bandit's periodic visits to the town. Now, as Francis reached the barracks, a bare dozen soldiers hung about, conspicuously without arms, in dirty grey-cotton tunics.

They stopped him at the gate. But nothing could withstand the fire which now consumed him. He forced his way to an inner chamber, where a young lieutenant in a clean and elegant uniform lounged by the paper-latticed window, reflectively polishing his white teeth with a willow twig.

Lieutenant Shon and the priest inspected one another, the young dandy with polite guardedness, his visitor with all the dark and hopeless ardour of his purpose.

"The city is threatened by a great sickness." Francis fought to inject his tone with deliberate restraint. "I am seeking for someone with courage and authority, to combat the grave danger."

Shon continued dispassionately to consider the priest. "General Wai-Chu has the monopoly of authority. And he is leaving for Tou-en-lai tomorrow."

"That will make it easier for those who remain. I beg of you to help me."

Shon shrugged his shoulders virtuously. "Nothing would afford me greater satisfaction than to work with the Shang-Foo entirely without prospect of reward, for the supreme benefit of suffering mankind. But I have no more than fifty soldiers. And no supplies."

"I have sent to Sen-siang for supplies." Francis spoke more

rapidly. "They will arrive soon. But meanwhile we must do all in our command to quarantine the refugees and prevent the pestilence from starting in the city."

"It has already started." Shon answered coolly. "In the Street of the Basket-makers there are more than sixty cases. Many dead. The rest dying."

A terrible urgency tautened the priest's nerves, a surge of protest, a burning refusal to accept defeat. He took a quick step forward.

"I am going to aid these people. If you do not come I shall go alone. But I am perfectly assured that you are coming."

For the first time the Lieutenant looked uncomfortable. He was a bold youngster, despite his foppish air, with ideas of his own advancement and a sense of personal integrity which had caused him to reject the price offered him by Wai-Chu, as dishonourably inadequate. Without the slightest interest in the fate of his fellow citizens, he had been, on the priest's arrival, idly debating the advisability of joining his few remaining men in the Street of the Stolen Hours. Now, he was disagreeably embarrassed and reluctantly impressed. Like a man moving against his own will, he rose, threw away his twig and slowly buckled on his revolver.

"This does not shoot well. But as a symbol it encourages the unswerving obedience of my most trusted followers."

They went out together into the cold grey day.

From the Street of the Stolen Hours they routed some thirty soldiers and marched to the teeming warrens of the basket-weavers' quarters by the river. Here the plague had already settled, with the instinct of a dunghill fly. The river dwellings, tiers of cardboard hovels, leaning one on top of another, against the high mud bank, were festering with dirt, vermin, and the disease. Francis saw that unless immediate measures were taken the contagion would spread in this congestion like a raging conflagration.

He said to the Lieutenant, as they emerged, bent double, from the end hovel of the row: —

"We must find some place to house the sick."

Shon reflected. He was enjoying himself more than he had expected. This foreign priest had shown much "face" in stooping close to the stricken persons. He admired "face" greatly.

"We shall commandeer the yamen of the *yu shih* — the imperial recorder." For many months Shon had been at violent enmity with this official, who had defrauded him of his share of the salt tax. "I am confident that my absent friend's abode will make a pleasing hospital."

They went immediately to the recorder's yamen. It was large and richly furnished, situated in the best part of the city. Shon effected entry by the simple expedient of breaking down the door. While Francis remained with half a dozen men to make some preparations for receiving the sick, he departed with the remainder. Presently the first cases arrived in litters and were arranged in rows on quilted mats upon the floor.

That night, as Francis went up the hill towards the mission, tired from his long day's work, he heard above the faint incessant death music the shouts of wild carousing and sporadic rifle shots. Behind him, Wai-Chu's irregulars were looting the shuttered shops. But presently the city fell again to silence. In the still moonlight he could see the bandits, streaming from the Eastern Gate, spurring their stolen ponies across the plains. He was glad to see them go.

At the summit of the hill the moon suddenly was dimmed. It began at last to snow. When he drew near the gateway in the kaolin fence the air was alive and fluttering. Soft dry blinding flakes came whirling out of the darkness, settling on eyes and brow, entering his lips like tiny hosts, whirling so dense and thick that in a minute the ground was carpeted in white. He stood outside, in the white coldness, rent by anxiety, and called in a low voice. Immediately Mother Maria-Veronica came to the gate, holding up a lantern which cast a beam of spectral brightness on the snow.

He scarcely dared to put the question. "Are you all well?"

"Yes."

His heart stopped pounding in sheer relief. He waited, suddenly conscious of his fatigue and the fact that he had not eaten all that day. Then he said: "We have established a hospital in the town . . .

not much . . . but the best we could do." Again he waited, as if
for her to speak, deeply sensible of the difficulty of his position, and
the greatness of the favour he must ask. "If one of the Sisters could
be spared . . . would volunteer to come . . . to help us with the
nursing . . . I should be most grateful."

There was a pause. He could almost see her lips shape themselves
to answer coldly: "You ordered us to remain in here. You forbade
us to enter the town." Perhaps the sight of his face, worn, drawn
and heavy-eyed, through the maze of snowflakes, restrained her.
She said: "I will come."

His heart lifted. Despite her fixed antagonism towards him she
was incomparably more efficient than Martha or Clotilde. "It
means moving your quarters to the yamen. Wrap up warmly. And
take all you need."

Ten minutes later he took her bag; they went down to the yamen
together in silence. The dark lines of their footprints in the fresh
snow were far apart.

Next morning sixteen of those admitted to the yamen were dead.
But three times that number were coming in. It was pneumonic
plague and its virulence surpassed the fiercest venom. People dropped
with it as if bludgeoned and were dead before the next dawn. It
seemed to congeal the blood, to rot the lungs, which threw up a thin
white speckled sputum, swarming with lethal germs. Often one hour
spaced the interval between a man's heedless laugh and the grin that
was his death-mask.

The three physicians of Pai-tan had failed to arrest the epidemic
by the method of acupuncture. On the second day they ceased
prickling the limbs of their patients with needles, and discreetly
withdrew to a more salubrious practice.

By the end of that week the city was riddled from end to end.
A wave of panic struck through the apathy of the people. The
southern exits of the city were choked with carts, chairs, over-
burdened mules and a struggling, hysterical populace.

The cold intensified. A great blight seemed to lie on the afflicted
land, here and beyond. Dazed with overwork and lack of sleep,

Francis nevertheless dimly sensed the calamity at Pai-tan to be but a portion of the major tragedy. He had no news. He did not grasp the immensity of the disaster: a hundred thousand miles of territory stricken, and half a million dead beneath the snow. Nor could he know that the eyes of the civilized world were bent in sympathy on China, that expeditions quickly organized in America and Britain had arrived to combat the disease.

His torturing suspense deepened daily. There was still no sign of Joseph's return. Would help never reach them from Sen-siang? A dozen times each day he plodded to the wharfside for the sight of the up-coming boat.

Then, at the beginning of the second week, Joseph suddenly appeared, weary and spent, but with a pale smile of achievement. He had encountered every obstacle. The countryside was in a ferment, Sen-siang a place of torment, the mission there ravaged by the disease. But he had persisted. He had sent his telegrams and bravely waited, hiding in his launch in a creek of the river. Now he had a letter. He produced it with a grimed and shaking hand. More: a doctor who knew the Father, an old and respected friend of the Father, would arrive on the supply boat!

With beating excitement, and a strange wild premonition, Father Chisholm took the letter from Joseph, opened it and read:—

> *Lord Leighton Relief Expedition*
> *Chek-kow*

Dear Francis,

I have been in China five weeks now with the Leighton expedition. This should not surprise you if you remember my youthful longings for the decks of ocean-going freighters and the exotic jungles that lay beyond. Quite truly, I thought I had forgotten all that nonsense myself. But at home, when they began asking for volunteers for the relief party, I suddenly surprised myself by joining up. It certainly was not the desire to become a National Hero which prompted the absurd impulse. Probably a reaction, long deferred, against my humdrum life in Tynecastle. And perhaps, if I may say it, a very real hope of seeing you.

Anyhow, ever since we arrived, I've been working my way up-country, trying to push myself into your sacred presence. Your telegram to Nankin was turned over to our headquarters there and word of it reached me at Hai-chang next day. I immediately asked Leighton, who is a very decent fellow, despite his title, if I might push off to give you a hand. He agreed and even let me have one of our few remaining power boats. I've just reached Sen-siang and am collecting supplies. I will be along full steam ahead, probably arriving twenty-four hours behind your servant. Take care of yourself till then. All my news later.

In haste,
Yours,

WILLIE TULLOCH

The priest smiled, slowly, for the first time in many days, and with a deep and secret warmth. He felt no great amazement; it was so typical of Tulloch to sponsor such a cause. He was braced, fortified by the unexpected fortune of his friend's arrival.

It was difficult to hold his eagerness in check. Next day when the relief boat was sighted he hastened to the wharf. Even before the launch drew alongside Tulloch had stepped ashore, older, stouter, yet unchangeably the same dour quiet Scot, careless as ever in his dress, shy, strong and prejudiced as a Highland steer, as plain and honest as homespun tweed.

The priest's vision was absurdly blurred.

"Man, Francis, it's you!" Willie could say no more. He kept on shaking hands, confused by his emotion, debarred by his Northern blood from more overt demonstration. At last he muttered, as if conscious of the need of speech: "When we walked down Darrow High Street we never dreamed we'd forgather in a place like this." He tried a half-laugh, but with little success. "Where's your coat and gumboots? You can't stroll through the pest in these shoes. It's high time I kept an eye on you."

"And on our hospital." Francis smiled.

"What!" The doctor's sandy eyebrows lifted. "You have a hospital of sorts? Let's see it."

"As soon as you are ready."

Instructing the crew of the launch to follow him with the supplies, Tulloch set off, at the priest's side, agile despite his increased girth, his eyes intent in his red hard-wearing face, his thinned hair showing a mass of freckles on his ruddy scalp as he punctuated his friend's brief report with comprehending nods.

At the end of it, as they reached the yamen, he remarked with a dry twinkle: "You might have done worse. Is this your centre?" Across his shoulder he told his bearers to bring in the cases.

Inside the hospital he made a quick inspection, his eyes darting right, left, and with an odd curiosity towards Mother Maria-Veronica, who now accompanied them. He took a swift glance at Shon, when the young dandy came in, then firmly shook hands with him. Finally as they stood, all four, at the entrance to the long suite of rooms which formed the main ward, he addressed them quietly.

"I think you have done wonders. And I hope you don't expect melodramatic miracles from me. Forget all your preconceived ideas and face the truth — I'm not the dark handsome doctor with the portable laboratory. I'm here to work with you, like one of yourselves, which means . . . flatly . . . like a navvy. I haven't a drop of vaccine in my bag — in the first place because it isn't one damn bit of good outside the story-books. And in the second because every flask we brought to China was used up in a week. Ye'll note," he inserted mildly, "it didn't check the epidemic. Remember! This is practically a fatal disease once it gets you. In such circumstances, as my old dad used to say," he smiled faintly, "an ounce of prevention is better than a ton of cure. That's why, if you don't mind, we'll turn our attention — not to the living — but to the dead."

There was a silence while they slowly grasped his meaning. Lieutenant Shon smiled.

"Cadavers are accumulating in the side streets at a disconcerting rate. It is discouraging to stumble in the darkness and fall into the arms of an unresponsive corpse."

Francis shot a quick glance at Maria-Veronica's expressionless face. Sometimes the young Lieutenant was a little indiscreet.

The doctor had moved to the nearest crate and, with stolid competence, was prying off the lid.

"The first thing we do is fit you out properly. Oh! I know you two believe in God. And the Lieutenant in Confucius." He bent and produced rubber boots from the case. "But I believe in prophylaxis."

He completed the unpacking of his supplies, fitting white overalls and goggles upon them, berating their negligence of their own
safety. His remarks ran on, matter-of-fact, composed. "Don't you
realize, you confounded innocents . . . one cough in your eye and
you're done for . . . penetration of the cornea. They knew that
even in the fourteenth century . . . they wore vizors of isinglass
against this thing . . . it was brought down from Siberia by a band
of marmoset hunters. Well, now, I'll come back later, Sister, and
have a real look at your patients. But first of all, Shon, the Reverend
and myself will take a peek round."

In his stress of mind, Francis had overlooked the grim necessity
of swift interment before the germ-infested bodies were attacked by
rats. Individual burial was impossible in that iron ground and the
supply of coffins had run out long ago. All the fuel in China would
not have burned the bodies — for as Shon again remarked, nothing
is less inflammable than frozen human flesh. One practical solution remained. They dug a great pit outside the walls, lined it with
quicklime, and requisitioned carts. The loaded carts, driven by
Shon's men, bumped through the streets and shot their cargo into
this common grave.

Three days later, when the city was cleared and the stray carcasses,
half-devoured and dragged away by dogs, collected from the ice-
encrusted fields, stricter measures were enforced. Afraid lest the
spirits of their ancestors be defiled by an unholy tomb, people were
hiding the bodies of their relatives, storing scores of infected corpses
under the floorboards of their houses and in the kaolin roofs.

At the doctor's suggestion Lieutenant Shon promulgated an edict
that all such hoarders would be shot. When the death carts rumbled
through the city his soldiers shouted: "Bring out your dead. Or you
yourselves will die."

Meanwhile, they were ruthlessly destroying certain properties
which Tulloch had marked as breeding grounds of the disease. Experience and dire necessity made the doctor vengefully efficient.
They entered, cleared the rooms, demolished the bamboo partitions
with axes, spread kerosene, and made a pyre for the rats.

The Street of the Basket-makers was the first they razed. Returning, scorched and grimed, a hatchet still in his hand, Tulloch cast a queer glance at the priest, walking wearily beside him through the deserted streets. He said, in sudden compunction: —

"This isn't your job, Francis. And you're worn so fine you're just about to drop. Why don't you get up the hill for a few days, back to those kids you're worrying yourself stiff over?"

"That would be a pretty sight. The man of God taking his ease while the city burns."

"Who is there to see you in this out-of-the-way hole?"

Francis smiled strangely. "We are not unseen."

Tulloch dropped the matter abruptly. Outside the yamen he swung round, gazing glumly at the redness still smouldering in the low dim sky. "The fire of London was a logical necessity." Suddenly his nerves rasped. "Damn it, Francis, kill yourself if you want to. But keep your motives to yourself."

The strain was telling on them. For ten days Francis had not been out of his clothes, they were stiff with frozen sweat. Occasionally he dragged his boots off, obeyed Tulloch's command to rub his feet with colza oil — even so his right great toe was inflamed with agonizing frostbite. He was dead with fatigue, but always there was more . . . more to be done.

They had no water, only melted snow, the wells were solid ice. Cooking was near impossible. Yet every day, Tulloch insisted that they all meet to have their midday meal together, to counteract the growing nightmare of their lives. At this hour, doggedly, he exerted himself to be cheerful, occasionally giving them Edison Bell selections on the phonograph he had brought out with him. He had a fund of North Country anecdotes, stories of the Tynecastle "Georgies," which he drew on freely. Sometimes he had the triumph of bringing a pale smile to Maria-Veronica's lips. Lieutenant Shon could never understand the jokes, though he listened politely while they were explained to him. Sometimes Shon was a little late in coming to the meal. Though they guessed that he was solacing some pretty lady who still, like themselves, survived, the empty chair took an unsuspected toll upon their nerves.

As the third week began Maria-Veronica showed signs of breaking down. Tulloch was bewailing the lack of floor space in the yamen, when she remarked: "If we took hammocks from the Street of the Netmakers we could house double our number of patients . . . more comfortably, too."

The doctor paused, gazed at her with grim approbation. "Why didn't I think of that before? It's a grand suggestion."

She coloured deeply under his praise, cast down her eyes and tried to go on with her dish of rice. But she could not. Her arm began to shake. It shook so violently the food dropped off her fork. She could not raise a grain of rice towards her lips. Her flush deepened, spread into her neck. Several times she repeated the attempt and failed. She sat with bent head, enduring the absurd humiliation. Then she rose without a word and left the table.

Later, Father Chisholm found her at work in the women's ward. He had never known such calm and pitiless self-sacrifice. She performed the most hateful duties for the sick, work which the lowest Chinese sweeper would have spurned. He dared not look at her, so unbearable had their relationship become. He had not addressed her directly for many days.

"Reverend Mother, Dr. Tulloch thinks . . . we all think you have been doing too much . . . that Sister Martha should come down to relieve you."

She had regained only a vestige of her cold aloofness. His suggestion disturbed her anew. She drew herself up. "You mean that I am not doing enough?"

"Far from it. Your work is magnificent."

"Then why attempt to keep me from it?" Her lips were trembling.

He said clumsily, "We are considering you."

His tone seemed to sting her to the quick. Holding back her tears, she answered passionately: "Do not consider me. The more work you give me . . . and the less sympathy . . . the better I shall like it."

He had to leave it at that. He raised his eyes to look at her but her gaze was fixedly averted. He sadly turned away.

The snow which had held off for a week suddenly began again. It fell and fell unendingly. Francis had never seen such snow, the flakes so large and soft. Each added snowflake made an added silence. Houses were walled up in the silent whiteness. The streets were choked with drifts, hindering their work, increasing the sufferings of the sick. His heart was wrung again . . . again. In the endless days he lost all sense of time and place and fear. As he bent over the dying, succouring them with deep compassion in his eyes, stray thoughts swam through his dizzy brain. . . . Christ promised us suffering . . . this life was given us only as a preparation for the next . . . when God will wipe all sorrow from our eyes, weeping and mourning shall be no more.

Now they were halting all nomads outside the walls, disinfecting and holding them in quarantine until assured of their freedom from the disease. As they came back from the isolation huts they had thrown up, Tulloch inquired of him, overtaxed, frayed to a raw anger: —

"Is hell any worse than this?"

He answered, through the fog of his fatigue, blundering forward, unheroic, yet undismayed: "Hell is that state where one has ceased to hope."

None of them knew when the epidemic eased. There was no climax of achievement, no operatic crowning of their efforts. Visible evidence of death no longer lingered in the streets. The worst slums lay as dirty ashes on the snow. The mass flight from the Northern Provinces gradually ceased. It was as if a great dark cloud, immovably above them, were at last rolling slowly to the southwards.

Tulloch expressed his feelings in a single dazed and jaded phrase. "Your God alone knows if we've done anything, Francis . . . I think . . ." He broke off, haggard, limp, and for the first time seemed about to break. He swore. "The admissions are down again today . . . let's take time off or I'll go mad."

That evening the two took a brief respite, for the first time, from the hospital and climbed to the mission to spend the night at the priest's house. It was after ten o'clock and a few stars were faintly visible in the dark bowl of sky.

The doctor paused on the brow of the snow-embowered hill, which they had ascended with great effort, studying the soft outlines of the mission, lit by the whiteness of the earth. He spoke with unusual quietness: "It's a bonny place you've made, Francis. I don't wonder you've fought so hard to keep your little brats safe. Well, if I've helped at all, I'm mortal glad." His lips twitched. "It must be pleasant to spend your days here with a fine-looking woman like Maria-Veronica."

The priest knew his friend too well to take offence. But he answered, with a strained and wounded smile: —

"I'm afraid she does not find it agreeable."

"No?"

"You must have seen that she loathes me."

There was a pause. Tulloch gave the priest a queer glance.

"Your most endearing virtue, my holy man, has always been your painful lack of vanity." He moved on. "Let's go in and have some toddy. It's something to have worked through this scourge and to have the end of it in sight. It sort of lifts one up above the level of the brutes. But don't try to use that on me as an argument to prove the existence of the soul."

Seated in Francis' room they knew a moment of exhausted exaltation, talked of home late into the night. Briefly, Tulloch satirized his own career. He had done nothing, acquired nothing but a taste for whiskey. But now, in his sentimental middle age, aware of his limitations, having proved the fallacy of the world's wide-open spaces, he was hankering for his home in Darrow and the greater adventure of matrimony. He excused himself with a shamed smile.

"My dad wants me in the practice. Wants to see me raise a brood of young Ingersolls. Dear old boy, he never fails to mention you, Francis . . . his Roman Voltaire."

He spoke with rare affection of his sister Jean, now married and comfortably settled in Tynecastle. He said, oddly, not looking at Francis: —

"It took her a long time to reconcile herself to the celibacy of the clergy."

His silence on the subject of Judy was strangely suspect. But he could not speak enough of Polly. He had met her six months ago in Tynecastle, still going strong. "What a woman!" He nodded across his glass. "Mark my words, she may astound you one day. Polly is, was, and always will be a holy trump." They slept in their chairs.

By the end of that week the epidemic showed further indications of abatement. Now the death carts seldom rattled through the streets, vultures ceased to swoop from the horizon and snow no longer fell.

On the following Saturday Father Chisholm stood again on his balcony at the mission, inhaling the ice-cold air, with a deep and blessed thankfulness. From his vantage he could see the children playing in complete unconsciousness behind the tall kaolin fence. He felt like a man towards whom sweet daylight slowly filters after a long and dreadful dream.

Suddenly his gaze was caught by a figure of a soldier, dark against the snowbanks, moving rapidly up the road towards the mission. At first he took the man for one of the Lieutenant's followers. Then, with some surprise, he saw that it was Shon himself.

This was the first time the young officer had visited him. A puzzled light hovered about Francis' eyes as he turned and went down the stairs to meet him.

On the doorstep, the sight of Shon's face stopped the welcome on his lips. It was lemon pale, tight-drawn, and of a mortal gravity. A faint dew of perspiration on the brow bespoke his haste, as did the half-unbuttoned tunic, an unbelievable laxity in one so precise.

The Lieutenant wasted no time. "Please come to the yamen at once. Your friend the doctor is taken ill."

Francis felt a great coldness, a cold shock, like the impact of a frigid blast. He shivered. He gazed back at Shon. After what seemed a long time he heard himself say: "He has been working too much. He has collapsed."

Shon's hard dark eyes winced imperceptibly. "Yes, he has collapsed."

There was another pause. Then Francis knew it was the worst. He turned pale. He set out, as he was, with the Lieutenant.

They walked half the way in complete silence. Then Shon, with a military precision that suppressed all feeling, revealed briefly what had occurred. Dr. Tulloch had come in with a tired air and gone to take a drink. While he poured the drink he had coughed explosively, and steadied himself against the bamboo table, his face a dingy grey, except for the prune-juice froth upon his lips. As Maria-Veronica ran to help him, he gave her before he collapsed a weak, peculiar smile: "Now is the time to send for the priest."

When they reached the yamen a soft grey mist was drooping, like a tired cloud, across the snow-banked roofs. They entered quickly. Tulloch lay in the small end room, on his narrow camp bed, covered with a quilted mat of purple silk. The rich deep colour of the quilt intensified his dreadful pallor, threw a livid shadow upon his face. It was agony for Francis to see how swiftly the fever had struck. Willie might have been a different man. He was shrunken, unbelievably, as though after weeks of wasting. His tongue and lips were swollen, his eyeballs glazed and shot with blood.

Beside the bed Maria-Veronica was kneeling, replenishing the pack of snow upon the sick man's forehead. She held herself erect — tensely, her expression rigid in its fixed control. She rose as Francis and the Lieutenant entered. She did not speak.

Francis went over to the bedside. A great fear was in his heart. Death had walked with them these past few weeks, familiar and casual, a dreadful commonplace. But now that death's shadow lay upon his friend, the pain that struck at him was strange and terrible.

Tulloch was still conscious, the light of recognition remained in his congested gaze. "I came out for adventure." He tried to smile. "I seem to have got it." A moment later, he added, half-closing his eyes, as a kind of afterthought: "Man, I'm weak as a cat."

Francis sat down on the low stool at the head of the bed. Shon and Maria-Veronica were at the end of the room.

The stillness, the painful sense of waiting, was insupportable, growing, alike, with a frightful feeling of intrusion upon the privacy of things unknown.

"Are you quite comfortable?"

"I might be worse. Spare me a drop of that Japanese whiskey. It'll help me along. Man, it's an awful conventional thing to die like this . . . me that damned the story-books."

When Francis had given him a sip of spirits he closed his eyes and seemed to rest. But soon he lapsed into a low delirium.

"Another drink, lad. Bless you, that's the stuff! I've drunk plenty in my time, round the slums of Tynecastle. And now I'm away home to dear old Darrow. On the banks of Allan Water, when the sweet springtime had fled. D'you mind that one, Francis . . . it's a bonny song. Sing it Jean. Come on, louder, louder . . . I cannot hear you in the dark." Francis gritted his teeth, fighting the tumult in his breast. "That's right, Your Reverence. I'll keep quiet and save my strength . . . It's a queer business . . . altogether . . . we've all got to toe the line sometime." Muttering, he sank into unconsciousness.

The priest knelt in prayer by the bedside. He prayed for help, for inspiration. But he was strangely dumb, gripped by a kind of stupor. The city outside was ghostly in its silence. Twilight came. Maria-Veronica rose to light the lamp, then returned to the far corner of the room outside the beam of lamplight, her lips unmoving, silent, but her fingers steadily enumerating the beads beneath her gown.

Tulloch was getting worse: his tongue black, his throat so swollen his bouts of vomiting were an agony to watch.

But suddenly he seemed to rally; he dimly opened his eyes.

"What o'clock is it?" His voice crouped huskily. "Near five . . . at home . . . that's when we had our tea. D'you mind, Francis, the crowd of us at the big round table . . . ?" A longer pause . . . "Ye'll write the old man and tell him that his son died game. Funny . . . I still can't believe in God."

"Does that matter now?" What was he saying? Francis did not know. He was crying and, in the stupid humiliation of his weakness, the words came from him, in blind confusion. "He believes in you."

"Don't delude yourself . . . I'm not repentant."

"All human suffering is an act of repentance."

There was a silence. The priest said no more. Weakly, Tulloch reached out his hand and let it fall on Francis' arm.

"Man, I've never loved ye so much as I do now . . . for not trying to bully me to heaven. Ye see — " His lids dropped wearily. "I've such an awful headache."

His voice failed. He lay on his back, exhausted, his breathing quick and shallow, his gaze upturned as though fixed far beyond the ceiling. His throat was closed, he could not even cough.

The end was near. Maria-Veronica was kneeling now, at the window, her back towards them, her gaze directed fixedly into the darkness. Shon stood at the foot of the bed. His face was set immovably.

Suddenly Willie moved his eyes, in which a lingering spark still flickered. Francis saw that he was trying, vainly, to whisper. He knelt, slipped his arm about the dying man's neck, brought his cheek close to the other's breath. At first he could hear nothing. Then weakly came the words: "Our fight . . . Francis . . . more than sixpence to get my sins forgiven."

The sockets of Tulloch's eyes filled up with shadow. He yielded to an unaccountable weariness. The priest felt rather than heard the last faint sigh. The room was suddenly more quiet. Still holding the body, as a mother might hold her child, he began blindly, in a low and strangled voice, the De Profundis.

"Out of the depths have I cried unto thee, O Lord. Lord, hear my voice . . . because with the Lord there is mercy: and with him plentiful redemption."

He rose at last, closed the eyes, composed the limp hands.

As he went out of the room he saw Sister Maria-Veronica still bowed at the window. As though still within a dream he gazed at the Lieutenant. He saw, in a kind of dim surprise, that Shon's shoulders were shaking convulsively.

VI

THE plague had passed, but a great apathy gripped the snow-bound land. In the country the rice fields were frozen lakes. The few remaining peasants could not work a soil so mercilessly entombed. There was no sign of life. In the town survivors emerged as from a painful hibernation, began dully to gather up their daily lives. The merchants and magistrates had not yet returned. It was said that many distant roads were quite impassable. None could remember such evil weather. All the passes were reported blocked and avalanches hurtled down the distant Kwangs like puffs of pure white smoke. The river, in its upper reaches, was frozen solid, a great grey wasteland over which the wind drove powder snow, in blinding desolation. Lower down there was a channel. Huge lumps of ice crashed and pounded in the current under the Manchu Bridge. Hardship was in every home and famine lurked not far behind.

One boat had risked the jagged floes and steamed up-river from Sen-siang, bringing food and medical comforts from the Leighton Expedition, and a long-delayed packet of letters. After a brief stay it had cast off, taking the remaining members of Dr. Tulloch's party back to Nankin.

In the mail which arrived one communication surpassed the others in importance. As Father Chisholm came slowly up from the end of the mission garden where a small wooden cross marked Dr. Tulloch's grave, he bore this letter in his hand and his thoughts were busy with the visit it announced. He hoped his work was satisfactory — the mission was surely worthy of his pride in it. If only the weather would break — thaw quickly — in the next two weeks!

When he reached the church Mother Maria-Veronica was coming down the steps. He must tell her — though he had come to dread these rare occasions when official business forced him to break the silence which lay between them.

"Reverend Mother . . . the provincial administrator of our Foreign Missions Society, Canon Mealey, is making a tour of inspection of the Chinese missions. He sailed five weeks ago. He will arrive in about a month's time . . . to visit us." He paused. "I thought you'd like to have notice . . . in case there is anything you wish to put before him."

Muffled against the cold, she raised her gaze, impenetrable, behind the rimed vapour of her breath. Yet she started faintly. Now she so seldom saw him closely, the change which those last weeks had brought was strikingly manifest. He was thin, quite emaciated. The bones of his face had become prominent, the skin drawn tighter, cheeks slightly sunken, so that his eyes seemed larger and oddly luminous. A terrible impulse took possession of her.

"There is only one thing I wish to put before him." She spoke instinctively, the sudden news lifting from the recesses of her soul a deeply buried thought. "I shall ask to be transferred to another mission."

There was a long pause. Though not wholly taken by surprise, he felt chilled, defeated. He sighed. "You are unhappy here?"

"Happiness has nothing to do with it. As I told you, when I entered the religious life I prepared myself to endure everything."

"Even the enforced association of someone whom you despise?"

She coloured with a proud defiance. That deep throbbing in her bosom drove her to continue. "You mistake me completely. It is obvious. It is something deeper . . . spiritual."

"Spiritual? Will you try to tell me?"

"I feel" — she took a quick breath — "that you are upsetting me . . . in my inner life . . . my spiritual beliefs."

"That is a serious matter." He stared at the letter unseeingly, twisting it in his bony hands. "It hurts me . . . as much, I am sure, as it hurts you to say it. But perhaps you have misunderstood me. To what do you refer?"

"Do you think I have prepared a list?" Despite her control she felt her agitation rising. "It is your attitude . . . For instance, some remarks you made when Dr. Tulloch was dying . . . and afterwards, when he was dead."

"Please go on."

"He was an atheist, and yet you virtually promised he would have his eternal reward . . . he who didn't believe . . . "

He said quickly: "God judges us not only by what we believe . . . but by what we do."

"He was not a Catholic . . . not even a Christian!"

"How do you define a Christian? One who goes to church one day of the seven and lies, slanders, cheats his fellow men the other six?" He smiled faintly. "Dr. Tulloch didn't live like that. And he died — helping others . . . like Christ himself."

She repeated stubbornly: "He was a free-thinker."

"My child, our Lord's contemporaries thought him a dreadful free-thinker . . . that's why they killed him."

She was pale now, quite distraught. "It is inexcusable to make such a comparison — outrageous!"

"I wonder! . . . Christ was a very tolerant man — and humble."

A rush of colour again flooded her cheek. "He made certain rules. Your Dr. Tulloch did not obey them. You know that. Why, when he was unconscious, at the end, you did not even administer extreme unction."

"No, I didn't! And perhaps I should have." He stood, thinking worriedly, rather depressed. Then he seemed to cheer up. "But the good God may forgive him none the less." He paused, with simple frankness. "Didn't you love him too?"

She hesitated, lowered her eyes. "Yes . . . Who could help that?"

"Then don't let us make his memory the occasion of a quarrel. There is one thing we most of us forget. Christ taught it. The Church teaches it . . . though you wouldn't think so to hear a great many of us today. No one in good faith can ever be lost. No one. Buddhists, Mohammedans, Taoists . . . the blackest cannibals who ever devoured a missionary . . . If they are sincere, according to their own lights, they will be saved. That is the splendid mercy of God. So why shouldn't He enjoy confronting a decent agnostic at the Judgement Seat with a twinkle in his eye: 'I'm here you see, in spite of all they brought you up to believe. Enter the

Kingdom which you honestly denied.'" He made to smile, then, seeing her expression, sighed and shook his head. "I'm truly sorry you feel as you do. I know I'm hard to get on with, and perhaps a little odd in my beliefs. But you've worked so wonderfully here . . . the children love you . . . and during the plague . . ." He broke off. "I know we haven't got on very well . . . but the mission would suffer terribly if you should go."

He gazed at her with a queer intentness, a sort of strained humility. He waited for her to speak. Then, as she did not, he slowly took his leave.

She continued on her way to the refectory where she superintended the serving of the children's dinner. Later, in her own bare room, she paced up and down in a strange continuance of her agitation. Suddenly, with a gesture of despair, she sat down and set herself to complete a further passage in another of those lengthy letters in which, from day to day, as the outlet for her emotions, a penance and a consolation, she compiled the record of her doings for her brother.

Pen in hand, she seemed calmer; the act of writing seemed to tranquillize her.

"I have just told him I must ask to be transferred. It came suddenly, a sort of climax to all I have suppressed, and something of a threat as well. I was amazed at myself, startled by the words issuing from my lips. Yet when the opportunity presented itself I could not resist, I wanted instantly to startle, to hurt him. But, my dear dear Ernst, I am no happier. . . . After that second of triumph when I saw dismay cloud his face I am even more restless and distressed. I look out at the vast desolation of these grey wastes — so different from our cosy winter landscape with its golden air, its sleighbells and clustered chalet roofs — and I want to cry . . . as if my heart would break.

"It is his silence which defeats me — that stoic quality of enduring, and of fighting, all without speech. I've told you of his work during the plague, when he went about amongst foul sickness and sudden repulsive death as carelessly as if he were walking down the main street of his dreadful Scottish village. Well, it wasn't merely his courage, but the muteness of that courage, which was so unbelievably heroic. When his friend, the doctor, died, he held him in his arms, unmindful of the contagion, of that final cough which spattered his cheek with clotted blood. And the look upon his face . . . in its compassion and utter selflessness . . . it pierced my heart. Only my pride saved me the humiliation of weeping in his sight! Then I became angry. What irks me most of all is that I once wrote you that he was despicable. Ernst, I was wrong, — what an admission from your stubborn sister! — I can no longer despise him. Instead I despise myself. But I detest him. And I won't, I won't let him beat me down to his level of harrowing simplicity.

"The two others here have both been conquered. They love him -- that is another mortification I must sustain. Martha, the stolid peasant, with bunions but no brains, is prepared to adore anything in a cassock. But Clotilde, shy and timid, flushing on the slightest provocation, a gently sweet and sensitive creature, has become a perfect devotee. During her enforced quarantine she worked him a thick quilted bed-mat, soft and warm, really beautiful. She took it to Joseph, his servant, with instructions to place it on the Father's bed — she is much too modest even to whisper the word 'bed' in his hearing. Joseph smiled: 'I am sorry, Sister, there is no bed!' It appears he sleeps upon the bare floor, with no covering but his overcoat, a greenish garment of uncertain age, which he is fond of, and of which, caressing the frayed and threadbare sleeves, he says proudly, 'Actually! I had it when I was a student at Holywell!'

"Martha and Clotilde have been making inquiries in his kitchen, nervous and perturbed, convinced that he does not look after himself. Their expressions, like shocked tabbies, almost made me laugh as they told me what I already knew, that he eats nothing but black bread, potatoes and bean curd.

" 'Joseph has instructions to boil a pot of potatoes and place them in a wicker basket,' Clotilde mewed. 'He eats one cold when he is hungry, dipping it in bean curd. Often they are quite musty before the basketful is finished.'

" 'Isn't it dreadful?' I answered curtly. 'But then some stomachs have never known a good cuisine — it is not hardship for them to do without it.'

" 'Yes, Reverend Mother,' murmured Clotilde, blushing, and retreating.

"She would do penance for a week to come and see him eat one nice hot meal. Oh, Ernst, you know how I abominate the sedulous and fawning nun who in the presence of a priest exposes the whites of her eyes and dissolves in obsequious rapture. Never, never, will I descend to such a level. I vowed it at Coblenz when I took the veil, and again at Liverpool . . . and will keep that vow . . . even in Pai-tan. But bean curd! *You* will not encounter it. A thin pinkish paste tasting of stagnant water and chewed wood!" She raised her head at an unexpected sound. "Ernst . . . It is unbeliev-able . . . it is raining . . ." She stopped writing, as if unable to continue, and slowly laid down her pen. With dark and self-distrustful eyes she sat watching the novelty of the rain, which trickled down the pane like heavy tears.

A fortnight later it was still raining. The skies, dull as tallow, were open sluices from which a steady deluge fell. The drops were large, pitting the upper crust of yellowish snow. It seemed everlasting . . . the snow. Great frozen slabs of it still came slid-ing from the church roof, with unpremeditated acceleration, land-ing soddenly upon the slushy snow beneath. Rivulets of rain went rushing across the dun-coloured sludge, channeling, undercutting the banks, which toppled with a slow splash into the stream beneath. The mission was a quagmire of slush.

Then the first patch of brown earth appeared, momentous as the tip of Ararat. Further patches sprouted and coalesced, form-ing a landscape of bleached grass and scabby desert all fissured and cratered with the flood. And still the rain continued. The mission roofs broke down at last and leaked incessantly. Water came in cataracts from the eaves. The children sat, green and miserable, in the class-room, while Sister Martha placed pails for the larger drips. Sister Clotilde had a dreadful cold and took lessons at her desk beneath Reverend Mother's umbrella.

The light soil of the mission garden could not withstand the scouring fusion of rain and thaw. It swept down the hill in a yellow turbulence on which floated uptorn sareta plants and oleander shrubs. Carp from the fish pond darted frightened, through the flood. The trees were slowly undermined. For a painful day the lychees and catalpas stood upright on their naked roots, which groped like pallid tentacles, then slowly toppled. The young white mulberries followed next, then the lovely row of flowering plum, these on the day that the lower wall was washed away. Only the toughened cedars stood, with the giant banyan, amidst the muddied desolation.

On the afternoon before Canon Mealey's arrival Father Chisholm heavily surveyed the dreary havoc, on his way to children's benediction. He turned to Fu, the gardener, who stood beside him.

"I wished for a thaw. The good God has punished me by sending one."

Fu, like most gardeners, was not a cheerful man. "The great Shang-Foo who arrives from across the seas will think much ill of us. Ah! If only he had seen my bloom of lilies last spring!"

"Let us be of good heart, Fu. The damage is not irreparable."

"My plantings are lost." Fu gloomed. "We shall have to begin all over again."

"That is life . . . to begin again when everything is lost!"

Despite his exhortation, Francis was deeply depressed as he went into the church. Kneeling before the lighted altar, while the rain still drummed upon the roof, he seemed to hear, above the childish treble of the Tantum Ergo, a liquid murmuring beneath him. But the sound of flowing water had long been echoing in his ears. His mind was burdened by the wretched appearance which the mission must present to his visitor upon the following day. He put the thing away as an obsession.

When the service was over and Joseph had snuffed the candles and left the sacristy he came slowly down the aisle. A dank vapour hung about the whitewashed nave. Sister Martha had taken the children across the compound for their supper. But still in prayer upon the damp boards were Reverend Mother and Sister Clotilde. He passed them in silence; then suddenly stopped short. Clotilde's running head catarrh made her a spectacle of woe and Maria-Veronica's lips were drawn with cold. He had an extraordinary inner conviction that they should neither of them be allowed to remain.

He stepped back to them and said: "I am sorry, I'm going to close the church now."

There was a pause. This interference was unlike him. They seemed surprised. But they rose obediently, in silence, and preceded him to the porch. He locked the front doors and followed them through the streaming dusk.

A moment later the sound broke upon them. A low rumble, swelling to a roll of subterranean thunder. As Sister Clotilde screamed, Francis swung round to see the slender structure of his church in motion. Glistening, wetly luminous, it swayed gracefully in the fading light; then, like a reluctant woman, yielded. His heart stood still in horror. With a rending crash, the undermined foundations broke. One side caved in, the roof's spire snapped, the rest was a blinding vision of torn timbers and shattered glass. Then his church, his lovely church, lay dissolved into nothing, at his feet.

He stood rooted, for an instant, in a daze of pain, then ran towards the wreckage. But the altar lay smashed to rubble, the tabernacle crushed to splinters beneath a beam. He could not even save the sacred species. And his vestments, the precious Ribiero relic, these were in shreds. Standing there, bare-headed in the teeming rain, he was conscious, amidst the frightened babble which now surrounded him, of Sister Martha's lamentation.

"Why . . . why . . . why has this come on us?" She was moaning, wringing her hands. "Dear God! What worse could you have done to us?"

He muttered, not moving, desperately sustaining his own faith rather than hers: —

"Ten minutes sooner . . . we should every one of us have been killed."

There was nothing to be done. They left the fallen wreckage to the darkness and the rain.

Next day, at three o'clock punctually, Canon Mealey arrived. Because of the turbulence of the flooded river, his junk had dropped anchor in a backwater five li below Pai-tan. There were no chairs available: only some wheelbarrows, long-shafted like ploughs, with solid wooden wheels which, since the plague, were used by the few remaining runners to transport their passengers. The situation was difficult for a man of dignity. But there was no alternative. The Canon, mud-spattered and with dangling legs, reached the mission in a wheelbarrow.

The modest reception rehearsed by Sister Clotilde — a song of welcome, with waving of little flags, by the children — had been abandoned. Watching from his balcony, Father Chisholm hurried to the gate to meet his visitor.

"My dear Father!" cried Mealey, stiffly straightening himself and warmly grasping both Francis' hands. "This is the happiest day in many months — to see you again. I told you I should one day run the gamut of the Orient. With the interest of the world centred upon suffering China it was inevitable my resolve should crystallize to action!" He broke off, his eye bulging across the other's shoulder at the scene of desolation. "Why . . . I don't understand. Where is the church?"

"You see all that is left of it."

"But this mess . . . You reported a splendid establishment."

"We have had some reverses." Francis spoke quietly.

"Why, really, it's incomprehensible . . . most disturbing."

Francis intervened with a hospitable smile. "When you have had a hot bath and a change I will tell you."

An hour later, pink from his tub, in a new tussore suit, Anselm sat stirring his hot soup, with an aggrieved expression.

"I must confess this is the greatest disappointment of my life . . . to come here, to the very outposts . . ." He took a mouthful of soup, meeting the spoon with plump, pursed lips. He had filled out in these last years. He was big now, full-shouldered and stately, still smooth-skinned and clear-eyed, with big palps of hands, hearty or pontifical at will. "I had set my heart on celebrating high mass in your church, Francis. These foundations must have been badly laid."

"It is a wonder they were laid at all."

"Nonsense! You've had lots of time to establish yourself. What in heaven's name am I to tell them at home?" He laughed shortly, dolefully. "I even promised a lecture at London Headquarters of the F.M.S. — 'St. Andrew's: or God in Darkest China.' I'd brought my quarter-plate Zeiss to get lantern slides. It places me . . . all of us . . . in a most awkward position."

There was a silence.

"Of course I know you've had your difficulties," Mealey continued between annoyance and compunction. "But who hasn't? I assure you we've had ours. Especially lately since we merged the two divisions . . . after Bishop MacNabb's death!"

Father Chisholm stiffened, as in pain.

"He's dead?"

"Yes, yes, the old man went at last. Pneumonia — this March. He was past his best, very muddled and queer, quite a relief to all of us when he went, very peacefully. The coadjutor, Bishop Tarrant, succeeded him. A great success."

Again a silence fell. Father Chisholm raised his hand to shield his eyes. Rusty Mac gone . . . A rush of unbearable recollection swept him: that day by the Stinchar, the glorious salmon, those kind wise peering eyes and the warmth of them when he was worried at Holywell; the quiet voice in the study at Tynecastle before he sailed, "Keep fighting, Francis, for God and good old Scotland."

Anselm was reflecting, with friendly generosity: "Well, well! We must face things, I suppose. Now that I'm here I'll do my best to get things straight for you. I've a great deal of organizing experience. It may interest you, some day, to hear how I have put the Society on its feet. In my personal appeals, delivered in London, Liverpool and Tynecastle, I raised thirty thousand pounds — and that is only the beginning." He showed his sound teeth in a competent smile. "Don't be so depressed, my dear fellow. I'm not unduly censorious . . . the first thing we'll do is have Reverend Mother over to lunch — she seems an able woman — and have a real round-table parochial conference!"

With an effort Francis pulled himself back from the dear forgotten days. "Reverend Mother doesn't care to take her meals outside the Sisters' house."

"You haven't asked her properly." Mealey gazed at the other's spare figure with a hearty, pitying kindliness. "Poor Francis! I'd hardly expect you to understand women. She'll come all right . . . just leave it to me!"

On the following day, Maria-Veronica did, in fact, present herself for lunch. Anselm was in high spirits after an excellent night's rest and an energetic morning of inspection. Still benevolent from his visit to the schoolroom, he greeted the Reverend Mother, though he had parted from her only five minutes before, with effusive dignity.

"This, Reverend Mother, is indeed an honour. A glass of sherry? No? I assure you it is fine — pale Amontillado. A little travelled perhaps," he beamed, "since it came with me from home. Coddlesome, maybe . . . but a palate, acquired in Spain, is hard to deny."

They sat down at table.

"Now, Francis, what are you giving us? No Chinese mysteries, I trust, no birds'-nest soup or purée of chopsticks. Ha! Ha!" Mealey laughed heartily as he helped himself to boiled chicken. "Though I must confess I am somewhat enamoured of the Oriental cuisine. Coming over on the boat — a stormy passage, incidentally; for four days no one appeared at the skipper's table but your humble servant — we were served with a quite delicious Chinese dish, chow mein."

Mother Maria-Veronica raised her eyes from the tablecloth. "Is chow mein a Chinese dish? Or an American edition of the Chinese custom of collecting scraps?"

He stared at her, mouth slightly agape. "My dear Reverend

Mother! Chow mein! Why . . ." He glanced at Francis for support, found none, and laughed again. "At any rate, I assure you, I chewed mine! Ha! Ha!"

Swinging round, for better access to the dish of salad which Joseph was presenting, he ran on: "Food apart, the lure of the Orient is immensely fascinating! We Occidentals are too apt to condemn the Chinese as a greatly inferior race. Now I for one will shake hands with any Chinaman, provided he believes in God and . . ." he bubbled . . . "carbolic soap!"

Father Chisholm shot a quick glance at Joseph's face, which, though expressionless, showed a faint tightening of the nostrils.

"And now," Mealey paused suddenly, his manner dropping to pontifical solemnity. "We have important business on our agenda. As a boy, Reverend Mother, our good mission father was always leading me into scrapes. Now it's my task to get him out of this one!"

Nothing definite emerged from the conference. Except, perhaps, a modest summary of Anselm's achievements at home.

Free of the limitations of a parish, he had set himself wholeheartedly to work for the missions, mindful that the Holy Father was especially devoted to the Propagation of the Faith and eager to encourage the workers who so selflessly espoused his favourite cause.

It had not been long before he won recognition. He began to move about the country, to preach sermons of impassioned eloquence in the great English cities. Through his genius for collecting friends, no contact of any consequence was ever thrown away. On his return from Manchester, or Birmingham, he would sit down and write a score of charming letters, thanking this person for a delightful lunch, the next for a generous donation to the Foreign Mission Fund. Soon his correspondence was voluminous, and employed a whole-time secretary.

Presently, London acknowledged him as a distinguished visitor. His debut, in the pulpit of Westminster, was spectacular. Women had always idolized him. Now he was adopted by the wealthy coterie of Cathedral spinsters who collected cats and clergymen in their rich mansions south of the Park. His manners had always been engaging. That same year he became a country member of the Athenæum. And the sudden engorgement of the F.M. money-bags evoked a most gracious token of appreciation, direct from Rome.

When he became the youngest canon in the Northern Diocese, few grudged him the success. Even the cynics who traced his ex-uberant rise to an overactive thyroid gland admitted his business acumen. For all his gush he was no fool. He had a level head for figures and could manage money. In five years he had founded two fresh missions in Japan and a native seminary in Nankin. The new F.M.S. offices in Tynecastle were imposing, efficient and completely free of debt.

In brief, Anselm had made a fine thing of his life. With Bishop Tarrant at his elbow there was every chance that his most admirable work would continue to expand.

Two days after his official meeting with Francis and Reverend Mother, the rain ceased and a watery sun sent pale feelers towards the forgotten earth. Mealey's spirits bounded. He joked to Francis.

"I've brought fine weather with me. Some people follow the sun around. But the sun follows me."

He unlimbered his camera and began to take countless photo-graphs. His energy was tremendous. He bounded out of bed in the morning shouting "Boy! Boy!" for Joseph to get his bath. He said mass in the schoolroom. After a hearty breakfast he departed in his solar topee, a stout stick in hand, the camera swinging on his hip.

He made many excursions, even poking discreetly for souvenirs amongst the ashes of Pai-tan's plague-spots. At each scene of blackened desolation he murmured reverently: "The hand of God!" He would stop suddenly, at a city gate, arresting his companion with a dramatic gesture. "Wait! I must get this one. The light is perfect."

On Sunday, he came in to lunch greatly elated. "It's just struck me, I can still give that lecture. Treat it from the angle of Dangers and Difficulties in the Mission Field. Work in the plague and the flood. This morning I got a glorious view of the ruins of the church. What a slide it will make, titled 'God Chastiseth His Own'! Isn't that magnificent?"

But on the eve of his departure Anselm's manner altered and his tone, as he sat with the mission priest on the balcony after supper, was grave.

"I have to thank you for extending hospitality to a wanderer, Francis. But I am not happy about you. I can't see how you are going to rebuild the church. The Society cannot let you have the money."

"I haven't asked for it." The strain of the past two weeks was beginning to tell on Francis, his stern self-discipline was wearing thin.

Mealey threw his companion a sharp glance. "If only you had been more successful with some of the better-class Chinese, the rich merchants. If only your friend Mr. Chia had seen the light."

"He hasn't." Father Chisholm spoke with unusual shortness. "And he has given munificently. I shall not ask him for another tael."

Anselm shrugged his shoulders, annoyed. "Of course that's your affair. But I must tell you, frankly, I'm sadly disappointed in your conduct of this mission. Take your convert rate. It doesn't compare with our other statistics. We run them as a graph at headquarters, and you're the lowest in the whole chart."

Father Chisholm gazed straight ahead, his lips firmly compressed. He answered with unusual irony: "I suppose missionaries differ in their individual capabilities."

"And in their enthusiasm." Anselm, sensitive to satire, was now justly incensed. "Why do you persist in refusing to employ catechists? It's the universal custom. If you had even three active men, at forty taels a month, why, one thousand baptisms would only cost you fifteen hundred Chinese dollars!"

Francis did not answer. He was praying desperately that he might control his temper, suffer this humiliation as something he deserved.

"You're not getting behind your work here," Mealey went on. "You live, personally, in such poor style. You ought to impress the natives, keep a chair, servants, make more of a show."

"You are mistaken." Francis spoke steadily. "The Chinese hate ostentation. They call it *ti-mien*. And priests who practice it are regarded as dishonourable."

Anselm flushed angrily. "You're referring to their own low heathen priests, I presume."

"Does it matter?" Father Chisholm smiled palely. "Many of these priests are good and noble men."

There was a strained silence. Anselm drew his coat about him with a shocked finality.

"After that, of course, there is nothing to be said. I must confess your attitude pains me deeply. Even Reverend Mother is embarrassed by it. Ever since I arrived it has been plain how much she is at variance with you." He got up and went into his own room.

Francis remained a long time in the gathering mist. That last remark had cut him worst of all: the stab of a premonition confirmed. Now he had no doubt that Maria-Veronica had submitted her request to be transferred.

Next morning Canon Mealey took his departure. He was returning to Nankin to spend a week at the Vicariate and would go from there to Nagasaki to inspect six missions in Japan. His bags were packed, a chair waited to bear him to the junk, he had taken his farewells of the Sisters and the children. Now, dressed for the journey, wearing sun-glasses, his topee draped with green gauze, he stood in final conversation with Father Chisholm in the hall.

"Well, Francis!" Mealey extended his hand in grudging forgiveness. "We must part friends. The gift of tongues is not given to all of us. I suppose you are a well-meaning fellow at heart."

He threw out his chest. "Strange! I'm itching to be off. I have travel in my blood. Good-bye. *Au revoir. Auf Wiedersehen.* And last but not least — God bless you!"

Dropping the mosquito veil he stepped into his chair. The runners groaningly bent their shoulders, supported him and shuffled off. At the sagging mission gates he leaned through the window of the chair, fluttered his white handkerchief in farewell.

At sundown, when he took his evening walk, his beloved hour of stealing twilight and far-off echoing stillness, Father Chisholm found himself meditating, amongst the débris of the church. He seated himself upon a lump of rubble, thinking of his old Headmaster — somehow he always saw Rusty Mac with schoolboy's eyes — and of his exhortation to courage. There was little courage in him now. These last two weeks, the perpetual effort to sustain his visitor's patronizing tone, had left him void. Yet perhaps Anselm was justified. Was he not a failure, in God's sight and in man's? He had done so little. And that little, so laboured and inadequate, was almost undone. How was he to proceed? A weary hopelessness of spirit took hold of him.

Resting there, with bent head, he did not hear a footstep behind him. Mother Maria-Veronica was compelled to make her presence known to him.

"Am I disturbing you?"

He glanced up, quite startled. "No . . . no. As you observe," — he could not suppress a wincing smile, — "I am doing nothing."

There was a pause. In the indistinctness her face had a swimming pallor. He could not see the nerve twitching in her cheek yet he sensed in her figure a strange rigidity.

Her voice was colourless. "I have something to say to you. I — "

"Yes?"

"This is no doubt humiliating for you. But I am obliged to tell you. I — I am sorry." The words, torn from her, gained momentum, then came in a tumbled flood. "I am most bitterly and grievously sorry for my conduct towards you. From our first meeting I have behaved shamefully, sinfully. The devil of pride was in me.

It's always been in me, ever since I was a little child and flung things at my nurse's head. I have known now for weeks that I wanted to come to you . . . to tell you . . . but my pride, my stubborn malice restrained me. These past ten days, in my heart, I have wept for you . . . the slights and humiliations you have endured from that gross and worldly priest, who is unworthy to untie your shoe. Father, I hate myself — forgive me, forgive me . . ." Her voice was lost, she crouched, sobbing into her hands, before him.

The sky was strained of all colour, except the greenish afterglow behind the peaks. This faded swiftly and the kind dusk enfolded her. An interval of time, in which a single tear fell upon her cheek. . . .

"So now you will not leave the mission?"

"No, no . . ." Her heart was breaking. "If you will let me stay. I have never known anyone whom I wished so much to serve . . . Yours is the best . . . the finest spirit I have ever known."

"Hush, my child. I am a poor and insignificant creature . . . you were right . . . a common man . . ."

"Father, pity me." Her sobs went choking into the earth.

"And you are a great lady. But in God's sight we are both of us children. If we may work together . . . help each other . . ."

"I will help with all my power. One thing at least I can do. It is so easy to write to my brother. He will rebuild the church . . . restore the mission. He has great possessions, he will do it gladly. If only you will help me . . . help me to defeat my pride."

There was a long silence. She sobbed more softly. A great warmth filled his heart. He took her arm to raise her but she would not rise. So he knelt beside her and gazed, without praying, into the pure and peaceful night where, across the ages, among the shadows of a garden, another poor and common man also knelt and watched them both.

VII

ONE sunny forenoon in the year 1912 Father Chisholm was separating beeswax from his season's yield of honey. His workshop, built in Bavarian style, at the end of the kitchen garden — trim, practical, with a pedal lathe and tools neatly racked, as much a source of delight to him as on the day Mother Maria-Veronica had handed him the key — was sweet with the fume of melted sugar. A great bowl of cool yellow honey stood among fresh shavings upon the floor. On the bench, setting, was the flat copper pan of tawny wax from which, tomorrow, he would make his candles. And such candles — smooth-burning and sweet-scented; even in St. Peter's one would not find the like!

With a sigh of contentment, he wiped his brow, his short fingernails blobbed with the rich wax. Then, shouldering the big honey jar, he pulled the door behind him and set off through the mission grounds. He was happy. Waking in the morning with the starlings chattering in the eaves, and the coolness of the dawn still dewed upon the grass, his second thought was that there could be no greater happiness than to work — much with his hands, a little with his head, but mostly with his heart — and to live, simply, like this, close to the earth which, to him, never seemed far from heaven.

The province was prospering and the people, forgetting flood, pestilence and famine, were at peace. In the five years which had elapsed since its reconstruction, through the generosity of Count Ernst von Hohenlohe, the mission had flourished in a quiet fashion. The church was bigger, stouter than the first. He had built it solidly, with grim compunction, using neither plaster nor stucco, after the monastic model which Queen Margaret had introduced to Scotland centuries before. Classic and severe, with a simple bell-tower, and aisles supported by groined arches, its plainness grew on him until he preferred it to the other. And it was safe.

The school had been enlarged, a new children's home added to the building. And the purchase of the two adjoining irrigated fields provided a model home farm with pigpen, byre, and a chicken run down which Martha stalked, thin-shanked, in wooden shoes and kilted habit, casting corn and clucking joyously in Flemish.

Now his congregation comprised two hundred faithful souls, not one of whom knelt under duress before his altar. The orphanage had trebled in size and was beginning to bear the first fruits of his patient foresight. The older girls helped the Sisters with the little ones, some were already novices, others would soon be going into the world. Why, last Christmas he had married the eldest, at nineteen, to a young farmer from the Liu village. He smiled ruefully at the implications of his cunning. At his recent pastoral visit to Liu — a happy and successful expedition from which he had returned only last week — the young wife had hung her head and told him he must return presently to perform another baptism.

As he shifted the heavy honey to his other shoulder, a bent little man of forty-three, growing bald, with rheumatism already nibbling at his joints, a bough of jessamine flailed him on the cheek. The garden had seldom been so lovely: that, also, he owed to Maria-Veronica. Admitting some adroitness with his hands, he could not remotely claim to have green fingers. But Reverend Mother had revealed an unsuspected skill in growing things. Seeds had arrived from her home in Germany, bundles of shoots wrapped tenderly in sacking. Her letters, begging for this cutting and for that, had sped to famous gardens in Canton and Peking — like his own swift white doves, importunate and homing. This beauty which now surrounded him, this sun-shot sanctuary, alive with twittering hum, was her work.

Their comradeship was not unlike this precious garden. Here, indeed, when he took his evening walk, he would find her, intent, coarsely gloved, cutting the full white peonies that grew so freely, training a stray clematis, watering the golden azaleas. There they would briefly discuss the business of the day. Sometimes they did not speak. When the fireflies flitted in the garden they had gone their separate ways.

As he approached the upper gate he saw the children march in twos across the compound. Dinner. He smiled and hastened. They were seated at the long low table in the new annex to the dormitory, twoscore little blue-black polls and shining yellow faces, with Maria-Veronica at one end, Clotilde at the other. Martha, aided by the Chinese novices, was ladling steaming rice broth into a battery of blue bowls. Anna, his foundling of the snow, now a handsome girl, handed round the bowls with her usual air of dark and frowning reserve.

The clamour stilled upon his entry. He shot a shamed boyish look at the Reverend Mother, craving indulgence, and placed the honey jar triumphantly on the table.

"Fresh honey today, children! It is a great pity. I am sure no one wishes it!"

Shrill, immediate denial rose like the chatter of little monkeys. Suppressing his smile, he shook his head dolefully at the youngest, a solemn mandarin of three who sat swallowing his spoon, swaying dreamily, his soft small buttocks unstable on the bench.

"I cannot believe a good child could enjoy such monstrous depravity! Tell me, Symphorien —" It was dreadful the way in which new converts chose the most resounding saint names for their children —"Tell me, Symphorien . . . would you not rather learn nice catechism than eat honey?"

"Honey!" answered Symphorien dreamily. He stared at the lined brown face above him. Then, surprised by his own temerity, he burst into tears and fell off the bench.

Laughing, Father Chisholm picked up the child. "There, there! You are a good boy, Symphorien. God loves you. And for speaking the truth you shall have double honey."

He felt Maria-Veronica's reproving gaze upon him. She would presently follow him to the door and murmur: "Father . . . we must consider discipline!" But today — it seemed so long since he stood outside the buzzing classroom, troubled and unhappy, afraid to penetrate the chill unfriendly air — nothing could restrain his manner with the children. His fondness towards them had always been absurd, it was what he named his patriarchal privilege.

As he expected, Maria-Veronica accompanied him from the room but, though her brow seemed unusually clouded, she did not even mildly rebuke him. Instead, after some hesitation, she remarked: "Joseph had a strange story this morning."

"Yes. The rascal wants to get married . . . naturally. But he is deafening me with the beauties and convenience of a lodge . . . to be built at the mission gate . . . not, of course, for Joseph or for Joseph's wife . . . but solely for the benefit of the mission."

"No, it isn't the lodge." Unsmiling, she bit her lip. "The building is taking place elsewhere, in the Street of the Lanterns—you know that splendid central site—and on a grander scale, much grander than anything we have accomplished here." Her tone was strangely bitter. "Scores of workmen have arrived, barges of white stone from Sen-siang. Everything. I assure you money is being spent as only American millionaires can spend it. Soon we shall have the finest establishment in Pai-tan, with schools, for both boys and girls, a playground, public rice kitchen, free dispensary, and a hospital with resident doctor!" She broke off, gazing at him with tears in her troubled eyes.

"What establishment?" He spoke automatically, stunned by a presage of her answer.

"Another mission. Protestant. The American Methodists."

There was a long pause. Secure in the remoteness of his situation, he had never contemplated even the possibility of such intrusion. Reverend Mother, recalled to the refectory by Clotilde, left him in painful silence.

He walked slowly towards his house, all the brightness of the morning dimmed. Where was his mediæval fortress now? In a quick throwback to his childhood, he had the same sensation of injustice as when, out berry-picking, another boy had encroached upon a secret bush of his own discovery and rudely begun to strip it of its fruit. He knew the hatreds which developed between rival missions, the ugly jealousies, above all, the bickerings on points of doctrine, the charge and countercharge, the raucous denunciation which made the Christian faith appear, to the tolerant Chinese mind, an infernal tower of Babel where all shouted at lung-pitch: "Behold, it is here! Here! Here!" But where? Alas! When one looked, there was nothing but rage and sound and execration.

At his house he found Joseph, duster in hand, idling about the hall, in pretence of work, waiting to bemoan the news.

"Has the Father heard of the hateful coming of these Americans who worship the false God?"

"Be silent, Joseph!" The priest answered harshly. "They do not worship the false God, but the same true God as we. If you speak such words again you will never get your gate-house!"

Joseph edged away, grumbling beneath his breath.

In the afternoon Father Chisholm went down to Pai-tan and, in the Street of the Lanterns, received the fateful confirmation of his eyes. Yes, the new mission was begun — was rising rapidly under the hands of many squads of masons, carpenters, and coolies. He watched a string of labourers, swaying along a strip of planking, bearing baskets of the finest Soochin glaze. He saw that the scale of operations was princely.

As he lingered there, with his thoughts for company, he suddenly discovered Mr. Chia at his elbow. He greeted his old friend quietly.

As they talked of the fineness of the weather and the general excellence of trade, Francis sensed more than usual kindness in the merchant's manner.

Suddenly, having appeased the proprieties, Mr. Chia guilelessly remarked: "It is pleasant to observe the excess growth of goodness, though many would consider it a superfluity. For myself I much enjoy walking in other mission gardens. Moreover, when the Father came here many years ago he received much ill-usage." A gentle and suggestive pause. "It seems highly probable, even to such an uninfluential and lowly-placed citizen as I, that the new missioners could receive such execrable treatment on their arrival that they might be most regretfully forced to depart."

A shiver passed over Father Chisholm as an unbelievable temptation assailed him. The ambiguity, the forced understatement, of
the merchant's remark was more significant than the direst threat.
Mr. Chia, in many subtle and subterranean ways, wielded the greatest power in the district. Francis knew that he need only answer,
gazing into space: "It would certainly be a great misfortune if
disaster befell the coming missioners . . . But then, who can prevent the will of heaven?" to foredoom the threatened invasion of
his pastorate. But he recoiled, abhorring himself for the thought.
Conscious of a cold perspiration on his brow, he replied as calmly
as he could: —

"There are many gates to heaven. We enter by one, these new
preachers by another. How can we deny them the right to practice
virtue in their own way? If they desire it, then they must come."

He did not observe that spark of singular regard which for
once irradiated Mr. Chia's placid eye. Still deeply disturbed, he
parted from his friend and walked homeward up the hill. He
entered the church and seated himself, for he was tired, before the
crucifix on the side altar. Gazing at the face, haloed with thorns,
he prayed, in his mind, for endurance, wisdom, and forbearance.

By the end of June the Methodist mission was near completion.
For all his fortitude, Father Chisholm had not brought himself to
view the successive stages of construction; he had sombrely avoided
the Street of the Lanterns. But when Joseph, who had not failed
as a baleful informant, brought news that the two foreign devils had
arrived, the little priest sighed, put on his one good suit, took his
tartan umbrella, and steeled himself to call.

When he rang the door bell the sound echoed emptily into the
new smell of paint and plaster. But after waiting indeterminately
for a minute under the green-glass portico, he heard hastening
steps within, and the door was opened by a small faded middle-aged
woman in a grey alpaca skirt and high-necked blouse.

"Good afternoon. I am Father Chisholm. I took the liberty of
calling to welcome you to Pai-tan."

She started nervously and a look of quick apprehension flooded her pale blue eyes.

"Oh, yes. Please come in. I am Mrs. Fiske. Wilbur . . . my husband . . . Dr. Fiske . . . he's upstairs. I'm afraid we are all alone, and not quite settled yet!" Hurriedly, she silenced his regretful protest. "No, no . . . you must step in."

He followed her upstairs to a cool, lofty room, where a man of forty, clean-shaven, with a short-cropped moustache, and of her own diminutive size, was perched on a stepladder methodically arranging books upon the shelves. He wore strong glasses over his intelligent, apologetic, short-sighted eyes. His baggy cotton knickers gave his thin little calves an indescribable pathos. Descending the ladder, he stumbled, almost fell.

"Do be careful, Wilbur!" Her hands fluttered protectively. She introduced the two men. "Now let's sit down . . . if we can." She unsuccessfully attempted a smile. "It's too bad not having our furniture . . . but then one gets used to anything in China."

They sat down. Father Chisholm said pleasantly: —

"You have a magnificent building here."

"Yes." Dr. Fiske deprecated. "We're very lucky. Mr. Chandler, the oil magnate, is most generous with us."

A strained silence. They so little fulfilled the priest's uneasy expectations, he felt taken unawares. He could not claim gigantic stature, yet the Fiskes, by the very sparseness of their physical economy, silenced the merest whisper of aggression. The little doctor was mild, with a bookish, even timid air, and a smile, deprecating, about his lips, as though afraid to settle. His wife, more clearly distinguishable in this good light, was a gentle, steadfast creature, her blue eyes easily receptive of tears, her hands alternating between her thin gold locket chain and a frizzy pad of rich, net-enclosed, brown hair which, with a slight shock, Francis perceived to be a wig.

Suddenly Dr. Fiske cleared his throat. He said, simply: "How you must hate our coming here!"

"Oh, no . . . not at all." It was the priest's turn to look awkward.

"We had the same experience once. We were up-country in the

Lan-hi province, a lovely place. I wish you'd seen our peach trees. We had it all to ourselves for nine years. Then another missionary came. Not," he inserted swiftly, "a Catholic priest. But, well . . . We did resent it, didn't we, Agnes?"

"We did, dear." She nodded tremulously. "Still . . . we got over it. We are old campaigners, Father."

"Have you been long in China?"

"Over twenty years! We came as an insanely young couple the day we were married. We have given our lives to it." The moisture in her eyes receded before a bright and eager smile. "Wilbur! I must show Father Chisholm John's photograph." She rose, proudly took a silver-framed portrait from the bare mantelpiece. "This is our boy, taken when he was at Harvard, before he went as Rhodes Scholar to Oxford. Yes, he's still in England . . . working in our dockland settlement in Tynecastle."

The name shattered his strained politeness. "Tynecastle!" He smiled. "That is very near my home."

She gazed at him, enchanted, smiling back, holding the photograph to her bosom with tender hands.

"Isn't that amazing? The world is such a small place after all." Briskly she replaced the photograph on the mantel. "Now I'm going to bring in coffee, and some of my very own doughnuts . . . a family receipt." Again she silenced his protests. "It's no trouble. I always make Wilbur take a little refreshment at this hour. He has had some bother with his duodenum. If I didn't look after him who would?"

He had meant to stay for five minutes; he remained for more than an hour.

They were New England people, natives of the town of Biddeford, in Maine, born, reared and married in the tenets of their own strict faith. As they spoke of their youth he had a swift and strangely sympathetic vision of a cold crisp countryside, of great salty rivers flowing between wands of silver birches to the misty sea, past white wooden houses amidst the wine of maples, and sumac, velvet-red in winter, a thin white steeple above the village, with bells and dark silent figures in the frosted street, following their quiet destiny.

But the Fiskes had chosen another and harder path. They had suffered. Both had almost died of cholera. During the Boxer rebellion, when many of their fellow missioners were massacred, they had spent six months in a filthy prison under daily threat of execution. Their devotion to each other, and to their son, was touching. She had, for all her tremulousness, an indomitable maternal solicitude towards her two men.

Despite her antecedents, Agnes Fiske was a pure romantic whose life was written in the host of tender souvenirs she so carefully preserved. Soon she was showing Francis a letter of her dear mother's, a quarter of a century old, with the formula for these doughnuts, and a curl from John's head worn within her locket. Upstairs in her drawer were many more such tokens: bundles of yellowing correspondence, her withered bridal bouquet, a front tooth her son had shed, the ribbon she had worn at her first Biddeford Church Social. . . .

Her health was frail and presently, once this new venture was established, she was leaving for a six months' vacation which she would spend in England with her son. Already, with an earnestness that presaged her goodwill, she pressed Father Chisholm to entrust her with any commissions he might wish executed at home.

When, at last, he took his leave, she escorted him beyond the portico, where Dr. Fiske stood, to the outer gate. Her eyes filled up with tears. "I can't tell you how relieved, how glad I am at your kindness, your friendliness in calling . . . especially for Wilbur's sake. At our last station he had such a painful experience . . . hatreds stirred up, frightful bigotry. It got so bad, latterly, when he went out to see a sick man he was struck and knocked senseless by a young brute of a . . . a missionary who accused him of stealing the man's immortal soul." She suppressed her emotion. "Let us help one another. Wilbur is such a clever doctor. Call on him any time you wish." She pressed his hand quickly and turned away.

Father Chisholm went home in a curious state of mind. For the next few days he had no news of the Fiskes. But on Saturday a batch of home-baked cookies arrived at St. Andrew's. As he took them, still warm and wrapped in the white napkin, to the children's refectory, Sister Martha scowled.

"Does she think we cannot bake here — this new woman?"

"She is trying to be kind, Martha. And we also must try."

For several months Sister Clotilde had suffered from a painful irritation of her skin. All sorts of lotions had been used, from calamine to carbolic, but without success. So distressing was the affliction, she made a special novena for a cure. The following week Father Chisholm saw her rubbing her red excoriated hands in a torment of itching. He frowned and, fighting his own reluctance, sent a note to Dr. Fiske.

The doctor arrived within half an hour, quietly examined the patient in Reverend Mother's presence, used no resounding words, praised the treatment that had been given and, having mixed a special physic to be taken internally every three hours, unobtrusively departed. In ten days the ugly rash had vanished and Sister Clotilde was a new woman. But after the first radiance she brought a troubling scruple to her confession.

"Father . . . I prayed to God so earnestly . . . and . . ."

"It was the Protestant missionary who cured you?"

"Yes, Father."

"My child . . . don't let your faith be troubled. God did answer your prayer. We are his instruments . . . every one of us." He smiled suddenly. "Don't forget what old Lao-tzŭ said — 'Religions are many, reason is one, we are all brothers.'"

That same evening as he walked in the garden Maria-Veronica said to him, almost unwillingly: —

"This American . . . he is a good doctor."

He nodded. "And a good man."

The work of the two missions marched forward without conflict. There was room for both in Pai-tan, and each was careful not to give offence. The wisdom of Father Chisholm's determination to have no rice-Christians in his flock was now apparent. Only one of his congregation betook himself to Lantern Street, and he was

returned with a brief note: "Dear Chisholm, The bearer is a bad
Catholic but would be a worse Methodist. Ever, Your friend in
the Universal God, Wilbur Fiske, M.D. *P.S.* If any of your people
need hospitalization send them along. They'll receive no dark hints
on the fallibility of the Borgias!"

The priest's heart glowed. Dear Lord, he thought, kindness and
toleration — with these two virtues how wonderful Thy earth would
be!

Fiske's accomplishments were not worn on his sleeve: he was
revealed gradually as an archeologist and Chinese scholar of the
first order. He contributed abstruse articles to the archives of obscure societies at home. His hobby was Chien-lung porcelain and
his collection of eighteenth-century *famille noire,* picked up with
unobtrusive guile, was genuinely fine. Like most small men ruled
by their wives, he loved an argument, and it was not long before
Francis and he were friends enough to debate, warily, with cunning
on both sides, and sometimes, alas, with rising heat, certain points
which separated their respective creeds. Occasionally, carried away
by the fervour of their opposite views, they parted with a certain
tightness of the lips — for the pedantic little doctor could be querulous when roused. But it soon passed.

Once, after such a disagreement, Fiske met the mission priest.
He stopped abruptly. "My dear Chisholm, I have been reflecting
on a sermon which I once heard from the lips of Dr. Elder Cummings, our eminent divine, in which he declared: 'The greatest
evil of today is the growth of the Romish Church through the
nefarious and diabolical intrigues of its priests.' I should like you to
know that since I have had the honour of your acquaintance I believe
the Reverend Cummings to have been talking through his hat."

Francis, smiling grimly, consulted his theological books and ten
days later formally bowed.

"My dear Fiske, in Cardinal Cuesta's catechism I find, plainly
printed, this illuminating phrase: 'Protestantism is an immoral
practice which blasphemes God, degrades man, and endangers
society.' I should like you to know, my dear Fiske, that even before

I had the honour of your acquaintance I considered the Cardinal unpardonable!" Raising his hat he solemnly marched off.

Neighbouring Chinese thought the "doubled-up-with-laughter small-foreign-devil Methody" had completely lost his reason.

One gusty day towards the end of October Father Chisholm met the doctor's good lady on the Manchu Bridge. Mrs. Fiske was returning from marketing, one hand holding a net bag, the other clasping her hat securely to her head.

"Goodness!" she exclaimed cheerfully. "Isn't this a gale? It does blow the dust into my hair. I shall have to shampoo it again tonight!"

Familiar now with this one eccentricity, this single blot upon a blameless soul, Francis did not smile. Upon every possible occasion she guilelessly assumed her dreadful toupee to be a perfect mane of hair. His heart went out to her for the gentle little lie.

"I hope you are all well."

She smiled, head inclined, being very careful of her hat. "I am in rude health. But Wilbur is sulking — because I am off tomorrow. He will be so lonely, poor fellow. But then you are always lonely — what a solitary life you have!" She paused. "Do tell me, now that I am going to England, if there is anything I can do for you. I am bringing Wilbur back some new winter underwear — there's no place like Britain for woollens. Shall I do the same for you?"

He shook his head, smiling; then an odd thought struck him. "If you have nothing better to do one day . . . look up a dear old aunt of mine in Tynecastle. Miss Polly Bannon is the name. Wait, I'll write down her address."

He scribbled the address with a stub of pencil on a scrap of paper torn from a package in her shopping bag. She tucked it into her glove.

"Shall I give her any message?"

"Tell her how well and happy I am . . . and what a grand place this is. Tell her I'm — next to your husband — the most important man in China."

Her eyes were bright and warm towards him. "Perhaps I shall

tell her more than you think. Women have a way of talking when they get together. Good-bye. See that you look in on Wilbur occasionally. And do take care of yourself."

She shook hands and went off, a poor weak woman with a will of iron.

He promised himself he would call on Dr. Fiske. But as the weeks slipped past he seemed never to have an hour of leisure. There was the matter of Joseph's house to be arranged, and, when the little lodge was nicely built, the marriage ceremony itself, a full nuptial mass with six of the youngest children as train-bearers. Once Joseph and his bride were suitably installed, he returned to the Liu village with Joseph's father and brothers. He had long cherished the dream of an outpost, a small secondary mission at Liu. There was talk of a great trade route being constructed through the Kwangs. At some future date he might well have a younger priest to help him, one who might operate from this new centre in the hills. He had a strange impulse to set his plans in motion by increasing the area of the village grain-fields, arranging with his friends in Liu to clear, plough and sow an additional sixty mu of arable upland.

These affairs offered a genuine excuse, yet he experienced a sharp twinge of self-reproach as, some five months later, he unexpectedly encountered Fiske. The doctor, however, was in good spirits, lit by a guarded, oddly jocose animation, which permitted only one deduction.

"Yes." He chuckled, then corrected himself to a fitting gravity. "You're quite right. Mrs. Fiske rejoins me at the beginning of next month."

"I'm glad. It has been a long journey for her to take alone."

"She was fortunate in finding a most congenial fellow-passenger."

"Your wife is a very friendly person."

"And with a great talent," Dr. Fiske seemed to suppress a preposterous tendency to giggle, "for not minding her own business. You must come and dine with us when she arrives."

Father Chisholm rarely went out, his mode of life did not permit it, but now compunction drove him to accept. "Thank you, I will."

Three weeks later he was reminded of his commitment, not altogether willingly, by a copper-plate note from the Street of the Lanterns: "Tonight, without fail, seven-thirty."

It was inconvenient, when he had arranged for vespers at seven o'clock. But he advanced the service by half an hour, sent Joseph to procure a chair, and that evening set out in formal style.

The Methodist Mission was brightly illuminated, exuding an unusual air of festivity. As he stepped out into the courtyard he hoped it would not be a large or lengthy affair. He was not anti-social, but his life had grown increasingly interior in these last years and that strain of Scots reserve, inherited from his father, had deepened into an odd guardedness towards strangers.

He was relieved, on entering the upper room, now gay with flowers and festoons of coloured paper, to find only his host and hostess, standing together on the hearth-rug, rather flushed from the warm room, like children before a party. While the doctor's thick lenses scintillated rays of welcome, Mrs. Fiske came quickly forward and took his hand.

"I am so glad to see you again, my poor neglected and misguided creature."

There was no mistaking the warmth of her greeting. She seemed quite taken out of herself. "You're happy to be back anyway. But I'm sure you've had a wonderful trip."

"Yes, yes, a wonderful trip. Our dear son is doing splendidly. How I wish he were with us tonight." She rattled on, ingenuous as a girl, her eyes bright with excitement. "Such things I have to tell you. But you'll hear . . . indeed, you'll hear . . . when our other guest comes in."

He could not prevent a questioning elevation of his brows.

"Yes, we are four tonight. A lady . . . in spite of our different viewpoints . . . now a most particular friend of mine. She is here on a visit." She stumbled, aware of his amazement, then faltered nervously. "My dear good Father, you are not to be cross with me." She faced the door and clapped her hands, in prearranged signal.

The door opened and Aunt Polly came into the room.

VIII

IN THE convent kitchen on that September day of 1914 neither Polly nor Sister Martha gave the slightest heed to the faint familiar sound of rifle-fire in the hills. While Martha cooked the dinner, using her spotless battery of copper pans, Polly stood by the window ironing a pile of linen wimples. In three months the two had become as inseparable as two brown hens in a strange farmyard. They respected each other's qualities. Martha had acclaimed Polly's crochet as the finest she had ever seen while Polly, after fingering Martha's cross-stitch, admitted her own inferior for the first time in her life. And they had, of course, a topic which never failed them.

Now, as Polly damped the linen and raised the iron expertly to her cheek to test its heat, she complained: "He is looking very poorly again." With one hand Martha put some more wood into the stove while she stirred the soup reflectively with the other. "What would one expect? He eats nothing."

"When he was a young man he had a good appetite."

The Belgian Sister shrugged her shoulders in exasperation. "He is the worst feeder of all the priests I have known. Ah! I have known some great feeders. There was our abbé at Metiers — six courses of fish in Lent. Of course I have a theory. When one eats little the stomach contracts. Thereafter it becomes impossible."

Polly shook her head in mild disagreement. "Yesterday when I took him some new baked scones he looked at them and said, 'How can one eat when thousands are hungry, within sight of this room?'"

"Bah! They are always hungry. In this country it is customary to eat grass."

"But now he says it will be worse because of all this fighting that is going on."

Sister Martha tasted the soup, her famous *pot-au-feu,* and her face registered critical approval. But as she turned to Polly she made a grimace. "There is always fighting. Just as there is always starving. We have bandits with our coffee in Pai-tan. They pop a few guns — like you hear now. Then the city buys them off and they go home. Tell me, did he eat my scones?"

"He ate one. Yes, and said it was excellent. Then he told me to give the set to Reverend Mother for our poor."

"That good Father will drive me to distraction." Though Sister Martha was, outside her kitchen, as mild as mother's milk, she scowled as if she were a creature of splendid rages. "Give, give, give! Until one's skin cracks with the strain. Shall I tell you what occurred last winter? One day in the town when it was snowing he took his coat off, his fine new coat that we sisters had made for him of best imported wool cloth, and gave it to some already half-frozen good-for-nothing. I would have let him have a tonguing, I assure you. But Mother Superior chose to correct him. He looked at her with those surprised eyes which hurt you deep inside. 'But why not? What's the use of preaching Christianity if we don't live as Christians? The great Christ would have given that beggar his coat. Why shouldn't I?' When Reverend Mother answered very crossly that the coat was a gift from us he smiled, standing there, shivering with cold. 'Then you are the good Christians — not I.' Was not that incredible? You wouldn't believe it, if like me you were brought up in a country where thrift is inculcated. Enough! Let us sit and drink our soup. If we wait until these greedy children have done we may faint for weakness."

Walking past the uncurtained window on his way back from the town Father Chisholm caught a glimpse of the two seated at their early lunch. The deep shadow of anxiety lifted momentarily from his face, his lips faintly smiled.

Despite his first premonitions, the accident of Polly's visit was an immense success; she fitted miraculously into the frame of the mission, and was enjoying herself with the same placidity that she would have displayed during a short week-end at Blackpool. Undismayed by clime or season, she would stalk silently to her seat in the kitchen garden and knit for hours among the cabbages with shoulders squared, elbows angled, and needles flashing, her mouth slightly pursed, her eyes remotely complacent, the yellow mission cat purring like mad, crouched half beneath her skirts. She was the closest crony of old Fu and became a hub round which the gloomy gardener revolved, exhibiting prodigious vegetables for her approval and prognosticating the weather with signs and baleful portents.

In her contact with the Sisters she never interfered, never assumed a privilege. Her tact was instinctive and beautiful, springing from her gift of silence, from the prosaic simplicity of her life. She had never been happier. She was realizing her cherished longing to see Francis at his missionary work, a priest of God, helped, perhaps, to the worthy end — though she would never have dreamed of voicing such a thought — by her own humble effort. The length of her stay, set primarily at two months, had been extended until January.

Her one regret, naïvely expressed, was that she had been unable to take this trip earlier in her life. Though she had served Ned hand and foot so long, his death had not freed her from responsibility. Judy remained, a constant anxiety, with her whims and giddiness, her capricious inconstancy of purpose. From her first employment with the Tynecastle Council she had passed through half a dozen secretarial positions, each acclaimed as perfect in the beginning, then presently thrown up in disgust. From a business career she had turned to pupil-teaching, but her course at the Normal College soon bored her, and she vaguely entertained the idea of entering a convent. At this stage, when twenty-seven years of age, she had suddenly discovered that her true vocation was to become a nurse and had joined the staff of the Northumberland General Hospital as a probationer. This was the circumstance which had provided Polly with her present opportunity — a freedom which, alas, seemed only momentary. Already, after four short months, the hardships of the probationer's life were discouraging Judy, and letters kept coming, full of petulance and grievance, hinting that Aunt Polly must return soon to look after her poor neglected niece.

As Francis pieced together the pattern of Polly's life at home —

gradually, for she was never garrulous — he came to see her as a saint. Yet her fixity was not that of a plaster image. She had her foibles, and her genius for the malapropos still remained. For instance, with remarkable initiative, and a loyal desire to aid Francis in his work, she had practically reconverted two errant souls, who on one of her staid excursions through Pai-tan obsequiously attached themselves to her person and her purse. It had cost Francis some trouble to rid her of Hosannah and Philomena Wang.

If only for the consolation of their daily conversations, he had reason to value this amazing woman. Now, in the trials which had suddenly confronted him, he clung to her common sense.

As he reached his house, there, awaiting him on the porch verandah, stood Sister Clotilde and Anna. He sighed. Was he never to have peace to consider the disquieting news he had received?

Clotilde's sallow face wore a nervous flush. She stood close to the girl, almost like a gaoler, restraining her with a freshly bandaged hand. Anna's eyes were dark with defiance. She also smelled of perfume.

Under his interrogating gaze Clotilde took a quick breath. "I had to ask Reverend Mother to let me bring Anna over. After all, in the basket workroom, she's under my special charge."

"Yes, Sister?" Father Chisholm forced himself to speak patiently. Sister Clotilde was quivering with hysterical indignation.

"I've put up with so much from her. Insolence and disobedience and laziness. Watching her upset the other girls. Yes, and steal! Why, even now she's reeking of Miss Bannon's Eau-de-Cologne. But this last — "

"Yes, Sister?"

Sister Clotilde reddened more deeply. It was a greater ordeal for her than for the graceless Anna.

"She's taken to going out at night. You know the place is infested with soldiers just now. She was out all last night with one of Wai-Chu's men, her bed not even slept in. And when I reasoned with her this morning, she struggled with me and bit me."

Father Chisholm turned his eyes on Anna. It seemed incredible that the little child he had held in his arms that winter night, who had come to him like a gift from heaven, should now confront him as a sulky and unruly young woman. In her teens, she was quite mature, with a full bosom, heavy eyes, and a plummy ripeness on her lips. She had always been different from the other children: uncaring, bold, never submissive. He thought: For once the copy-books are wrong — Anna has turned out no angel.

The heavy burden upon his mind made his voice mild. "Have you anything to say, Anna?"

"No."

"No, Father," Sister Clotilde hissed. Anna gave her a sullen glance of hatred.

"It seems a pity, after all we've tried to do for you, Anna, that you should repay us like this. Aren't you happy here?"

"No, I am not."

"Why?"

"I didn't ask to come to the Convent. You didn't even buy me. I came for nothing. And I am tired of praying."

"But you don't pray all the time. You've got your work."

"I don't want to make baskets."

"Then we'll find something else for you to do."

"What else? Sewing? Am I to go on sewing all my life?"

Father Chisholm forced a smile. "Of course not. When you've learned all those useful things, one of our young men will want to marry you."

She gave him a sullen sneer, which said plainly: "I want something more exciting than your nice young men."

He was silent; then he said, somewhat bitterly, for her lack of gratitude hurt him: "No one wishes to keep you against your will. But until the district is more settled you must remain. Great trouble may be coming to the town. Indeed, great trouble may be coming to the world. While you are here you are safe. But you must keep the rule. Now go with Sister and obey her. If I find that you do not I shall be very angry."

He dismissed them both, then as Clotilde turned he said: "Ask Reverend Mother to come and see me, Sister." He watched them cross the compound, then went slowly to his room. As if he had not enough to weigh him down!

Five minutes later when Maria-Veronica entered he stood at the window viewing the city below. He let her join him there, keeping silent. At last he said: "My dear friend, I have two bad pieces of news for you, and the first is that we are likely to have a war here — before the year is out."

She gazed at him calmly, waiting. He swung round and faced her. "I have just come from Mr. Chia. It is inevitable. For years the province has been dominated by Wai-Chu. As you know, he has bled the peasants to death with taxation and forced levies. If they didn't pay, their villages were destroyed — whole families slaughtered. But — brute though he is — the merchants of Pai-tan have always managed to buy him off." He paused. "Now another war lord is moving into the district — General Naian, from the lower Yangtze. He's reported to be not so bad as Wai — in fact our old friend Shon has gone over to him. But he wants Wai's province, that is, the privilege of squeezing the people there. He will march into Pai-tan. It is impossible to buy off both leaders. Only the victor can be bought off. So this time they must fight it out."

She smiled slightly. "I knew most of this before. Why are you so ominous today?"

"Perhaps because war is in the air." He gave her a queer strained glance. "Besides, it will be a bitter battle."

Her smile deepened. "Neither you nor I are afraid of a battle."

There was a silence. He glanced away. "Of course, I am thinking of ourselves, exposed here outside the city walls — if Wai attacks Pai-tan we shall be in the middle of it. But I am thinking more of the people — so poor, so helpless and so hungry. I have come to love them here with all my heart. They only beg to be left in peace, to get a simple living from the soil, to live in their homes quietly with their families. For years they've been oppressed by one tyrant. Now, because another appears on the scene, guns are being thrust into their hands, yes, into the hands of the men of our congregation, flags are being waved, the usual cries are already raised — Freedom and Liberty. Hatreds are being worked up. Then, because two dictators wish it, these poor creatures will fall upon one another. And to what purpose? After the slaughter, when the smoke and the shooting have cleared away, there will be more taxation, more oppression, a heavier yoke than before." He sighed, "Can one help feeling sad for poor mankind?"

She moved somewhat restively. "You have not a great opinion of war. Surely some wars can be just and glorious? History proves it. My family has fought in many such."

He did not answer for a long time. When at last he turned to her the lines about his eyes had deepened. He spoke slowly, heavily. "It is strange you should say that at this moment." He paused, averting his eyes. "Our little trouble here is only the echo of a greater disorder." He found it difficult, most difficult, to continue. But he forced himself on. "Mr. Chia has had word by special courier from his business associates in Sen-siang. Germany has invaded Belgium and is at war with France and Britain."

There was a short pause. Her face altered, she did not speak, but stood silent, her head immobile, unnaturally arrested.

At length he said: "The others will soon know. But we must not let it make any difference to us at the mission."

"No, we must not." She answered mechanically, as though her gaze were fixed thousands of miles away.

The first sign came some days later: a small Belgian flag, sewn hurriedly with coloured threads upon a square of silk, and placed prominently in Sister Martha's bedroom window. That same day, indeed, Martha scurried in early to the Sisters' house from the dispensary, with her new eagerness, then gave a cluck of nervous satisfaction. They had come — what she looked forward to with all her soul: the newspapers. It was the *Intelligence,* an American daily published in Shanghai, and it arrived, in batches, erratically, about once a month. Hurriedly, her fingers trembling between expectation and apprehension, she undid the wrappers at the window.

For a minute she turned the pages, hastily. Then she gave an outraged cry.

"What monsters! Oh my God, it is insupportable!" She beckoned urgently, not lifting her head, to Clotilde, who had come quickly into the room, drawn by the same magnetic force. "Look, Sister! They are in Louvain — the Cathedral is in ruins — shelled to pieces. And Metrieux — ten kilometers from my home — destroyed to the ground. Oh, dear God! Such a fine and prosperous town!"

Linked by common calamity, the two Sisters bent over the sheets, punctuating their reading with exclamations of horror.

"The very altar blown to pieces!" Martha wrung her hands. "Metrieux! I drove there with my father in the high cart when I was a little thing of seven. Such a market! We bought twelve grey geese that day . . . so fat and beautiful . . . and now . . ."

Clotilde, with dilated eyes, was reading of the battle of the Marne. "They are slaughtering our brave people. Such butchery, such vileness!"

Though Reverend Mother had entered and seated herself quietly at the table, Clotilde remained unconscious of her presence. But Martha saw her, from the corner of her eye, and Martha was beside herself.

Suffused with indignation, her voice shaking, she pointed her finger to a paragraph. "Consider this, Sister Clotilde. 'It is reliably reported that the convent of Louvain was violated by the German invaders. Unimpeachable sources confirm the fact that many innocent children have been mercilessly butchered.'"

Clotilde was pale as ivory. "In the Franco–Prussian War it was the same. They are inhuman. No wonder, in this good American journal, they already call them Huns." She hissed the word.

"I cannot allow you to speak in such terms of my people."

Clotilde spun round, supporting herself on the window frame, taken aback. But Martha was prepared.

"Your people, Reverend Mother? I would not be so proud to

own them if I were you. Brutal barbarians. Murderers of women and little children."

"The German Army is comprised of gentlemen. I do not believe that vulgar sheet. It is not true."

Martha spread her hands on her hips; her harsh peasant voice grated with resentment. "Is it true when the vulgar sheet reports the ruthless invasion of a little peaceful country by your gentlemanly army?"

Reverend Mother was paler now than Clotilde.

"Germany must have her place in the sun."

"So she kills and plunders, blows up cathedrals, and the market place I went to as a girl, because she wants the sun and the moon, the greedy swine — "

"Sister!" Dignified even in her agitation, Reverend Mother rose up. "There is such a thing as justice in this world. Germany and Austria have never had justice. And do not forget that my brother is fighting even now to forge the new Teutonic destiny. Therefore I forbid you both, as your superior, to speak any such slanders as have just defiled your lips."

There was an intolerable pause, then she turned to leave the room. As she reached the door Martha cried: "Your famous destiny isn't forged yet. The Allies will win the war."

Maria-Veronica gave her a cold and pitying smile. She went out.

The feud intensified, fanned by the stray news that filtered to the far-off mission itself under threat of war. Though the French Sister and the Belgian had never greatly liked each other, now they were linked in bosom friendship. Martha was protective towards the weaker Clotilde, solicitous for her health, dosing her troublesome cough, giving her choice pieces from every dish. Together, openly, they knitted mittens and socks to be sent to the brave *blessés*. They would talk of their beloved countries, over Reverend Mother's head, with many sighs and innuendoes — careful, oh so careful to give no offence. Then Martha with a strange significance would remark: "Let us go over a moment to pray for our intention."

Maria-Veronica endured it all with a proud silence. She, too, prayed for victory. Father Chisholm could see the three faces in a row, beatifically upturned, praying for opposing victories while he, careworn and harassed, watching Wai's forces march and countermarch amongst the hills, hearing of Naian's final mobilization, prayed for peace . . . safety for his people . . . and enough food for the children.

Presently Sister Clotilde began to teach her class the *Marseillaise*. She did it secretly, when Reverend Mother was engaged in the basket room at the other end of the mission. The class, being imitative, picked it up quickly. Then, one forenoon as Maria-Veronica came slowly across the compound, her air fatigued and noticeably constrained, there burst, through the open windows of Clotilde's class-room, to the accompaniment of a thumped piano, the full-throated blast of the French national anthem.

"Allons, enfants de la patrie . . ."

For an instant Maria-Veronica's step faltered; then her figure, which showed signs of softening, became steeled. All her fortitude was summoned to sustain her. She walked on with her head high.

One afternoon towards the end of the month, Clotilde was again in her schoolroom. The class, having given its daily rendering of the *Marseillaise*, had now concluded its catechism lesson. And Sister Clotilde, following her recently instituted custom, remarked: —

"Kneel down, dear children, and we will say a little prayer for the brave French soldiers."

The children knelt down obediently and repeated the three Hail Marys after her.

Clotilde was about to signal them to rise when, with a slight shock, she became aware of Reverend Mother standing behind her. Maria-Veronica was calm and pleasant. Gazing across Sister Clotilde's shoulder she addressed the class.

"And now, children, it is only right that you should say the same prayer for the brave German soldiers."

Clotilde turned a dirty green. Her breath seemed to choke her. "This is my class-room, Reverend Mother."

Maria-Veronica ignored her. "Come now, dear children, for the brave Germans, 'Hail Mary full of Grace . . .'"

Clotilde's breast heaved, her pale lips retracted from her narrow teeth. Convulsively, she drew back her hand and slapped her superior on the face.

There was a terrified hush. Then Clotilde burst into tears and ran sobbing from the room.

Maria-Veronica moved not a muscle. With that same agreeable smile she said to the children: —

"Sister Clotilde is unwell. You see how she knocked against me. I will finish the class. But first, children, three Hail Marys for the good German soldiers."

When the prayer concluded she seated herself, unruffled, at the high desk and opened the book.

That evening, entering the dispensary unexpectedly, Father Chisholm surprised Sister Clotilde measuring herself a liberal dose of chlorodyne. She whipped round at his step and almost dropped the full minim glass, her cheek flooded by a painful flush. The episode in the class-room had strung her to breaking pitch.

She stammered: "I take a little for my stomach. We have so much to worry us these days." He knew, from the measure and her manner, that she was using the drug as a sedative.

"I wouldn't take it too often, Sister. It contains a good deal of morphine."

When she had gone he locked the bottle in the poison cupboard. As he stood in the empty dispensary, torn by the anxiety of their danger here, weighed down by the sheer futility of that far-off, awful war, he felt a slow surge of anger at the senseless rancour of these women. He had hoped it would settle. But it had not settled. He compressed his lips in sudden resolution.

After school that day he sent for the three Sisters. He made them stand before his desk, his face unusually stern, choosing his words, almost with bitterness.

"Your behaviour at a time like this is greatly distressing me. It must cease. You have no justification for it whatsoever."

There was a short pause. Clotilde was shaking with contention. "But we have justification." She fumbled in the pocket of her robe and agitatedly thrust into his hand a much-creased, cut-out section of newsprint. "Read this, I beg of you. From a prince of the Church."

He scanned the cutting, slowly read it aloud. It was the report of a pronouncement by Cardinal Amette, from the pulpit of the Cathedral of Notre Dame in Paris. " 'Beloved Brethren, Comrades in Arms of France and her Glorious Allies, Almighty God is upon our side. God has helped us to our greatness in the past. He will help us once again in our hour of need. God stands beside our brave soldiers in the battlefield, strengthening their arms, girding them against the enemy. God protects his own. God will give us victory . . .' "

He broke off, he would go no further.

A rigid silence followed. Clotilde's head trembled with nervous triumph and Martha's face was dogged with vindication. But Maria-Veronica remained undefeated. Stiffly, from the black cloth bag she wore upon her girdle, she unfolded a neat square clipping.

"I know nothing of the prejudiced opinion of any French Cardinal. But here is the joint statement to the German people of the Archbishops of Cologne, Munich and Essen." In a cold and haughty voice she read: " 'Beloved People of the Fatherland, God is with us in this most righteous struggle which has been forced upon us. Therefore we command you in God's name to fight to the last drop of your blood for the honour and glory of our country. God knows in his wisdom and justice that we are in the right and God will give us . . .' "

"That is enough."

Francis stopped her, struggling for self-control, his soul suffused by wave upon wave of anger and despair. Here, before him, was the essence of man's malice and hypocrisy. The senselessness of life seemed suddenly to overwhelm him. Its hopelessness crushed him.

He remained with his head resting upon his hand, then in a low

voice he said: "God knows God must get sick of all this crying out
to God!"

Mastered by his emotion he rose abruptly and began to pace
the room. "I can't refute the contradictions of cardinals and archbishops with still more contradictions. I wouldn't presume to. I'm
nobody — an insignificant Scottish priest stuck in the wilds of
China on the edge of a bandit's war. But don't you see the folly
and the baseness of the whole transaction? We, the Holy Catholic
Church — yes, all the great Churches of Christendom — condone
this world war. We go further — we sanctify it. We send millions
of our faithful sons to be maimed and slaughtered, to be mangled
in their bodies and their souls, to kill and destroy one another, with
a hypocritical smile, an apostolic blessing. Die for your country
and all will be forgiven you. Patriotism! King and Emperor! From
ten thousand smug pulpits: 'Render to Cæsar the things that are
Cæsar's . . .'" He broke off, hands clenched, eyes remotely burning.
"There is no Cæsar nowadays — only financiers and statesmen who
want diamond mines in Africa and rubber in the slave-driven
Congo. Christ preached everlasting love. He preached the brotherhood of man. He did not climb the mountain and shout, 'Kill! kill!
Go forth in hatred and plunge a bayonet into thy brother's belly!'
It isn't His voice that resounds in the churches and high cathedrals
of Christendom today — but the voice of time-servers and cowards."
His lips quivered. "How in the name of the God we serve can we
come to these foreign lands, the lands we call pagan, presuming to
convert the people to a doctrine we give the lie to by our every
deed? Small wonder they jeer at us. Christianity — the religion of
lies! Of class and money and national hatreds! Of wicked wars!"
He stopped short, perspiration beading his brow, his eyes dark with
anguish. "Why doesn't the Church seize her opportunity? What
a chance to justify herself as the Living Bride of Christ! Instead of
preaching hatred and incitement, to cry, in every land, with the
tongues of her pontiff and all her priests: 'Throw down your
weapons. Thou shalt not kill. We command you *not* to fight.' Yes,
there would be persecutions and many executions. But these would

be martyrdoms — not murders. The dead would decorate, not desecrate, our altars." His voice dropped, his attitude was calmer, strangely prophetic. "The Church will suffer for its cowardice. A viper nourished in one's bosom will one day strike that bosom. To sanction the might of arms is to invite destruction. The day may come when great military forces will break loose and turn upon the Church, corrupting millions of her children, sending her down again — a timid shadow — into the Catacombs."

There was a strained stillness when he concluded. Martha and Clotilde hung their heads, as though touched, against their will. But Maria-Veronica, with something of the arrogance that marked those early days of strife, faced him with a cold clear gaze, hardened by a glint of mockery.

"That was most impressive, Father . . . worthy of these cathedrals you decry. . . . But aren't your words rather empty if you don't live up to them . . . here in Pai-tan?"

The blood rushed to his brow, then quickly ebbed. He answered without anger.

"I have solemnly forbidden every man in my congregation to fight in this wicked conflict which threatens us. I have made them swear to come with their families inside the mission gates, when trouble breaks. Whatever the consequences I shall be responsible."

All three Sisters looked at him. A faint tremor passed over Maria-Veronica's cold still face. Yet, as they filed from the room, he could see they were not reconciled. He suddenly felt a shiver of unnameable fear. He had the strange sensation that time swung suspended, balanced in fateful expectation of what might come to pass.

IX

On a Sunday morning, he was awakened by a sound which he had dreaded for many days — the dull concussion of artillery in action. He jumped up and hurried to the window. On the western hills, a few miles distant, six light field-pieces had begun to shell the city. He dressed rapidly and went downstairs. At the same moment Joseph came running from the porch.

"It has begun, Master. Last night General Naian marched into Pai-tan and the Wai forces are attacking him. Already our people are arriving at the gates."

He glanced swiftly over Joseph's shoulder. "Admit them at once."

While his servant went back to unlock the gates he hastened over to the home. The children were collected at breakfast and amazingly undisturbed. One or two of the smaller girls whimpered at the sudden distant banging. He went round the long tables, forcing himself to smile. "It is only firecrackers, children. For a few days we are going to have big ones."

The three Sisters stood apart at the head of the refectory. Maria-Veronica was calm as marble but he saw at once that Clotilde was upset. She seemed to hold herself in, and her hands were clenched in her long sleeves. Every time the guns went off she paled. Nodding toward the children, he joked expressly for her. "If only we could keep them eating all the time!"

Sister Martha cackled too quickly: "Yes, yes, then it would be easy." As Clotilde's stiff face made the effort to smile the far-off guns rolled again.

After a moment he left the refectory and pressed on to the lodge where Joseph and Fu stood at the wide-open gates. His people were pouring in with their belongings, young and old, poor humble illiterate creatures, frightened, eager for safety, the very substance of suffering mortality. His heart swelled as he thought of the sanctuary he was giving them. The good brick walls would afford them sound protection. He blessed the vanity which had made him build them high. With a queer tenderness, he watched one aged ragged dame, whose withered face bespoke a patient resignation to a long life of privation, stumble in with her bundle, establish herself quietly in a corner of the crowded compound, and painstakingly begin to cook a handful of beans in an old condensed-milk can.

At his side, Fu was imperturbable but Joseph, the valiant, showed a slight variation of his normal colour. Marriage had altered him, he was no longer a careless youth, but a husband and a father, with all the responsibilities of a man of property.

"They should hurry," he muttered restively. "We must lock and barricade the gates."

Father Chisholm put his hand on his servant's shoulder. "Only when they are all inside, Joseph."

"We are going to have trouble," Joseph answered with a shrug. "Some of our men who have come in were conscripted by Wai. He will not be pleased when he finds they prefer to be here rather than to fight."

"Nevertheless they will not fight." The priest answered firmly. "Come, now, don't be despondent. Run up our flag, while I watch at the gate."

Joseph departed, grumbling, and in a few minutes the mission flag, of pale blue silk with a deeper blue St. Andrew's cross, broke and fluttered on the flagstaff. Father Chisholm's heart gave an added bound of pride, his breast was filled with a quick elation. That flag stood for peace and goodwill to all men, a neutral flag, the flag of universal love.

When the last straggler had entered they locked the gates provisionally. At that moment Fu drew the priest's attention to the cedar grove, some three hundred yards to the left, on their own Jade hillside. In this clump of trees a long gun had unexpectedly appeared. Indistinctly, between the branches, he could see the quick movements of soldiers, in Wai green tunics, trenching and fortifying the position. Though he knew little of such matters the gun seemed a far more powerful weapon than the ordinary field-pieces now in action. And even as he gazed there came a swift flash, followed instantly by a terrifying concussion and the wild scream of the shell overhead.

The change was devastating. As the new heavy gun deafeningly pounded the city, it was answered by a Naian battery of ineffectual range. Small shells, falling short of the cedar grove, rained about the mission. One plunged into the kitchen garden, erupting a shower of earth. Immediately a cry of terror rose in the crowded compound and Francis ran to shepherd his congregation from the open into the greater safety of the church.

The noise and confusion increased. In the class-room the children were in a milling stampede. It was Reverend Mother who stemmed the panic. Calm and smiling, but shouting above the bursting shells, she drew the children round her, made them close their ears with their fingers and sing at the pitch of their lungs. When they became calmer they were herded quickly across the courtyard into the cellars of the convent. Joseph's wife and the two children were already there. It was strange to see all these small yellow faces, in the half-light, amongst stores of oil and candles and sweet potatoes, below the long shelves on which stood Sister Martha's preserves. The screaming of the shells was less down below. But from time to time there was a heavy shock, the building shook to its foundations.

While Polly remained below with the children, Martha and Clotilde scurried to fetch them lunch. Clotilde, always highly strung, was now almost out of her wits. As she crossed the compound a spent piece of metal struck her lightly on her cheek.

"Oh, God!" she cried, sinking down. "I'm killed!" Pale as death she began to make an act of contrition.

"Don't be a fool." Martha shook her fiercely by the shoulder. "Come and get these wretched brats some porridge."

Father Chisholm had been called by Joseph to the dispensary. One of the women had been slightly wounded in the hand. When the bleeding was controlled and the wound bandaged, the priest sent both Joseph and the patient over to the church, then hurried to the window, anxiously gauging the effects of the bursts, damaging puffs of débris, as the shells from the Wai gun exploded in Pai-tan. Sworn to neutrality, he could not repress a terrible desire, surging and devastating, that Wai, the unspeakable, might be defeated.

Suddenly, as he stood there, he saw a detachment of Naian soldiers strike out from the Manchu Gate. They flowed out like a stream of grey ants, perhaps two hundred of them, and began in a ragged line to mount the hill.

He watched them with a dreadful fascination. They came quickly, at first, in little sudden rushes. He could see them vividly against the untroubled green of the hillside. Bent double, each man bolted forward, carrying his rifle, for a dozen yards, then flung himself, desperately, upon the earth.

The Wai gun continued firing into the city. The grey figures drew nearer. They were crawling now, flat on their stomachs, completing their toiling ascent in that blazing sun. At a distance of a hundred paces from the cypress grove they paused, hugging the slope, for a full three minutes. Then their leader gave a sign. With a shout they jumped erect and rushed on the emplacement.

They covered half the distance rapidly. A few seconds and they would have reached their objective. Then the harsh vibration of machine guns resounded in the brilliant air.

There were three, manned and waiting, in the cypress grove. At their jarring impact the rushing grey figures seemed to stop, to fall in sheer bewilderment. Some fell forwards, others on their backs, some for a moment upon their knees, as though in prayer. They fell all ways, comically, then lay still, in the sunshine. At that, the rattling of the Maxims ceased. All was stillness, warm and quiet, until the heavy concussion of the big gun boomed again, reawakening everything to life — all but those quiet little figures on the green hillside.

Father Chisholm stood rigid, consumed by the torment of his mind. This was war. This toylike pantomime of destruction, magnified a million times, was what was happening now on the fertile plains of France. He shuddered, and prayed passionately: O Lord, let me live and die for peace.

Suddenly his haggard eye picked up a sign of movement on the hill. One of the Naian soldiers was not dead. Slowly and painfully, he was dragging himself down the slope in the direction of the mission. It was possible to observe the ebbing of his strength in the gradual slowing of his progress. Finally he came to rest, utterly spent, lying on his side, some sixty yards from the upper gate.

Francis thought, He is dead . . . this is no time for mock-heroics, if I go out there I will get a bullet in my head . . . I must not do it. But he found himself leaving the dispensary and moving towards the upper gate. He had a shamed consciousness as he opened the gate: fortunately no one was watching from the mission. He walked out into the bright sunshine upon the hillside.

His short black figure and long black shadow were shockingly obvious. If the mission windows were blank he felt many eyes upon him from the cypress grove. He dared not hurry.

The wounded soldier was breathing in sobbing gasps. Both hands were pressed weakly against his lacerated belly. His human eyes gazed back at Francis with an anguished interrogation.

Francis lifted him on his back and carried him into the mission. He propped him up while he relocked the gate. Then he pulled him gently into shelter. When he had given him a drink of water he found Maria-Veronica and told her she must prepare a cot in the dispensary.

That afternoon another unsuccessful raid was made on the gun position. And when night fell Father Chisholm and Joseph brought in five more wounded men. The dispensary assumed the appearance of a hospital.

Next morning the shelling continued without interruption. The noise was interminable. The city took severe punishment, and it looked as if a breach were being driven in the western wall. Suddenly, at the angle of the Western Gate, about a mile away, Francis saw the main body of the Wai forces bearing in upon the broken parapet. He thought with a sinking heart, They are in the city. But he could not judge.

The remainder of the day passed in a state of sick uncertainty. In the late afternoon he liberated the children from the cellar and his congregation from the church to let them have a breath of air. At least they were unharmed. As he went among them, heartening them, he buoyed himself with this simple fact.

Then, as he finished his round, he found Joseph at his side, wearing for the first time a look of unmistakable fear.

"Master, a messenger has come over from the Wai gun in the cedar grove."

At the main gate three Wai soldiers were peering between the bars while an officer, whom Father Chisholm took to be the captain of the gun crew, stood by. Without hesitation Francis unlocked the gate and went outside.

"What do you wish of me?"

The officer was short, thickset and middle-aged, with a heavy face and thick mulish lips. He breathed through his mouth, which hung open, showing his stained upper teeth. He wore the usual peaked cap and green uniform with a leather belt, bearing a green tassel. His puttees ended in a pair of broken canvas plimsols.

"General Wai favours you with several requests. In the first place you are to cease sheltering the enemy wounded."

Francis flushed sharply, nervously. "The wounded are doing no harm. They are beyond fighting."

The other took no notice of this protest. "Secondly, General Wai affords you the privilege of contributing to his commissariat. Your first donation will be eight hundred pounds of rice and all American canned goods in your storerooms."

"We are already short of food." Despite his resolution, Francis felt his temper rise; he spoke heatedly. "You cannot rob us in this fashion."

As before, the gun captain let the argument pass unheeded. He had a way of standing sideways, with his feet apart, delivering each word across his shoulder, like an insult.

"Thirdly, it is essential that you clear your compound of all whom you are protecting there. General Wai believes you are harbouring deserters from his forces. If this is so they will be shot. All other able-bodied men must enlist immediately in the Wai army."

This time Father Chisholm made no protest. He stood tense and pale, his hands clenched, his eyes blazing with indignation. The air before him vibrated on a red haze. "Suppose I refuse to comply with these most moderate solicitations?"

The obstinate face before him almost smiled. "That, I assure you, would be a mistake. I should then most reluctantly turn our gun upon you and in five minutes reduce your mission, and all within, to an inconsiderable powder."

There was a silence. The three soldiers were grimacing, making signs to some of the younger women in the compound. Francis saw the situation as cold and clear-cut as a picture etched on steel. He must yield, under threat of annihilation, to these inhuman demands. And that yielding would be but the prelude to greater and still greater demands. A dreadful sweep of anger conquered him. His mouth went dry, he kept his burning eyes on the ground.

"General Wai must realize that it will take some hours to make ready these stores for him . . . and to prepare my people . . . for their departure. How much time does he afford me?"

"Until tomorrow." The officer answered promptly. "Provided you deliver to me before midnight at my gun position a personal offering of tinned goods together with sufficient valuables to constitute a suitable present."

Again there was a silence. Francis felt a dark choking swelling of his heart. He lied in a suppressed voice: "I agree. I have no alternative. I will bring you your gift tonight."

"I commend your wisdom. I shall expect you. And I advise you not to fail."

The captain's tone held a heavy irony. He bowed to the priest, shouted a command to his men, and marched off squatly towards the cedar grove.

Francis re-entered the mission in a trembling fury. The clang of the heavy iron gate behind him set a chain of febrile echoes ringing through his brain. What a fool he had been, in his fatuous elation, to imagine he could escape this trial. He . . . the dove-like pacifist. He gritted his teeth as wave after wave of pitiless self-anger assailed him. Abruptly, he rid himself of Joseph and of the silent gathering who timidly searched his face for the answer to their fears.

Usually he took his troubles to the Church, but now he could not bow his head and tamely murmur: Lord, I will suffer and submit. He went to his room and flung himself violently into the wicker chair. His thoughts for once ran riot, without the rein of meekness or forbearance. He groaned as he thought of his pretty gospel of peace. What was to happen to his fine words now? What was to happen to them all?

Another barb struck him — the needlessness, the crass inanity of Polly's presence in the mission at such a time. Under his breath he cursed Mrs. Fiske for the interfering officiousness which had subjected his poor old aunt to this fantastic tribulation. God! He seemed to have the cares of all the world upon his bent incompetent shoulders. He jumped up. He could not, he would not, yield, weakly, to the maddening menace of Wai's threat and the deadlier menace of that gun which grew in his feverish imagination, swelled to such gigantic size it became the symbol of all wars, and of every brutal weapon built by man for the slaughter of mankind.

As he paced his room, tense and sweating, there came a mild knock at his door. Polly entered the room.

"I don't like to disturb you, Francis . . . but if you have a minute to spare. . . ." She smiled remotely, using the privilege of her affection to disturb his privacy.

"What is it, Aunt Polly?" He composed his features with a great effort. Perhaps she had further news, another message from Wai.

"I'd be glad if you'd try on this comforter, Francis. I don't want to get it too large. It should keep you nice and warm in the winter." Under his bloodshot gaze she produced a woollen Balaclava helmet she was knitting him.

He scarcely knew whether to weep or laugh. It was so like Polly. When the crack of doom resounded she would no doubt pause to offer him a cup of tea. There was nothing for it but to comply. He stood and let her fit the half-finished capote upon his head.

"It looks all right," she murmured critically. "Maybe a trifle wide about the neck." With her head on one side and her long wrinkled upper lip pursed, she counted the stitches with her bone knitting-needle. "Sixty-eight. I'll take it in four. Thank you, Francis. I hope I haven't troubled you."

Tears started to his eyes. He had an almost irresistible desire to put his head on her hard shoulder and cry brokenly, outrageously: "Aunt Polly! I'm in such a mess. What in God's name am I to do?"

As it was, he gazed at her a long time. He muttered: "Don't you worry, Polly, about the danger we're all in here?"

She smiled faintly. "Worry killed the cat. Besides . . . aren't you looking after us?"

Her ineradicable belief in him was like a breath of pure cold air. He watched her wrap up her work, skewer it with needles and, giving her competent nod, silently withdraw. Somehow, beneath her casualness, her air of commonplace, there lay a hint of deeper knowledge. He had no doubts now as to what he must do. He took his hat and coat, made his way secretly towards the lower gate.

Outside the mission the deep darkness blindfolded him. But he went down the Brilliant Green Jade road towards the city, rapidly, heedless of any obstacle.

At the Manchu Gate he was sharply halted and a lantern thrust close against his face, while the sentries scrutinized him. He had counted on being recognized — he was, after all, a familiar figure in the city — yet his luck went further still. One of the three soldiers was a follower of Shon who had worked all through the plague epidemic. The man vouched for him immediately and after a short exchange with his companions agreed to take him at once to the Lieutenant.

The streets were deserted, choked in parts with rubble and ominously silent. From the distant eastern section there came occasional bursts of firing. As the priest followed the quick padding footsteps of his guide he had a strange exhilarating sense of guilt.

Shon was in his old quarters at the cantonment, snatching a short rest, fully dressed, on that same camp bed which had been Dr. Tulloch's. He was unshaven, his puttees white with mud, and there were dark shadows of fatigue beneath his eyes. He propped himself upon his elbow as Francis entered.

"Well!" he said slowly. "I have been dreaming about you, my friend, and your excellent establishment on the hill."

He slid from the bed, turned up the lamp and sat down at the table. "You do not want some tea? No more do I. But I am glad to see you. I regret I cannot present you to General Naian. He is leading an attack on the East section . . . or perhaps executing some spies. He is a most enlightened man."

Francis sat down at the table, still in silence. He knew Shon well enough to let him talk himself out. And tonight the other had less to say than usual. He glanced guardedly at the priest. "Why don't you ask it, my friend? You are here for help which I cannot give. We should have been in your mission two days ago except that then we should merely have been blown to pieces together by that infamous Sorana."

"You mean the gun?"

"Yes, the gun," Shon answered with polite irony. "I have known it too well for a period of years . . . It came originally from a French gunboat. General Hsiah had it first. Twice I took it from him with great trouble, but each time he bought it back from my commandant. Then Wai had a concubine from Pekin who cost him twenty thousand silver dollars. She was an Armenian lady, very beautiful, named Sorana. When he ceased to regard her with affection he exchanged her to Hsiah for the gun. You saw us try to capture it yesterday. It is not possible. . . . Fortified . . . Across that open country . . . with only our *piff-paff* battery to protect us. Perhaps it is going to lose us our war . . . just when I am making a great personal advancement with General Naian."

There was a pause. The priest said stiffly: "Suppose it were possible to capture the gun?"

"No. Do not entice me." Shon shook his head with concealed bitterness. "But if ever I get near that dishonourable weapon I shall finish it for good."

"We can get very near the gun."

Shon raised his head deliberately, sounding Francis with his eyes. A glint of excitement enlivened him. He waited.

Father Chisholm leaned forward, his lips making a tight line. "This evening under threat of shelling the mission, the Wai officer who commands the gun crew ordered me to bring food and money to him before midnight . . ."

He went on, gazing at Shon, then abruptly broke off, conscious that he need say no more. For a full minute nothing was said. Shon was thinking, behind his careless brow. At last he smiled — at least the muscles of his face went through the act of smiling, but there was nothing of humour in his eyes.

"My friend, I must continue to regard you as a gift from heaven."

A cloud passed over the priest's set face. "I have forgotten about heaven tonight."

Shon nodded, not thinking of that remark. "Now listen and I will tell you what we shall do."

An hour later Francis and Shon left the cantonment and made their way through the Manchu Gate towards the mission. Shon had changed his uniform for a worn blue blouse and a pair of coolie's slacks, rolled to the knee. A flat pleated hat covered his head. On his back he carried a large sack, tightly sewn with twine. Following silently, at a distance of some three hundred paces, were twenty of his men.

Halfway up the Brilliant Green Jade road Francis touched his companion on the arm. "Now it is my turn."

"It is not heavy." Shon shifted the bundle tenderly to his other shoulder. "And I am perhaps more used to it than you."

They reached the shelter of the mission walls. No lights were showing, the outline which compassed everything he loved lay shadowy and unprotected. The silence was absolute. Suddenly, from within the lodge, he heard the melodious strike of the American chiming clock he had given Joseph for a wedding present. He counted automatically. Eleven o'clock.

Shon had given the men a final word of instruction. One of them, squatting against the wall, suppressed a cough which seemed to echo out across the hill. Shon cursed him in a violent whisper. The men were not important. It was what Shon and he must do together that mattered. He felt his friend peering at him through the silent darkness.

"You know exactly what is going to occur?"

"Yes."

"When I fire into the can of gasoline it will ignite instantly and explode the cordite. But before that, even before I raise my revolver, you must begin to move away. You must be well away. The concussion will be extreme." He paused. "Let us go if you are ready. And for the love of your Lord of Heaven keep the torch away from the sack."

Nerving himself, Francis took matches from his pocket and let the split reed flare. Then, holding it up, he stepped from the cover of the mission wall and walked openly towards the cypress grove. Shon came behind him, like a servant, bearing the sack on his back, as if groaning beneath its weight, taking care to make a noise.

The distance was not great. At the edge of the grove he halted, called out into the watchful stillness of the invisible trees: —

"I have come as requested. Take me to your leader."

There was an interval of silence; then, close behind them, a sudden movement. Francis swung round and saw two of Wai's men standing in the pool of smoky glare.

"You are expected, Bewitcher. Proceed without undue fear."

They were escorted through a formidable maze of shallow trenches and sharp-ended bamboo stakes to the centre of the grove. Here the priest's heart sharply missed a beat. Behind a breastwork of earth and cedar branches, the crew dispersed in attitudes of care beside it, stood the long-muzzled gun.

"Have you brought all that was demanded of you?"

Francis recognized the voice of his visitor earlier that evening. He lied more readily this time.

"I have brought a great load of tinned goods . . . which will certainly please you."

Shon exhibited the sack, moving nearer, a trifle nearer, to the gun.

"It is not so great a load." The captain of the gun crew stepped into the light. "Have you brought money also?"

"Yes."

"Where is it?" The captain felt the neck of the sack.

"Not there." Francis spoke hurriedly, with a start. "I have the money in my purse."

The captain gazed at him, diverted from his examination of the sack, his expression lit by a sudden cupidity. A group of soldiers had collected, their staring faces all bent upon the priest.

"Listen, all of you." Francis held their attention, with a desperate intensity. He could see Shon edging imperceptibly into the fringe of shadow, closer, still closer to the gun. "I ask you — I beg you — to leave us unmolested in the mission."

Contempt showed in the captain's face. He smiled derisively. "You shall be unmolested . . . until tomorrow." Someone laughed in the background. "Then we shall protect your women."

Francis hardened his heart. Shon, as though exhausted, had unloaded the sack under the breech of the gun. Pretending to wipe the perspiration from his brow he came back a little towards the priest. The crowd of soldiers had increased and were growing impatient. Francis strove to gain one minute of extra time for Shon.

"I do not doubt your word but I should value some assurance from General Wai."

"General Wai is in the city. You will see him later."

The captain spoke curtly and stepped out to get the money. From the corner of his eye, Francis saw Shon's hand go beneath his blouse. It is coming now, he thought. In the same moment, he heard the loud report of the revolver shot and the impact of the bullet as it struck the oil tin inside the sack. Braced for the convulsion, he could not understand. There was no explosion. Shon in swift succession fired three further shots into the tin. Francis saw the gasoline flood all over the sacking. He thought, with a kind of sick disillusionment yet quicker than the thudding shots: Shon was mistaken, the bullets won't ignite the gasoline, or perhaps it is only kerosene they put inside the tin. He saw Shon shooting into the crowd now, struggling to free his gun, shouting hopelessly to his own men to rush in. He saw the captain and a dozen soldiers closing on him. It all happened as swiftly as his thought. He felt a final, devastating wave of anger and despair. Deliberately, as though casting with a salmon rod, he drew back his arm and threw his torch.

His accuracy was beautiful. The blazing flare arched like a comet through the night and hit the oil-soaked sacking squarely in the centre. Instantly a great sheet of sound and light struck at him. He no more than sensed the brilliant flash when the earth erupted and amidst a frightful detonation a blast of scorching air blew him backwards into crashing darkness. He had never lost consciousness before. He seemed falling, falling, into space and blackness, clutching for support and finding none, falling to annihilation, to oblivion.

When his senses returned he found himself stretched in the open, limp but unhurt, with Shon pulling his ear-lobes to bring him round. Dimly he saw the red sky above him. The whole cypress grove was ablaze, crackling and roaring like a pyre.

"Is the gun finished?"

Shon stopped the ear-tweaking and sat up, relieved.

"Yes, it is finished. And some thirty of Wai's soldiers blown to pieces with it." His teeth showed white in his scorched face. "My friend, I congratulate you. I have never seen such a lovely killing in my life. Another such and you may have me for a Christian."

The next few days brought a terrible confusion of mind and spirit to Father Chisholm. The physical reaction to his adventure almost prostrated him. He was no virile hero of romantic fiction but a stubby, short-winded little man well over forty. He felt shaken and dizzy. His head ached so persistently he had to drag himself to his room several times a day to plunge his splitting brow in the tepid water of his ewer. And through this bodily suffering ran the greater anguish of his soul, a chaotic mixture of triumph and remorse, a heavy and relentless wonder that he, a priest of God, should have raised his hand to slay his fellow men. He could barely find self-vindication in the safety of his people. His strangest torment lay in the stabbing recollection of his own unconsciousness under the shock of the explosion. Was death like that? A total oblivion . . .

No one but Polly suspected that he had left the mission grounds that night. He could feel her tranquil gaze travelling from his own silent and diminished form to the charred cedar stumps which marked the remnants of the gun emplacement. There was infinite understanding in the banal phrase she spoke to him: —

"Somebody has done us a good turn by getting that nuisance out of the way."

Fighting continued in the outskirts of the city and in the hills to the eastward. By the fourth day reports reaching the mission indicated that the struggle was turning against Wai.

The end of that week came grey and overcast, with heavy gathering clouds. On Saturday the firing in Pai-tan dwindled to a few spasmodic rattles. Watching from his balcony Father Chisholm saw strings of figures in the Wai green retreating from the Western Gate. Many of these had thrown away their arms in the fear of being captured and shot as rebels. This Francis knew to be an indication of Wai's reverses and of his inability to effect a compromise with General Naian.

Outside the mission, behind the upper wall where some bamboo canes screened them from observation from the city, a number of these scattered soldiers had collected. Their voices, indeterminate and plainly frightened, could be heard inside the mission.

Towards three o'clock in the afternoon Sister Clotilde came with renewed agitation to Father Chisholm as he paced the courtyard, too disturbed to rest.

"Anna is throwing food over the upper wall." She wailed out the complaint. "I am sure her soldier is there . . . they were talking together."

His own nerves were near to breaking point. "There is no harm in giving food to those who need it."

"But he is one of those dreadful cut-throats. Oh, dear, we shall all be murdered in our beds!"

"Don't think so much about your own throat." He flushed with annoyance. "Martyrdom is an easy way to heaven."

As twilight fell, masses of the beaten Wai forces poured from all the city gates. They came by the Manchu Bridge, swarming up the Brilliant Green Jade road past the mission, in great confusion. The dirty faces of the men were stamped with the urgency of flight.

The night that followed was one of darkness and disorder, filled with shouting and shots, with galloping horses and the flare of torches on the far-off plain below. The priest watched with a strange melancholy from the lower mission gate. Suddenly, as he stood there, he heard a cautious step behind him. He turned. As he had half-expected, it was Anna, her mission coat buttoned closely to her chin, a cloth-wrapped bundle in her hand.

"Where are you going, Anna?"

She drew back with a stifled cry, but immediately regained her sullen boldness.

"It is my own affair."

"You will not tell me?"

"No."

His mood had fallen to quieter key, his attitude was changed. What was the use of more compulsion here?

"You have made up your mind to leave us, Anna. That is evident. And nothing that I can say or do will change it."

She said bitterly: "You have caught me now. But the next time you will not do so."

"There need be no next time, Anna." He took the key from his pocket and unlocked the gate. "You are free to go."

He could feel her start in sheer amazement, feel the impact of those full sultry eyes. Then without a word of gratitude or farewell she gripped her bundle and darted through the opening. Her running form was lost in the crowded roadway.

He stood, bare-headed, while the rabble swept past him. Now the exodus had turned to a rout. Suddenly there was a louder shouting, and he saw in the bobbing glare of upheld torches a group of men on horses. They approached rapidly, beating their way through the slow unmounted stream that hindered them. As they reached the gate one of the riders wrenched his lathered pony to a stop. In the torchlight the priest had a vision of incredible evil, a death's-head face, with narrowed slits of eyes, and a low receding brow. The horseman shouted at him, an insult charged with hatred, then raised his hand with immediate deadly menace. Francis did not move. His perfect immobility, uncaring and resigned, seemed to disconcert the other. While he hesitated for an instant a pressing cry was raised from behind. "On, on, Wai . . . to Tou-en-lai . . . they are coming!"

Wai dropped his hand, holding the weapon, with a queer fatalism. As he spurred his beast forward he bent in the saddle and spat venomously in the priest's face. The night enclosed him.

Next morning, which dawned bright and sunny, the mission bells were ringing gaily. Fu, of his own accord, had clambered to the tower. He swung on the long rope, his thin beard wagging with delight. Most of the refugees were ready to go home, their faces jubilant, waiting only to have the mission Father's word before departing. All the children were in the compound, laughing and skipping, watched by Martha and Maria-Veronica, who had patched up their differences sufficiently to stand no more than six feet apart.

Even Clotilde was playing, the gayest of all, bouncing a ball, running with the little ones, giggling. Polly, upright in her favourite place in the vegetable garden, sat winding a new skein of wool as though life were nothing but a round of calm normality.

When Father Chisholm came slowly down the steps of his house Joseph met him joyfully, carrying his chubby infant on his arm. "It is over, Master. Victory for the Naians. The new general is truly great. No more war in Pai-tan. He promises it. Peace for all of us in our time." He bounced the baby tenderly, triumphantly. "No fighting for you my little Joshua, no more tears and blood. Peace! Peace!"

Inexplicably, a shaft of utter sadness pierced the priest's heart. He took the babe's tiny cheek, soft and golden, between his thumb and finger, caressingly. He stifled his sigh and smiled. They were

all running towards him, his children, his people whom he loved
— whom, at the cost of his dearest principle, he had saved.

X

THE end of January brought the first glorious fruits of victory to
Pai-tan. And Francis felt relief that Aunt Polly was spared the
sight of them. She had departed for England the week before, and
although the parting had been difficult he knew in his heart that it
was wiser for her to go.

This morning as he crossed to the dispensary he speculated on
the length of the rice line. Yesterday it had stretched the whole
length of the mission wall. Wai, in the fury of defeat, had burned
every stalk of grain for miles around. The sweet potato crop was
poor. The rice fields, tended only by the women, with men and
water-oxen commandeered by the army, had produced less than
half the usual yield. Everything was scarce and costly. In the city,
the value of tinned goods had multiplied five times. Prices were
soaring daily.

He hastened into the crowded building. All three Sisters were
there, each with a wooden measure and a black japanned bin of
rice, engaged in the interminable task of scooping three ounces of
the grain, running it into the proffered bowls.

He stood watching. His people were patient, quite silent. But the
motion of the dry kernels made a constant hissing in the room. He
said in a low voice to Maria-Veronica: "We can't keep this up. Tomorrow we must cut the allowance in half."

"Very well." She made a gesture of acquiescence. The strain
of the past weeks had taken toll of her, he thought her unusually
pale. She kept her eyes on the bin.

He went to the outer door, once or twice, counting the numbers.
At last, to his relief, the line began to thin. He recrossed the compound, and descended to the store cellars, recasting the inventory of
their supplies. Fortunately he had placed an order with Mr. Chia

two months ago and it had been faithfully delivered. But the stock of rice and sweet potatoes, which they used in great quantity, was dangerously low.

He stood thinking. Though prices were exorbitant, food could still be purchased in Pai-tan. He took a sudden resolution and decided, for the first time in the mission's history, to cable the Society for an emergency grant.

A week later he received the answering cable: —

Quite impossible allocate any monies. Kindly remember we are at war. You are not and therefore extremely lucky. Am immersed Red Cross work. Best regards Anselm Mealey.

Francis crumpled the green slip with an expressionless face. That afternoon he mustered all the available financial resources of the mission and went to the town. But now it was too late — he could buy nothing. The grain market was closed. The principal shops showed only a minimum of perishable produce: some melons, radishes, and small-river fish.

Disturbed, he stopped at the Lantern Street mission, where he had a long conversation with Dr. Fiske. Then, on his way back, he visited Mr. Chia's house.

Mr. Chia made Francis welcome. They drank tea together in the latticed little office, smelling of spice and musk and cedar.

"Yes," Mr. Chia agreed gravely, when they had fully discussed the shortage. "It is a matter of some small concern. Mr. Pao has gone to Chek-kow to endeavour to procure certain assurances from the new government."

"With some chance of success?"

"With every chance." The mandarin added, with the nearest approach to cynicism Father Chisholm had heard from him: "But assurances are not supplies."

"It was reported that the granary held many tons of reserve grain."

"General Naian took every bushel for himself. He has gutted the city of food."

"But surely," the mission Father spoke frowningly, "he cannot see the people starve. He promised them great benefit if they fought for him."

"Now he has mildly expressed the belief that some slight depopulation might benefit the community."

There was a silence. Father Chisholm reflected. "At least it is a blessing that Dr. Fiske will have large supplies. He is promised three full junkloads from his headquarters in Pekin."

"Ah!"

Again the silence.

"You are dubious?"

Mr. Chia responded with his gentle smile. "It is two thousand li from Pekin to Pai-tan. And there are many hungry people on the way. In my unworthy opinion, my most esteemed friend, we must prepare for six months of greatest hardship. These things come to China. But what matter? We may go. China remains."

Next morning Father Chisholm was obliged to turn back the rice line. It cut him to the heart to do so, yet he had to close the doors. He instructed Joseph to paint a notice that cases of utter destitution might leave their names at the lodge. He would investigate them personally.

Back in his house he set himself to work out a plan for rationing the mission. And the following week he introduced it. As the scheme began to operate the children wondered, then passed through fretfulness into a kind of puzzled dullness. They were lethargic and they asked for more at every meal. The insufficiency of sugar and starchy stuffs seemed to cause them most discomfort. They were losing weight.

From the Methodist mission came no word of the relief stores. The junks were now nearly three weeks overdue, and Dr. Fiske's anxiety was too significant to be mistaken. His public rice-kitchen had been closed for more than a month. In Pai-tan the people had a sluggish air, a heavy apathy. There was no light upon their faces, no briskness in their movements.

Then it began and gradually gathered strength: the timeless transmigration, old as China itself, the silent departure of men and women with their children from the city towards the South.

When Father Chisholm saw this symptom his heart chilled. A horrible vision attacked him of his little community, emaciated, relaxed in the final debility of starvation. He drew the lesson, swiftly, from the slow procession now beginning before his eyes.

As in the days of plague, he summoned Joseph to him, spoke to him and sped him upon an urgent errand.

On the morning following Joseph's departure he came over to the refectory and ordered an extra portion of rice to be given to the children. One last box of figs remained in the larder. He went down the long table giving each child a sweet sticky mouthful.

This sign of better feeding made the community more cheerful. But Martha, with one eye on the almost empty store-cellar and the other upon Father Chisholm, muttered her perplexity.

"What is in the wind, Father? There's something . . . I'm sure."

"You shall know on Saturday, Martha. Meanwhile, please tell Reverend Mother we shall continue on the extra rice for the remainder of this week."

Martha went off to do his bidding but could not find Reverend Mother anywhere. It was strange.

All that afternoon Maria-Veronica did not appear. She failed to take her weaving class, which was always held on Wednesdays, in the basket room. At three o'clock she could not be found. Perhaps it was an oversight. Shortly after five, she came in for refectory duty as usual, pale and composed, offering no explanation of her absence. But that night in the convent both Clotilde and Martha were awakened by a startling sound which came, unmistakably, from Maria-Veronica's room.

Appalled, they talked of it next morning in whispers, in the corner of the laundry, watching Reverend Mother through the window as she crossed the courtyard, dignified and upright, yet much slower than before.

"She has broken at last." Martha's words seemed constricted in her throat. "Blessed Virgin, did you hear her weep last night?"

Clotilde stood twisting an end of linen in her hands. "Perhaps she has news of a great German defeat we have not heard of yet."

"Yes, yes . . . it is something terrible." Martha's face suddenly puckered up. "Truly, if she were not an accursed Boche I would feel almost sorry for her."

"I have never known her to weep before." Clotilde meditated, her fingers twisting indecisively. "She is a proud woman. That must make it doubly hard."

"Pride goeth before a fall. Would she have had sympathy for us if we had yielded first? Nevertheless I must admit — Bah! Let us continue with our ironing."

Early on Sunday morning a small cavalcade approached the mission, winding downwards from the mountains. Advised by Joseph of its arrival, Father Chisholm hastened to the lodge to welcome Liu-Chi and his three companions from the Liu village. He clasped the old shepherd's hands as though he would never let them go.

"This is true kindness. The good God will bless you for it."

Liu-Chi smiled, naïvely pleased by the warmth of his reception. "We would have come sooner. But we took much time to collect the ponies."

There were perhaps thirty of the short shaggy uplands ponies, bridled but unsaddled, with big double panniers strapped upon their backs. They were contentedly munching the swathes of dried grass strewn for them. The priest's heart lifted. He pressed the four men to the refreshments which Joseph's wife had already prepared in the lodge, told them they must rest when they had eaten.

He found Reverend Mother in the linen room silently passing out fresh white bundles of the week's requirements: tablecovers, sheets and towels, to Martha, Clotilde and one of the senior students. He no longer attempted to conceal his satisfaction.

"I must prepare you for a change. Because of the threat of famine we are moving to the Liu village. You'll find plenty there, I assure you." He smiled. "Sister Martha, you'll find many ways of cooking mountain mutton before you return. I know you will enjoy the experience. And for the children . . . it will be a fine holiday."

There was a moment's sheer surprise. Then Martha and Clotilde both smiled, conscious of a coming break in the monotony of life, already stirring to the excitement of the adventure.

"Doubtless you will expect us to be organized in five minutes," Martha grumbled amiably, casting her eye instructively, for the first time in many weeks, upon Reverend Mother, as if for her approval.

It was the first faint gesture of atonement. But Maria-Veronica, standing by, with a colourless face, gave no answering sign.

"Yes, you must look sharp." Father Chisholm spoke almost gaily. "The little ones will be packed into the panniers. The others must take turns of walking and riding. The nights are warm and fine. Liu-Chi will look after you. If you leave today you should reach the village in a week."

Clotilde giggled. "We shall be like one of the tribes of Egypt."

The priest nodded. "I am giving Joseph a basket of my fantails. Every evening he must release one to bring me a message of your progress."

"What!" Martha and Clotilde exclaimed together. "You are not coming with us?"

"I may follow at a later date." Francis felt happy that they should want him. "You see, someone must remain at the mission. Reverend Mother and you two will be the pioneers."

Maria-Veronica said slowly: "I cannot go."

There was a silence.

At first he thought it a continuation of her pique, a disinclination to accompany the other two, but one glance at her face told him otherwise.

He said persuasively: "It will be a pleasant trip. The change would do you good."

She shook her head slowly. "I shall be obliged to take a longer trip . . . quite soon."

There was a longer pause. Then standing very still, she spoke with a toneless lack of emotion. "I must return to Germany . . . to see about the disposal . . . to our order . . . of my estate." She gazed into the distance. "My brother has been killed in action."

The previous silence had been deep, but now there was a mortal stillness. It was Clotilde who burst into violent tears. Then Martha, as though trapped, like an animal, hung her head unwillingly, in sympathy. Father Chisholm glanced from one to the other in deep distress, then walked silently away.

A fortnight after the party had arrived at Liu the day of Maria-Veronica's departure was, incredibly, upon him. The latest information from the village, received by pigeon post, indicated that the children were primitively yet comfortably billeted, and wild with health in the keen high air. Father Chisholm had good reason to congratulate himself upon his own resourcefulness. Yet as he walked beside Maria-Veronica to the landing steps, preceded by two bearers with long poles, supporting her baggage upon their shoulders, he felt a desperate forlornness.

They stood on the jetty while the men placed the bundles in the sampan. Behind them the city lay, murmuring in still dejection. Before them, in mid-river, lay the outgoing junk. The dun water which lapped its hull reached out to a grey horizon.

He could find no words to express himself. She had meant so much to him, this gracious and distinguished woman, with her help, encouragement, and comradeship. The future had stretched before them, indefinitely, a future filled with their work together. Now she was going, unexpectedly, almost furtively, it seemed, in a haze of darkness and confusion.

He sighed, at last, giving her his troubled smile. "Even if my country remains at war with yours . . . remember . . . I am not your enemy."

The understatement was so like him, and all that she admired in him, it shook her determination to be strong. As she gazed at his spare figure, gaunt face and thinning hair, tears clouded her beautiful eyes.

"My dear . . . dear friend . . . I will never forget you."

She gave him her warm firm clasp and stepped quickly into the little craft which would take her to the junk.

He stood there, leaning on his old tartan umbrella, his eyes screwed against the water's glitter, until the vessel was a speck, float-ing, vanishing beyond the rim of the sky.

Unknown to her, he had placed amongst her baggage the little antique figure of the Spanish Virgin which Father Tarrant had given him. It was his sole possession of any value. She had often admired it.

He turned and slowly plodded home. In the garden which she had made and loved so much, he paused, grateful for the silence and the peace there. The scent of lilies was in the air. Old Fu, the gardener, his sole companion in the deserted mission, was pruning the azalea bushes with gentle, inquiring hands. He felt worn-out by all that he had lately undergone. A chapter in his life was ended; for the first time, he dimly sensed that he was growing old. He seated himself on the bench beneath the banyan tree, rested his elbows on the pinewood table she had placed there. Old Fu, prun-ing the azaleas, pretended not to see him as, after a moment, he laid his head upon his arms.

XI

THE broad leaves of the banyan tree still shaded him as he sat at the garden table turning the pages of his journal with hands which, as by some strange illusion, were veined and vaguely tremulous. Of course, old Fu no longer watched him, unless through a chink of heaven. Instead, two young gardeners bent by the azalea bed while Father Chou, his Chinese priest, small, gentle and demure, pacing with his breviary at a respectful distance, kept a warm brown filial eye upon him.

In the August sunshine the mission compound was aquiver with dry light, like the sparkle of a golden wine. From the playground the happy shouts of the children at their playtime told him the fore-noon hour: eleven o'clock. His children, or rather, he corrected him-self wryly, his children's children . . . How unfairly time had flashed across him, tumbling the years into his lap, one upon an-other, too fast for him to marshal them.

A jolly red face, plump and smiling, swam into his abstracted vision, above a tumblerful of milk. He forced a frown as Mother Mercy Mary drew near, annoyed to be reminded of his age by another of her coddling tricks. He was only sixty-seven . . . well, sixty-eight next month . . . a mere nothing . . . and fitter than any youngster.

"Haven't I told you not to bring me that stuff?"

She smiled soothingly — vigorous, bustling, and matronly. "You need it today, Father, if you will insist on taking that long unnecessary trip." She paused. "I don't see why Father Chou and Dr. Fiske couldn't go themselves?"

"Don't you?"

"No, indeed."

"Dear Sister, that's too bad. Your mind must be breaking up." She laughed indulgently and tried to coax him.

"Shall I tell Joshua you've decided not to go?"

"Tell him to have the ponies saddled in an hour."

He saw her depart, shaking her head reproachfully. He smiled again, with the dry triumph of a man who has had his way. Then, sipping his milk, without, now that she was gone, the necessity of a grimace, he resumed his leisured perusal of the diary before him. It was a habit into which he had lately fallen, a kind of wilful retrospection, evoked by turning the frayed and dog-eared pages at random.

This morning it opened, strangely, first at the date *October 1917*.

"Despite the improving conditions in Pai-tan, the good rice crop and the safe homecoming of my little ones from Liu, I have been downcast lately; yet today a simple incident gave me preposterous happiness.

"I had been away for four days at the annual conference which the Prefect Apostolic has thought fit to institute at Sen-siang. As the farthest outpost of the Vicariate I had fancied myself immune from such junketings. Indeed, we missioners are so widely scattered and so few — only Father Surette, poor Thibodeau's successor, the three

Chek-kow Chinese priests and Father Van Dwyn the Dutchman from Rakai — that the occasion seemed scarcely worth the long river journey. But there we were 'exchanging viewpoints.' And naturally I talked indiscreetly against 'aggressive Christianizing methods,' got hot under the collar and quoted Mr. Pao's cousin: 'You missionaries walk in with your Gospel and walk off with our land.' I fell into disgrace with Father Surette, a bustling Father who rejoices in his muscles, which he has used to destroy all the pleasant little Buddhist wayside shrines within twenty li of Sen-siang, and who in addition claims the amazing record of 50,000 pious ejaculations in one day.

"On my return trip I was overcome with remorse. How often have I had to write in this journal: 'Failed again. Dear Lord, help me restrain my tongue!' And they thought me such a queer fish at Sen-siang!

"To mortify myself I had dispensed with a cabin on the boat. Next to me on deck was a man with a cage of prime rats which he dined on, progressively, under my jaundiced eye. In addition it rained hard, blew down streams and I was, as I deserved to be, extremely sick.

"Then, as I stepped off the vessel at Pai-tan, more dead than alive, I found an old woman waiting for me on the drenched, deserted jetty. As she approached I saw her to be my friend, old mother Hsu, she who cooked beans in the milk-can in the compound. She is the poorest, the lowest person in my parish.

"To my amazement her face was illuminated at the sight of me. Quickly she told me she had missed me so much she had stood there in the rain these past three afternoons, waiting my arrival. She produced six little ceremonial cakes of rice flour and sugar, not for eating — the kind they place before the images of Buddha — the same images that Father Surette knocks down. A comic gesture . . . But the joy of knowing that to one person at least one is dear . . . and indispensable . . .

"*May 1918.* This lovely morning my first batch of young settlers departed for Liu, twenty-four in all, — I might discreetly add, twelve of each kind, — amidst great enthusiasm and many knowing nods and practical admonitions from our good Reverend Mother Mercy Mary. Though I resented her coming intensely — weighing her sulkily against the memory of Maria-Veronica — she is a fine, capable, cheerful person, and for a holy nun she has an amazing insight into the exigencies of the marriage bed.

"Old Meg Paxton, the Cannelgate fishwife, used to reassure me that I wasn't such a fool as I looked; and I'm quite proud of my inspiration to colonize Liu — with the finest produce of this mission of St. Andrew's. There simply aren't enough jobs here for my growing-up young people. It would seem the worst kind of stupidity, having pulled them out of the gutter, to throw them back again, benevolently, now they are educated. And Liu itself will profit by an infusion of fresh blood. There is ample land, a stirring climate. Once the numbers are adequate I shall establish a young priest there. Anselm must send me one, until he does so I shall deafen him with my importunities. . . .

"I am tired tonight from the excitement and the ceremonies — these mass marriages are no joke, and Chinese ceremonial oratory leaves the vocal cords in ruins. Perhaps my depression is reactionary, perhaps physical. I do need a holiday quite badly, I am a little stale. The Fiskes have gone off for their routine six months' rest, to visit their son, now established in Virginia. I miss them. Their relief, the Reverend Ezra Salkins, makes me realize how fortunate I am to have such sweet and gentle neighbours. Shang-Foo Ezra is neither — a big man with a fixed beam, a Rotarian handshake, and a smile like melting lard. He boomed at me as he cracked my finger-bones: 'Anything I can do to help you, brother, anything at all.'"

The Fiskes would be my honoured guests at Liu. But to Ezra I am dumb. In just sixty seconds he would have Father Ribiero's tomb plastered with bill-heads: *Brother are you saved?* Oh, blow! I am crabbed and sour, it's that plum pie Mercy Mary made me eat at the wedding breakfast. . . .

"I have been made truly happy by a long letter dated June 10th, 1922 from Mother Maria-Veronica. After many vicissitudes, the trials of the war and the humiliations of the armistice, she has at last been rewarded by her appointment as Superior of the Sistine Convent in Rome. This is the mother house of her order, a fine old foundation on the high slopes between the Corso and the Quirinal overlooking the Saporelli and the lovely church of Santi Apostoli. It is an office of the first importance but no more than she deserves. She seems contented . . . at peace. Her letter brings me such a fragrance of the Holy City — that might be one of Anselm's phrases! — always the object of my tender longings, I have dared to make a plan. When my sick-leave, already twice postponed, does arrive, what is to prevent my visiting Rome, wearing my boots out on the mosaics of St. Peter's, and seeing Mother Maria-Veronica in the bargain? When I wrote in April congratulating Anselm on his appointment as Rector of the Tynecastle Cathedral Church he assured me, in his reply, that I should have an assistant priest within six months and my 'much-needed vacation' before the year was out.

"An absurd thrill pervades my sun-bleached bones when I think that such happiness may be in store for me. Enough! I must start to save to buy myself a suit of clothes. What would the good Abbess of Santi Apostoli think if the little bricklayer who claimed her acquaintance turned out to have a patch on the backside of his pants. . . .

"*September 17th, 1923.* Breathless excitement! Today, my new priest arrived, at last I have a colleague, and it seems almost too good to be true.

"Although, at first, Anselm's voluminous hieratics gave me hope of a stout young Scot, preferably with freckles and sandy hair, later advices had prepared me for a native Father from the College at Pekin. It was like my perverted humour to tell the Sisters nothing of the coming dénouement. For weeks they had been gathering themselves to coddle the young missioner from home — Clotilde and Martha wanted something Gallic with a beard, but poor Mother Mercy Mary had made a very special novena for an Irish one. The look on her honest Hibernian face as she burst into my room, purple with tragedy! 'The new Father is a Chinese!'

"But Father Chou seems a splendid little fellow, not only quiet and amiable, but conveying a deep sense of that extraordinary interior life which is such an admirable characteristic of the Chinese. I have met several native priests on my infrequent pilgrimages to Sen-siang and I have always been impressed. If I wished to be pompous I should say that the good ones appear to combine the wisdom of Confucius with the virtue of Christ.

"And now I am off to Rome, next month . . . my first holiday in nineteen years. I am like a Holywell schoolboy, at the end of term, banging his desk and chanting: —

> 'Two more weeks and I shall be,
> Outside the gates of mis-er-ee.'

"I wonder if Mother Maria-Veronica has lost her taste for fine stem ginger. I shall take her a jar and risk being told she has turned to macaroni. Heigh-ho! This life is most jolly. Through my window I see the young cedars swaying in the wind with a wild joy. I must write now to Shanghai for my tickets. Hurrah!

"*October 1923.* Yesterday the cable came cancelling my trip to Rome and I have just returned from my evening walk by the riverbank where I stood a long time in a soft mist watching the cormorant fishers. It is a sad way of catching fish, or perhaps I had a sad way of looking at it. The great birds are ringed by the neck to prevent their swallowing the fish. They crouch indolently on the gunwale of the boat as though dreadfully bored with the whole proceeding. Suddenly there is a dip and a splutter and up comes the great bill, pouched with fish, a tail wriggling at the tip. An embarrassing undulation of the neck follows next. When relieved of their catch the birds shake their heads, disconsolate, yet as though experience had taught them nothing. Then they squat again, brooding blackly, recuperating for a fresh defeat.

"My own mood was dark and defeated enough, God knows. As I

stood by the slaty water, from which the night wind threw waves upon the weed coiled like hair upon the shore, my thoughts, strangely, were not of Rome but of the streams of Tweedside, with myself, barefoot in the rippling crystal, casting a withy rod for trout.

"More and more of late I find myself living in the memory of my childhood, recollected so vividly it might be yesterday — a sure symptom of approaching age! . . . I even dream, tenderly, wistfully — isn't this unbelievable? — of my boyish love: my own dear Nora.

"You see, I have reached the sentimental stage of disappointment, which is next to getting over it, but when the telegram arrived, in old Meg's words, 'it was hard to thole.'

"Now I am almost resigned to the utter finality of my exile. The principle is probably correct that a return to Europe unsettles the missionary priest. After all, we give ourselves entirely, there is no retreat. I am here for life. And I'll lay myself, at last, in that little piece of Scotland where Willie Tulloch rests.

"Moreover, it is certainly logical and just that Anselm's trip to Rome is more necessary than mine. The funds of the Society cannot sustain two such excursions. And he can better tell the Holy Father of the advances of 'his troops' — as he calls us. Where my tongue would be stiff and clumsy his will captivate — garner funds and support for all the F. S. missions. He has promised to write me fully of his doings. I must enjoy Rome vicariously, have my audience in imagination, meet Maria-Veronica in spirit. I could not bring myself to accept Anselm's suggestion of a short vacation in Manila. Its gaiety would have troubled me, I should have laughed at the solitary little man, poking round the harbour, fancying himself on the Pontine Hill. . . .

"*A month later.* . . . Father Chou is nicely established in the Liu village and our pigeons pass one another at celestial speed. What a joy that my scheme is working so beautifully. I wonder if Anselm will mention it, perhaps, when he sees the Holy Father, just a word of that tiny jewel, set in the great wilderness, once forgotten . . . by all but God. . . .

"*22d November, 1928.* How can one compass a sublime experience in mere words — in one bald and arid phrase? Last night Sister Clotilde died. Death is a topic I have not often dwelt upon in this sketchy record of my own imperfect life.

"Thus, twelve months ago when Aunt Polly passed away in her sleep at Tynecastle, uneventfully and of pure goodness and old age, and the news reached me in Judy's tear-smudged letter, I made no comment here beyond the simple entry: '*Polly died, 17th October, 1927.*' There is an inevitability in the death of those whom we know to be good. But there are others . . . sometimes we tough old priests are staggered, as by a revelation.

"Clotilde had been ailing, slightly it seemed, for several days. When they called me just after midnight I was shocked to see the change in her. I sent at once to tell Joshua, Joseph's eldest boy — to run for Dr. Fiske. But Clotilde, with a strange expression, restrained me. She indicated, with a peculiar smile, that Joshua might spare himself the journey. She said very little; but enough.

"When I recollected how, years ago, I tartly reproached her for that inexplicable recourse to chlorodyne, I could have wept for my stupidity. I had never thought enough of Clotilde: the tension of her manner, which she could not help, her morbid dread of flushing, of people, of her own overcharged nerves, made her superficially unattractive, even ridiculous. One should have reflected on the struggles of such a nature to overcome itself, one should have thought of the invisible victories. Instead, one thought only of the visible defeats.

"For eighteen months she had been suffering from a growth of the stomach arising out of a chronic ulcer. When she learned from Dr. Fiske that nothing could be done she pledged him to secrecy and set herself to fight an unsung battle. Before I was called the first bad hemorrhage had prostrated her. At six next morning she had the second and succumbed quite quietly. Between, we talked . . . but I dare not make a record of that conversation. Broken and disjointed, it would seem meaningless . . . a prey for easy sneers . . . and alas, the world cannot be reformed by a sneer . . .

"We are all much upset, Martha especially. She is like me, strong as a mule, and will go on forever. Poor Clotilde! I think of her as a gentle creature so strung to sacrifice that sometimes she vibrated harshly. To see a face become at peace, a quiet acceptance of death, without fear . . . it ennobles the heart of man.

"*November 30th, 1929.* Today Joseph's fifth child was born. How life flies on! Who would have dreamed that my shy, brave, garrulous, touchy youngster had in him the makings of a patriarch? Perhaps his early fondness for sugar should have warned me! Really, he is quite a personage now — officious, uxorious, a little pompous, very curt to callers he thinks I should not see — I am rather scared of him myself. . . .

"*A week later.* More local news . . . Mr. Chia's dress boots have been hung up at the Manchu Gate. This is a tremendous honour here . . . and I rejoice for my old friend, whose ascetic, contemplative, generous nature has always been devoted to the reasonable and the beautiful, to that which is eternal.

"Yesterday the mail came in. Even without the presage of his immense success in Rome, I had long realized that Anselm must achieve high honour in the Church. And at last his work for the foreign missions has earned him a fitting reward from the Vatican. He is the new Bishop of Tynecastle. Perhaps the greatest strain is thrown upon our moral vision by the spectacle of another's success. The dazzle hurts us. But now, in my approaching old age, I'm short-sighted. I don't mind Anselm's lustre, I'm rather glad, because I know that he will be supremely glad himself. Jealousy is so hateful a quality. One should remember that the defeated still have everything if they still have God.

"I wish I might take credit for my magnanimity. But this is not magnanimity, merely an awareness of the difference between Anselm and myself . . . of the ridiculous presumption of myself aspiring to the crozier. Though we started from the same mark

Anselm has far outstripped me. He has developed his talents to the full, is now, I observe from the *Tynecastle Chronicle,* 'an accomplished linguist, a notable musician, a patron of arts and science in the diocese, with a vast circle of influential friends.' How lucky! I have had no more than six friends in my uneventful life, and all except one were humble folk. I must write to Anselm to congratulate him, making it clear, however, that I do not presume upon our friendship and have no intention of asking for preferment. *Viva Anselmo!* I am sad when I think how much you have made of your life and how little I have made of mine. I have bumped my head so often . . . and so hard, in my strivings after God.

"*December 30, 1929.* I have not written in this journal for almost a month . . . not since the news of Judy arrived. I still find it difficult to set down even the barest outline of what has taken place at home . . . and here, within myself.

"I flattered myself I had achieved a beatific resignation towards the finality of my exile. Two weeks ago today, I was remarkably complacent. Having made a survey of my recent additions to the mission, the four rice-fields by the river which I bought last year, the enlarged stockyard beyond the white mulberry grove, and the new pony farm, I came into the church to help the children make the Christmas crib. This is a job I particularly enjoy, partly from that lamentable obsession which has stuck to me all my life, I suppose the ribald would call it a suppressed paternal instinct: a love of children — from the dear Christ child down to the meanest little yellow waif who ever crawled into this mission of St. Andrew's.

"We had made a splendid manger with a snowy roof of real cotton wool and were arranging the ox and ass in their stall behind. I had all sorts of things up my sleeve too, coloured lights, and a fine crystal star to hang on the spruce-branched sky. As I saw the shining faces about me and listened to the excited chatter — this is one of the occasions when distractions are permissible in church — I had a wonderful sense of lightness, a vision of all the Christmas cribs in all the Christian churches of the world, dignifying this sweet festival of the Nativity, which, even to those who cannot believe, must at least be beautiful as the feast of all motherhood.

"At that moment one of the bigger boys, sent by Mother Mary Mercy, hurried in with the cablegram. Surely ill-tidings come fast enough without flashing them round the earth. As I read my expression must have changed. One of the smallest girls began to cry. The brightness in my breast was quenched.

"Perhaps I might be judged absurd for taking this so much to heart. I lost Judy when in her teens, on my departure for Pai-tan. But I have lived her life with her in thought. The infrequency of her letters made them stand out like beads upon a chain.

"The hand of heredity propelled Judy forward without mercy. She never quite knew what she wanted or where she was going. But so long as Polly stood beside her she could not become the victim of her own caprice. All through the war she prospered, like many other young women, working for high wages in a munitions factory. She bought a fur coat and a piano—how well I recollect the letter in which the joyful information reached me—and was keyed to sustain her effort by the sense of emergency in the air. This was her heyday. When the war ended, she was over thirty, opportunities were scarce, she gradually abandoned all thought of a career and lapsed into a quiet life with Polly, sharing the small flat in Tynecastle and gaining, one hoped, with maturity, an added balance.

"Judy seemed always to have a queer suspicion towards the other sex and had never been attracted by the thought of marriage. She was forty when Polly died and one never dreamed that she would change her single state. Nevertheless, within eight months of the funeral, Judy was married . . . and later deserted.

"One does not disguise the brutal fact that women do strange things before the climacteric. But this was not the explanation of the pitiful comedy. Polly's legacy to Judy was some two thousand pounds, enough to provide a modest annual competence. Not until

Judy's letter arrived did I guess how she had been persuaded to realize her capital, to transfer it to her sober, upright and gentlemanly husband whom she had first met, apparently, in a boarding house at Scarborough.

"No doubt whole volumes might be written on this basic mundane theme . . . dramatic . . . analytical . . . in the grand Victorian manner . . . perhaps with that sly smirk which sees a rich deep humour in the gullibility of our human nature. But the epilogue was briefly written in ten words on the telegraph form that I held in my hands before the Christmas crib. A child had been born to Judy of this belated, transitory union. And she had died in bearing it.

"Now I reflect there had always been a dark thread running through the flimsy fabric of Judy's inconsequential life. She was the visible evidence, not of sin — how I detest and distrust that word! — but of man's weakness and stupidity. She was the reason, the explanation of our presence here on earth, the tragic evidence of our common mortality. And now, differently, yet with the same essential sadness, that mortal tragedy is again perpetuated.

"I cannot bring myself to contemplate the fate of this unlucky infant, with no one to look after it but the woman who attended Judy — she who has now sent me the news. It is easy to fit her to the pattern of events: one of those handywives who take in expectant mothers, in straitened, slightly dubious circumstances. I must reply to her at once . . . send some money, what little I have. When we bind ourselves to holy poverty we are strangely selfish, forgetful of the awful obligations which life may place upon us. Poor Nora . . . poor Judy . . . poor unnamed little child . . .

"*June 19th, 1930.* A grand day of early summer sunshine and my heart is lighter for the letter received this afternoon. The child is baptized Andrew, after this same infamous mission, and the news makes me chuckle with senile vanity, as though I, myself, were the little wretch's grandfather. Perhaps, whether I wish it or not, this relationship will devolve on me. The father has vanished and we shall make no attempt to trace him. But if I send a certain sum each month, this woman, Mrs. Stevens, who seems a worthy creature, will care for Andrew. Again I can't help smiling . . . my priestly career has been a hotch-potch of peculiarities . . . to rear an infant at a distance of eight thousand miles will be its crowning oddity!

"Wait a moment! I've flicked myself on the raw with that phrase: 'my priestly career.' The other day, during one of our friendly tiffs, on Purgatory I think it was, Fiske declared — heatedly, for I was getting the better of him: 'You argue like a mixed Convention of Holy Rollers and High Anglicans!'

"That brought me up short. I daresay my upbringing, and that early bit of the uncalculable influence of dear old Daniel Glennie, shaped me towards undue liberality. I love my religion, into which I was born, which I have taught, as best I could, for over thirty years, and which has led me unfailingly to the source of all joy, of everlasting sweetness. Yet in my isolation here my outlook has simplified, clarified with my advancing years. I've tied up, and neatly tucked away, all the complex, pettifogging little quirks of doctrine. Frankly, I can't believe that any of God's creatures will grill for all Eternity because of eating a mutton chop on Friday. If we have the fundamentals — love for God and our neighbour — surely we're all right? And isn't it time for the churches of the world to cease hating one another . . . and unite? The world is one living, breathing body, dependent for its health on the billions of cells which comprise it . . . and each tiny cell is the heart of man . . .

"*December 15th, 1932.* Today the new patron saint of this mission was three years old. I hope he had a pleasant birthday and didn't eat too much of the toffee I wrote Burley's, in Tweedside, to send him.

"*September 1st, 1935.* Oh Lord, don't let me be a silly old man . . . this journal is becoming more and more the fatuous record of a child I have not seen and shall never see. I cannot return and he cannot come here. Even my obstinacy balks at that absurdity . . . though I did in fact inquire of Dr. Fiske, who told me that the climate would be deadly for an English child of such tender years.

"Yet I must confess I'm troubled. Reading between her letters it would seem as though Mrs. Stevens had lately come down a little in her luck. She has moved to Kirkbridge, which, as I remember it, is a cotton town, not prepossessing, near Manchester. Her tone has altered, too, and I am beginning to wonder if she is more interested in the money she receives than in Andrew. Yet her parish priest gave her an excellent character. And hitherto she has been admirable.

"Of course, it's all my own fault. I could have secured Andrew's future, after a fashion, by turning him over to one of our excellent Catholic institutions. But somehow . . . he's my one 'blood relation,' a living memento of my dear lost Nora . . . I can't and I won't be so impersonal . . . it's my inveterate crankiness, I suppose, which makes me fight against officialdom. Well . . . if that is so . . . I . . . and Andrew . . . must take the consequences . . . we are in God's hands and he will . . ."

Here, as Father Chisholm turned another page, his concentration was disturbed by the sound of ponies stamping in the compound. He hesitated, listening, half unwilling to relinquish his mood of precious reverie. But the sound increased, mingled with brisk voices. His lips drew together in acceptance. He turned to the last entry in the journal and, taking his pen, added a paragraph.

"*April 30th, 1936.* I am on the point of leaving for the Liu settlement with Father Chou and the Fiskes. Yesterday Father Chou came in, anxious for my advice about a young herdsman he had isolated at the settlement, fearing he might have the smallpox. I decided to go back with him myself — with our good ponies and the new trail, it is only a two days' journey. Then I amplified the idea. Since I have repeatedly promised to show Dr. and Mrs. Fiske our model village, I decided we might all four take the trip. It

will be my last opportunity to fulfill my long-outstanding pledge
to the doctor and his wife. They are returning home to America
at the end of this month. I hear them calling now. They are looking forward to the excursion . . . I'll tackle Fiske en route on his
confounded impudence . . . Holy Roller, indeed! . . ."

XII

THE sun was already dropping towards the bare rim of the hills
which enclosed the narrow valley. Riding ahead of the returning
party, occupied by thoughts of Liu, where they had left Father
Chou with medicine for the sick herdsman, Father Chisholm had resigned himself to another night encampment before reaching the
mission when, at a bend of the road, he met three men in dirty
cotton uniforms slouching head-down with rifles on their hips.

It was a familiar sight: the province was swarming with irregulars, disbanded soldiers with smuggled weapons who had
formed themselves into roving gangs. He passed them with a muttered, "Peace be with you," and slowed down till the others of the
party made up to him. But as he turned he was surprised to see
terror on the faces of the two porters from the Methodist mission
and a sudden anxiety in his own servant's eyes.

"These look like followers of Wai." Joshua made a gesture
towards the road ahead. "And there are others."

The priest swung round stiffly. About twenty of the grey-green
figures were approaching down the path kicking up a cloud of
slow white dust. On the shadowed hill, straggling in a winding
line, were at least another score. He exchanged a glance with
Fiske.

"Let's push on."

The two parties met a moment later. Father Chisholm, smiling,
with his usual greeting, kept his beast moving steadily down the
middle of the path. The soldiers, gaping stupidly, gave way automatically. The only mounted man, a youngster with a broken peaked

cap and some air of authority, enhanced by a corporal's stripe misplaced upon his cuff, halted his shaggy pony indecisively.

"Who are you? And whither are you going?"

"We are missionaries, returning to Pai-tan." Father Chisholm gave the answer calmly across his shoulder, still leading the others forward. They were now almost through the dirty, puzzled, staring mob: Mrs. Fiske and the doctor behind him, followed by Joshua and the two bearers.

The corporal was uncertain but partly satisfied. The encounter was robbed of danger, reduced to commonplace, when suddenly the elder of the two porters lost his head. Prodded by a rifle butt in his passage between the men, he dropped his bundle with a screech of panic and bolted for the cover of the brushwood on the hill.

Father Chisholm suppressed a bitter exclamation. In the gathering twilight, there was a second's dubious immobility. Then a shot rang out, another, and another. The echoes went volleying down the hills. As the blue figure of the bearer, bent double, vanished into the bushes, a loud defrauded outcry broke amongst the soldiers. No longer dumbly wondering, they crowded around the missionaries, in furious, chattering resentment.

"You must come with us." As Father Chisholm had foreseen, the corporal's reaction was immediate.

"We are only missionaries," Dr. Fiske protested heatedly. "We have no possessions. We are honest people."

"Honest people do not run away. You must come to our leader, Wai."

"I assure you — "

"Wilbur!" Mrs. Fiske interposed quietly. "You'll only make it worse. Save your breath."

Bundled about, surrounded by the soldiers, they were roughly pushed along the path which they had recently traversed. About five li back, the young officer turned west into a dry watercourse which took a tortuous and stony course into the hills. At the head of the gully the company halted.

Here perhaps a hundred ill-conditioned soldiers were scattered about in postures of ease — smoking, chewing betel nut, scraping lice from their armpits and caked mud from between their bare toes. On a flat stone, cross-legged, eating his evening meal before a small dung fire, with his back against the wall of the ravine, was Wai-Chu.

Wai was now about fifty-five, gross but full-bellied, with a greater and more evil immobility. His ghee-oiled hair, worn long and parted in the middle, fell over a forehead so drawn down by a perpetual frown as to narrow the oblique eyes to slits. Three years before, a bullet had sheared away his front teeth and upper lip. The scar was horrible. Despite it, Francis plainly recognized the horseman who had spat into his face at the mission gate that night of the retreat. Hitherto he had sustained their detention with composure. But now, under that hidden, subhuman gaze, charged beneath its blankness with an answering recognition, the priest was conscious of a sharp constriction of his heart.

While the corporal volubly related the circumstances of the capture, Wai continued unfathomably to eat, the twin sticks sending a stream of liquid rice and pork lumps into his gullet from the bowl pressed beneath his chin. Suddenly two soldiers broke up the ravine at the double, dragging the fugitive bearer between them. With a final heave they threw him into the circle of fire-glow. The unhappy man fell on his knees close to Wai, his arms skewered behind him, panting and gibbering, in an ecstasy of fear.

Wai continued to eat. Then, casually, he pulled his revolver from his belt and fired it. Caught in the act of supplication, the porter fell forward, his body still jerking against the ground. A creamy pinkish pulp oozed from his blasted skull. Before the stunning reverberations of the report had died Wai had resumed his meal.

Mrs. Fiske had screamed faintly. But beyond a momentary lifting of their heads, the resting soldiers took no notice of the incident. The two who had brought in the bearer now pulled his corpse away and systematically dispossessed it of boots, clothing, and a string of copper cash. Numb and sick, the priest muttered to Dr. Fiske, who stood, very pale, beside him.

"Keep calm . . . show nothing . . . or it is hopeless for all of us."

They waited. The cold and senseless murder had charged the air with horror. At a sign from Wai the second bearer was driven forward and flung upon his knees. The priest felt his stomach turn with a dreadful premonition. But Wai merely said, addressing them all, impersonally: —

"This man, your servant, will leave immediately for Pai-tan and inform your friends that you are temporarily in my care. For such hospitality a voluntary gift is customary. At noon on the day following tomorrow two of my men will await him, half a li outside the Manchu Gate. He will advance, quite alone." Wai paused blankly. "It is to be hoped he will bring the voluntary gift."

"There is little profit in making us your guests." Dr. Fiske spoke with a throb of indignation. "I have already indicated that we are without worldly goods."

"For each person five thousand dollars is requested. No more." Fiske breathed more easily. The sum, though large, was not impossible to a mission as wealthy as his own.

"Then permit my wife to return with the messenger. She will ensure that the money is paid."

Wai gave no sign of having heard. For one apprehensive moment the priest thought his overwrought companion was about to make a scene. But Fiske stumbled back to his wife's side. The messenger was dispatched, sent bounding down the ravine with a last forceful injunction from the corporal. Wai then rose and, while his men made preparations for departure, walked forward to his tethered pony, so casually that the dead man's bare upturned feet, protruding from an arbutus bush, struck the eye like a hallucination.

The missionaries' ponies were now brought up, the four prisoners forced to mount, then roped together by long hemp cords. The cavalcade moved off into the gathering night.

Conversation was impossible at this bumping gallop. Father

Chisholm was left to the mercy of his thoughts, which centred on the man now holding them for ransom.

Lately Wai's waning power had driven him to many excesses. From a traditional war lord, dominating the Chek-kow district of the province with his army of three thousand men, bought off by the various townships, levying taxes and imposts, living in feudal luxury in his walled fortress at Tou-en-lai, he had slowly fallen to ruinous days. At the height of his notoriety he had paid fifty thousand taels for a concubine from Pekin. Now he lived from hand to mouth by petty forays. Beaten decisively in two pitched battles with neighbouring mercenaries, he had thrown in his lot first with the *Min-tuan,* then, in a fit of malice, with the opposing faction, the *Yu-chi-tui.* The truth was that neither desired his doubtful aid. Degenerate, vicious, he fought solely for his own hand. His men were steadily deserting. As the scale of his operations dwindled his ferocity intensified. When he reached the humiliation of a bare two hundred followers, his round of pillage and burnings stood as a dreadful theme of terror. A fallen Lucifer, his hatreds fed on the glories he had lost, he was at enmity with mankind.

The night was interminable. They crossed a low range of hills, forded two rivulets, spattered for an hour through low-lying swamplands. Beyond that, and his conjecture from the pole star that they were travelling due west, Father Chisholm had no knowledge of the terrain they traversed. At his age, used to the quiet amble of his beast, the rapid jolting shook his bones until they rattled. But he reflected, with commiseration, that the Fiskes, too, were enduring the bone-shaking, for the good God's sake. And Joshua, poor lad, though supple enough, was so young he must be sadly frightened. The priest told himself that on the return to the mission he would assuredly give the boy the roan pony he had coveted, silently, these past six months. Closing his eyes, he said a short prayer for the safety of their little party.

Dawn found them in a wilderness of rock and windblown sand, quite uninhabited, with no vegetation but scattered clumps of yellowish tuft grass. But within an hour, the sound of rushing water reached them and there, behind an escarpment, was the ruined citadel of Tou-en-lai, a huddle of ancient mud-brick houses on the cliff slope, surrounded by a crenellated wall, scarred and scorched by many sieges, the old glazed pillars of a Buddhist temple standing roofless, by the riverside.

Within the walls, the party dismounted, and Wai, without a word, entered his house, the only habitable dwelling. The morning air was raw. As the missionaries stood shivering on the hard mud courtyard, still roped together, a number of women and older men came crowding from the little caves which honeycombed the cliff and joined the soldiers in a chattering inspection of the captives.

"We should be grateful for food and rest." Father Chisholm addressed the company at large.

"Food and rest." The words were repeated, passed from mouth to mouth, amongst the onlookers, as an amusing curiosity.

The priest proceeded patiently. "You observe how weary is the missionary woman." Mrs. Fiske was, indeed, half-fainting, on her feet. "Perhaps some well-disposed person would offer her hot tea."

"Tea . . . hot tea," echoed the mob, crowding closer.

They were now within touching distance of the missionaries and suddenly, with a simian acquisitiveness, an old man in the front rank snatched at the doctor's watch-chain. It was the signal for a general spoliation — money, breviary, Bible, wedding ring, the priest's old silver pencil — in three minutes the little group stood divested of everything except their boots and clothing.

As the scramble ended, a woman's eye was caught by the dull sparkle of a jet buckle on the band of Mrs. Fiske's hat. Immediately, she clutched at it. Aware, desperately, of her awful hazard, Mrs. Fiske struggled, with a shrill defensive cry. But in vain. Buckle, hat and wig came off together in her assailant's tenacious grasp. In a flash her bald head gleamed, like a bladder of lard, with grotesque and terrible nakedness, in the remorseless air.

There was a hush. Then a babble of derision broke, a paroxysm of shrieking mockery. Mrs. Fiske covered her face with her hands and burst into scalding tears. The doctor, attempting tremulously to cover his wife's scalp with his handkerchief, saw the coloured silk snatched away. Poor woman, Father Chisholm thought, compassionately averting his eyes.

The sudden arrival of the corporal ended the hilarity as quickly as it had begun. The crowd scattered as the missionaries were led into one of the caves, which possessed the distinction of a hatch. This heavy-ribbed door was slammed and fastened. They were left alone.

"Well," said Father Chisholm after a pause, "at least we have this to ourselves."

There was a longer silence. The little doctor, seated on the earth floor with his arm about his weeping wife, said dully: "It was scarlet fever. She caught it the first year we were in China. She was so sensitive about it. We took such pains never to let a soul know."

"And no one will know," the priest lied swiftly. "Joshua and I are silent as the grave. When we return to Pai-tan the — the damage can be repaired."

"You hear that, Agnes, dear? Pray stop crying, my dearest love."

A slackening, then cessation of the muffled sobs. Mrs. Fiske slowly raised her tear-stained eyes, red-rimmed in that ostrich orb.

"You are very kind," she choked.

"Meanwhile, they seem to have left me with this. If it can be of any service." Father Chisholm produced a large maroon bandana from his inner pocket.

She took it humbly, gratefully; tied it, like a mob-cap, with a butterfly knot behind her ear.

"There now, my dear." Fiske patted her on the back. "Why, you look quite captivating again."

"Do I, dear?" She smiled wanly, coquettishly. Her spirits lifted. "Now let's see what we can do to put this wretched *yao-fang* in order."

There was little they could do: the cave, no more than nine feet deep, held nothing but some broken crockery and its own

dank gloom. The only light and air came from chinks in the barricaded entry. It was cheerless as a tomb. But they were worn-out.
They stretched themselves on the floor. They slept.

It was afternoon when they were wakened by the creak of the
opening hatch. A shaft of fantastic sunshine penetrated the *yao-fang,*
then a middle-aged woman entered with a pitcher of hot water and
two loaves of black bread. She stood watching as Father Chisholm
handed one loaf to Dr. Fiske, then silently broke the other between
Joshua and himself. Something in her attitude, in her dark and
rather sullen face, caused the priest to gaze at her attentively.

"Why!" He gave a start of recognition. "You are Anna!" She
did not answer. After sustaining his gaze, boldly, she turned and
went out.

"Do you know that woman?" Fiske asked quickly.

"I am not sure. But yes, I am sure. She was a girl at the mission
who . . . who ran away."

"Not a great tribute to your teaching." For the first time Fiske
spoke acidly.

"We shall see."

That night they all slept badly. The discomforts of their confinement grew hourly. They took turns lying next to the hatch, for the
privilege of breathing in the damp moist air. The little doctor kept
groaning: "That awful bread! Dear heaven, it's tied my duodenum
in a knot."

At noon, the next day, Anna came again with more hot water
and a bowl of millet. Father Chisholm knew better than to address
her by name.

"How long are we to be kept here?"

At first it seemed as though she would make no reply, then
she said, indifferently: —

"The two men have departed for Pai-tan. When they return you
will be free."

Dr. Fiske interposed restively: "Cannot you procure better food
for us and blankets? We will pay."

She shook her head, scared off. But when she had retreated and let down the hatch she said, through the bars: "Pay me if you wish. It is not long to wait. It is nothing."

"Nothing." Fiske groaned again when she had gone. "I wish she had my insides."

"Don't give way, Wilbur." From the darkness beyond Mrs. Fiske exhorted him. "Remember, we've been through this before."

"We were young, then. Not old crocks on the verge of going home. And this Wai . . . he's got his knife in us missionaries especially . . . for changing his good old order when crime paid."

She persisted: "We must all keep cheerful. Look, we've got to distract ourselves. Not talk — or you two will start quarrelling about religion. A game. The silliest we can think of! We'll play 'animal, vegetable or mineral.' Joshua, are you awake? Good. Now listen and I'll explain how it goes."

They played the guessing game with heroic vigour. Joshua showed surprising aptitude. Then Mrs. Fiske's bright laugh cracked suddenly. They all fell very quiet. A dragging apathy succeeded; snatches of fitful sleep; uneasy, restless movements.

"Dear God, they must surely be back by now." All next day that phrase fell incessantly from Fiske's lips. His face and hands were hot to the touch. Lack of sleep and air had made him feverish. But it was evening before a loud shouting and the barking of dogs gave indication of a late arrival. The silence which followed was oppressive.

At last, footsteps approached and the hatch was flung open. On being commanded, they scrambled out on their hands and knees. The freshness of the night air, the sense of space and freedom, induced a delirium, almost, of relief.

"Thank heaven!" Fiske cried. "We're all right now."

An escort of soldiers took them to Wai-Chu.

He was seated, in his dwelling, on a coir mat, a lamp and a long pipe beside him, the lofty dilapidated room impregnated with the faintly bitter reek of poppy. Beside him was a soldier with a soiled blood-stained rag tied round his forearm. Five others of his troop, including the corporal, stood by the walls with rattans in their hands.

A penetrating silence followed the introduction of the prisoners. Wai studied them with deep and meditative cruelty. It was a hidden cruelty, sensed rather than seen, behind the mask of his face.

"The voluntary gift has not been paid." His voice was flat, unemotional. "When my men advanced to the city to receive it one was killed and the other wounded."

A shiver passed over Father Chisholm. What he had dreaded had come to pass. He said: —

"Probably the message was never delivered. The bearer was afraid and ran away to his home in Shansee without going to Pai-tan."

"You are too talkative. Ten strokes on the legs."

The priest had expected this. The punishment was severe, the edge of the long square rod, wielded by one of the soldiers, lacerating his shins and thighs.

"The messenger was our servant." Mrs. Fiske spoke with suppressed indignation, a high spot of colour burning on her pale cheek. "It is not the Shang-Foo's fault if he ran away."

"You are also too talkative. Twenty slaps on the face."

She was beaten hard with the open palm on both cheeks while the doctor trembled and struggled beside her.

"Tell me, since you are so wise. If your servant ran away why should my emissaries be waited upon and ambushed?"

Father Chisholm wished to say that, in these times, the Pai-tan garrison was perpetually on the alert and would shoot any of Wai's men on sight. He knew this to be the explanation. He judged it wiser to hold his tongue.

"Now you are not so talkative. Ten strokes on the shoulders for keeping unnatural silence."

He was beaten again.

"Let us return to our missions." Fiske threw out his hands, gesticulating, like an agitated woman. "I assure you on my solemn oath that you will be paid without the slightest hesitation."

"I am not a fool!"

"Then send another of your soldiers to Lantern Street with a message which I will write. Send him now, immediately."

"And have him slaughtered also? Fifteen blows for assuming that I am a fool."

Under the blows the doctor burst into tears. "You are to be pitied," he blubbered. "I forgive you but I pity, I pity you."

There was a pause. It was almost possible to observe the dull flicker of gratification in Wai's contracted pupils. He turned to Joshua. The lad was healthy and strong. He desperately needed recruits.

"Tell me. Are you prepared to make atonement by enlisting under my banner?"

"I am sensible of the honour." Joshua spoke steadily. "But it is impossible."

"Renounce your foreign devil god and you will be spared."

Father Chisholm endured an instant of cruel suspense, preparing himself for the pain and humiliation of the boy's surrender.

"I will die gladly for the true Lord of Heaven."

"Thirty blows for being a contumacious wretch."

Joshua did not utter a cry. He took the punishment with eyes cast down. Not a moan escaped him. But every blow made Father Chisholm wince.

"Now will you advise your servant to repent?"

"Never." The priest answered firmly, his soul illuminated by the boy's courage.

"Twenty blows on the legs for reprehensible obduracy."

At the twelfth blow, delivered on the front of his shins, there was a sharp brittle crack. An agonizing pain shot through the broken limb. Oh Lord, thought Francis, that's the worst of old bones.

Wai considered them with an air of finality. "I cannot continue to shield you. If the money does not arrive tomorrow I have a foreboding that some evil may befall you."

He dismissed them blankly. Father Chisholm could barely limp across the courtyard. Back in the *yao-fang* Mrs. Fiske made him sit down and, kneeling beside him, stripped off his boot and sock. The doctor, somewhat recovered, then set the broken limb.

"I've no splint . . . nothing but these rags." His voice had a high and tremulous ring. "It's a nasty fracture. If you don't rest it'll turn compound. Feel how my hands are shaking. Help us, dear Lord! We're going home next month. We're not so — "

"Please, Wilbur." She soothed him with a quiet touch. He completed dressing the injury in silence. Then she added: "We must try to keep our spirits up. If we give in now, what's going to happen to us tomorrow?"

Perhaps it was well that she prepared them.

In the morning the four were led out into the courtyard, which was lined with the population of Tou-en-lai, and humming with the promise of a spectacle. Their hands were tied behind their backs and a bamboo pole passed between their arms. Two soldiers then seized the ends of each spit and, raising the prisoners, marched them in procession round the arena six times, in narrowing circles, bringing up before the bullet-pocked façade of the house where Wai was seated.

Sick with the pain of his broken leg, Father Chisholm felt, through the stupid ignominy, a terrible dejection, amounting to despair, that the creatures of God's hand should make a careless festival out of the blood and tears of others. He had to still the dreadful whisper that God could never fashion men like this . . . that God did not exist.

He saw that several of the soldiers had their rifles, he hoped that a merciful end was near. But after a pause, at a sign from Wai, they were turned about and frog-marched down the steep path, past some beached sampans on a narrow spit of shingle, to the river. Here, before the reassembled crowd, they were dragged through the shallows and each secured with cord to a mooring stake in five feet of running water.

The switch from the threat of sudden execution was so unexpected, the contrast to the filthy squalour of the cave so profound, it was impossible to escape a sensation of relief. The shock of the water restored them. It was cold from mountain springs, and clear as crystal. The priest's leg ceased to pain him. Mrs. Fiske smiled feebly. Her courage was heartrending.

Her lips shaped the words: "At least we shall get clean."

But after half an hour a change set in. Father Chisholm dared not look at his companions. The river, at first so refreshing, gradually grew colder, colder, losing its gentle numbness, compressing their bodies and lower limbs in an algid vice. Each heartbeat, straining to force the blood through frozen arteries, was a throb of pulsing agony. The head, engorged, floated disembodied, in a reddish haze. With his swimming senses the priest still strove to find the reason of this torture, which now he dimly recollected as "the water ordeal," an intermittent sadism, hallowed by tradition, first conceived by the tyrant Tchang. It was a punishment well suited to Wai's purpose, since it probably expressed his lingering hope that the ransom might still be paid. Francis suppressed a groan. If this were true, their sufferings were not yet over.

"It's remarkable." With chattering teeth the doctor tried to talk. "This pain . . . perfect demonstration of angina pectoris . . . intermittent blood supply through constricted vascular system. O blessed Jesus!" He began to whimper. "O Lord God of Hosts — why hast thou forsaken us? My poor wife . . . thank God she has fainted. Where am I? . . . Agnes . . . Agnes . . ." He was unconscious.

The priest painfully turned his eyes towards Joshua. The boy's head, barely visible to his congested gaze, seemed decapitated, the head of a young Saint John the Baptist on a streaming charger. Poor Joshua — and poor Joseph! How he would miss his eldestborn. Francis said gently: —

"My son, your courage and your faith — they are very pleasing to me."

"It is nothing, Master."

A pause. The priest, deeply moved, made a great effort to stem the torpor stealing over him.

"I meant to tell you, Joshua. You shall have the roan pony when we return to the mission."

"Does the Master think we shall ever return to the mission?"

"If not, Joshua, the good God will give you a finer pony to ride in heaven."

Another pause. Joshua said faintly: —

"I think, Father, I should prefer the little pony at the mission."

A great surging flowed into Francis' ears, ending their conversation with waves of darkness. When the priest came to himself again they were all back in the cave, flung together in a sodden heap. As he lay a moment, gathering his senses, he heard Fiske talking to his wife, in that querulous plaint to which his speech had fallen.

"At least we are out of it . . . that dreadful river."

"Yes, Wilbur dear, we are out of it. But unless I mistake that ruffian, tomorrow we shall be into it again." Her tone was quite practical as though she were discussing the menu for his dinner. "Don't let's delude ourselves, dearest. If he keeps us alive it's only because he means to kill us as horribly as possible."

"Aren't you . . . afraid, Agnes?"

"Not in the least, and you mustn't be either. You must show these poor pagans . . . and the Father . . . how good New England Christians die."

"Agnes dear . . . you're a brave woman."

The priest could feel the pressure of her arm about her husband. He was greatly stirred, reshaken by a passionate concern for his companions, these three people, so different, yet each so dear to him. Was there no way of escape? He thought deeply, with gritted teeth, his brow pressed against the earth.

An hour later when the woman entered with a dish of rice he placed himself between her and the door.

"Anna! Do not deny that you are Anna! Have you no gratitude for all that was done for you at the mission? No —" She tried to push past him. "I shall not let you go until you listen. You are still a child of God. You cannot see us slowly murdered. I command you in His name to help us."

"I can do nothing." In the darkness of the cave it was impossible to see her face. But her voice, though sullen, was subdued.

"You can do much. Leave the hatch unfastened. No one will think to blame you."

"To what purpose? All the ponies are guarded."

"We need no ponies, Anna."

A spark of inquiry flashed in her lowering gaze. "If you leave Tou-en-lai on foot you will be retaken next day."

"We shall leave by sampan . . . and float down-river."

"Impossible." She shook her head with vehemence. "The rapids are too strong."

"Better to drown in the rapids than here."

"It is not my business where you drown." She answered with sudden passion: "Nor to help you in any manner whatsoever."

Unexpectedly, Dr. Fiske reached out in the darkness and gripped her hand. "Look, Anna, take my fingers and give heed. You must make it your business. Do you understand? Leave the door free tonight."

There was a pause.

"No." She hesitated, slowly withdrew her hand. "I cannot tonight."

"You must."

"I will do it tomorrow . . . tomorrow . . . tomorrow." With an odd change of manner, a sudden wildness, she bent her head and darted from the cave. The hatch closed behind her with a heavy slam.

And a heavier silence settled upon the cave. No one believed that the woman would keep her word. Even if she meant it, her promise was a feeble thing to weigh against the prospects of the coming day.

"I'm a sick man," Fiske muttered peevishly, laying his head against his wife's shoulder. In the darkness they could hear him percussing his own chest. "My clothes are still sopping. D'you hear that . . . it's quite dull . . . lobar consolidation. Oh, God, I thought the tortures of the inquisition were matchless."

Somehow the night passed. The morning was cold and grey. As the light filtered through and sounds were heard in the courtyard, Mrs. Fiske straightened herself with a look of sublime resolution on her peaked and pallid face, still girded by the shrunken headdress. "Father Chisholm, you are the senior clergyman here. I ask you to say a prayer before we go out to what may be our martyrdom."

He knelt down beside her. They all joined hands. He prayed, as best he could, better than he had prayed in all his life. Then the soldiers came for them.

Weakened as they were, the river seemed colder than before. Fiske shouted hysterically as they drove him in. To Father Chisholm it now became a hazy vision.

Immersion, his thoughts ran mazily, purification by water, one drop and you were saved. How many drops were here? Millions and millions . . . four hundred million Chinese all waiting to be saved, each with a drop of water. . . .

"Father! Dear good Father Chisholm!" Mrs. Fiske was calling him, her eyes glassy with a sudden feverish gaiety. "They are all watching us from the bank. Let us show them. An example. Let us sing. What hymn have we in common? The Christmas Hymn, of course. A sweet refrain. Come, Joshua . . . Wilbur . . . all of us."

She struck up, in a high quavering pipe: —

"Oh, come, all ye faithful,
Joyful and triumphant . . ."

He joined with the others: —

"Oh, come ye, oh, come ye, to Bethlehem."

Late afternoon. They were back in the cave again. The doctor lay on his side. His breath came raspingly. He spoke with an air of triumph.

"Lobar pneumonia. I knew it yesterday. Apical dullness and crepitations. I'm sorry, Agnes, but . . . I'm rather glad."

No one said anything. She began to stroke his hot forehead with her bleached sodden fingers. She was still stroking when Anna came to the cave. This time, however, the woman brought no food with her.

She did no more than stand in the entrance staring at them with a kind of grudging sullenness. At last she said: —

"I have given the men your supper. They think it is a great joke. Go quickly before they discover their mistake."

There was an absolute silence. Father Chisholm felt his heart bound in his racked, exhausted body. It seemed impossible that they might leave the cave of their own free will. He said: "God will bless you, Anna. You have not forgotten Him and He has not forgotten you."

She gave no answer. She stared at him with her darkly inscrutable eyes which he had never read, even on that first night amidst the snow. Yet it gave him a burning satisfaction that she should justify his teaching, openly, before Dr. Fiske. She stood for a moment, then glided silently away.

Outside the cave it was dark. He could hear laughter and low voices from the neighbouring *yao-fang*. Across the courtyard there was a light in Wai's house. The adjacent stables and soldiers' quarters showed a feeble illumination. The sudden barking of a dog sent a shock through his tortured nerves. This slender hope was like a new pain, suffocating in its intensity.

Cautiously, he tried to stand upon his feet. But it was impossible, he fell heavily, beads of perspiration breaking on his brow. His leg, swollen to three times its natural size, was quite unusable.

In a whisper he told Joshua to take the half-unconscious doctor on his back and carry him very quietly to the sampans. He saw them go off, accompanied by Mrs. Fiske, Joshua bent under his sacklike burden, keeping cleverly to the dense shadows of the rocks. The faint clatter of a loose stone came back to him, so loud it seemed to wake the dead. He breathed again; no one had heard it but himself. In five minutes Joshua returned. Leaning on the boy's shoulder, he dragged slowly and painfully down the path.

Fiske was already stretched out on the bottom of the sampan with his wife crouched beside him. The priest seated himself in the stern. Lifting his useless leg with both hands he arranged it out of the way, like a piece of timber, then propped himself against the gunwale with his elbow. As Joshua climbed into the bow and began to untie the mooring rope he seized the single stern oar in readiness to push off.

Suddenly a shout rang out from the top of the cliff, followed by another and the sound of running. A loud commotion broke, dogs

set up a violent barking. Then two torches flared in the upper darkness and came rapidly, amidst shrill voices and excited, clattering
footsteps, down the river path.

The priest's lips moved, in the anguished immobility of his body.
But he remained silent. Joshua, fumbling and tearing at the matted
rope, knew the danger, without the added confusion of a command.

At last, with a wild gasp, the boy pulled the rope loose, falling
backwards against the thwarts. Instantly, Father Chisholm felt the
sampan float free and with all his remaining strength he fended it
into the current. Out of the slack water, they spun aimlessly, then
began to slide downstream. Across and behind them, the flares now
showed a group of running figures on the bank. A rifle-shot
cracked, followed by an irregular volley. The lead skipped the water
with a twanging hum. They were sliding faster now, much faster;
they were almost out of range. Father Chisholm was staring into
the dark wall ahead with almost feverish relief when suddenly,
amidst the scattered shooting, a great weight struck at him out of
the night. His head rocked under the impact of what seemed a heavy
flying stone. Beyond the crashing blow he had no pain. He raised
his hand to his wet face. The bullet had smashed through his upper
jaw, torn out by his right cheek. He kept silent. The firing ceased.
No one else was hit.

The river now moved them forward at intimidating speed. He
was quite sure in his own mind that it must ultimately join the
Hwang — no other outlet was possible. He leaned forward towards
Fiske and, seeing him conscious, made an effort to cheer him.

"How do you feel?"

"Pretty comfortable, considering I'm dying." He repressed a
short cough. "I'm sorry I've been such an old woman, Agnes."

"Please don't talk, dear."

The priest straightened himself, sadly. Fiske's life was ebbing
away. His own resistance was almost gone. He had to fight an almost irresistible impulse to weep.

Presently an increase in the volume of the river's sound heralded their approach to broken water. The noise seemed to blot out what vision was left him. He could see nothing. With his single oar he pulled the sampan straight with the current. As they shot down, he commended their souls to God.

He was beyond caring, beyond realizing how the craft lived in that unseen thunder. The roar dulled him into stupor. He clung to the useless oar as they lurched and plunged, invisibly. At times they seemed to drop through empty space, as if the bottom had fallen from the boat. When a splintering crash arrested their momentum, he thought numbly that they must founder. But they plunged off again, the boiling water surging in on them as they whirled, down, down. Whenever he felt they must be free, a new roaring reared itself ahead, reached out, engulfed them. At a narrow bend they hit the rocky bank with stunning force, ripping low branches from overhanging trees, then bounced, spun, crashed on again. His brain was caught in the swirl, battered and jarred, down, down, down.

The peace of the quiet water, far below, brought him feebly to his senses. A faint streak of dawn lay ahead of them, limning a broad expanse of gentle pastoral waters. He could not guess what distance they had come, though dimly he surmised it must be many li. All he knew was this: they had reached the Hwang and were floating calmly on its bosom towards Pai-tan.

He tried to move, but could not, his weakness held him fettered. His damaged limb felt heavier than lead, the pain of his smashed face was like a raging toothache. But with incredible effort he turned and pulled himself slowly down the boat with his hands. The light increased. Joshua was huddled in the bow, his body limp, but breathing. He was asleep. In the bottom of the sampan Fiske and his wife lay together, her arm supporting his head, her body shielding him from the water they had shipped. She was awake and calmly reasonable. The priest was conscious of a great wonder as he gazed at her. She had shown the highest endurance of them all. Her eyes answered his unspoken inquiry with a wan negation. He could see that her husband was almost gone.

Fiske was breathing in little staccato spasms, with intervals when he did not breathe at all. He muttered constantly but his eyes, though fixed, were open. And, suddenly, there appeared in them a vague, uncertain light of recognition. The shadow of a movement crossed his lips — nothing, yet in that nothingness hovered the suggestion of a smile. His muttering took on coherent form.

"Don't pride yourself . . . dear fellow . . . on Anna." A little gasp of breathing. "Not so much your teaching as — " Another spasm. "I bribed her." Weakly, the flutter of a laugh. "With the fifty-dollar bill I always carried in my shoe." A feeble triumphant pause. "But God bless you, dear fellow, all the same."

He seemed happier now he had scored his final point. He closed his eyes. As the sun rose in a flood of sudden light they saw that he was gone.

Back in the stern Father Chisholm watched Mrs. Fiske compose the dead man's hands. He looked dizzily at his own hands. The backs of both his wrists were covered peculiarly with raised red spots. When he touched them they rolled like buckshot beneath his skin. He thought, Some insect has bitten me while I slept.

Later, through the rising morning vapours, he saw down-river, in the distance, the flat boats of cormorant fishers. He closed his throbbing eyes. The sampan was drifting . . . drifting in the golden haze, towards them.

XIII

ONE afternoon six months later the two new missionary priests, Father Stephen Munsey, M.B. and Father Jerome Craig, were earnestly discussing the arrangements over coffee and cigarettes.

"Everything has got to be perfect. Thank God the weather looks good."

"And settled." Father Jerome nodded. "It's a blessing we have the band."

They were young, healthy, full of vitality, with an immense

belief in themselves and God. Father Munsey, the American priest, with a medical degree from Baltimore, was slightly the taller of the two, a fine six-footer, but Father Craig's shoulders had gained him a place in the Holywell boxing team. Though Craig was British he had a pleasant touch of American keenness, for he had taken a two years' missionary preparatory course at the College of St. Michael's in San Francisco. Here, indeed, he had met Father Munsey. The two had felt, instinctively, a mutual attraction, had soon become, affectionately, "Steve" and "Jerry" to each other — except on those occasions when a burst of self-conscious dignity induced a more formal tone. "Say, Jerry, old boy, are you playing basketball this afternoon? — And oh, er, by the way, Father, what time is your mass tomorrow?" To be sent to Pai-tan together had set the seal upon their friendship.

"I asked Mother Mercy Mary to look in." Father Steve poured himself fresh coffee. He was clean-cut and virile, two years senior to Craig, admittedly the leader of the partnership. "Just to discuss the final touches. She's so cheery and obliging. She's going to be a great help to us."

"Yes, she's a grand person. Honestly, Jerry, we'll make things hum here when we have it to ourselves."

"Hist! Don't talk so loud," Father Steve warned. "The old boy's not so deaf as you'd think."

"He's a case." Father Jerry's blunt features melted to a reminiscent smile. "Of course I know you pulled him through. But at his age to shake off a broken leg, a smashed jaw, and the smallpox on top of it — well! — it says something for his pluck."

"He's terribly feeble though." Munsey spoke seriously. "It's quite finished him. I'm hoping the long voyage home'll do him good."

"He's a funny old devil — sorry, Father, I mean fogy. D'you remember, when he was so sick and Mrs. Fiske sent up the four-poster bed before she left for home? The awful trouble we had to get him into it? Remember how he kept saying 'How can I rest if I'm comfortable?'" Jerry laughed.

"And that other time he threw the beef tea at Mother Mercy

Mary's head —" Father Steve stifled his grin. "No, no, Father, we mustn't let our tongues get the better of us. After all he's not so bad if you take him the right way. Anybody would get a bit queer in the topknot after being over thirty years out here alone. Thank God we're a pair. Come in."

Mother Mercy Mary entered, smiling, red-cheeked, her eyes friendly and merry. She was very happy with her new priests, whom she thought of, instinctively, as two nice boys. She would mother them. It was good for the mission to have this infusion of young blood. It would be more human for her to have a proper priest's laundry to oversee, decent thick underwear to darn.

"Afternoon, Reverend Mother. Can we tempt you to the cup that cheers but doesn't inebriate? Good. Two lumps? We'll have to watch that sweet tooth of yours in Lent. Well now, about tomorrow's farewell ceremonies for Father Chisholm."

They talked together, amicably and earnestly, for half an hour. Then Mother Mercy Mary seemed to prick up her ears. Her expression of maternal protectiveness deepened. Listening acutely, she sounded a note of concern with her tongue.

"Do you hear him about? I don't. God bless my soul, I'm sure he's away out without telling us." She rose. "Excuse me, Fathers. I'll have to find out what he's up to. If he goes and gets his feet wet it'll ruin everything."

Leaning on his old rolled umbrella, Father Chisholm had made a last pilgrimage of his mission of St. Andrew's. The slight exertion fatigued him absurdly; he realized, with an inward sigh, how sadly useless his long illness had left him. He was an old man. The thought was quite staggering — he felt so little different, within his heart, so unchanged. And tomorrow he must leave Pai-tan. Incredible! When he had made up his mind to lay his bones at the foot of the mission garden alongside Willie Tulloch. Phrases in the Bishop's letter recurred to him: ". . . not up to it, solicitous your health, deeply appreciative, end your labours in the foreign mission field." Well, God's will be done!

He was standing, now, in the little churchyard, swept by a flood of tender, ghostly memories, noting the wooden crosses — Willie's, Sister Clotilde's, the gardener Fu's, a dozen more, each an end and a beginning, the milestones of their common pilgrimage.

He shook his head like an old horse amidst a hum of insects in a sunny field: really he must not yield to reverie. He fixed his gaze across the low wall in the new pasture field. Joshua was putting the roan pony through its paces while four of his younger brothers watched admiringly. Joseph himself was not far off. Fat, complacent and forty-five, shepherding the remainder of his nine children back from their afternoon stroll, he slowly pushed a wicker perambulator towards the lodge. What richer instance, thought the priest with a faint slow smile, of the subjugation of the noble male?

He had made the grand tour, as unobtrusively as possible, for he guessed what lay in store for him tomorrow. School, dormitory, refectory, the lace and mat-making workrooms, the little annex he had opened last year to teach basket-weaving to the blind children. Well . . . why continue the meagre tally? In the past he had judged it some small achievement. In his present mood of gentle melancholy he measured it as nothing. He swung round stiffly. From the new hall came the ominous stertor of wind on brass. Again he suppressed a crooked smile, or was it perhaps a frown? These young curates with their explosive ideas! Only last night, when he was trying — vainly, of course — to instruct them in the topography of the parish, the doctor one had whispered: *Aeroplane.* What were things coming to! Two hours by air to the Liu village. And his first trip had taken him two weeks on foot!

He ought not to go farther, for the afternoon was turning chill. But, though he knew his disobedience would earn a merited scolding, he pressed harder on his umbrella and went slowly down the Hill of Brilliant Green Jade towards the deserted site of the first forgotten mission. Though the compound was now rank with bamboo, the lower edge eroded to a muddy swamp, the mud-brick stable still remained.

He bowed his head and passed under the sagging roof, assailed, immediately, by another host of recollections, seeing a young priest, dark, eager and intent, crouched before a brazier, his sole companion a Chinese boy. That first mass he had celebrated here, on his japanned tin trunk without bell or server, no one but himself — how sharply it struck the taut chords of his memory. Clumsily, a stiff ungainly figure, he knelt down, and begged God to judge him less by his deeds than by his intention.

Back at the mission he let himself in by the side porch and went softly upstairs. He was fortunate; no one saw him come in. He did not wish "the grand slam," as he had come to call it, a flurry of feet and doors, with hot-water bottles and solicitous profferings of soup. But, as he opened the door of his room, he was surprised to find Mr. Chia inside. His disfigured face, now grey with cold, lit up to a sudden warmth. Heedless of formality, he took his old friend's hand and pressed it.

"I hoped you would come."

"How could I refrain from coming?" Mr. Chia spoke in a sad and strangely troubled voice. "My dear Father, I need not tell you how deeply I regret your departure. Our long friendship has meant much to me."

The priest answered quietly: "I, too, shall miss you much. Your kindness and benefactions have overwhelmed me."

"It is less than nothing," Mr. Chia waved the gratitude away, "beside your inestimable service to me. And have I not always enjoyed the peace and beauty of your mission garden? Without you, the garden will hold a great sadness." His tone lifted to a fitful gleam. "But then . . . perhaps, on your recovery . . . you may return to Pai-tan?"

"Never." The priest paused, with the suspicion of a smile. "We must look forward to our meeting in the celestial hereafter."

An odd silence fell. Mr. Chia broke it with constraint. "Since our time together is limited it might not be unfitting if we talked a moment regarding the hereafter."

"All my time is dedicated to such talk."

Mr. Chia hesitated, beset by unusual awkwardness. "I have never pondered deeply on what state lies beyond this life. But if such a state exists it would be very agreeable for me to enjoy your friendship there."

Despite his long experience, Father Chisholm did not grasp the import of the remark. He smiled but did not answer. And Mr. Chia was forced in great embarrassment to be direct.

"My friend, I have often said: There are many religions and each has its gate to heaven." A faint colour crept beneath his dark skin. "Now it would appear that I have the extraordinary desire to enter by your gate."

Dead silence. Father Chisholm's bent figure was immobilized, rigid.

"I cannot believe that you are serious."

"Once, many years ago, when you cured my son, I was not serious. But then I was unaware of the nature of your life . . . of its patience, quietness and courage. The goodness of a religion is best judged by the goodness of its adherents. My friend . . . you have conquered me by example."

Father Chisholm raised his hand to his forehead, that familiar sign of hidden emotion. His conscience had often reproached him for his initial refusal to accept Mr. Chia, even without a true intention. He spoke slowly. "All day long my mouth has been bitter with the ashes of failure. Your words have rekindled the fires in my heart. Because of this one moment I feel that my work has not been worthless. In spite of that I say to you . . . don't do this for friendship — only if you have belief."

Mr. Chia answered firmly. "My mind is made up. I do it for friendship and belief. We are as brothers, you and I. Your Lord must also be mine. Then, even though you must depart tomorrow, I shall be content, knowing that in our Master's garden our spirits will one day meet."

At first the priest was unable to speak. He fought to conceal the depth of his feeling. He reached out his hand to Mr. Chia. In a low uncertain tone he said: —

"Let us go down to the church." . . .

Next morning broke warm and clear. Father Chisholm, awakened
by the sound of singing, escaped from the sheets of Mrs. Fiske's
bed and stumbled to the open window. Beneath his balcony twenty
little girls from the junior school, none more than nine years of
age, dressed in white and blue sashes, were serenading him: *Hail,
Smiling Morn* . . . He grimaced at them. At the end of the tenth
verse he called down:—

"That's enough. Go and get your breakfast."

They stopped, smiled up at him, holding their music sheets. "Do
you like it, Father?"

"No . . . Yes. But it's time for breakfast."

They started off again from the beginning and sang it all through
with extra verses while he was shaving. At the words "on thy fresh
cheek" he cut himself. Peering into the minute mirror at his own
reflection, pocked and cicatrized, and now gory, he thought mildly,
Dear me, what a dreadful-looking ruffian I've become, I really must
behave myself today.

The breakfast gong sounded. Father Munsey and Father Craig
were both waiting on him, alert, deferential, smiling—the one
rushing to pull out his chair, the other to lift the cover from the
kedgeree. They were so anxious to please they could scarcely sit
still. He scowled.

"Will you young idiots kindly stop treating me like your great-
grandmother on her hundredth birthday?"

Must humour the old boy, thought Father Jerry. He smiled
tenderly. "Why, Father, we're just treating you like one of ourselves. Of course you can't escape the honour due to a pioneer who
blazed the first trails. You don't want to, either. It's your natural
reward and don't you have any doubt about it."

"I have a great many doubts."

Father Steve said heartily: "Don't you worry, Father. I know how
you feel, but we won't let you down. Why, Jerry—I mean Father
Craig and I have schemes in hand for doubling the size and efficiency
of St. Andrew's. We're going to have twenty catechists—pay them
good wages too—start a rice kitchen in Lantern Street, right op-

posite your Methodist pals there. We'll poke them in the eye all right." He laughed good-naturedly, reassuringly. "It's going to be downright, honest, foursquare Catholicism. Wait till we get our plane! Wait till we start sending you our conversion graphs. Wait till — "

"The cows come home," said Father Chisholm dreamily.

The two young priests exchanged a sympathetic glance. Father Steve said kindly: —

"You won't forget to take your medicine in the trip home, Father? One tablespoonful *ex aqua,* three times a day. There's a big bottle in your bag."

"No, there isn't. I threw it out before I came down." Suddenly Father Chisholm began to laugh. He laughed until he shook. "My dear boys, don't mind me. I'm a cantankerous scoundrel. You'll do grandly here if you're not too cocksure . . . if you're kind and tolerant, and especially if you don't try to teach every old Chinaman how to suck eggs."

"Why . . . yes . . . yes, of course, Father."

"Look! I have no aeroplanes to spare but I'd like to leave you a useful little souvenir. It was given me by an old priest. It's been with me on most of my travels." He left the table, handed them from the corner of the room the tartan umbrella Rusty Mac had given him. "It has a certain status amongst the state umbrellas of Pai-tan. It may bring you luck."

Father Jerry took it gingerly as though it were a sort of a relic.

"Thank you, thank you, Father. What pretty colours. Are they Chinese?"

"Much worse, I'm afraid." The old priest smiled and shook his head. He would say no more.

Father Munsey put down his napkin with a surreptitious signal to his colleague. There was an organizing glitter in his eye. He rose.

"Well, Father, if you'll excuse Father Craig and myself. Time is getting on, and we're expecting Father Chou any moment now . . ."

They departed briskly.

He was due to leave at eleven o'clock. He returned to his room.

When he had completed his modest packing he had still an hour in which to wander round. He descended, drawn instinctively towards the church. There, outside his house, he drew up, genuinely touched. His entire congregation, nearly five hundred, stood awaiting him, orderly and silent, in the courtyard. The contingent from the Liu village, under Father Chou, stood on one flank, the older girls and handicraft workers upon the other, with his beloved children, shepherded by Mother Mercy Mary, Martha, and the four Chinese Sisters, in front. There was something in the mass attention of their eyes, all bent affectionately upon his insignificant form, which gripped him with a sudden pang.

A deeper hush. From his nervousness it was clear that Joseph had been entrusted with the honour of the address. Two chairs were produced like a conjuring trick. When the old Father was seated in one, Joseph mounted unsteadily upon the other, almost overbalancing, and unrolled the vermilion scroll.

"Most Reverend and Worthy Disciple of the Lord of Heaven, it is with the utmost anguish that we, thy children, witness thy departure across the broad oceans . . ."

The address was no different from a hundred other eulogies suffered in the past except that it was lachrymose. Despite a score of secret rehearsals before his wife, Joseph's delivery was vanquished by the open courtyard. He began to sweat and his paunch quivered like a jelly. Poor dear Joseph, thought the priest, staring at his boots and thinking of a slim young boy running, unfaltering, at his bridle rein thirty years ago.

When it was over the entire congregation sang the *Gloria laus* quite beautifully. Still looking at his boots, as the clear voices ascended, the priest felt a melting of his old bones. "Dear God," he prayed, "don't let me make a fool of myself."

For the presentation, they had chosen the youngest girl in the basket-weaving centre for the blind. She came forward, in her black skirt and white blouse, uncertain yet sure, guided by her instinct and Mother Mercy Mary's whispered instructions. As she knelt before him, holding out the ornate gilt chalice of execrable design, bought by mail order from Nankin, his eyes were sightless as her own. "Bless you, bless you, my child," he muttered. He could say no more.

Mr. Chia's number-one chair now swam into the orbit of his hazy vision. Disembodied hands helped him into it. The procession formed and set off amidst the popping of firecrackers and a sudden burst of Sousa from the new school band.

As he swayed slowly down the hill, borne pontifically on the shoulders of the men, he tried to rivet his consciousness upon the gimcrack comedy of the band: twenty schoolboys in sky-blue uniforms, blowing their cheeks out, preceded by a Chinese majorette aged eight in fleecy shako and high white boots, strutting, twirling a cane, kicking up her knees. But somehow, his sense of the ridiculous had ceased to function. In the town the doorways were crowded with friendly faces. More firecrackers welcomed him at every street crossing. As he neared the landing stage flowers were cast before him.

Mr. Chia's launch lay waiting at the steps, the engines quietly running. The chair was lowered, he stepped out. It had come at last. They were surrounding him bidding him farewell: the two young priests, Father Chou, Reverend Mother, Martha, Mr. Chia, Joseph, Joshua . . . all of them, some of the women of the congregation weeping, kneeling to kiss his hand. He had meant to say something. He could not mumble one incoherent word. His breast was overflowing.

Blindly, he boarded the launch. As he turned again to face them there fell a bar of silence. At a prearranged signal, the children's choir began his favourite hymn: the *Veni Creator*. They had saved it till the last.

> "Come, Holy Spirit, Creator, come,
> From thy bright heav'nly throne."

He had always loved these noble words, written by the great Charlemagne in the ninth century, the loveliest hymn of the Church. Everyone on the landing was singing now.

"Take possession of our souls,
And make them all thy own."

Oh, dear, he thought, yielding at last, that's kind, that's sweet of them . . . but oh, how wickedly unfair! A convulsive movement passed over his face.

As the launch moved away from the stage and he raised his hand to bless them, tears were streaming down his battered face.

V

THE RETURN

I

His Grace Bishop Mealey was extremely late. Twice a nice young priest of the household had peeped round the parlour door to explain that His Lordship and His Lordship's secretary were detained, unavoidably, at a Convocation. Father Chisholm blinked formidably over his copy of the *Tablet*.

"Punctuality is the politeness of prelates!"

"His Lordship is a very busy man." With an uncertain smile, the young priest withdrew, not quite sure of this old boy from China, half-wondering if he could be trusted with the silver. The appointment had been for eleven. Now the clock showed half-past twelve.

It was the same room in which he had awaited his interview with Rusty Mac. How long ago? Good heavens . . . thirty-six years! He shook his head dolefully. It had amused him to intimidate the pretty stripling, but his mood was far from combative. He felt rather shaky this morning, and desperately nervous. He wanted something from the Bishop. He hated asking favours, yet he must ask this one, and his heart had jumped when the summons to the interview arrived at the modest hotel where he had been staying since the ship unloaded him at Liverpool.

Valiantly, he straightened his wrinkled vest, spruced up his tired collar. He was not really old. There was plenty of go in him yet. Now that it was well past noon, Anselm would undoubtedly ask him to remain to luncheon. He would be spry, curb his outrageous tongue, listen to Anselm's stories, laugh at his jokes, not be above a little, or perhaps a lot of, flattery. He hoped to God the nerve wouldn't start twitching in his damaged cheek. That made him look a perfect lunatic!

It was ten minutes to one. At last there came a commotion of importance in the corridor outside and, decisively, Bishop Mealey entered the room. Perhaps he had been hurrying; his manner was brisk, his eye beaming towards Francis, not unconscious of the clock.

"My dear Francis. It's splendid to see you again. You must pardon this little delay. No, don't get up, I beg of you. We'll talk here. It's . . . it's more intimate than in my room."

Briskly, he pulled out a chair and seated himself with an easy grace beside Father Chisholm at the table. As he rested his fleshy, well-tended hand affectionately upon the other's sleeve, he thought: Good heavens, how old and feeble he has become!

"And how is dear Pai-tan? Not unflourishing, Monsignor Sleeth tells me. I vividly remember when I stood in that stricken city, amidst deadly plague and desolation. Truly the hand of God lay upon it. Ah, those were my pioneering days, Francis. I pine for them sometimes. Now," he smiled, "I'm only a Bishop. Do you see much change in me since we parted on that Orient strand?"

Francis studied his old friend with an odd admiration. There was no doubt of it — the years had improved Anselm Mealey. Maturity had come late to him. His office had given him dignity, toned his early effusiveness to suavity. He had a fine presence and held his head high. The soft full ecclesiastic face was lit by the same velvety eye. He was well preserved, still had his own teeth, and a supple vigorous skin.

Francis said simply, "I've never seen you look better."

The Bishop inclined his head, pleased. "*O tempora! O mores!* We're neither of us so young as we were. But I don't wear too badly. Frankly, I find perfect health essential to efficiency. If you knew what I have to cope with! They've put me on a balanced diet. And I have a masseur, a husky Swede, who literally pummels the fear of God into me. . . . I'm afraid," with a sudden genuine solicitude, "you've been very careless of yourself."

"I feel like an old ragman beside you, Anselm, and that is God's truth. . . . But I keep young in heart . . . or try to. And there's still some service left in me. I . . . I hope you're not altogether dissatisfied with my work in Pai-tan."

"My dear Father, your efforts were heroic. Naturally we're a little disappointed in the figures. Monsignor Sleeth was showing me only yesterday . . ." The voice was quite benevolent. ". . . In all your thirty-six years you made less conversions than Father Lawler made in five. Please don't think I'm reproaching you — that would be too unkind. Someday when you have leisure we'll discuss it thoroughly. Meanwhile — " His eye was hovering round the clock. "Is there anything we can do for you?"

There was a pause; then, in a low tone, Francis answered: "Yes . . . There is, your Grace . . . I want a parish."

The Bishop almost started out of his benign, affectionate composure. He slowly raised his brows as Father Chisholm continued, with that quiet intensity: "Give me Tweedside, Anselm. There's a vacancy at Renton . . . a bigger, better parish. Promote the Tweedside priest to Renton. And let me . . . Let me go home."

The Bishop's smile had become fixed, rather less easy, upon his handsome face. "My dear Francis, you seem to wish to administer my diocese."

"I have a special reason for asking you. I would be so very grateful . . ." To his horror Father Chisholm found his voice out of control. He broke off, then added huskily: "Bishop MacNabb promised I should have a parish if ever I came home." He began to fumble in his inside pocket. "I have his letter . . ."

Anselm raised his hand. "I can't be expected to honour the posthumous letters of my predecessor." A silence; then, with kindly urbanity, His Lordship continued: "Naturally, I will bear your request in mind. But I cannot promise. Tweedside has always been very dear to me. When the weight of the pro-cathedral is off my shoulders I had thought of building myself a retreat there — a little Castle Gondolfo." He paused — his ear, still keen, picking up the sound of an arriving car, followed by voices in the hall outside. Diplomatically his eye sought the clock. His pleasant manner quickened. "Well . . . It is all in God's hands. We shall see, we shall see."

"If you would let me explain — " Francis protested humbly. "I'm
. . . rather anxious to make a home . . . for someone."

"You must tell me some other time." Another car outside and
more voices. The Bishop gathered up his violet cassock, his tone
honeyed with regret. "It is quite a calamity, Francis, that I must
slip away, just as I was looking forward to our long and interesting
talk. I have an official luncheon at one. The Lord Mayor and City
Council are my guests. More politics, alas . . . school board, water
board, finance . . . a *quid pro quo* . . . I have to be a stockbroker
these days . . . But I like it Francis, I like it!"

"I wouldn't take more than a minute . . ." Francis stopped short,
dropped his gaze to the floor.

The Bishop had risen blandly. With his arm lightly on Father
Chisholm's shoulder he aided him affectionately to the door. "I can't
express what a great joy it has been for me to welcome you home.
We will keep in touch with you, never fear. And now, I must leave
you. Good-bye, Francis . . . and bless you."

Outside, a stream of large dark limousines flowed up the drive
towards the high portico of the palace. The old priest had a vision of
a purple face beneath a beaver hat, of more faces, hard and bloated,
of miniver, gold chains of office. A wet wind was blowing and it
cut his old bones, used to sunshine and covered only by his thin
tropic suit. As he moved away a car-wheel churned near the curb
and a spurt of mud flew up and hit him in the eye. He wiped it off
with his hand, gazing down the arches of the years, reflecting, with
a faint grim smile: Anselm's mud bath is avenged.

His breast was cold, yet through his disappointment, his sinking
weakness, a white flame burned, unquenchably. He must find a
church at once. Across the street the great domed bulk of the new
cathedral loomed, a million pounds in sterling, transmuted to massive stone and marble. He limped urgently towards it.

He reached the broad entrance steps, mounted them, then suddenly drew up. Before him, on the wet stone of the topmost step, a
ragged cripple crouched in the wind, with a card pinned upon his
chest: *Old Soldier, Please Help.*

Francis contemplated the broken figure. He pulled out the solitary shilling from his pocket, placed it in the tin cup. The two unwanted soldiers gazed at each other in silence, then each gazed away.

He entered the pro-cathedral, an echoing vastness of beauty and silence, pillared in marble, rich in oak and bronze, a temple of towering and intricate design, in which his mission chapel would have stood unnoticed, forgotten, in a corner of the transept. Undaunted, he marched towards the high altar. There he knelt and fiercely, with unshaken valour, prayed.

"Oh, Lord, for once — not Thy will, but mine, be done."

II

FIVE weeks later Father Chisholm made his expedition, long deferred, to Kirkbridge. As he left the railway station the cotton-thread mills of that large industrial centre were disgorging their workers for the dinner hour. Hundreds of women with shawls wrapped about their heads went hurrying through the drenching rain, yielding only to an occasional tram clanging over the greasy cobbles.

At the end of the main street he inquired his way, then took to the right, past an enormous statue erected to a local thread magnate, and entered a poorer locality: a squalid square imprisoned by high tenements. He crossed the square and plunged into a narrow alley, fetid with smells, so dark that, on the brightest day, no gleam of sun could penetrate. Despite his joy, his high excitement, the priest's heart sank. He had expected poverty but not this. . . . He thought: What have I done in my stupidity and neglect! Here, it was like being at the bottom of a well.

He inspected the numbers on the tenement entrances, singled out the right one, and began to climb the stairs, which were without light or air, the windows foul, the gas brackets plugged. A cracked soil pipe had drenched one landing.

Three flights up he stumbled and almost fell. A child was seated upon the stairs, a boy. The priest stared through the foggy gloom at the small rachitic figure, supporting his heavy head with one hand, bracing his sharp elbow against his bony knee. His skin was the colour of candle tallow. He was almost transparent. He looked like a tired old man. He might have been seven years of age.

Suddenly the boy lifted his head so that a shaft from the broken skylight fell upon him. For the first time Francis saw the child's face. He gave a stifled exclamation and a heavy wave of terrible emotion broke over him, he felt it as a ship might feel the buffet of a heavy wave. That pallid upturned face was unmistakable in its likeness to Nora's face. The eyes, especially, enormous in the pinched skin, could never be denied.

"What is your name?"

A pause. The boy answered: "Andrew."

Behind the landing door there was a single room where, cross-legged on a dirty mattress stretched on the bare boards, a woman stitched rapidly, her needle flying with deadly, automatic speed. Beside her, on an upturned egg-box, was a bottle. There was no furniture, only a kettle, some sacking, and a cracked jug. Across the egg-box lay a pile of half-finished coarse serge trousers.

Torn by his distress, Francis could barely speak. "You are Mrs. Stevens?" She nodded. "I came . . . about the boy."

She let her work fall nervously into her lap: a poor creature, not old, nor vicious, yet worn-out by adversity, sodden through and through. "Yes, I had your letter." She began to whimper out an explanation of her circumstances, to exonerate herself, to produce irrelevant evidence proving how misfortune had lowered her to this.

He stopped her quietly; the story was written in her face. He said: "I'll take him back with me today."

At this quietness, she dropped her eyes to her swollen hands, the fingers blue-stippled by countless needle-pricks. Though she made an effort to conceal it, his attitude agitated her more than any rebuke. She began to weep.

"Don't think I'm not fond of him. He helps me in a heap of ways. I've treated him well enough. But it's been a sore struggle." She looked up with sudden defiance, silent.

Ten minutes later he left the house. Beside him, clutching a paper bundle to his pigeon chest, was Andrew. The priest's feelings were deep and complex. He sensed the child's dumb alarm at the unprecedented excursion, yet felt he could best reassure him by silence. He thought, with a slow deep joy: God gave me my life, brought me from China . . . for this!

They walked to the railway station without a word between them. In the train, Andrew sat staring out of the window, hardly moving, his legs dangling over the edge of the seat. He was very dirty, grime was ingrained into his thin pallid neck. Once or twice he glanced sideways at Francis, then immediately he glanced away again. It was impossible to guess his thoughts, but in the depths of his eyes there lurked a dark glimmer of fear and suspicion.

"Don't be afraid."

"I'm not afraid." The boy's underlip quivered.

Once the train had quitted the smoke of Kirkbridge it sped across the country and down the riverside. A look of wonder dawned slowly on the boy's face. He had never dreamed that colours could be so bright, so different from the leaden squalor of the slums. The open fields and farmlands gave place to a wilder scene, where woods sprang up about them, rich with green bracken and the part's-tongue fern, where the glint of rushing water showed in little glens.

"Is this where we are going?"

"Yes, we're nearly there."

They ran into Tweedside towards three in the afternoon. The old town, clustered on the riverbank, so unchanged he might have left it only yesterday, lay basking in brilliant sunshine. As the familiar landmarks swam into his gaze Francis' throat constricted with a painful joy. They left the little station and walked to St. Columba's Presbytery together.

VI

END OF THE BEGINNING

FROM the window of his room Monsignor Sleeth frowned down towards the garden where Miss Moffat, basket in hand, stood with Andrew and Father Chisholm, watching Dougal fork up the dinner vegetables. The tacit air of companionship surrounding the little group heightened his fretful feeling of exclusion, hardened his resolution. On the table behind him, typed on his portable machine, lay his finished report — a terse and lucid document, crammed with hanging evidence. He was leaving for Tynecastle in an hour. It would be in the Bishop's hands this evening.

Despite the keen, incisive satisfaction of accomplishment it was undeniable that the past week at St. Columba's had been trying. He had found much to annoy, even to confuse him. Except for a group centred round the pious yet obese Mrs. Glendenning, the people of the parish had some regard, he might even say affection, for their eccentric pastor. Yesterday, he had been obliged to deal severely with the delegation that waited on him to protest their loyalty to the parish priest. As if he didn't know that every native son must have his claque! The height of his exasperation was touched that same evening when the local Presbyterian minister dropped in and, after hemming and hawing, ventured to hope that Father Chisholm was not "leaving them" — the "feeling" in the town had lately been so admirable. . . . Admirable — indeed!

While he meditated, the group beneath his eye broke up and Andrew ran to the summerhouse to get his kite. The old man had a mania for making kites, great paper things with waving tails, which flew — Sleeth grudgingly admitted — like monster birds. On Tuesday, coming upon the two breezily attached to the clouds by humming twine, he had ventured to remonstrate.

"Really, Father. Do you think this pastime dignified?"

The old man had smiled — confound it, he was never rebellious: always that quiet, maddeningly gentle smile.

"The Chinese do. And they're a dignified people."

"It's one of their pagan customs, I presume."

"Ah, well! Surely a very innocent one!"

He remained aloof, his nose turning blue in the sharp wind, watching them. It appeared that the old priest was merging pleasure with instruction. From time to time, while he held the string, the boy would sit in the summerhouse taking down dictation on strips of paper. Completed, these laboured scrawls were threaded on the string, sent soaring to the sky, amidst joint jubilation.

An impulse of curiosity had mastered him. He took the latest missive from the boy's excited hands. It was clearly written and not ill-spelled. He read: "I faithfully promise to oppose bravely all that is stupid and bigoted and cruel. Signed, ANDREW. *P.S.* Toleration is the highest virtue. Humility comes next."

He looked at it bleakly, for a long time, before surrendering it. He even waited with a chilled face until the next was prepared. "Our bones may moulder and become the earth of the fields but the Spirit issues forth and lives on high in a condition of glorious brightness. God is the common Father of all mankind."

Mollified, Sleeth looked at Father Chisholm. "Excellent. Didn't Saint Paul say that?"

"No." The old man shook his head apologetically. "It was Confucius."

Sleeth was staggered. He walked away without a word.

That night he misguidedly began an argument, which the old man evaded with disconcerting ease. At the end he burst out, provoked: —

"Your notion of God is a strange one."

"Which of us has any notion of God?" Father Chisholm smiled. "Our word 'God' is a human word . . . expressing reverence for our Creator. If we have that reverence, we shall see God . . . never fear."

To his annoyance, Sleeth had found himself flushing. "You seem to have a very slight regard for Holy Church."

"On the contrary . . . all my life I have rejoiced to feel her arms about me. The Church is our great mother, leading us forward . . . a band of pilgrims, through the night. But perhaps there are other mothers. And perhaps even some poor solitary pilgrims who stumble home alone."

The scene, of which this was a fragment, seriously disconcerted Sleeth and gave him, when he returned that night, a shockingly distorted nightmare. He dreamed that while the house slept his guardian angel and Father Chisholm's knocked off for an hour and went down to the living room for a drink. Chisholm's angel was a slight cherubic creature, but his own was an elderly angel with discontented eyes and a ruffled angry plumage. As they sipped their drink, wings at rest on the elbows of their chairs, they discussed their present charges. Chisholm, although indicted as a sentimentalist, escaped lightly. But he . . . he was torn to shreds. He sweated in his sleep as he heard his angel dismiss him with a final malediction. "One of the worst I ever had . . . prejudiced, pedantic, overambitious, and worst of all a bore."

Sleeth wakened with a start in the darkness of his room. What a hateful, disgusting dream. He shivered. His head ached. He knew better than to give credence to such nightmares, no more than odious distortions of one's waking thoughts, altogether different from the good, authentic scriptural dreams, that of Pharaoh's wife, for instance. He dismissed his dream violently, like an impure thought. But it nagged him now, as he stood at the window: *Prejudiced, pedantic, over-ambitious, and worst of all, a bore.*

Apparently he had misjudged Andrew, for the child emerged from the summerhouse bearing, not his kite, but a large wicker trug into which, with Dougal's aid, he began to place some fresh-picked plums and pears. When the task was accomplished the boy moved towards the house, carrying the long basket on his arm.

Sleeth had an inexplicable impulse to retreat. He sensed that the gift was for him. He resented it, was vaguely, absurdly disconcerted. The knock on his door made him pull his scattered wits together.

"Come in."

Andrew entered the room and put the fruits upon the chest of drawers. With the shamed consciousness of one who knows himself suspected he delivered his message, memorized all the way up-stairs. "Father Chisholm hopes you will take these with you — the plums are very sweet — and the pears are the very last we'll get."

Monsignor Sleeth looked sharply at the boy, wondering if a double meaning were intended in that final simple phrase.

"Where is Father Chisholm?"

"Downstairs. Waiting on you."

"And my car?"

"Dougal has just brought it round for you to the front door." There was a pause. Andrew began, hesitantly, to move away.

"Wait!" Sleeth drew up. "Don't you think it would be more convenient . . . altogether politer . . . if you carried down the fruit and put it in my car?"

The boy coloured nervously and turned to obey. As he lifted the basket from the chest one of the plums fell off and rolled below the bed. Darkly red, he stooped and clumsily retrieved it, its smooth skin burst, a trickle of juice upon his fingers. Sleeth watched him with a cold smile.

"That one won't be much good . . . will it?"

No answer.

"I said, will it?"

"No, sir."

Sleeth's strange pale smile deepened. "You are a remarkably stubborn child. I've been watching you all the week. Stubborn and ill-bred. Why don't you look at me?"

With a tremendous effort the boy wrenched his eyes from the floor. He was trembling, like a nervous foal, as he met Sleeth's gaze.

"It is the sign of a guilty conscience not to look straight at a

THE WAR OF
THE REVOLUTION

By *CHRISTOPHER WARD*

Edited by *JOHN RICHARD ALDEN*

IN TWO VOLUMES

VOLUME TWO

THE MACMILLAN COMPANY : NEW YORK

1952

The maps on pages 217, 299, 345, 367, 583, 601, 607, 727, 759, 789, 805, 819, and 829 also appear in *The Delaware Continentals, 1776–1783*, by Christopher L. Ward, copyright, 1941, by the Historical Society of Delaware.

Contents

VOLUME TWO

The War in the South

Maps

VOLUME TWO

C H A P T E R   3 8

Stanwix and Oriskany

It will be remembered that there was a third element in Burgoyne's plan for the conquest of the Hudson: an expedition from Canada by way of Lake Ontario, Oswego, and the Mohawk River to meet Burgoyne at Albany. Its purpose was also the occupation of the extensive and important Mohawk valley, the gateway to the great western country and to the territory of the powerful Six Nations of Indians, whose support in the war Great Britain was seeking. We must now turn to that valley.

The American border settlements in the West were not left undisturbed during the War of Independence. Rather the war was waged there with the ferocity and cruelty characteristic of the chief components of the British forces in that section, that is to say the Indians enlisted with them, not to mention their Tory allies. A ruthlessness, one regrets to say, that was matched at last by the great American punitive expedition finally sent against the Indian towns in that section.

Tryon County in New York was one of the chief seats of the conflict in the West. It was a vast tract, comprising the land west and northwest of Schenectady and extending to Lake Ontario. Through it ran the Mohawk River in a beautiful and fertile valley. Its great area was sparsely settled, harboring perhaps 5,000 people. They were of diverse nationalities. A numerous element of Germans from the Rhenish Palatinate, indicated by the name of one of the chief settlements, German Flats, lived chiefly along the upper reaches of the river. In its lower reaches the population was largely of Dutch extraction. Everywhere there were people of English descent. The Irish were well represented, also the Scotch-Irish. Scottish Highlanders were numerous, particularly in the neighborhood of Johnstown.

As in the South under similar conditions, the political sentiments of the people were divided, in part along lines of nationality, in part by individual or family preferences. The Germans and many of the Dutch were inclined to favor the royal government; the Highlanders were as loyal to the King as their kinsmen in the Carolinas. The whole county was generally regarded as a Tory stronghold. One historian says that "the loyalists in that [Mohawk] valley were probably more numerous, in proportion to the whole . . . population, than in almost any other section of the northern states." [1] And yet the fact that the course of the war forced so many of them, including the most powerful and influential, to flee to Canada would seem to prove the existence of a majority of patriots, unless as elsewhere they were merely better organized and more vigorous in their activities.

To the west of Tryon County was the seat of the great Iroquois League, the Six Nations, the Mohawks, Onondagas, Cayugas, Senecas, Oneidas, and Tuscaroras. Their towns and their "castles," the headquarters of the various tribes or of their component clans, were numerous over a wide extent of country.

The ruling family in the county were the Johnsons, headed by Sir William, the British Superintendent of Indian Affairs, until his death in 1774 and after that by his son, Sir John, and his son-in-law, Colonel Guy Johnson, who was his successor in office. The Johnsons were strongly and unitedly Tory. Sir William had been the greatest landholder and the wealthiest man in the county. His handsome mansion house at Johnstown was the center of governmental relations with the Indians, the symbol of the wealth and power of the great nation he officially represented. While his influence was strong in determining the attitude of many of the whites toward the conflict between Britain and the colonists, it was predominant among the Indians.

This influence over the Indians was based not only on his official position, but also on a lifelong, sympathetic study of their ways, habits, and dispositions. It was also powerfully backed by his left-handed family relationship with two of their great chieftains. After the death of his first wife, a German, he took to himself, successively, two Indian mistresses, Caroline, the daughter of Hendrick, the famous Mohawk "King," and Molly, sister of Joseph Brant, also called Thayendanegea, chief war leader of the Mohawks and as such of the whole Iroquois League. Molly, indeed, may have been actually married to Sir William in Indian fashion; at all events she had a recognized position as the head of his household. She was a woman of considerable mental ability and great shrewdness, and her influence among the Indians was freely exerted and very potent.

Her brother, Joseph Brant, was a figure of distinction, a remarkable man.

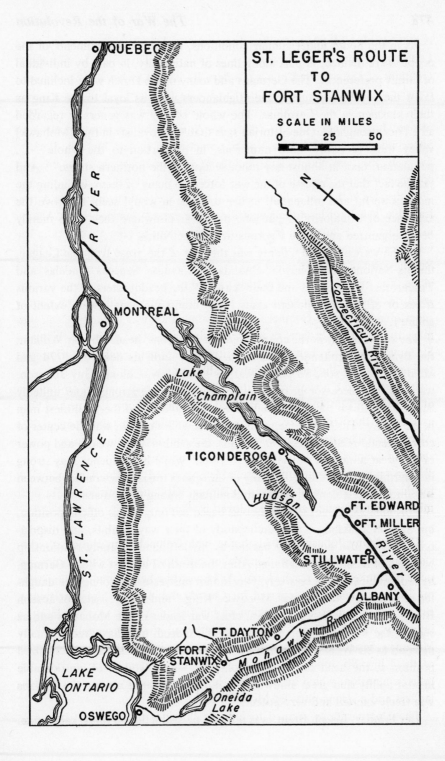

ST. LEGER'S ROUTE
TO
FORT STANWIX

SCALE IN MILES
0   25   50

N

QUEBEC

RIVER

MONTREAL

Lake
Champlain

Connecticut River

TICONDEROGA

ST. LAWRENCE

Hudson

FT. EDWARD

FT. MILLER

STILLWATER

River

ALBANY

FT. DAYTON

FORT
STANWIX

Mohawk   R.

LAKE
ONTARIO

Oneida
Lake

OSWEGO

A full-blooded Mohawk, he had been educated in English at a school in Lebanon, Connecticut, under the tutelage of Dr. Eleazar Wheelock (founder of Dartmouth College), where he is said to have assisted in the translation of religious books into the Indian tongue. He had visited England, had been entertained by James Boswell, and had had his portrait painted by Romney. On his return to America he became secretary to Superintendent Guy Johnson. Yet he remained an Indian. He went back to live with his own people and distinguished himself as one of their most courageous warriors and undoubtedly their ablest strategist.

Both sides in the war solicited the aid of the Six Nations or, on the American side, sought at least their neutrality. The great "council-fire" at Albany in August, 1775, at which the Indians agreed "not to take any part" in the war because they deemed it "a family affair," has already been mentioned. But the spirit of that agreement was observed by the Oneidas and Tuscaroras alone. The other four Indian nations yielded to the powerful influence of the Johnsons and of Daniel Claus, also a son-in-law of Sir William and deputy superintendent under Colonel Guy. This influence was backed by the munificent gifts to the Indians of arms, clothing, and other desirable things by Sir Guy Carleton on behalf of the British government, which the Congress was possibly unwilling and certainly unable to match.

It must be said, however, that the alliance was not unnatural on the part of the Indians. For more than a hundred years the Iroquois League had been assisted by the British forces in their long conflict with their enemies, the Algonquins. This new alliance was, in effect, but the continuance of a long-standing cooperation. It is rather to be wondered at that the Oneidas and Tuscaroras should decide to adhere, at least passively, to the American side; for this much credit must be given to Samuel Kirkland, a missionary in their midst, much respected and indeed loved by them.

Colonel Guy Johnson left his home with Colonel John Butler, an outstanding Tory leader, Butler's son Walter, and Joseph Brant shortly after the news of Bunker's Hill reached him. At Oswego he held a great council with the Indians. Thence he departed for Canada, taking with him the Butlers, Brant, and a numerous delegation of his Indian friends. At Montreal an interview with Sir Guy Carleton strengthened the determination of the Mohawks, Senecas, Cayugas, and Onondagas to join in the war on the side of the King. Sir John Johnson, however, remained at Johnson Hall, his father's mansion, which he fortified. He was guarded by 150 armed Highlanders and a strong party of Mohawks.

These preparations seemed to indicate "designs of the most dangerous tendency to the rights, liberties, property and even lives" of the patriots, as General Schuyler wrote to Sir John in January, 1776. He ordered out the county militia under General Herkimer, to the number of more than 3,000, and marched to a point near Johnson Hall, where he met Sir John. At the meeting Sir John agreed to surrender all his armament and submitted to being taken prisoner. He was soon thereafter liberated upon his parole not to engage in hostilities against the Americans. Within four months from the time of his agreement, he broke his parole and, with a large number of his tenants and other Tories, took to the woods on his way to Montreal, where he arrived after a journey of great hardship lasting nearly three weeks.

By the departure of the Johnsons, the Butlers, Brant, and their adherents, Tryon County was relieved of the most powerful members of its Tory element; but the dangers to its peace and the welfare of its patriot inhabitants were thereby increased rather than lessened. Their Tory enemies were now in touch with the British forces in Canada and thus able to concert measures for hostile operations with more facility and greater effectiveness than if they had remained in the midst of their former neighbors, where they could have been observed and more readily suppressed. This was soon made evident when Sir John received a commission as colonel in the British service and raised a Tory regiment of two battalions, entitled the Royal Greens from the color of their coats, which conformed to the customary uniforms of the Loyalist troops attached to the British army. Colonel John Butler also raised a corps of Tory Rangers, similarly clad.[2]

Hostile invasion of the county was not, however, immediately begun. Two years were to elapse before Johnson and Butler appeared in arms against their former neighbors. That was in August, 1777, when their troops formed a part of the British expedition auxiliary to Burgoyne's plan for the conquest of the Hudson.

The principal defensive post in the Mohawk valley was Fort Stanwix, built in 1758 to hold the portage, the Great Carrying Place, between the river and Wood Creek, which runs into Lake Ontario. Originally a strong fortification with bomb-proof bastions, a glacis, a covered way, and a well picketed ditch, it had, as usual, been allowed to decay. When in April, 1777, Colonel Peter Gansevoort with the 3rd New York Continental regiment took over its command, he found it "not only indefensible, but untenable." [3] Gansevoort, energetic and resolute, a competent soldier, was a young officer, no more than twenty-eight years old. He was ably seconded by his courageous, enterprising lieutenant colonel, Marinus Willett, spirited and active. They put their men to work on the old fort, and before its day of supreme trial it was restored to a defensible condition. Standing athwart the way from Oswego to Albany, it must first be reduced before invaders from the west could proceed to the Hudson. The task of reducing it fell to Barry St. Leger, who was appointed by Burgoyne to lead the auxiliary expedition forward from Oswego.

Barry St. Leger was an experienced soldier; more than half of his forty years had been spent in the King's service. He had taken part in the siege of Louisburg and in the capture of Quebec. His regular and permanent rank was lieutenant colonel of the 34th Foot; but temporarily and locally he had the title of brigadier general.

The force allotted to St. Leger was made up of detachments of 100 men each from the 8th and the 34th regiments, a regiment of 133 Tories of Sir John Johnson's "Royal Greens," a company of Tory Rangers under Colonel John Butler, and about 350 Hanau jägers. Forty artillerists were equipped with two 6-pounders, two 3-pounders, and four very small mortars, called "cohorns" or "royals." Some Canadian irregulars, a large number of axmen, and other noncombatants were added.[4] As he started with only one company of the jägers, about 100 men, the rest being delayed, his force of white men numbered about 875 of all ranks. The Indian contingent, under Joseph Brant, between 800 and 1,000 strong, met him at Oswego on his arrival July 25. The next day he started for Fort Stanwix, which he had been led to believe was in a ruinous condition and garrisoned by only 60 men.

Thomas Spencer, a half-breed chief of the Oneidas, was present at a council of the Six Nations where Daniel Claus urged the Indians to join St. Leger, and he brought word of this to the inhabitants of the valley. The result was unfortunate for the American cause: the Tories became bolder and more active. The less courageous and the uncertain patriots either professed neutrality or secretly allied themselves with the Tories. There was a general paralysis of the patriot effort throughout the valley.

To counteract this sad effect was the task of Nicholas Herkimer, brigadier general of the county militia. The son of a Palatine German immigrant named Ergheimer who had secured large grants of land along the river, he was now, in his fiftieth year, a moderately wealthy man. He had fought in the French and Indian War. He has been described as "short, slender, of dark complexion, with black hair and bright eyes." [5] Like many of the people of the valley, he was better acquainted with the tongue of his ancestors than with the English language.

On July 17 Herkimer issued a brief but vigorous and stirring proclamation calling on all able-bodied men between the ages of sixteen and sixty to prepare for mobilization; all invalids and old men were to be ready to defend their homes, and all Tories and slackers were to be arrested and confined. This appeal, powerfully backed by the dread prospect of an Indian invasion, had the desired effect. The fighting spirit of the rebels of Tryon County was fully aroused.

St. Leger's march was conducted with much caution, with great regularity, and in excellent formation. Five single-file columns of Indians, widely spaced, preceded the advance guard of soldiers by about a quarter of a mile. A middle single file, its members ten paces apart, followed these soldiers, to ensure communication with the main body. The regulars' advance guard, 60 marksmen of the Royal Greens, marched in two columns a hundred yards ahead of the British regulars, whose two detachments marched side by side. Indian flankers covered both sides of the main body, and a guard of regulars brought up the rear. All the columns were in single file. Though St. Leger moved cautiously, he moved swiftly. His force marched ten miles a day, excellent progress in a wilderness of forests, streams, and swamps.

But he wished for an even swifter movement to surprise the fort and cut off its communications with the lower country, and especially to intercept a convoy of provisions and supplies on the way to it. Accordingly, he pushed forward a detachment of 30 regulars of the 8th Regiment under Lieutenant Bird, and 200 Indians led by Brant. They reached Stanwix on the 2nd, just too late to cut off the convoy of five bateaux and a reenforcement of 200 men, which got safely into the fort, although one of several bateaumen lingering about the boats was killed. Two others were wounded, and the captain of the boats was captured. The next day St. Leger and his full force arrived.

His first move was an attempt to intimidate the garrison by a review of his troops in plain sight of the palisaded earthwork. The varied uniforms, scarlet for the British, blue for the Germans, green for the jägers, the rangers, and Johnson's Tories, made a gay display; but the naked bodies of a thousand savages were more impressive. Impressive, however, in a way contrary to St. Leger's intentions. They were visible indications of the cruel fate of the men of the garrison and of their families in the settlements behind them, if the fort were not held against the invaders. And so that parade stiffened the determination of the 750 defenders not to let the savages and their allies pass.

St. Leger's second move was to send a proclamation, under a flag, into the fort. It rivaled Burgoyne's similar effort in pomposity. Indeed, most of it was a copy of that sample of "enlightened absurdity." It received no answer.

Perceiving that the fort was too strong and too strongly held to yield to an assault, St. Leger disposed his force to besiege it. It stood on a slight elevation on the north side of the river and close to the road from Wood Creek to the Lower Landing on the Hudson, being the important portage or Great Carrying Place. Behind it there was a somewhat higher elevation on which he established the camp of his regular troops. At the Lower Landing, most of the Canadians, Tories, and Indians were posted. Another detachment of Tories held a position on Wood Creek to the west of the fort. Little groups of Indians were strung along from that place to the Lower Landing. Thus the fort was surrounded. But it was not closely invested, for the circuit of the investment was nearly three miles long and there was heavily wooded and swampy ground on the southwest, which could not be tightly held.

St. Leger's next thought was for his communications with Lake Ontario. A road sixteen miles long through the forest had to be cut before he could bring up his artillery and heavy supplies. Also Wood Creek had to be cleared of the trees that Gansevoort had felled to obstruct it. Besides his Canadian axmen and other noncombatants, he put so many of his men to work at that job that on August 5, when he had news of a relieving force on its way to the fort, he had in camp fewer than 250 regular troops to oppose it.

In the meantime, the Indians along with their friends, the German jägers, had been enjoying a safe kind of warfare. Taking cover as near the fort as possible, they fired at the Americans who were piling sods on the parapet to increase its height, and wounded several of them. To reply, marksmen were posted at different parts of the works; and a brisk, though desultory, fire was kept up throughout the 4th and 5th.

On July 30 Herkimer, having news of St. Leger's advance, summoned his militia to rendezvous at Fort Dayton on the Mohawk about thirty miles below Stanwix. They turned out in satisfactory numbers, about 800 of them, and marched on August 4. Although encumbered by a train of oxcarts,[6] they made good progress, about twenty-two miles in two days. On the way, they were joined by 60 Oneida Indians, who were to act as scouts.

Herkimer sent forward four runners to inform Gansevoort of his approach. In reply Gansevoort was to fire three cannon shots, acknowledging receipt of the news and signaling his readiness to make a sortie when the relief column was near, then to engage the enemy about the fort and prevent them from concentrating on Herkimer's troops.

On the morning of the 6th Herkimer held a council of war. No gunshots from the fort had been heard. The question was whether the relieving force should, nevertheless, immediately advance or await the expected signal. Herkimer was for waiting; but in that opinion he stood almost alone. His subordinate officers were for going on, regardless of the lack of reply by Gansevoort.

The matter was debated with acerbity which developed into hot anger on the part of those urging an immediate advance. Herkimer seems to have kept his temper, but stubbornly held to his opinion. The others charged him with cowardice, called him a Tory at heart, brought up the fact that one of his brothers was an officer in a Tory company under St. Leger. At last he could no longer withstand their urgency, coupled with accusations of pol-- troonery. He yielded and gave the order.

The Oneida scouts went ahead. Herkimer, conspicuously mounted on a white horse, showed that he was no coward by taking the lead of his men. After him, 600 marched in double file. Then came the wagon train, followed by a rear guard of 200.

At the news of the advance of Herkimer's men St. Leger prepared to receive them before they got to the fort. Six miles short of Stanwix, and near Oriskany village, the road crossed a wide ravine, fifty feet deep with steep sides. Through it ran a small stream bordered by a morass. Across that bottom, the road was corduroyed with loose logs, offering a difficult and a narrow passage. Here St. Leger proposed to check, indeed to annihilate, Herkimer's force. To this work he detailed a part of his Royal Greens, a detachment of Butler's Rangers, and the whole force of Indians under Joseph Brant.

The plan was to post the white men on the west of the ravine and the savages in hiding along its western margin in a curve almost encircling it, but leave the eastern side open for Herkimer's troops to enter the trap. When the middle of the column was deep in the ravine, the Tories and Rangers were to check its head, and the Indians were to close the circle around the rear on the east. Thus Herkimer would be completely surrounded by enemies under cover of rocks and trees, their fire converging on his trapped column. It was a well conceived scheme, admirably fitted to the character of those who were to execute it and likely to be successful.

It is difficult to understand why the Oneida scouts did not discover some signs of that ambuscade; but they did not. If the Americans had thrown out any flankers, they must have stumbled upon some of the ambushed Indians and given the alarm. It seems probable that no such precautions were taken, that the long thin column was confined to the narrow road.

The main body, led by Herkimer, had made its way down into the ravine and up the other side, and the groaning, creaking supply train of oxcarts was negotiating the difficult passage when the trap was sprung. The Indians east of the ravine leaped from their cover, delivered their fire, and rushed in with whoops and yells to close the circle—rushed in a little too soon for complete encirclement, for they closed upon the rear of the wagon train, between it and the rear guard. Cut off from the main body, the guard fled along the road, pursued by some of the savages.

Herkimer, at the head of the column, heard the firing in the rear, turned his horse, and hurried to investigate the situation. As he did so, the Tories and Indians on the west of the ravine pushed forward and began shooting. On the western slope of the ravine, his horse fell dead; his own leg was wounded.

The circle was now complete. Hemmed in on every side, the Americans broke from their ordered line. Singly or in groups they took cover behind trees. There was no front to this fight. Behind a tree, a man was not covered from the bullets of the enemy in his rear. And the Indians were coming closer on every side, ready to charge upon the disorganized mass with tomahawk and knife.

To protect their rear, groups of the Americans formed little circles, facing out from behind trees. Herkimer was carried into their midst. His saddle was brought. Astride it, his back against a tree, he lit his pipe and with great coolness directed his men to form one great circle and thus oppose their fire to all those around them.

But it was not a compact circle after the manner of a British square. It was irregular and widely spaced. The attack was irregular, too, and there was much hand-to-hand fighting, Indian tomahawks and knives and Tory bayonets against clubbed muskets. At this work, the Indians were experts. As soon as an American had fired, an Indian would rush in upon him and cut him down with a tomahawk before he could reload.

But after three-quarters of an hour of this desperate conflict there was a sudden and complete cessation of fire on both sides. The lowering clouds of that hot, sultry day had broken and discharged a downpour that wet the priming of the flintlocks. No gun could be discharged. For a full hour, this armistice lasted. Then the sun came out and the fight began again, but with a slight difference. Herkimer had ordered his men to take cover by twos, so that, when one had fired and was reloading, the other would be ready to shoot any of the savages that attempted their favorite trick.

The Indians had been suffering severely and had begun to lose interest in such a well contested struggle. Their fire slackened; they showed signs of uneasiness. At this juncture Major Watts came up with a second detachment of Royal Greens. He had them turn their coats inside out, so that their uni-

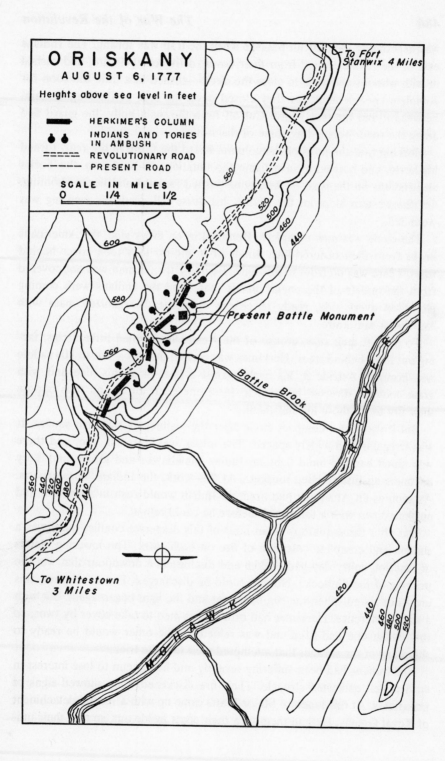

form color was concealed. So they advanced in the guise of a friendly sortie from the fort. But when they were near the ruse was discovered; they were boldly attacked, and a terrific hand-to-hand fight ensued, with bayonets, gun butts, and knives doing their deadly work.

But by this time the Indians had had enough. The cry of retreat, *"Oonah! Oonah!"* was raised. They drew back and disappeared into the woods. The Tories gave up the fight and followed them. The Tryon County men could not pursue them. Besides their general, they had some fifty wounded men to care for. On rude litters they bore them away in a march back to Fort Dayton.

While the fight at Oriskany was going on, there had been activity at Stanwix. Herkimer's messengers had been unable to get into the fort until late in the morning of that same day. The three guns were then promptly fired, but seem to have been unheard amid the noise of the battle. Marinus Willett with 250 men and a fieldpiece issued from the fort. The British regular troops in the main camp, reduced by those working on the roads and those at Oriskany, numbered rather less. The camp of the Tories and Canadians at the Lower Landing was but lightly guarded, the Indian camps hardly at all, except by their squaws. At these there was hardly a show of resistance. At Willett's approach their occupants fled to the woods; Sir John Johnson departed in his shirt sleeves.

Methodically and completely, Willett looted the camps. He destroyed all their provisions, and carried off twenty-one wagonloads of spoils, muskets and weapons of all sorts, ammunition, camp kettles, blankets, and clothing. He stripped the Indians' tents of everything movable, including their deer-skins and their packs, thus giving them ground for deep discontent with their allies. He got all Sir John Johnson's papers and five flags. Before troops from the main British camp could arrive to cut him off from the fort, he was back in it with his spoils and without losing a man. The five flags were hoisted on the fort's flagstaff "under the Continental flag." [7]

On the return of his men from Oriskany, St. Leger again disposed them for the siege. The next day he sent Colonel Butler, Major Ancron, and another officer to the fort, under a flag. They were received by Gansevoort and Willett and as many other officers as could crowd into a small room. Ancron delivered the message.

Its effect was that Colonel St. Leger had, with difficulty, prevailed upon the Indians to agree that if the fort were surrendered its garrison would be secured in their lives, their persons, and their private property. But if the fort had to be taken by force he could not restrain his savage allies from an indiscriminate massacre of its defenders. Indeed, he went on, the Indians were so provoked by their recent losses of several favorite chiefs that they threatened to march down the valley and destroy all the settlements and their inhabitants, men, women, and children; and he could not prevent it.

Willett answered for the garrison: "Do I understand you, sir? I think you say you come from a British Colonel, who is commander of the army that invests this fort; and by your uniform you appear to be an officer in the British service. . . . You come from a British colonel to the commandant of this garrison to tell him that, if he does not deliver up the garrison . . . he will send his Indians to murder our women and children." With blistering scorn, Willett told Ancron that he had brought a message degrading for any British officer to send and disreputable for any British officer to carry. No, they would not surrender.[8]

St. Leger set about building new redoubts more closely to invest the fort and establishing batteries to bombard it. But his guns were too light to have any effect on its sod-covered walls. He then began digging trenches, regular approaches by parallels, which would allow him to undermine the walls of the fort and breach them.

While this was going on, Willett and one companion undertook to penetrate the enemy's lines with an appeal to the militia of Tryon County for help. Working their way by night through the swamps and across the streams in the ground held by the Indians, they got to Fort Dayton in two days and there learned that a relieving force of Continental troops was already on its way.

Schuyler at Stillwater had received news of the investment of Stanwix. He called a council of war and proposed to send a detachment to relieve it. Most of his officers opposed this as weakening the army already too weak to resist Burgoyne. They muttered among themselves that it was an intentional weakening. The insinuation was in line with the charges of cowardice and even of treason, which had been leveled against the general on account of his successive retreats. Schuyler, who was pacing the room in agitation at the opposition to his plan for succor, overheard the remarks. In his anger he bit the stem of his clay pipe in two. Casting away the fragments, he stopped and looked the council in the face. "Gentlemen," he said, "I shall take the responsibility upon myself. Fort Stanwix and the Mohawk Valley shall be saved! Where is the brigadier who will command the relief? I shall beat up for volunteers to-morrow." [9]

Benedict Arnold, angry at the false imputations cast upon Schuyler and ever ready for action in the field, instantly offered his services. Although a major general, second in command to Schuyler, he was more than willing to take up the duties of a brigadier. Volunteers to the number of 950 were eager to follow a leader whom they admired and trusted. Brigadier General Ebenezer Learned of Massachusetts took the second command.

At Fort Dayton, on the 21st, they were joined by a hundred Tryon County militia and were informed that St. Leger had 1,700 men to oppose them. It seemed even to Arnold, that fighting man, that prudence called for reinforcements. Yet, the next day, hearing that St. Leger's approaches were very near their objective, and that the fort was in grave danger, Arnold decided to go forward with what men he had. On the 23rd he started, with a part of his force, on a forced march up the Mohawk. He had gone but ten miles when he got word that a ruse he had employed had been successful.

A Mohawk Valley German, Hon Yost Schuyler, had been sentenced to death for trying to recruit men for the British cause. He was generally esteemed a half-idiot, and was therefore regarded by the Indians with the respect and awe that they always accorded to the insane. Yet he was both cunning and shrewd. Arnold promised him a pardon if he would go to St. Leger's camp and spread a report of the approach of a relief force overwhelming in numbers.

Hon Yost took off his coat and had it shot through by several bullets. With an Oneida Indian as assistant, he started for Stanwix. Entering the Indians' camp alone, he said he had narrowly escaped from Arnold's force, and showed the bullet holes as proof. He had come, he said, to warn his red brothers that they were in danger. Thousands of troops were about to attack them. To St. Leger he told a circumstantial story of his escape while on the way to the gallows.

The Oneida assistant came in to tell *his* red brothers of their danger, repeating the story the other had told. The Indians took alarm, began to pack up for immediate departure. St. Leger's attempts to quiet them had no effect. Rumors that Arnold was coming with 3,000 men, that he was only two miles away, ran through the camp. He was feared by the white soldiers and the red warriors alike as was no other American officer. A panic ensued. The Indians rioted, seized the officers' supplies of liquor and even their clothing. They became, as St. Leger said, "more formidable than the enemy!" Two hundred of them fled to the woods. The chiefs of those remaining insisted on an immediate retreat. St. Leger gave the order.

Leaving their tents standing, their artillery, ammunition, and supplies, the whole force started for their boats on Wood Creek, with only such baggage as they could carry on their backs. So they made their way back to Oswego.

That was the story Arnold got from the crazy Hon Yost, who slipped away and came back to meet him. There was nothing now to do but push on to Stanwix and be received by its garrison with cheers and a salute from the artillery.

The losses on both sides at Oriskany were never accurately ascertained. It was as bloody a battle in proportion to the numbers engaged as any in the war. Fought at close quarters with unusual ferocity, the usual relative proportions of killed and wounded were reversed. Perhaps as good a guess as any is that the Tryon militia had 150 to 200 killed and 50 wounded, while of the Indians and Tories 150 may have fallen. Herkimer died shortly after his wounded leg was amputated.

But one thing was certain. Part of Burgoyne's plan had been knocked into a cocked hat. St. Leger had been beaten back. There would be no one to meet Burgoyne at Albany. He had to see it through alone.

CHAPTER 39

Danbury

Before the narrative of the movements of the two armies towards their final meeting at Saratoga, two incidents that occurred previously must have their place here, for, though they were slight in proportion to the magnitude of the Hudson River campaign, both had important effects upon it.

The first of these occurred in April, 1777. General Howe directed William Tryon, royal governor of New York, lately commissioned a major general, to destroy a magazine of American stores and provisions at Danbury in Connecticut. Detachments of 250 men each were drawn from the 4th, 15th, 23rd, 27th, 44th, and 64th British infantry regiments, and of 300 from Brown's Tory regiment. A few light dragoons and some fieldpieces were added. Generals Agnew and Erskine were appointed to commands under Tryon. Convoyed by two frigates, the expedition sailed from New York on the 23rd and landed near Norwalk in the evening of the 25th.

The march to Danbury was unopposed. Its garrison of 150 Continentals removed a small part of the stores before they retired on Tryon's approach. About three o'clock in the afternoon of the 26th the work of destruction was begun; and it was continued until the next morning. Nineteen dwelling houses and twenty-two storehouses and barns, as well as great quantities of pork, beef, flour, wheat, clothing, and tents were burned. At ten o'clock the next morning the return march to the ships was begun.

In New Haven, Brigadier General Benedict Arnold, the Achilles of the American army, was sulking in his tent, that is to say in the house of his sister. Despite his brilliant services in the war, five brigadiers, all junior to him in rank and one a mere militia general, had been made major generals

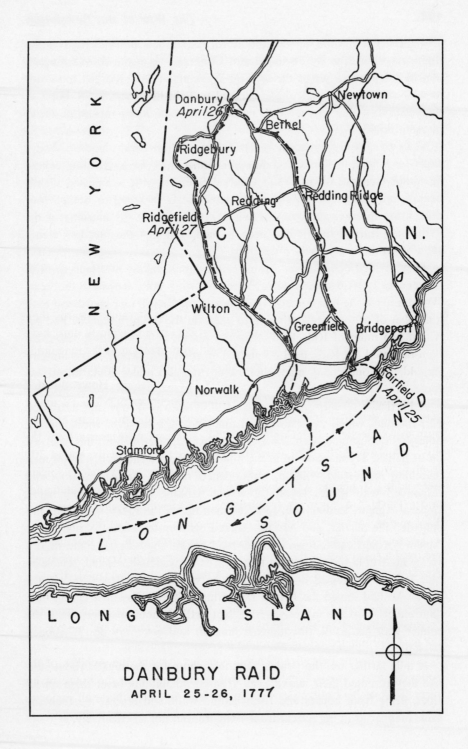

NEW YORK

Danbury
April 26

Newtown

Bethel

Ridgebury

Redding Ridge

Redding

Ridgefield
April 27

C O N N.

Wilton

Greenfield   Bridgeport

Norwalk

Fairfield
April 25

L O N G   I S L A N D   S O U N D

Stamford

L O N G   I S L A N D

DANBURY RAID
APRIL 25-26, 1777

on February 19, while he was unnoticed. Astonished and indignant at the slight put upon him by an ungrateful Congress, he wrote to Washington that he intended to resign the service. Washington having urged him "not to take any hasty steps," [1] he consented to hold his place in the hope of rectification of the "error." But, naturally, he was in the meantime in no pleasant mood.

News of Tryon's invasion reached him at his sister's house. Always eager for a fight, he at once mounted his horse and rode to Redding, where he found General Wooster and General Silliman with a hundred Continentals and about 500 militia. They immediately marched to Bethel, four miles from the ravaged town. Arriving there at two in the morning of the 27th, they learned that it had been burned, and that the invaders would soon be on their way back to the ships.

They divided their forces, Arnold and Silliman taking 400 men to meet the enemy at Ridgefield, while Wooster, with 200, harassed the rear. Wooster made the first contact. He attacked the British rear guard and took a number of prisoners. Continuing to press on the enemy's rear, he had got within two miles of Ridgefield when he was mortally wounded. His force then retreated. At Ridgefield a hundred more militia, proud of the fame of Arnold, a Connecticut man, and eager to fight under him, joined his force.

A barricade of carts, logs, stones, and earth was thrown up across the narrow road, which was flanked on one side by a ledge of rocks, on the other by a house and barn. Two hundred were posted behind this, the rest on its flanks. Tryon came up in the middle of the afternoon, his 2,000 men marching in a solid column, and opened fire on the Americans, who responded with spirit. Tryon threw out flanking parties on both sides. General Agnew, leading one, took his men up on the rocky ledge. His fire enfiladed the barrier, and Arnold ordered his men to retreat. A platoon of Agnew's troops came down into the road behind the barricade and fired a volley at Arnold, no more than thirty yards away. His horse fell, struck by nine bullets. Entangled in the stirrups, he was struggling to arise when a Tory who had joined the British ran at him with the bayonet, crying out: "Surrender! You are my prisoner!" "Not yet!" Arnold answered, shot the soldier with his pistol, disentangled himself, and got away into a wooded swamp.

A mile farther on, the British went into camp for the night. About sunrise they resumed their march. The aroused inhabitants beset them on all sides, firing from houses and from behind walls and fences, in much the same manner as in the retreat from Concord, but not so effectively.

In the meantime, Arnold had collected his men and secured three field-pieces with their appropriate companies of artillerists. He posted his force so as to command both of two roads by which Tryon might gain the waterside where his ships awaited him. But a Tory guide showed Tryon a circuitous way around Arnold's position to Compo Hill near the landing place. There the British stood on the defensive. The Americans formed in two columns for the attack. But before it could be launched, General Erskine led 400 of his men in a bayonet charge, which despite the valiant efforts of Colonel John Lamb's artillery to check it, broke the American ranks, and Tryon was enabled to embark his men.

Howe admitted no greater loss than 60 killed and wounded, but Stedman, the English historian, figured their casualties at "near two hundred men, including ten officers." The Americans lost perhaps 20 killed and 40 wounded.[2]

The results of this expedition reflected no credit upon the Connecticut people, who allowed the British to make a leisurely march through their country without opposition until its objects had been accomplished, and failed to remove the precious stores from Danbury before they could be taken and destroyed. The contrast between such pusillanimous behavior and that of the men of Massachusetts on a similar occasion is painful to contemplate.

Lamb and Wooster, however, and especially Arnold, deserved much praise. Of Arnold's services the Congress took notice immediately. Within a week, it made him a major general and shortly afterward ordered the gift of a horse "properly caparisoned as a token of . . . approbation of his gallant conduct . . . in the late enterprize to Danbury."[3] This was balm to Arnold's injured feelings, yet not a complete assuagement of his resentment, for he was still junior to the five major generals who had been promoted over his head. He still sought for the restoration of his proper rank, but in vain. Again he offered his resignation, driven to it, he said, by a sense of injustice. "Honor is a sacrifice no man ought to make," said he. "As I received, so I wish to transmit it to posterity."[4]

But on the very day that his letter was presented to the Congress, that body received a letter from Washington suggesting the sending of Arnold, "an active, spirited officer . . . judicious and brave," to the northern army opposing Burgoyne. "I am persuaded his presence and activity will animate the militia greatly."[5] This praise from his chief calmed Arnold. He asked leave to suspend his resignation and even agreed to serve "faithfully" under St. Clair, one of the juniors who had been promoted over his head. So it came about that Arnold had a part in the affairs at Saratoga.

The second incident was a tragedy, in which a woman played the leading part. Jane McCrea was the daughter of a Presbyterian minister of New Jersey. On the death of her mother and her father's marriage to a second wife, she went to live with her brother, who had settled in the Hudson valley about halfway between Fort Edward and Saratoga. At the time of Burgoyne's invasion, her brother, a colonel in the militia, decided to move to Albany. But she was engaged to marry David Jones, who had fled to Canada and become an officer in one of the Tory contingents then on the march with Burgoyne.

Jane refused to go with her brother, went instead up to Fort Edward, evidently hoping to greet her lover on his arrival. In one of two or three cabins near the fort lived a cousin of the British General Fraser, an old woman, Mrs. McNeil, who received her as a guest.

On July 27, two days before Burgoyne's army took over the abandoned fort, a group of his Indian forerunners came to it. They seized Mrs. McNeil and Jane and started back towards the British army at Fort Ann. They had not gone far when two of them "disputed who should be her guard," [6] and one shot her, scalped her, and stripped the clothing from her body.

They took Mrs. McNeil and Jane's scalp to the British camp, where General Fraser received his cousin and, it is said, David Jones recognized his fiancée's hair. Burgoyne ordered the arrest of the murderer and proposed to execute him, but St. Luc La Corne advised him that if this were done all the Indians would desert the army. Burgoyne pardoned the culprit, who is said to have borne the suitable name of Wyandot Panther.

That is the story of Jane McCrea as related by the most credible historians. In itself, it was but a minor incident in the list of Indian atrocities on that march. There was, for example, the slaughter of the whole family of John Allen—himself, his wife, three children, and three Negroes—on the day when Jane was killed. No one ever hears of them, yet not a history of the war fails to tell of Jane McCrea's murder. The difference lies in the results of the two outrages. The massacre of the Allen family was but one of a familiar type that had happened all along the frontier ever since the white man came to America; but Jane McCrea's murder was different, and for propaganda purposes it was made to measure.

She was young, twenty-three years of age, beautiful, "tall and noted for her long lustrous hair, which could reach to the floor when she stood up and let it down." [7] Or at least, if "not lovely in beauty of face," she was "so lovely in disposition, so graceful in manners and so intelligent in features, that she was a favorite of all who knew her." And her hair, an important element even if it did not reach to the ground, "was of extraordinary length and beauty, measuring a yard and a quarter . . . darker than a raven's wing," [8] says one authority; but another sees her locks, not as long and dark, but as "clustering curls of soft blonde hair." [9] Still another says "she was finely formed, dark hair, and uncommonly beautiful." [10] Another description makes her "a beauty in her bridal dress, hastening to her lover." [11] These descriptions are all from reputable histories. It matters not that James Wilkinson, who must have seen her, describes her as simply "a country girl of honest family in circumstances of mediocrity, without either beauty or accomplishments." [12]

The beautiful Jenny McCrea of the general run of the historians is the Jenny McCrea that was important, and she was very important. To the Americans she became more real than the real Jenny had ever been—a martyred saint in the patriotic hierarchy. Gates was the one most responsible for her prompt canonization. He had lately received a letter from Burgoyne complaining of the treatment of some of the prisoners taken by Stark at Bennington. To that he replied:

That the savages of America should in their warfare mangle and scalp the unhappy prisoners who fall into their hands is neither new nor extraordinary; but that the famous Lieutenant General Burgoyne, in whom the fine gentleman is united with the soldier and the scholar, should hire the savages of America to scalp Europeans and the descendants of Europeans, nay more, that he should pay a price for each scalp so barbarously taken, is more than will be believed in England until authenticated facts shall in every gazette convince mankind of the truth of this horrid tale. Miss McCrae, a young lady lovely to the sight, of virtuous character and amiable disposition, engaged to be married to an officer of your army was, with other women and children, taken out of a house near Fort Edward, carried into the woods, and there scalped and mangled in the most shocking manner. . . . The miserable fate of Miss McCrae was partly aggravated by her being dressed to receive her promised husband; but met her murderers employed by you.[13]

Gates was proud of that letter. He showed it to Lincoln and to Wilkinson. When they suggested it was rather personal, he exclaimed, "By God! I don't believe either of you can mend it." And he had a right to be proud. It was a prize bit of propaganda, and it worked. That letter was printed and reprinted in newspapers all over New England.

The story got about. It was "told at every village fireside and no detail of pathos or horror was forgotten. The name of Jenny McCrea became a watchword." [14] "It seems to have been the one thing needed to inflame the patriot imagination." [15] Washington added fuel to the flame when he wrote urging the brigadiers of militia in Massachusetts and Connecticut to "re‑pel an enemy from your borders, who not content with hiring mercenaries to lay waste your country, have now brought savages, with the avowed and expressed intention of adding murder to desolation." [16] A general statement; but in the common mind it was Jenny McCrea he was writing about.

Trevelyan says that the men of New England were "determined that the story of Jane MacCrea should not be repeated in their own villages. They arrived at the very sound conclusion that, in order to protect their families from the Wyandot Panther and his brother warriors, the shooting must be done, not from the windows of farm-houses . . . but in the line of battle outside the borders of New England. Before the middle of August, a sixth of the militia of several counties marched off to reinforce the Northern army." [17] They came to it, says John Fiske, "inflamed with such wrath as had not filled their bosoms since the day when all New England had rushed to besiege the enemy in Boston." [18] They were also encouraged to come by the fact that Gates, whom they trusted, was now in command.

A few days after the murder of Jenny McCrea another important incident occurred—Gates was chosen commander of the northern American army. A tug of war in the Congress between the friends of Schuyler (that is to say, the delegates from New York and the more southerly colonies) and the friends of Gates (the New Englanders) had been won temporarily by the Schuyler men when on May 22 their favorite was ordered to the command of the northern army; [19] but since that time the fortunes of war had run against him.

The precipitate evacuation of Ticonderoga, that famous fortress which had bulked so large in the imagination of the Americans, had caused astonishment and spread dismay throughout the country. For this St. Clair might be held primarily responsible; but Schuyler, as chief commander of the northern army, must also bear the blame. Added to that, the continuous series of retreats was certainly Schuyler's work. Moreover his reports to Congress were tinged with defeatism. New England raged against him, with the result that he was displaced from his command, and on August 4 Gates was elected "by the vote of eleven States." Subsequently both Schuyler and St. Clair were "called down" to face a committee of the Congress appointed to conduct an inquiry into their conduct "at the time of surrendering Ticonderoga and Mount Independence." [20]

Horatio Gates, English-born, was the son of an upper servant in the family of the Duke of Leeds. Although his membership in the servant class apparently debarred him from elevation in the aristocratic military profession, he succeeded in obtaining a captaincy at the age of twenty-seven in a provincial regiment in Nova Scotia. He saw service in Braddock's expedition and in the capture of Martinique, and achieved the rank of major. In 1772, resigning from the British army, he crossed the Atlantic and settled in Virginia on an estate of modest dimensions. There he renewed an acquaintance with George Washington which had begun in the Braddock affair, and in 1775 he enthusiastically threw himself into the American cause.

Gates was one of the few American generals who had seen service in a regular army. Probably at Washington's suggestion the Congress, in 1775, made him adjutant general of the army with the rank of brigadier.[21] In that position, so especially important in the organization of a new army, Gates rendered excellent service. He was acquainted, as were few of the American officers, with military paper work and seems to have been indefatigable in the performance of his duties. He had undoubted ability as an administrator, and he was not without talent in the field.

In May, 1776, Gates was raised to the rank of major general and, in the next month, after the disaster at Trois Rivières, was ordered to the command of the American forces in Canada. How that order failed to take effect, because all the American troops had been driven out of Canada, and how he obtained only a subordinate command under Schuyler, have been already noted in this narrative. Gates, always ambitious, was disappointed. With the support of New Englanders in Congress who admired him and despised Schuyler he succeeded in displacing Schuyler to his own advantage, only to lose out two months later when his rival was reinstated. Now he had again achieved the high command.

It is not proposed here to follow his subsequent career. It is enough to say that he was more at home and more effective in the lobby of the Congress, that source of promotion and preferment, than on the field of battle. What seems to be an example of Gates's preference of intrigue to combat is furnished by his conduct in December, 1776. Washington was then, with a sadly deficient force, trying to hold the Delaware River in the neighborhood of Trenton against any attempted crossing by Howe's army on the way to Philadelphia. Schuyler ordered Gates to march with certain regiments to reenforce Washington. Gates's regiments arrived a few days before that Christmas Day on which Washington planned to attack the Hessian troops at Trenton. In expectation of his coming, Washington had allotted to him the command of the right wing of the attacking force. Gates did not fancy committing himself to so desperate an enterprise, and he seems not to have had the courage to present his excuses to Washington in person. He sent a letter by Wilkinson, his aide-de-camp, begging off on the plea of illness. He wished to go to Philadelphia to recover his health. What he actually did was immediately to go on to Baltimore, where the Congress was in session after its flight from Philadelphia. There he busied himself in an effort to secure the command of the northern army.

In person, Gates was of medium height, his body not muscular, his shoulders somewhat stooped. He seemed older than fifty, his age at that time. His face was rather long, his features heavy, especially his aquiline nose with its drooping tip and his long chin. His eyes were somewhat hooded by heavy lids. In the excellent portrait of him by Gilbert Stuart, his face wears a shrewdly calculating expression, the eyes as if watching an opponent narrowly, the slightly smiling lips confident, as if he had an ace up his sleeve.[22]

Gates, whatever his faults, was jolly and kindly.

Gates arrived in the camp at the mouth of the Mohawk on August 19. There he found an army of about 4,500 rank and file, less one brigade posted about five miles up the Mohawk. Arnold had not yet returned from Stanwix. Lincoln, with about 500 militia, was in Vermont ready to act against Burgoyne's rear. Stark and his brigade still lingered at Bennington.

Arnold, having left a garrison of 700 men at Stanwix, brought 1,200 men to the camp in the first week of September. About the same time came a contingent, sent by Washington, which, though small, added vastly to Gates's strength. It was a corps of Pennsylvania, Maryland, and Virginia riflemen led by that redoubtable warrior Daniel Morgan numbering 331 effectives, with 36 on the sick-list. To strengthen it, 250 "vigorous young men" [23] equipped with muskets and bayonets were selected from the army. Major Henry Dearborn, a veteran of Arnold's march to Quebec, was assigned to their command under Morgan.

Gates wanted to add Stark's brigade to the main force. Lincoln again undertook to induce that difficult soldier to take his men over to the Hudson, but Stark would not give up his independent position. To be sure, his brigade was enlisted for only two months, its term expiring in the middle of September; but there was still need for his men in the army, even for so short a time. And, with the fateful conflict with Burgoyne so imminent, Stark should have been able to induce them to extend their time. But his ingrained cantankerousness had the upper hand of his patriotism. He felt that he and his men had been "slighted" in the report of the Bennington battle made by Lincoln. He made various excuses: his men had the "meazels," he himself was ill, he had only 800 men, too few to march so close to Burgoyne, and so on.[24] At last, in the morning of September 18, he appeared. At noon, he and all his troops departed. Their time was up. The very next day the Americans were locked in combat with the enemy.

The effect of Bennington on Burgoyne's army had been immediate and severe. In general orders he said that Baum's expedition to procure stocks of food, which "might have enabled the Army to proceed without waiting for the arrival of the Magazines" from the north, having failed "thro the chances of War, the Troops must necessarily halt some days, for bringing forward the Transport of Provisions." [25] So they remained in camp at the so-called Fort Miller a short distance above the Batten Kill and about four miles above Saratoga.

The shortage of provisions was not the only cause for concern on the part of Burgoyne. Bennington had deprived him of more than 800 men, of whom nearly 450 were regulars. Severe restrictions which he had imposed on the independent operations of his Indians, in consequence of the McCrea murder, had disgruntled his savage allies, and the Bennington affair had not encouraged them. They held a council and decided to go home. Soon there were left to him no more than 80 out of his original 500.

The Tories in his ranks were few and unreliable. "I have about 400 (but not half of them armed), who may be depended upon," he wrote to Germain after Bennington. "The rest are trimmers merely actuated by interest." [26] His belief in a prevailing mood of loyalism in Tryon County and in Vermont had been shattered. He could not rely on any uprisings to assist him.

He had begun to doubt, more than doubt, the success of his expedition with only his present force. "Had I a latitude in my orders," he wrote to Germain, "I should think it my duty to wait in this position, or perhaps as far back as Fort Edward, where my communication with Lake George would be perfectly secure, till some event happened to assist my movement forward; but my orders being positive to 'force a junction with Sir William Howe,' I apprehend I am not at liberty to remain inactive longer than shall be necessary to collect twenty-five days' provision" and to receive the reenforcement of certain new German auxiliaries coming down from Canada. But he added, "I yet do not despond." If he could get to Albany, he would fortify it and wait for Howe to get in touch with him.[27]

Gates's army had been built up to about 6,000 rank and file, say 7,000 in all. The Mohawk, since the Stanwix affair, was no longer a threat in his rear. His position at its mouth offered no satisfactory ground for the

American style of fighting, being rather fit for the British regular formations. He decided to move north to a more suitable and more easily defensible terrain. On September 9 he was at Stillwater again, and his chief
engineer, Kosciuszko, began to lay out defenses; but it was not a good
choice. The wide river meadows offered too favorable an opportunity for
turning the chosen position. He therefore moved again, on the 12th, about
three miles north to a point where the river ran through a narrow defile
dominated on the west by bluffs rising steeply more than a hundred feet,
called Bemis Heights from the name of the owner of a tavern by the
riverside.[28]

The plateau above the bluffs rose again in steep slopes to greater heights,
200 to 300 feet above the river. These heights were irregularly shaped
and were separated from one another by ravines, in which small streams
flowed down to the Hudson. One of the ravines, that of Mill Creek, reached
through the bluffs northwestwardly, in front of the position taken by the
American army, and thence northerly to the final position of the British.
Another, the widest and deepest, called the Great Ravine, started somewhat farther north and reached northwestwardly behind the ground on
which the British army was first deployed. On the bluffs and the plateau
were thick woods of pine, maple, and oak, interspersed with a few small
clearings. Certain roads, or rather wagon tracks, ran from the main river
road up the sides of the ravines and interlaced on the plateau above in a
complicated and irregular pattern.

At the southern end of this area, on a 200-foot elevation south of the
Mill Creek ravine, the American position was taken. It is said to have been
selected by Arnold and Kosciuszko, who laid out plans for its fortification.
Beginning at the river's edge, near Bemis's tavern, an entrenchment was
drawn across the main river road; and at its eastern end a battery was
erected. From this point a bridge of boats was swung across the Hudson.

Connected with this, trenches were dug; and breastworks of logs and
earth were erected in a line running at a right angle with the river up the
bluff to the higher level of the main fortification. This was constructed of
the same materials in the form of three sides of a square about three-
quarters of a mile on each side. The rear, which was somewhat protected
by a ravine, was left open. A small redoubt, mounting artillery, was built at
the middle of each of the three fortified sides. At the northwest angle there
was a house belonging to one Neilson. A log barn near by was stockaded
and named Fort Neilson.[29]

The ground was well chosen to oppose Burgoyne's advance down the
west side of the river, except in one respect. To the west and not far distant

was a greater height, which dominated the fortification. If it should be occupied with artillery in sufficient force, the American stronghold would be in a precarious situation. This point had been incompletely entrenched and was not occupied by the Americans when Burgoyne pushed forward in force, on September 19.

Gates established his headquarters in "a small hovel, not ten feet square" [30] in the side of a slope near the rear end of the western side of the fortification and awaited the arrival of the enemy.

CHAPTER 40

Freeman's Farm

For his southward march from Fort Miller, Burgoyne had a choice between the road on the east side of the Hudson, where he was, and that on the west. Gates had blocked the west road at Bemis Heights and held a position dominating it; the east road was open. But Albany, Burgoyne's objective, was on the west side. If he marched down the east side, he would find the Hudson at Albany greatly increased in volume and width by the inflow of the Mohawk, and the American army would certainly have moved down to oppose him. The crossing there would be difficult and hazardous.

On the other hand, if he now crossed to the west side and took that road he would have to fight his way past his enemy. In either case, he would have to cut his already too long and too tenuous communications with Lake Champlain and Canada. Choice was difficult, but it had to be made promptly: he could not winter where he was, having no proper shelter for his troops, nor any certainty of food even from Canada after Champlain froze over—a supply sufficient for thirty days already brought down was all he could rely upon.[1] Unless he retreated, Albany was his only hope for the winter. He boldly chose the west road and a fight at Bemis Heights.

Strengthened by the arrival of the guns from Fort George and by a new draft of 300 regulars from Canada, Burgoyne threw a bridge of boats across the river; and his right wing, the British troops, crossed to Saratoga on the 13th, followed shortly after by the Germans. On the 15th the bridge was dismantled, and the whole army resumed its southward march in three columns: the right wing taking the right of the road; the left wing the meadows between the road and the river; the artillery, the road itself. The supplies and baggage were committed to the bateaux. So they proceeded about three miles to a farm called Dovecote—or "Dovegat." Two days later they made another three miles and camped about the house of one Sword.[2] Up to this time, although he was now within four miles of Gates's position, Burgoyne seems to have had no definite idea of his enemy's whereabouts. His intelligence had formerly been derived from his Indian scouts, of whom few were left to him. But now he heard of the Americans.

A small party of British soldiers and some women went out to dig potatoes on an abandoned farm. An American patrol surprised them, fired on them, killed several, and took 20 prisoners.[3] So Burgoyne knew that the Americans were close at hand. He soon ascertained their exact position and made his dispositions to attack them.

The right wing, under General Fraser, was made up of the light infantry companies of the 9th, 20th, 21st, 24th, 29th, 31st, 34th, 47th, 53rd, and 62nd British regiments, under command of Major the Earl of Balcarres; the grenadiers of the same regiments, commanded by Major John Dyke Acland; also the battalion companies of the 24th Regiment, Lieutenant Colonel Breymann's Brunswick riflemen, and an artillery brigade of four 6-pounders and four 3's. Being the advance corps, it received the few remaining Indians (about 50), the 70 to 80 Canadians, the Tories (perhaps 150), and 50 of the British "marksmen." All told, there were about 2,000 in this wing.

The center, under command of General Hamilton, included battalion companies of the 20th, 21st, and 62nd British regiments, with the 9th regiment in reserve. It had six light fieldpieces, 6's and 3's under Captain Jones. General Burgoyne was to accompany this section.

The left, led by General Phillips and General Riedesel, comprised the Brunswick infantry regiments of Riedesel, Specht, and Rhetz, and Captain Pausch's Hesse Hanau artillery, six 6-pounders and two 3's. Six battalion companies of the British 47th were detailed to guard the 200 bateaux containing the provisions and supplies. The wheeled carriages for the rest of the baggage were to be protected by the Hesse Hanau infantry. The center and left wings numbered about 1,100 each, rank and file. Fifty Brunswick dragoons, the relics of Baum's expedition, "shabbily mounted, attended (occasionally)" General Burgoyne. All in all, the British army now numbered only about 6,000 rank and file.[4]

On the morning of September 19, the sun rose bright and clear; the air was cool and bracing, and hoarfrost whitened the grass.[5] The British army prepared for its advance, but it was not until some time after ten o'clock that the discharge of a gun called for a simultaneous movement of the three divisions.[6] Led by a party of the "shabbily mounted" dragoons and a hundred light infantry, Riedesel's division, accompanied by a detachment of pioneers and followed by the heavy artillery and the baggage, took its way in two columns down the road that ran under the bluffs and through the alluvial meadows by the riverside. Bridges, destroyed by the Americans, had to be replaced and guarded. Dispositions of troops on the heights above the road to protect the workers had to be made at each halt. Thus the progress of the division was much delayed. By one o'clock it reached a point about a quarter-mile below Wilbur's Basin, the farthest south that any part of Burgoyne's army ever penetrated.[7]

Meanwhile, Fraser's division had left the riverside by a rough road running west from Sword's house. Crossing the head of the Great Ravine, it marched nearly three miles until it met a crossroad on which it swung to the left, then south for a short distance to take a position on a height of land west of Freeman's Farm.[8]

The center division followed the right for about a mile, took a southward road for a half-mile, crossed the stream in the bottom of the Great Ravine on a bridge that the Americans had failed to destroy, and halted at noon for an hour on the south side of the ravine to give Fraser time to make his more circuitous march.

In the American camp, the right wing was composed chiefly of the Continental troops of Brigadier General John Glover, Colonel John Nixon and Brigadier General John Paterson. It occupied the heights near the river and the narrow level ground below them, under personal command of Gates.

The left wing, commanded by Arnold, included the New Hampshire regulars of Colonels Joseph Cilley, Nathan Hale,[9] and Alexander Scammell; Colonel Philip Van Cortlandt's and Colonel Henry Livingston's New Yorkers; the Connecticut militia under Colonel Jonathan Lattimer and Colonel Thaddeus Cook; Colonel Daniel Morgan's riflemen; and Lieutenant Colonel Henry Dearborn's light infantry.

The center was held by Brigadier General Ebenezer Learned's Continental brigade, the Massachusetts Continental regiments of Colonel John Bailey, Colonel Henry Jackson, and Colonel James Wesson, and Colonel James Livingston's New Yorkers. The total number of effectives in Gates's army was about the same as that in Burgoyne's, perhaps a thousand more.[10]

Burgoyne's army, divided into three widely spaced parts, its communications so difficult because of the broken terrain, was really in a precarious condition. It would seem, for example, that a swift attack in sub-stantial force down the slope and upon Riedesel's division, in its narrow space by the waterside, might have routed it before it could have help from the right or center, Fraser or Burgoyne. Or that a strong detachment might have turned either the right or the left of the British center division and fought it successfully in the woods, in which neither its artillery nor its bayonets would have been of much use. But Gates undertook no such bold enterprises. To be sure, the defense would probably be less costly, and time then seemed to be on the American side.

Gates is said to have been subject to "the fatal attraction which the apparent security of a fortress has so often exercised upon the mind of a timid and incompetent general." It is argued that he proposed to con-centrate his army either altogether within his fort or in that and on the narrow ground between it and the river, in "the insensate belief that his adversaries would run their heads, wantonly and obstinately, against his impenetrable bulwarks." [11] But it is asserted only by Gates's enemies, friends of Schuyler and Arnold, with whom he was now on bad terms, that he was not properly concerned about his left flank and the possibility that it might be turned.

Burgoyne planned an attack. Phillips and Riedesel were to advance along the river road and engage the American right. Burgoyne and Hamilton, with their four regiments, were to attack in the center, while Fraser's light infantry and grenadiers, the 24th British regiment, and his mixed auxiliary force of Tories, Canadians, and Indians swept around the American left and occupied that undefended higher ground to the west of the fort. From it Fraser could bring his guns to bear on the entrenchments, enfilade their front lines, and finally assault them in flank and rear, in the hope of push-ing the Americans down the slope and into the river.[12] It was a bold plan, yet not unfeasible.

The movements of the British army into its chosen positions could not be concealed from the American scouts perched in treetops. The brilliant colors of the uniforms and the flash of sunlight reflected from their polished steel gave notice for three hours of its continuing advance; yet Gates gave not a single order to meet the developing emergency. Arnold was not so complacent. He could not have known what Burgoyne planned. Indeed, he seems to have been at fault in permitting that western dominating height to remain partly fortified and entirely undefended; or, at least, if he could not induce Gates to occupy it, in making no protest. But he did argue with his superior against remaining on the defensive in and about the fortifica-tions. Letting Burgoyne approach the fort unopposed would permit him to bring up his heavy guns to bombard it. And if the camp were stormed successfully there would be no natural rallying place for the defeated Americans, no chosen position to which they could withdraw. But if the fight were made in the woods—where their superior marksmanship would tell and the British could not fight in close ranks with orderly volleys and finally with the bayonet—and they were beaten off they could still retire to the fort and defend themselves.[13]

Arnold was vehement in his argument and, according to a bitter enemy of Gates, "urged, begged and entreated" [14] permission to attack with his division. Whether or not he had any influence upon Gates is not clear. Gates did send Morgan's riflemen and Dearborn's light infantry to cover his left and to meet the enemy's flanking move, Arnold's division to be called on for support when needed.

It was after one o'clock when Burgoyne in his temporary position on the southern side of the Great Ravine concluded, or was informed, that Fraser had gained his appointed post. As a signal for the advance, three guns were fired; and Burgoyne's division marched west along a road towards Freeman's Farm.[15]

In the meantime, Morgan's riflemen, seconded by Dearborn's light infantry, had set out from the American left wing through the woods towards Freeman's Farm. The riflemen divided into parties to comb the woods and deployed in a long irregular line, Morgan taking his accustomed place close behind its center, where he could best observe and control his men. In a ravine south of Freeman's Farm, the riflemen came upon a picket of Fraser's irregulars, Canadians, Indians, and Tories. Under a crackling, deadly fire from the riflemen, every officer of the picket and many of its men fell, dead or wounded. The rest fled.

With too great impetuosity and in no order at all, Morgan's riflemen rushed after the fleeing enemy. From Fraser's position, Major Forbes led out a strong detachment of Tories and struck the disorganized Americans with such force that they were dispersed and scattered through the woods, leaving Morgan almost alone. He stood there, tears of chagrin and anger on his face, sounding the turkey call, an instrument used to decoy wild turkeys, which he most appropriately substituted for trumpet or drum. His men soon responded and began to gather about him.[16]

In the meantime Cilley's and Scammell's New Hampshire Continentals in Arnold's division came out. They went to the left of Morgan's and Dearborn's reorganized line, extending beyond Fraser's right, which they

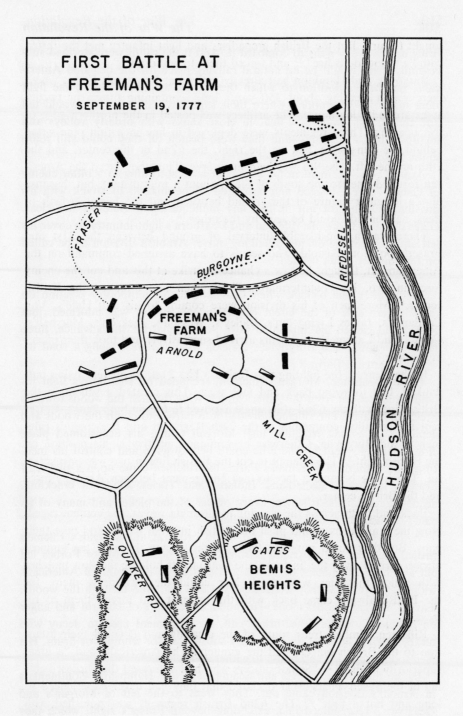

FIRST BATTLE AT
FREEMAN'S FARM
SEPTEMBER 19, 1777

FRASER

BURGOYNE

RIEDESEL

FREEMAN'S
FARM
ARNOLD

MILL CREEK

HUDSON RIVER

QUAKER RD.

GATES
BEMIS
HEIGHTS

sought to turn. But the British grenadiers and light infantry met the thrust with "a tremendous fire" [17] and forced them to withdraw.

Burgoyne and Hamilton had already arrived at Freeman's Farm, where there was a clearing about 350 yards long, containing fifteen or twenty acres around a log house. The artillery was posted in the northern edge of this opening. Three regiments were deployed in line in a thin pine wood behind the guns—the 21st on the right, the 62nd in the center, and the 20th on the left. The 9th was held in reserve. Thus they faced the American fortified lines to the south of them, about a mile distant, but, because of the irregular nature of the ground between and the heavy growth of trees, neither side could be seen by the other.[18]

There was a considerable interval of ground between the 21st and Fraser's position. Arnold, who seems to have assumed command on the American left, thought he saw a chance to strike at this and cut the enemy force in two. He "countermarched" his men and attacked the British center.[19] More men of his division were coming to his aid; Hale's, Van Cortlandt's, James Livingston's, Bailey's, Wesson's, Jackson's, Marshall's, Cook's, and Lattimer's regiments arrived successively and took their places in the line.[20]

In the clearing the fighting was furious. The 21st, to prevent being outflanked, had to swing back and face west. This created a salient in the British line, with the 62nd at its angle exposed to fire on both flanks. Fraser sent the battalion companies of the 24th Regiment and Breymann's riflemen to aid Burgoyne. Otherwise he remained inactive in his position on the British right.[21] The attempt to cut the British line in two was unsuccessful. The battle became a face-to-face engagement between Arnold's force and the British center.

Back and forth across the clearing in alternate waves, the combat raged. Now the Americans would push the British into the woods and take their guns. But they could not turn them on the enemy, because the gunners always carried away the linstocks, the instruments holding the slow matches with which the guns were fired. Nor could they withdraw them, for the British always came back with the bayonet and forced them to retreat.

Riflemen climbed trees south of the clearing and devoted their attention to the British officers and the gunners. The Americans had "a great superiority of fire." [22] "Senior officers who had witnessed the hardest fighting of the Seven Years' War declared that they had never experienced so long and hot a fire." [23] The 62nd British regiment was punished with especial severity. It almost broke. Once it tried a bayonet charge, but carried it too far beyond its supporting regiments and lost 25 men as prisoners.[24]

General Phillips had ridden up from his and Riedesel's division, to see what was going on in the center. He found a deplorable condition.[25] Every officer of the British artillery in the center save one and 36 out of 48 gunners and matrosses had been shot down. The guns had been silenced. Phillips called on Riedesel for four more. They came, but were soon also out of action for want of ammunition.[26]

In person, Phillips led the 20th out into the clearing in a bayonet charge to rescue the 62nd, enable it to withdraw and re-form.[27] Yet, for all he could do and for all Burgoyne and Hamilton could do, repeatedly exposing themselves to the American fire,[28] the center remained in a desperate situation.

Arnold believed that only a little more force was needed to break through and throw the enemy's line into complete confusion; but his entire division was already engaged—he wanted more men. He applied for a reenforcement.

Gates "deemed it prudent not to weaken" his lines.[29] Late in the afternoon he sent General Learned's brigade. Instead of striking at the British center, Learned led his men in a futile attack on Fraser's wing and was beaten off. All other aid, Gates refused.

But Riedesel down by the river was not so "prudent." When he had word of the precarious condition of the British line he ordered his own regiment to follow two companies of the Rhetz regiment which he led through the woods a mile and a half to a height where he could see the field of battle. The fight was "raging at its fiercest." "The three brave English regiments had been, by the steady fire of fresh relays of the enemy, thinned down to one-half and now formed a small band surrounded by heaps of dead and wounded." Without waiting for the support of his own regiment, he called on the two companies to charge. "With drums beating and his men shouting 'Hurrah!' he attacked the enemy on the double-quick." [30]

This sudden and unexpected attack on the flank drove the Americans back into the woods. Captain Pausch of the Hesse Hanau artillery was coming up with two 6-pounders. Officers and privates of the British regiments and some of the Brunswick jägers seized the dragropes and hauled the guns up the steeps and through the forest into position in the British line. They opened fire on the Americans with grape, "within good pistol-shot distance." [31] Riedesel's own regiment came up and fired a volley of musketry. That was about the end. It was growing dark. Hopeless of achieving a decisive victory, the Americans ceased firing and withdrew. The British bivouacked on the field.

The British loss was extraordinarily heavy. With as many as 2,500 men on the field, only three of the four regiments in the center—about 800 men—were deeply and continuously engaged. Yet the casualties of the whole British force amounted to about 600 killed, wounded, or captured. Of these, 350 were in the three regiments, the 20th, 21st, and 62nd. The 62nd was reduced from about 350 to scarcely 60 men.[32]

Of the Americans, 8 officers and 57 noncoms and privates were killed, 21 officers and 197 noncoms and privates were wounded; 36 others were reported missing.[33]

The incapacity of Gates as commander of a fighting force was convincingly demonstrated that day. If Arnold's persistent importunity had not forced his hand, the battle would have been fought on Burgoyne's own terms, in accordance with his plan, with the Americans trying to hold their works under a heavy, enfilading fire from that undefended western height. All the advantages which the Americans enjoyed in woods fighting, where marksmanship counted for so much and where the artillery and the bayonets of the British were of little avail, would have been lost.

Again, his failure to send to Arnold, at the crucial moment of the battle, a substantial reenforcement prevented the Americans from achieving a complete victory. Sir John Fortescue, the English military historian, says, "Had Gates sent to Arnold the reinforcements for which he asked, Arnold must certainly have broken the British centre, which, even as things were, could barely hold its own."

There was also open to Gates an opportunity to act on his own in a decisive manner. When Riedesel withdrew his own regiment, the two Rhetz companies, and Pausch's guns to go to Burgoyne's aid, there were left on the low ground by the riverside to protect all the baggage, provisions, and supplies of the entire British army only the 47th British regiment, the regiment of Specht, the Hesse Hanau infantry, and the rest of the Rhetz, perhaps eight or nine hundred in all. Gates had at least 4,000 on the height above. A swift descent by half of these could hardly have failed to capture and destroy all the British bateaux and land carriages with all their contents, leaving Burgoyne, bereft of food and supplies of every kind, to surrender or starve.[34]

Fort Clinton and Fort Montgomery

From the day after the fight at Freeman's Farm until the 7th day of October, the opposing forces lay in their respective positions, facing each other at a distance of little more than a mile, without any hostile move except frequent little affairs of outposts and continual sniping. But, in that interval, there occurred a conflict at a place somewhat distant, yet closely related to the principal contest between Burgoyne and Gates. This must be described before returning to the major scene.

It will be remembered that Burgoyne received a letter dated July 17 in which General Howe announced his intention of going south to Pennsylvania instead of up the Hudson to Albany, writing, "Sir Henry Clinton remains in command here and will act as occurrences direct." This unpromising reference gave no assurance that Clinton would move northward; nor did Howe give Clinton any orders in that respect.

Certain letters to Clinton vaguely referred to the possibility of Clinton's "acting offensively"; and on July 30 Howe had written, "If you can make any diversion in favor of General Burgoyne's approaching Albany, I need not point out the utility of such a measure." [1] Clinton accepted this merely permissive, casual suggestion at its face value. He later wrote to General Hervey, "I have not heard from Howe for six weeks and have no orders to co-operate with Burgoyne." [2]

Howe had left in New York no more than 7,000 troops, including 3,000 Tories, with whom Clinton had to hold Manhattan Island and the various outposts on Long Island, Staten Island, and Paulus Hook. This was not a force sufficient to be divided for offensive operations elsewhere. But Clin-

ton was expecting reenforcements from England, and when he heard that
Burgoyne was no farther advanced than Saratoga on September 12 he wrote
a reassuring message: "You know my good will and are not ignorant of
my poverty. If you think 2000 men can assist you effectually, I will make a
push at [Fort] Montgomery in about ten days." [3] Burgoyne got this on the
21st and immediately dispatched a message urging Clinton to hasten his
advance. The messenger failed to arrive. Another messenger, sent on the
27th, was so long delayed by the difficulties of travel and of escaping
American patrols that he did not find Clinton until October 8, the day after
Burgoyne's surrender at Saratoga. But Clinton had not awaited an answer.
His reenforcements came in on September 24 or thereabouts, bringing his
force of regulars up to nearly 7,000 men—2,700 British and 4,200 Germans. He at once began preparations for the projected advance.

Sir Henry Clinton was by now in his fortieth year. Behind him were one
signal failure, his repulse at Fort Moultrie, and one signal success, his
part as commander of the flanking column in the Battle of Long Island. He
had been too often hindered by an abundance of caution, as at Kip's Bay
and at White Plains and on the whole had scarcely distinguished himself.
He was, however, competent and hard-working, apt to the burdens of
administration and thoroughly reliable, a man normal in every respect save
one; namely, his curious *idée fixe* that General Howe had slighted and
wronged him. Troyer Anderson concludes from a perusal of Clinton's
papers that he was "almost mentally unbalanced on this subject." Perhaps
because of this unfortunate (and completely unjustified) prepossession, or
perhaps through less partisan judgment, he had opposed Howe's move
southward and had urged a junction with Burgoyne. He had no fondness for
Burgoyne; indeed, he seems to have been disappointed that he himself had
not received the Canadian command. But he was strong in force, temporarily unrestrained by Howe's presence, and in every way perfectly situated
for a vigorous stroke.[4]

Though he "never showed that he possessed the tactical ability" [5] of
Howe, Clinton was a skillful soldier, especially in such an enterprise as he
was now about to embark upon, capable of striking hard and effectively.
He conducted his operation "with more energy than most of the military
operations that took place in America." [6] He was not handicapped in his
activities by Howe's sloth, nor by such dissipated habits as characterized
both Howe and Burgoyne.

Clinton's immediate objectives were two forts about forty miles above
New York in the Highlands of the Hudson. A lofty height of land, a huge

massif about fifteen miles wide, extends like a great wall across the course of the Hudson, which flows through a narrow cleft in it. On both sides of the river steep, rocky eminences arise to heights of a thousand feet or more, the southernmost on the west side being Dunderberg. Next above that is Bear Mountain, which slopes sharply downward on its northern side to a deep ravine through which little Popolopen Kill flows into the Hudson. On the northeast shoulder of Bear Mountain, about 120 feet above the water, stood Fort Clinton. Across the ravine was Fort Montgomery, on a similar, somewhat lower, shoulder a half-mile distant. These guarded the half-mile width of the river, which was blocked by a chevaux-de-frise of heavy timbers, strengthened by a log boom and a great iron chain extending to Anthony's Nose on the opposite side. Montgomery was the larger and the more elaborately planned of the forts but was yet unfinished, so that Clinton was the stronger. Both had been planned especially for offense and defense on the waterside to hold this narrow gateway to the upper Hudson. The approaches on the land side were through narrow, steep, and rugged defiles extremely difficult to penetrate and very easy to defend.

The two forts were under the command of Brigadier General George Clinton, who was also governor of New York. His brother, Brigadier General James Clinton, was in particular charge of Fort Montgomery. They were garrisoned by a few regulars, a number of militia from the surrounding country, many of them unarmed, and a company of Colonel John Lamb's 2nd Continental Artillery, a force "not a tenth part enough to defend them." [7] In the river above the boom a little American flotilla of two frigates, the *Congress* and the *Montgomery*, a sloop, and two galleys rode at anchor.

On the other side of the Hudson, in and about Peekskill, Major General Putnam had been posted in May with a strong force to cooperate with the forts in guarding the Highlands. But that force had been reduced, by drafts in aid of Gates and Washington, to 1,200 Continentals and 300 incompletely armed militia.

Sir Henry Clinton did not expect to be able to fight his way through to Albany. To create a diversion in Gates's rear, in the hope of relieving the pressure on Burgoyne, was as much as he considered feasible. Indeed, he regarded even so much as "a desperate attempt on a desperate occasion." [8] For this purpose, he detached 4,000 men, including some of his Tory regiments.

The first contingent, 1,100 men, embarked in flatboats and bateaux at

Spuyten Duyvil Creek in the evening of October 3 and reached Tarrytown on the Hudson, about halfway to Peekskill, at daybreak. There it was joined by a second division of equal strength, which had marched overland from Kingsbridge. The third division embarked on the 4th in transports, convoyed by the frigates *Preston, Mercury*, and *Tartar* under the command of Commodore William Hotham, and arrived off Tarrytown on the same day. In the evening of the 5th, the convoy of transports, flatboats, bateaux, and galleys carrying the entire force proceeded up the river to Verplanck's Point, where there was a little breastwork mounting two guns. There 400 men were landed, and the small force of Americans holding the point retired without any resistance.

This concentration of attention upon the east side of the river was intended to make the Americans think that the expedition was against Putnam at Peekskill, and it succeeded. Putnam hastily withdrew to the hills four miles inland and sent a message to George Clinton asking for all the troops he could spare from the forts, and actually obtained some of them. Having accomplished this initial purpose of deception, Sir Henry proceeded vigorously and without delay against his real objective.

Leaving a thousand of his men, chiefly Tories, to hold Verplanck's Point against Putnam, he carried the rest early in the morning of the 6th, under cover of a thick fog, across the river to Stony Point, whence a rugged road ran west for two miles and then turned to the north behind Dunderberg and towards the forts. The British column took this northern road under the guidance of Brom Springster, a Tory. The advance was led by Lieutenant Colonel Campbell, with the 27th and 52nd British regiments, Colonel Andreas von Emmerich's Hessian jägers, and 400 of Colonel Beverley Robinson's Loyal Americans (Tories), a force of 900 in all. General Sir John Vaughan followed with the main body, the light infantry, the Koehle and Anspach grenadiers, the 26th and 63rd British regiments, a company of the 71st, a troop of dismounted men of the 17th Light Dragoons, and a number of Hessian jägers, making up 1,200 rank and file. General Tryon brought up the rear, with the 7th British and the Trumbach Hessian regiments. Sir Henry marched with the main body.

The road soon degenerated into a wagon track so narrow that the troops could march only three abreast. After three miles, it came to a 500-foot, almost precipitous ascent to a notch called the Timp. Up this, for three-quarters of a mile, scrambled the heavily laden men—the British carrying sixty pounds of equipment each, the Germans even more. A handful of determined opponents posted at the top of the acclivity could have held them off; but the road was not guarded, not even picketed.

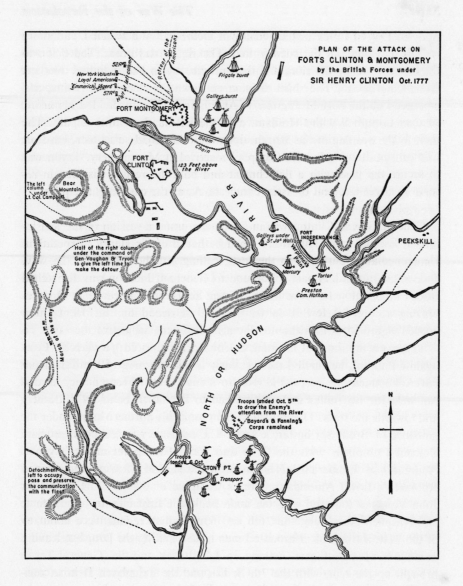

PLAN OF THE ATTACK ON
FORTS CLINTON & MONTGOMERY
by the British Forces under
SIR HENRY CLINTON Oct. 1777

52 R.

New York Volunt.
Loyal Americans
Emmerich, Jägers
57 R.

Retreat of the Americans

FORT MONTGOMERY

Frigate burnt

Galleys burnt

Poplopen Kill

Boom Chain

FORT CLINTON

123 Feet above the River

POND

The left column under Lt. Col. Campbell

Bear Mountain

Half of the right column under the command of Gen. Vaughan & Tryon to give the left time to make the detour

March of the army

RIVER

Galleys under Sr Jas Wallace

FORT INDEPENDENCE

Verplanck's Point

Mercury

Tartar

Preston
Com. Hotham

PEEKSKILL

NORTH OR HUDSON

Troops landed Oct. 5th to draw the Enemy's attention from the River

Bayard's & Fanning's Corps remained

N

Troops landed 6 Oct.

STONY PT.

Transport

Detachment left to occupy pass and preserve the communication with the fleet

A mile or so farther, at Doodletown in the valley between Dunderberg and Bear Mountain, the road forked. The right-hand branch led down to the low ground by the river and then up directly to Fort Clinton. The left fork passed around Bear Mountain, came down the Popolopen ravine, and emerged behind Fort Montgomery. At this fork Clinton divided his army, sending Campbell with the advance on the left-hand, circuitous path. The main body was to time its march along the other road so as to reach Fort Clinton simultaneously with Campbell's arrival at Montgomery. Tryon was to secure the pass with a detachment and hold the rest of his men in reserve to cover a retreat or assist either attack, as the case might require.

General George Clinton was in attendance upon a session of the legislature at Esopus (now Kingston) when he heard of Sir Henry's expedition. He immediately hastened to the forts, calling out the militia on the way, and took command. A party of 30 under Lieutenant Jackson was dispatched from Fort Clinton to reconnoiter. It met Sir Henry's advance at Doodletown, exchanged a few shots with it, and retreated to the fort. Clinton hoped for aid from Putnam, to whom he had sent an urgent message. To delay the enemy, he sent Lieutenant Colonel Jacobus Bruyn with 50 Continentals, and Lieutenant Colonel James McLarey with 50 militia from Fort Clinton, back along the Doodletown road. From Montgomery he dispatched Captain John Fenno with 60 men, later reenforced by 40, and a brass fieldpiece to meet Campbell in the pass behind Bear Mountain.

Bruyn and McLarey had little success. Though they fought courageously, they were promptly driven back to their fort, at the point of the bayonet. Fenno did better. He posted his men on the side of a ravine and opened fire with musketry and his one gun on Campbell's advance. The American fire was hot and well sustained, and checked Campbell's troops at first; but they divided, climbed the hill on Fenno's flanks, and were about to surround his little force when it retreated, first spiking the gun, but leaving its captain a prisoner.

Captain Lamb had brought out a 12-pounder and placed it in a commanding position. To it Fenno's men rallied, but from it they were again driven, leaving it, spiked, to the enemy. That was the end of resistance outside the forts.

Although Sir Henry's force had left its landing early in the morning and had reached Doodletown by ten o'clock, it was half past four when the divisions were in position before their respective forts. A summons to surrender having been refused by General George Clinton, simultaneous attacks were begun.

Sir Henry sent the 63rd Regiment around Fort Clinton to attack it on the northwest. The rest he formed for an assault on the southern side, the flank companies of the 7th and 26th British regiments and a company of Anspach grenadiers in the van, backed by the battalion companies of the 26th, the dragoons, and some Hessian jägers, with a Hessian battalion and the battalion companies of the British 7th in the rear. Between a small lake and the river there was a space no wider than 400 yards. It was blocked by an abatis and commanded by ten of the fort's guns. Through this space Sir Henry sent his men with orders to fire no shot, but to assault the works with the bayonet alone.

In the face of all the fire the insufficient garrison could bring to bear on them, the British regulars gallantly pressed forward. The defenders were too few—a few Continentals and 600 militia divided between the two forts —but their fire was deadly. The attackers fell by tens and twenties; but unfalteringly the rest came on. They reached the fort, pushed and pulled one another up through its embrasures, and swept into the works. The defenders immediately threw down their arms.

At Montgomery, Campbell had placed his German jägers in the center, his two British regiments on the right, and Robinson's Tories on the left. Thus he led them to the assault, only to be shot down before he reached the works. Colonel Robinson took command, and, with gallantry equal to that of Sir Henry's men, the fort was stormed successfully. The two forts fell almost at the same time.

It was now late in the day. Under cover of darkness General George and General James Clinton escaped with the greater part of their troops, some taking to the woods, others crossing the river in boats.

The American loss was heavy. Of the 600-odd men in the two garrisons, 250 were reported killed, wounded, or missing.[9] Also lost were sixty-seven guns and a considerable amount of stores.

The British lost about 40 killed and 150 wounded.[10] Whether these figures include the Hessian casualties, not usually included in the British returns, is uncertain.

The American vessels in the river tried to get away, but they were insufficiently manned, and the wind was against them. One of the sloops was captured, and one of the frigates went aground. They were all burned. "As every sail was set, the vessels soon became magnificent pyramids of fire." The loaded guns were set off by the heat in succession until the fire reached the magazines and "the whole was sublimely terminated by the explosions that left all to darkness." [11]

The next day, Sir Henry cut through the river barrier, chevaux de frise, boom and chain, and sent a flag, with a demand for surrender, to little Fort Constitution on an island opposite West Point. The tiny garrison fired on the flag, but set fire to the works and fled the following day on the approach of the enemy.

The two American Clintons, bringing Lamb's artillery company and some others that had escaped from the forts, joined Putnam at New Windsor. General George Clinton tried to arouse him to active measures; but he was gloomy. He thought he saw Sir Henry pushing on vigorously to a junction with Burgoyne, and did not see how he could be stopped. He was for standing on the defensive where he was.[12]

But Sir Henry Clinton had no intention of going farther. He had carried out a diversion, and he believed he could do no more. Beyond sending Vaughan to burn Esopus, some barracks at Continental Village, and residences of conspicuous rebels, he engaged in no further hostilities. He garrisoned the forts and returned to New York. But first he wrote a short note from Fort Montgomery on the 8th to cheer and encourage Burgoyne: "*Nous y voici* and nothing now between us and Gates; I sincerely hope this little success of ours may facilitate your operations. . . . I heartily wish you success." But Burgoyne did not derive from the debonair epistle the encouragement intended. The messenger, having been captured by the Americans, tried the silver bullet trick; it was recovered in the usual manner, and its bearer met the prescribed fate. In any event, the encouragement, such as it was, would have been too late. The day before it was written, Burgoyne had finally put his fortunes on the wheel and had lost everything.

C H A P T E R   4 2

Bemis Heights

Burgoyne was of a mind to attack Gates in full force on the day after the Battle of Freeman's Farm. Had he done so, it is quite possible that he would have won. The ill organized American army was in confusion. Though heartened and inspirited by their demonstrated ability to cope with the British and German regulars, the men who had fought through that long afternoon of the 19th were tired out and in no condition to fight again the next day. So were the British, especially the three regiments that had borne the brunt of the battle; but there is a greater resilience in the regular soldier than in the militiaman. Accustomed to checks, which doubtless they longed to avenge, the British regulars, well disciplined to obey orders to the utmost of their strength, would have gone forward with the same dogged courage that had characterized the repeated attacks on Bunker Hill. Fraser, however, was opposed to immediate action. He said his grenadiers and light infantry who were to make the first move, against the American left wing, would do better after a day's rest. So Burgoyne decided to wait a day.

On the 21st his army was drawn up in battle array and an attack seemed imminent; but Burgoyne was digesting the contents of a dispatch received from Sir Henry Clinton early that morning. It was that note, dated September 12, in which Clinton had written that he expected to "make a push" against the two forts, Montgomery and Clinton, "in about ten days." That "push" might be the turning point of the campaign; it might draw men from Gates and leave him too weak to defend his position. So Burgoyne canceled the orders for the attack; he would await the outcome of Clinton's move. And by that decision he lost the last chance for success in his enter-

525

prise, the last chance even for a safe retreat, for from that time onward the American army gained strength by the continued arrival of reenforcements, while under the usual attrition of sickness and desertions the British force grew steadily weaker.

To hold his position while awaiting good news from Clinton, Burgoyne at once began to entrench. From Freeman's Farm on the right, the lines were run across the British front to the bluffs at the riverside. They began, on the right, with a short entrenchment facing west, then turned at an angle to face south and ran eastward to their end on the river bluffs. Redoubts strengthened the angle and the extremities of the line. One of considerable size in a horseshoe shape was erected well in the rear of the right end of the lines, facing north to prevent that wing from being outflanked. "A deep, muddy ditch" [1] covered the entire front and ran in a curve around the angle at the right. All trees within a hundred yards of the front of the lines were felled. Fraser's corps of light infantry and grenadiers held its old position on the extreme right, beyond the angle and outside the ditch. The Earl of Balcarres held the angle with more of the British light infantry. Breymann's corps was posted in the horseshoe, which was separated from Balcarres by an interval defended only by two stockaded log cabins held by some Canadians. The rest of the army manned the lines to the river bluff.[2]

On the bluffs by the riverside redoubts were built to protect the boats and baggage. A floating bridge spanning the Hudson was contrived. The Hesse Hanau regiment, the British 47th, and a corps of Tories were encamped in the meadows by the stream. "An abundance of artillery" [3] was distributed along the lines. These positions were held until the final battle.

There was no change in the American lines, except that the western height outside them, which had been Burgoyne's objective in the first battle, was occupied and fortified. But within the camp there was enough discord in the high command to wreck an army.

Ill feeling had existed for some time between Gates and Arnold. After Freeman's Farm, Gates was angered because friends of Schuyler and Arnold in the army gave the whole credit in that affair to Arnold. He did not even mention Arnold's name in his report to Congress on the engagement. Arnold wrote to him protesting and asking for a pass for himself and two aides to Philadelphia. Gates responded by offering a letter to the president of Congress. But Arnold was unsatisfied with this document, technically not what he had requested. He called at headquarters to protest.

Gates laughed at Arnold's pretensions; expressed the view that he did not consider him a major general since he had submitted his resignation to the Congress, that he had in fact never received any command in that army, that he was of little consequence anyhow, and that the command of the left wing was to be given to General Lincoln; and wound up by saying that he would gladly give Arnold a pass to Philadelphia whenever he wanted it.[4]

Arnold was enraged, and there was a bitter quarrel with high words on both sides. Following that there was an exchange of foolish, quibbling letters. "Gates was irritating, arrogant and vulgar; Arnold indiscreet, haughty and passionate." [5] Finally came an order relieving Arnold of all command and excluding him from headquarters. Brockholst Livingston, one of Gates's enemies, wrote that most of the other officers and many of the men "had lost all confidence in Gates and had the highest opinion of Arnold"; and he declared that all the general officers except Lincoln signed a letter urging Arnold to remain, "for another battle seemed imminent." [6] In any case Arnold stayed, an idle hanger-on in the camp waiting for that coming fight.

General Benjamin Lincoln had been sent in July by Schuyler at Washington's suggestion to encourage and to command the militia in Vermont; and he had remained in that territory ever since. He had collected 2,000 men whom he held inactive as a menace to Burgoyne's flank and rear until the middle of September. Then he sent three detachments of 500 men each, under Colonel Woodbridge, Colonel Johnson, and Colonel John Brown, against Skenesboro and Ticonderoga.

Skenesboro had been abandoned by the British, and Woodbridge occupied it without opposition. But Brigadier General Powell still held Ticonderoga and its outposts with the 53rd British regiment and some Canadians, also Mount Independence with the Prince Frederick Regiment of Brunswickers—in all, about 900 rank and file.

Brown rushed the Lake George landing place at daybreak on September 18, occupied Mount Defiance (Sugar Loaf Hill), captured 300 of the enemy, 200 bateaux, a sloop, and some gunboats, drove all the rest of the garrison into the fort, and released a hundred American prisoners. Johnson, coming a little later in the day, kept the Germans on Independence busy under a continuous fire. But the main defenses were too strong to invite an assault, and both forces withdrew. Johnson went back to Lincoln's camp Brown sailed up Lake George in the captured British boats, tried to surprise two companies of the British 47th, under Captain Aubrey on Diamond Island; but he was expected and was beaten off.[7]

This was a minor affair; but such an operation in Burgoyne's rear encouraged the army at Bemis Heights, which celebrated it by prolonged cheering and a salute of thirteen guns. To Burgoyne, the news brought no comfort.

Gates now called on Lincoln to bring his men over to the main army. Between the 22nd and the 29th they arrived, and this was not the only addition to the army. Aroused by the story of Jennie McCrea—which had been published throughout the country—encouraged by the news of Burgoyne's plight, and eager to serve under Gates as they had not been to serve under Schuyler, the militia of New England and New York were flocking to Bemis Heights. They came singly, in groups, in companies, armed men looking nothing like soldiers, but each with his musket or fowling piece and as much powder and lead as he owned. They were ready and fit to take their places in the ranks. They could shoot from behind a tree better than the best of their enemies. By October 4 Gates had more than 7,000 men— about 2,700 Continentals, the rest militia—and they were still coming. By the 7th he had 11,000. His slender store of ammunition had been replenished by Schuyler from Albany. His men were well fed; they rejoiced in their gathering strength; and they were ready, eager, to try conclusions with the redcoats and the bluecoats again.

In Burgoyne's camp the case was far otherwise. Three months in the bushes and brambles of the wilderness had reduced their uniforms, the pride of the regulars, to tatters. Their food was salt pork and flour, and even that was running out. On October 3 their rations were reduced by one-third.[8] The grass in the meadows had been very soon eaten by their horses. There was no more forage to be had, and many horses died of starvation. Of the 8,000 rank and file with whom Burgoyne had appeared before Ticonderoga, there were perhaps fewer than 5,000 now in the camp; and even this number was continually sapped by desertions. It was easy enough to slip off into the surrounding forest. Every man in the British camp must have known that the invasion had been stopped, and that even a retreat was hardly possible.

To those discouraged men the Americans gave no rest. Day after day and night after night their outposts were under fire so close to their camp that the sleep of the men within the lines was disturbed. Burgoyne described this continual harassment:

From the 20th of September to the 7th of October, the armies were so near, that not a night passed without firing, and sometimes concerted attacks, on our advanced picquets; no foraging party could be made without great detachments to cover it; it was the plan of the enemy to harrass the army by constant alarms and their superiority of numbers enabled them to attempt it without fatigue to themselves. . . . I do not believe that either officer or soldier ever slept during that interval without his cloaths, or that any general officer, or commander of a regiment, passed a single night without being upon his legs occasionally at different hours and constantly an hour before daylight." [9]

On the 4th of October, Burgoyne called Riedesel, Phillips, and Fraser into a council of war and proposed action. His plan was to leave 800 men to defend the low ground by the river where were the boats and the army's store of supplies, and to march with all the rest against the American left wing in an effort to flank it and get to its rear.

It was an audacious plan; it was, indeed, a foolhardy plan, as the other generals more than intimated. In the first place, none of them knew anything about the American position. Time after time parties had been sent out on reconaissance, but had not succeeded in approaching near enough to get more than the sketchiest idea of the position and shape of the lines, hidden as they were by the dense forest.[10] In the second place, leaving so few men to guard the boats and supplies would amount to an urgent invitation to the Americans to attack them. While the main force was making a slow and difficult march around the American left, the Americans could capture the whole store of provision and ammunition and destroy the bridges across two streams running into the Hudson above and below the riverside defenses, and thus cut the British army off from its only means of retreat and leave it to starve and surrender. To clinch this argument, an inspection of the British works by the riverside was proposed and made. They were found to be badly placed for protection of the supplies, and the plan was abandoned.[11]

Riedesel now proposed a retreat to their old position at the mouth of Batten Kill, where communication with Lake George might be reopened and the hoped-for arrival of Sir Henry Clinton's force could be awaited. Fraser seconded him. Phillips declined to give any opinion.

Burgoyne refused to agree to a retreat before he had made one more attempt to find out whether there was not a way through or around the Americans.[12] He presented another plan, a "reconnoisance in force" to discover the American position and find out its weak point. There was that much discussed height on the American left, the objective of the attempted movement of September 19: it might be seized, fortified, and armed with artillery to fire down into the American works. He evidently did not know that since September 19th it had been strongly occupied by the Americans.[13]

His plan was to draw out 1,500 regulars and some of his irregular auxiliaries and approach near enough to learn whether the American left was vulnerable. If it were, an attack in force could be made on the following day. If not, a retreat to Batten Kill would be in order. That was the final decision. To hearten the troops for the adventure, twelve barrels of rum were broken out of the stores and distributed.

In the morning of the 7th the reconnoitering party was made up. The British light infantry, led by Lord Balcarres, composed the right. The 24th Regiment, a detachment of Brunswickers chosen from all their regiments and from Breymann's jägers, made up the center, commanded by Riedesel. The left was composed of the British grenadiers under Major Acland.[14] First having sent out Captain Fraser with his rangers and 600 Canadian and Indian auxiliaries on a long circuit to westward to divert the Americans and keep them in check, the expedition moved southwest from Freeman's Farm in three columns, supported by six 6-pounders, two 12's, and two howitzers.[15] When they had gone about three-quarters of a mile they halted in a wheat field on a low ridge, deployed into line, and sat down to wait while foragers cut the wheat for its straw. At the same time the generals, mounted on the roof of a log cabin, strained their eyes to see through their glasses something of the American position and saw absolutely nothing. As a reconnaissance, the expedition was a complete fiasco. As an invitation to attack, it could hardly have been better. As a preparation for defeat, it was an outstanding success.

The British line extended about a thousand yards with only two men to hold every three yards. Though its front was cleared of trees and was a good field for artillery practice or for a bayonet charge, its flanks rested on thick woods, which gave cover for the kind of fighting favored by the Americans. So they sat there, discovering nothing, doing nothing, a "meaningless and objectless military expedition which, on Burgoyne's part, was a counsel of despair." [16]

The first news of this movement of the enemy came to Gates from an outpost on Mill Creek. He sent Major James Wilkinson out to investigate. Receiving an account of the enemy's disposition, he ordered Morgan "to begin the game." Morgan suggested that his men should attack the British right. Gates agreed, and directed that Poor's brigade should go against the flank of the enemy's left. The two detachments were to move secretly through the dense forest, so as to strike by surprise at the same moment.

To secure a proper position from which to launch his attack, Morgan had to make a wide circuit. Poor's march was much shorter. His brigade, comprising Scammell's, Hale's, and Cilley's New Hampshire Continental regiments, Van Cortlandt's and Livingston's New Yorkers and Cook's and

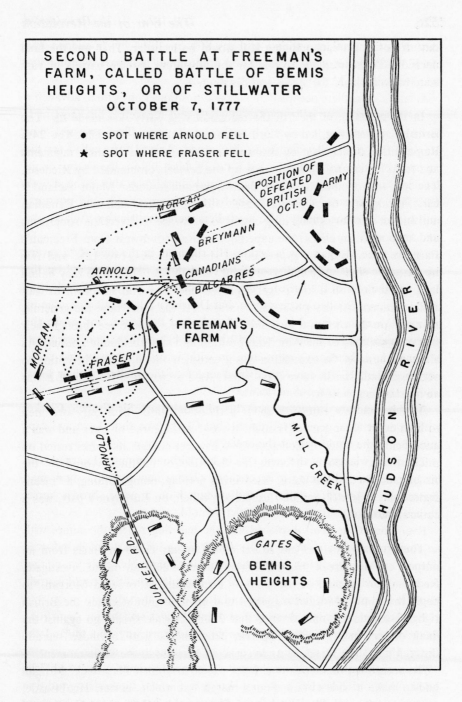

SECOND BATTLE AT FREEMAN'S
FARM, CALLED BATTLE OF BEMIS
HEIGHTS, OR OF STILLWATER
OCTOBER 7, 1777

● SPOT WHERE ARNOLD FELL
★ SPOT WHERE FRASER FELL

MORGAN

POSITION OF
DEFEATED
BRITISH
ARMY
OCT. 8

BREYMANN

ARNOLD

CANADIANS

BALCARRES

MORGAN

FREEMAN'S
FARM

FRASER

ARNOLD

MILL CREEK

HUDSON RIVER

QUAKER RD.

GATES

BEMIS
HEIGHTS

Lattimer's Connecticut militia—perhaps 800 in all [17]—by "a sudden and rapid" [18] movement gained the desired point about half past two and immediately attacked.

Acland's grenadiers occupied an elevated position. Poor's men, advancing up the slope, received a heavy fire of grape and musketry; but most of it flew high, cutting the leaves and branches of the trees. They reserved their fire until this first volley had been discharged. Acland then called for the bayonet, but the Americans loosed a deadly blast before the charge could develop. Many of the grenadiers fell. Acland himself was shot through both legs. The Americans, shouting, rushed the position, seized a 12-pounder, and turned it on the enemy. The grenadiers were swept away. Acland was taken prisoner.

By this time Morgan was in action. His riflemen, in the face of "a severe fire of grape-shot and small arms," "poured down like a torrent" on the flank and the rear of the British right, posted behind a rail fence.[19] Balcarres tried to change front to receive them, but Dearborn's light infantry, coming up after Morgan, poured in a close fire, leaped the fence, and drove the enemy in disorder. Balcarres rallied his force behind a second fence, but Morgan's and Dearborn's men came on with fierce impetuosity that could not be denied. His troops retired in disorder to the shelter of their lines, leaving their guns to the Americans.[20]

At this juncture Burgoyne sent his aide-de-camp, Sir Francis Clarke, with an order for a general retirement; but Clarke was shot down and captured before he could deliver the order.

The Brunswickers in the center were left without support. Learned with his brigade was advancing to meet them when a new figure, a small man dressed in a general's uniform and mounted on a great, brown horse, flashed onto the field. It was Benedict Arnold.

Ever since Gates had displaced him, he had lingered in the camp, with no command, no status at all in the army, eating his heart out in enforced idleness and disgrace. Now, with a battle raging before his very eyes, neither the lack of orders nor consideration for his irregular condition could restrain him. He had put spurs to his horse and dashed into the conflict.

Fearing that he "might do some rash thing," Gates sent Major Armstrong to order him back to the camp. Arnold saw Armstrong and spurred the faster. He first came up with one of Poor's Connecticut militia regiments. "Whose regiment is that?" he shouted. "Colonel Lattimer's, sir." "Ah!" he cried. "My old Norwich and New London friends. God bless you! I'm glad to see you." [21] They gave their old general a hearty cheer as he swept on to overtake the head of Learned's brigade.

Three regiments were in advance. Arnold called on them to follow him. They responded with shouts and cheers, charged across Mill Creek and up the opposite slope full upon Riedesel's Brunswickers, commanded by Colonel Specht. But these had been strengthened by detachments of the Rhetz and Hesse Hanau regiments and manfully withstood the shock. The Americans were repulsed.

Specht's right was uncovered when Balcarres's light infantry were driven back to the lines, and the Americans came back. Though exposed to fire on three sides, the Germans fought bravely until, when about to be surrounded, they were ordered to retreat to the works.

General Fraser had been conspicuous throughout the fight, riding to and fro and encouraging his troops. Now he tried, with the British 24th and the light infantry, to form a second line. Arnold saw him and said to Morgan, "That man on the gray horse is a host in himself and must be disposed of." Morgan called on one of his riflemen, Tim Murphy, an old Indian fighter and a noted marksman.

Murphy climbed a tree and took aim with his double-barreled rifle. His first shot cut the crupper of Fraser's horse. The second went through the horse's mane. One of Fraser's aides told his chief that he was the object of dangerous personal attention and urged him to withdraw. Fraser answered that his duty compelled him to remain there. The third shot passed through his body, wounding him mortally.[22]

At this point Brigadier General Abraham Ten Broeck, with his brigade of 3,000 New York militia lately arrived in camp, appeared on the field; but they were not needed. At Fraser's fall the last hope of British resistance had died. The whole line gave way and retreated to the shelter of the breastworks, just fifty minutes from the time the first shot was fired.

The fighting seemed to be over, and if Gates had commanded in the field it would have been over; but Arnold was of different stuff. He was not content with driving the enemy from the field; he wanted a smashing victory. "With true military instinct, [he] seized the opportunity for a general attack upon the British entrenchments." [23]

With a part of the brigades of Patterson and Glover he assaulted that part of the works held by Balcarres and his light infantry, and drove through the abatis. But though Arnold, raging with the ardor of battle, exposing himself to the rain of grapeshot and musketry, animated his men to the last degree of courage, the defense was too strong. They were driven back, and the fight settled down to continued hot firing at musket range.

While this was going on, Learned's brigade appeared off to the left, marching toward the extreme British right. Arnold clapped spurs to his horse and galloped straight across the line of fire, exposing himself to what seemed certain death. With his complete disregard of all military conventions he took charge of Learned's men and led them past Balcarres's right and against the two stockaded log cabins between Balcarres and Breymann's horseshoe redoubt. They had been and were still held by a weak force of unreliable Canadian irregulars. The Americans swept them away.

Now Breymann was exposed on all sides. His force had been reduced from 500 to 200 by drafts for the British line of battle. Arnold took over two regiments, Wesson's and Livingston's, and Morgan's riflemen, who had made a complete circuit of the British right, and ordered them forward. At the head of Brooks's Massachusetts regiment, just then coming up, he swung to the left and attacked Breymann's redoubt. "His impetuous onset carried everything before it." [24] He rode around the redoubt and entered the sally port. There his horse was shot down, and he himself received a bullet in his leg that fractured his thigh bone. It was the same leg that had been wounded at Quebec. It is said that the shot was fired by a wounded German, and that Arnold called out, "Don't hurt him! He's a fine fellow. He only did his duty." [25] Here at last Armstrong caught up with the man who had successfully avoided him up to this time. There was no need to deliver Gates's order to return to the camp. Arnold went willingly enough on a litter, with the glory of that mad afternoon coruscating about him.

Breymann had been mortally wounded in the attack, and his small force had given up the redoubt. Burgoyne's main position was thus open to the Americans, both on the right and in the rear. But it was growing dark, and, besides, they had no Arnold to lead them. Colonel Specht with a small force of Brunswickers made an attempt to recover the redoubt; but they were easily driven off, and he himself taken prisoner. That ended the battle.

The losses of the British army amounted to about 600 killed, wounded, and captured. They also lost every one of the ten guns they brought into the action. The Americans suffered about 150 casualties.

From the time when Arnold had come onto the field, he was never for a moment idle. Exercising command without warrant, but most effectively, over whatever brigade, regiment, or company he came across, he was incessantly active wherever the fighting was heaviest. He seemed to be endowed with the headlong energy of a madman,[26] exposing himself to the enemy's fire with the utmost temerity, flourishing his sword, shouting encouragement to the troops, and inspiring them with his own intrepidity and dash. He was exactly the sort of leader needed by the untrained militia and by the half-trained Continentals as well. The British were, of course, heavily outnumbered, and their defeat was in the cards before ever Arnold injected himself into the battle; but that it would have been so quickly and so completely accomplished without him is more than doubtful. Certainly to him and to Morgan belongs the credit for the victory.

Gates, on the other hand, was never on the field of battle at any time during the fighting. He remained in his headquarters, about three-quarters of a mile behind the front line of the American entrenchments and fully two miles from the scene of action. From there he could not even see what was going on; and, except for that first order to Morgan to attack and the subsequent sending out of other detachments, he exercised no control over the conduct of his troops nor over the tactics of the battle.

It may have been Gates's idea that a general commander should remain in a safe place, where reports of the progress of the fight could be brought to him and where he would be safe from injury. That is doubtless the correct principle in warfare, where enormous numbers have to be guided by a master-mind, but it was not the principle generally observed in the battles of the Revolution. Howe at Bunker Hill did not disdain to lead his men to the attack in person and to share their dangers. Washington exposed himself fearlessly at Kip's Bay and at Princeton; so did Burgoyne and Phillips and Riedesel at Bemis Heights; so did Arnold and Montgomery at Quebec. Someone has said that Gates never once heard the whistle of an enemy's bullet through his whole term of command of the northern army.[27]

That to Arnold is due the credit for the victory at Bemis Heights is the considered opinion of a distinguished military historian, Sir John W. Fortescue:

> In natural military genius neither Washington nor Greene are to my mind comparable with Benedict Arnold. The man was, of course, shallow, fickle, unprincipled and unstable in character, but he possessed all the gifts of a great commander. To boundless energy and enterprise he united quick insight into a situation, sound strategic instinct, audacity of movement, wealth of resource, a swift and unerring eye in action, great personal daring and true magic of leadership. It was he and no other who beat Burgoyne at Saratoga and, with Daniel Morgan to command the militia, Benedict Arnold was the most formidable opponent that could be matched against the British in America.[28]

The opinions of some others regarding Arnold's behavior before Saratoga are not so favorable.

CHAPTER 43

Saratoga

The loss of Breymann's redoubt threw the British wide open to attack in flank and in the rear, so that Burgoyne's position was no longer tenable. During the night of October 7 he withdrew his army in good order to a position north of the Great Ravine, on the riverside bluffs where strong redoubts had been erected to protect the train of artillery, the provisions, the bateaux, and the hospital. The next day, the Americans took over his old campground.[1] Lincoln occupied the bluff and the river meadows nearby, threatening an attack, of which Burgoyne was apprehensive. He wrote afterward that he had offered battle,[2] but that his position was too strong for the Americans to risk it. There was, however, "a great deal of cannonading"[3] of the enemy's camp and some skirmishing between the outposts, in which Lincoln was wounded.

That same morning Gates dispatched Brigadier General John Fellows and his brigade of 1,300 Massachusetts militia up the east side of the Hudson to the mouth of the Batten Kill, with orders to cross the river and entrench a position on the west side at Saratoga. Brigadier General Jacob Bayley, with 2,000 New Hampshire militia, was already posted on a height north of Fort Edward. Thus Burgoyne was menaced both in the front and in the rear; but Fellows in the rear was too weak to offer effective opposition.[4]

Anticipating the necessity of further retreat, Burgoyne sent Lieutenant Colonel Sutherland with the 9th and 47th British regiments to reconnoiter the road up to Fort Edward.

The movement of Fellows's troops had been observed by the British.

Burgoyne interpreted it as a preliminary to an attack on his rear. To obviate that, he decided to withdraw at once to the heights of Saratoga.

The retreat began about nine o'clock in the evening of the 8th. Captain Fraser's Rangers and the few remaining Tories and Indians led the van, followed by the Brunswickers, the heavy artillery, and the baggage train. The British regiments under Balcarres, marching in two columns, Burgoyne with them, closed the rear. While they were on the march Sutherland's detachment returned and fell in behind the Brunswickers.[5] The bateaux were laboriously rowed upstream alongside the marching men. The hospital, with more than 300 sick and wounded men, was left, in the care of a surgeon, to the mercy of the Americans.[6]

The progress of the British army was slow beyond belief, not more than a mile an hour. At Dovecote—now Coveville—a halt was ordered at two o'clock in the morning to let the bateaux carrying the provisions catch up. The march was not resumed until four o'clock in the afternoon. It was a dolorous march. Rain was falling heavily. The road, bad enough before, was now a bog. The tired men could hardly drag their feet out of the mud. The wagons stuck fast and were unable to go on.[7] The tents and baggage were therefore left behind. Parties of Americans hung on the rear of the retreating army, waylaying the bateaux, many of which were captured and looted. It was late in the evening of the 9th when the beaten army reached the mouth of the Fish Kill, forded the stream, and found itself in its desired position on the heights of Saratoga—where Schuylerville is today, near Saratoga Springs on the north. Wet to the skin and almost dead-beat, the men "had not strength or inclination to cut wood and make fires, but rather sought sleep in their wet cloaths and on the wet ground, under a heavy rain that still continued"; so says one that was with them.[8]

From that place Burgoyne sent Sutherland, with the 9th and 47th, some Canadians, and a corps of artificers, up the river again to the neighborhood of Fort Edward to build a bridge by which the retreating army could cross the Hudson to the only practicable northward road, that on the east side.[9]

The position taken was favorable for a defensive stand. It was on a rise of ground north of Fish Kill, with much open ground before it, which would afford a field of fire for the artillery and permit of battle formation in the classic style and the free use of the bayonet, the favorite weapon of the British and Brunswick regulars. It had already been fortified by Burgoyne's troops when they lay there on September 13 and 14. These works were now strengthened. Fellows and his brigade, who were there before Burgoyne, forded the river on his approach and took a position on a height opposite the British camp.

Gates was slow in his pursuit, lingering in camp until after noon of the 10th; but his men marched faster than the British and came in sight of them by four o'clock.[10] Burgoyne had left the 20th, 21st, and 62nd British regiments south of Fish Kill as a guard for headquarters established in Schuyler's great house near the river. These were now withdrawn to the main position, and Schuyler's house, being in the way of artillery fire from the heights, was burned.

After all his seeming dilatoriness and lack of energy Gates now suddenly grew bold. The movement of Sutherland's detachment up the river had been reported to him, and he assumed that it was the main body of the British, and that he faced only the rear guard. Without any reconnaissance to determine the true state of affairs, he drew up orders for an attack at dawn the next day.[11]

At that season of the year a morning fog always overhangs the river country; and so it did on the morning of October 11 when Morgan advanced along the edge of the bluffs and the rest of the army moved up the road by the riverside. They were going blindly against a strong position strongly held and mounting twenty-seven guns of various calibers with a clear field of fire when, by mere chance, Brigadier General John Glover learned the truth. His men had picked up a lone British deserter, who told them that the whole British army was in the entrenchments they intended to attack, even Sutherland's two regiments having been recalled. Glover sent the news back to Gates and to Nixon, whose brigade had already crossed Fish Kill. He suggested a return. Nixon halted. At that moment the fog lifted, disclosing the British position. The enemy opened fire, and Nixon's men hurriedly withdrew to the south side of the Kill.[12]

Learned's brigade had meanwhile proceeded according to orders, and was advancing in the fog up the slope against the enemy when James Wilkinson, Gates's youthful aide, overtook them bringing news of the true situation. Learned, with some reluctance, ordered a withdrawal, which was made under fire. There can be little doubt that, if the attack had been made according to Gates's orders, it would have resulted in a defeat.[12]

Concentrating their attention on Burgoyne's fleet of bateaux, the Americans captured most of them that day. Morgan, who had remained north of Fish Kill, now took post to the west of the British position and was joined by Learned's brigade and some Pennsylvania regiments. Burgoyne was thus invested on three sides, but his way to the north was still open. For the first time in the campaign he called a council of war—always before he had made his own decisions without asking his generals' advice.

Riedesel proposed abandonment of the baggage and retreat up the west side of the river, to cross above Fort Edward and go on to Fort George. But Burgoyne would not agree.[13] The Americans established three batteries at Fellows's position on the opposite side of the river and opened fire on the British camp, and there was constant fighting of outposts.

In the afternoon of the 12th Burgoyne called another council, including Riedesel, Phillips, and the two brigadiers, Gall and Hamilton. He placed before it the situation of his army: It was facing 14,000 rebels equipped with "considerable artillery" and was threatened with attack by them; other forces were between the British position and Fort Edward; the bateaux were either ruined or captured; the way up the west side of the river was impracticable, except for "small parties of Indians"; to get the artillery away, bridges would have to be built across the affluents of the Hudson under the fire of the enemy and with Gates attacking their rear; nothing had been heard from Clinton. He now asked for opinions on five propositions: (1) to wait in this position for coming, fortunate events; (2) to attack the enemy; (3) to retreat, repair the bridges on the march and thus, with artillery and baggage, force the fords at Fort Edward; (4) to retreat by night, leaving the artillery and baggage behind, cross above Fort Edward or march round Lake George; (5) in case the enemy should move to the left, to force a passage to Albany.

The first, second, and third propositions were promptly rejected as impracticable. Burgoyne, Phillips, and Hamilton were inclined toward the fifth; but its execution depended on a foolish move by Gates, and he could not be relied upon to make it. Riedesel insisted on the adoption of the fourth, and it was approved, the march to begin that night "with the greatest secrecy and quietness," each soldier carrying his own provision for six days.[14]

At ten o'clock Riedesel sent word to headquarters that the rations had been distributed and asked for marching orders. The answer was: "The retreat is postponed; the reason why is not known." [15] So Burgoyne lost his last chance to get away, for by the next day he was entirely surrounded.[16] In the night American troops had crossed from the mouth of Batten Kill on the east side of the river and erected a battery on the west side. They were commanded by John Stark, that unpredictable person having arrived with 1,100 New Hampshire militia.

"Numerous parties of American militia . . . swarmed around the little adverse army like birds of prey," says Sergeant Lamb, who was there. "Roaring of cannon and whistling of bullets from their rifle pieces were heard constantly by day and night." [17] And according to Riedesel:

Every hour the position of the army grew more critical, and the prospect of salvation grew less and less. There was no place of safety for the baggage; and the ground was covered with dead horses that had either been killed by the enemy's bullets or by exhaustion, as there had been no forage for several days. . . . Even for the wounded, no spot could be found which could afford them a safe shelter—not even, indeed, for so long a time as might suffice for a surgeon to bind up their ghastly wounds. The whole camp was now a scene of constant fighting. The soldier could not lay down his arms day or night, except to exchange his gun for the spade when new entrenchments were thrown up. The sick and wounded would drag themselves along into a quiet corner of the woods and lie down to die on the damp ground. Nor even here were they longer safe, since every little while a ball would come crashing down among the trees.[18]

Small wonder it is that "order grew more and more lax."

On the 13th another council was assembled, including not only the general officers but also "the field-officers and captains commanding corps of the army." [19] Burgoyne presented the same five propositions, but added a statement of the increased difficulties. He also said that he believed that some of the officers were in favor of capitulation, but he would not consider that without the assent of those in the council. He asked three questions. (1) Could an army of 3,500 effective combatants enter into an agreement with the enemy without detriment to the national honor? They all answered "Yes." (2) Was this now the case for this army? They all agreed that it was. (3) Was this army's situation such as to make an honorable capitulation really detrimental? They replied in the negative.[20]

Burgoyne sent Gates a letter asking for a meeting with a staff officer "in order to negotiate matters of high importance to both armies," [21] and in the morning of the 14th Major Kingston met Wilkinson between the lines and was conducted to Gates's headquarters. Kingston said that his chief knew Gates's superiority of numbers and their disposition, which would render a retreat "a scene of carnage on both sides," [22] and proposed a cessation of hostilities to consider terms. To his surprise, Gates presented a paper already drawn up, containing his terms.

They included a surrender of the troops as prisoners of war, grounding their arms within the camp and marching out to such destination as should be directed. Other provisions allowed the officers and soldiers to keep their personal baggage, admitted the officers to parole, and required the delivery of all public stores, arms, ammunition "&c &c." [23] But the two terms first mentioned amounted to a demand for unconditional surrender, and Burgoyne's officers made violent objection. The terms were "inadmissible in any extremity. Sooner than this the army will ground their arms in their encampment, they will rush on the enemy, determined to take no quarter." [24] So Burgoyne replied to Gates.

In thus presenting his terms, Gates made a tactical error. It was customary to let the besieged propose terms, which the besiegers could modify or reject. Now Gates had either to stand on the terms he proposed and take the consequences, or to let Burgoyne do the revising and accept what he offered. Burgoyne sent back his terms, to which, he said, he would accept no amendment. His troops were to march out of the camp with the honors of war and ground their arms by the riverside at the command of their own officers. Moreover, they were not to be considered as prisoners of war, but were to be granted passage back to Great Britain from the port of Boston, on British transports "whenever General Howe shall so order," on condition of "not serving again in North America during the present contest." [25] They were to have rations at American expense while on the march to Boston and while quartered there. The officers were to retain their carriages and horses, and "no baggage was to be molested, General Burgoyne giving his honour that their are no public stores secreted therein." The Canadians were to be permitted to return to Canada, being supplied by the Americans on the march. There were other similarly generous provisions, but those mentioned constitute the gist of the proposal.

To the amazement of Burgoyne and his officers, Gates immediately accepted the proposal, with only one addition: the surrender was to take place at two o'clock in the afternoon of the following day. This precipitate abandonment of his former demands and acceptance of the extraordinary proposals of the enemy aroused Burgoyne's suspicions. He thought that Gates must have heard that Clinton was coming up to relieve his compatriots. To gain time he asked for a postponement of the ceremony. Gates agreed, and the articles were drawn up in form and signed by representatives of both armies.

Then Burgoyne asked one more concession. The agreement must not be called a "capitulation" but rather a "convention." Again Gates consented. His willingness to yield was indeed, as Burgoyne suspected, prompted by news of movements of Clinton's army.

Although Clinton himself had returned to New York after capturing the two forts, he had sent a detachment up the river as far as Esopus. From this fact Gates deduced an intention to push on to Burgoyne's relief. Burgoyne had also heard of this. Hopes that relief was coming burgeoned in his mind, and he began to regret his proposal to give up. He went so far as to ask his council whether, at this stage of the proceedings, he could honorably withdraw from the negotiations. The council voted that he could not, and that the advantageous terms agreed to by Gates should not be rejected. Still Burgoyne delayed signing. He called another council, but found his officers still of the same mind. Then he yielded and signed.[26]

In the afternoon of the 16th, Burgoyne and his staff in their "rich, royal uniforms" rode out to the American camp and met Gates in "a plain, blue frock." "The fortune of war, General Gates," said Burgoyne, "has made me your prisoner." To which Gates replied, "I shall ever be ready to testify that it has not been through any fault of your Excellency," and invited the party to dine with him.[27]

In the morning of the 17th, the British army marched out of its camp to the appointed place in the meadows by the river and, at the command of its own officers, piled its arms and emptied its cartridge boxes. In order that the conquered troops might be humiliated as little as possible, Gates had ordered his men to remain within their own lines. The British then marched through the American camp between two lines of troops drawn up in order, from whom they received not "the least disrespect, or even a taunting look, but all was mute astonishment and pity." [28]

One of the Brunswickers has described the appearance of the American troops:

Not one of them was properly uniformed, but each man had on the clothes in which he goes to the field, to church or to the tavern. But they stood like soldiers, erect, with a military bearing which was subject to little criticism. All their guns were provided with bayonets, and the riflemen had rifles. The people stood so still that we were greatly amazed. Not one fellow made a motion as if to speak to his neighbor; furthermore, nature had formed all the fellows who stood in rank and file, so slender, so handsome, so sinewy, that it was a pleasure to look at them and we were all surprised at the sight of such a finely built people. And their size! . . . The officers . . . wore very few uniforms and those they did wear were of their own invention. All colors of cloth . . . brown coats with sea-green facings, white linings and silver sword-knots; also gray coats with straw facings and yellow buttons were frequently seen. . . . The brigadiers and generals have special uniforms and ribbons which they wear like bands of orders over their vests . . . most colonels and other officers, on the other hand, were in their ordinary clothes.

He was amazed at the variety and size of the wigs worn by the older Americans "between their fiftieth and sixtieth year," who had "perhaps at this age followed the calfskin [drum] for the first time" and "cut a droll figure under arms"; yet "it is no joke to oppose them . . . they can cold-bloodedly draw a bead on anyone." He noted the variety of "standards with all manner of emblems and mottoes, some of which seemed to us very caustic. . . .

There was not a man among them who showed the slightest sign of mockery, malicious delight, hate or any other insult; it seemed rather as if they wished to do us honor." [29]

When the beaten army came to a large tent, Gates and Burgoyne emerged from it, turned and faced each other. Silently, Burgoyne drew his sword and tendered it to Gates, who received it with a bow and returned it. So the ceremonies of the "convention" were completed, and the British army set out on its march to Boston.

For the Americans it was a stupendous victory. Two lieutenant generals, two major generals, three brigadiers, with their staffs and aides, 299 other officers ranging from colonels to ensigns, chaplains and surgeons, 389 non-commissioned officers, 197 musicians, and 4,836 privates passed out of the armed forces of Great Britain in America. The matériel captured was of vast importance, including 27 guns of various calibers, 5,000 stand of small arms, great quantities of ammunition, and military stores and equipment of all kinds.[30]

Even more important were its psychological effects among the patriots. Coming close after Washington's defeats at Brandywine and Germantown, it was a needed restorative of confidence in the American cause; and it acted as such. The ill organized, ill disciplined, ill supplied American amateur soldiers had defeated the British and German regulars in two battles in the open field. To be sure, the enemy was greatly outnumbered; but that fact did not affect the rejoicing, nor did it reduce the newborn confidence in the American armies. They had a great store of men to draw upon and might again produce armies greater in numbers than their foes.

Upon the disposition of the British troops in America, Burgoyne's defeat had an immediate effect. Ticonderoga and Crown Point were evacuated, and their garrisons were withdrawn to Canada. Sir Henry Clinton recalled Vaughan's detachment, which had got within forty miles of Albany and withdrew the garrison he had left in Fort Clinton, thus abandoning his hold on the Highlands and retaining only the town and island of New York, with their outlying posts. Only there, in Rhode Island, and in Philadelphia had His Majesty's forces any hold upon the revolted colonies.

In England the news of Bennington had already called forth from the politicians and newspapers of the Opposition "croaking prophecies of disaster to Burgoyne." When Saratoga's news arrived the Opposition in Parliament received it with "a howl of insulting triumph." But upon the country in general it had a tonic effect. There was considerable apprehension that the defeat would bring France into the war on the side of America. It was evident that a greater army would be needed, in that case, to carry on the struggle. Towns and cities volunteered to raise regiments at their own expense. In Scotland a number of noblemen and wealthy gentlemen offered to enroll battalions, though not at their own expense. Thus 15,000 men were added to the royal army.[31]

In France the effect was more encouraging to the Americans. Although for a long time, secretly and by various subterfuges, that country had been supplying the Americans with great quantities of arms and war matériel, it had refrained from entering the conflict even to the extent of recognizing their national existence. Now it acted with almost dizzy haste. Within two days after the arrival of the news of Saratoga, the King of France signed a short note extending such recognition and virtually making his country the ally of the United States. On February 6, 1778, a formal treaty was signed. Upon its publication, in March, the British ambassador was recalled from Paris. France and England were now at war, and after a considerable delay Spain and then Holland came into the conflict on the American side. Saratoga thus fairly earned the epithet of Turning Point of the Revolution.

Although the subsequent treatment by the Congress of the troops surrendered at Saratoga is a political matter, not within the strict scope of this account of the military operations of the Revolution, it is so intimately connected with the war itself and is of such interest and importance that it should be briefly discussed.

While the victory was received with rejoicings, the terms granted to the defeated were thought by the Congress and by the people generally to be far too liberal. It was too plain to be overlooked that, though they were under engagement not to serve against the Americans in the war, there was nothing to prevent the government of Great Britain from employing them elsewhere and so releasing other troops that might be sent to America. The Congress was indisposed to give Britain this advantage by ratifying and carrying out the terms of the convention, if any subterfuge could be hit upon to justify refusal. "The public wished to have some pretence for detaining them." [32]

Having scanned the returns of the matériel surrendered, a committee of the Congress reported, on November 22, that they included only 648 cartridge boxes, a manifestly insufficient number for over 5,000 men. This evident failure to give them all up was esteemed to be a breach of the convention. Yet, at that time, the committee did not regard that state of facts as warranting delaying the embarkation.[33]

Unfortunately for the captive troops, Burgoyne himself furnished a reason deemed by the Congress sufficient to justify a refusal to carry out the agreement. Boston was already overcrowded with American troops when Burgoyne's soldiers arrived. There was a consequent delay in securing for the British officers quarters "according to their rank," as specified in the agreement. They were crowded together, without regard to rank, in huts made of boards, poorly built, and quite open to the wintry weather.[34] Burgoyne took offense and wrote a haughty letter to General Heath, in command there, charging that, by this failure in the matter of quarters, "the public faith is broke." [35]

Howe contributed his share to the difficulties of the situation. Instead of at once dispatching to Boston a fleet of transports to carry the British troops back to England, he delayed for months in an effort to change the plan so that the embarkation might be made in some port in British possession—Newport or New York. This meant, in the minds of the delegates to the Congress, that his real intention was to get Burgoyne's troops within the British lines and keep them as an addition to his own army.[36] But, chiefly, it was Burgoyne's words that were seized upon as an excuse for disregarding the agreement. "Congress had now obtained what they wanted, a plea for detaining the convention troops." [37]

On January 8, 1778, a committee of the Congress reported that "this charge of a breach of public faith is of a most serious nature, pregnant of alarming consequences," affording grounds for a belief that Burgoyne intended to rely upon such breach of faith to absolve himself and his army from the obligations of the contract, including the agreement that his troops should not serve again in America. The Congress, with this in mind, but falling back upon the missing cartridge boxes as a concrete breach, resolved that "the convention, on the part of the British, has not been strictly complied with." [38]

Yet it had not the resolution boldly to denounce the agreement as broken by the other side. It merely suspended the embarkation "till a distinct and explicit ratification of the convention of Saratoga shall be properly notified by the court of Great Britain to Congress." [39] When the British transports arrived off Boston, late in December, they were not admitted to the harbor.[40]

His Majesty sent orders to Clinton, Howe's successor, to signify his ratification of the convention. Clinton did so, whereupon the Congress was driven to declaring that it had "no evidence" that Clinton "had any orders from his King for the ratification of the Convention, that the whole might be, for what they knew, a forgery" and that "a responsible witness" must be produced "to swear he saw the King sign the order"; until then "they would not believe a word that he [Clinton] advanced," [41] which was surely as miserable a pretense of honorable dealing as was ever put forth.

Burgoyne and a few of his officers were allowed to go home, but the rest of his troops were marched down into Virginia and held as prisoners until the end of the war. The action of the Congress in this regard reflected great discredit upon the nation. The public faith had been broken without justifiable excuse or palliation. It was, indeed, a dirty business altogether.

CHAPTER 44

Valley Forge

Although the distance from Whitemarsh to Valley Forge is not more than thirteen miles, the American army under Washington was on the road to its new camp site for more than a week. It first marched north three miles to Gulph Mills and bivouacked. Its tents and baggage, sent from Whitemarsh at the time of the threatened attack on that position, were now at Trappe, eighteen miles to the northwest. For four days and nights of snow and sleet, the wretched, ill clad, tired soldiers huddled around campfires, trying to cook their meager provisions or to sleep, unsheltered and in wet clothes, thousands of them blanketless, on the snow-covered ground.[1] The night after the tents came up, the snowfall turned to rain; but before morning the temperature fell below freezing point, and the rutted, slush-covered roads were congealed in icy ridges. The army waited three days more for weather that would permit its barefoot men to march.

On December 19, 1777, its march was resumed. That oft-repeated story of bloody footprints was unimpeachably confirmed by Washington himself. Years later he told William Gordon, the historian, that "you might have tracked the army from White Marsh to Valley Forge by the blood of their feet." [2]

It is impossible to exaggerate the misery of the troops at this time. General Greene wrote: "One half of our troops are without breeches, shoes and stockings; and some thousands without blankets." A quarter of the whole number were reported unfit for duty, "because they are barefoot and otherwise naked." [3] The quartermaster's department, as well as the commissariat, had completely broken down. "While the army was suffering . . . for want of shoes &c., hogsheads of shoes, stockings and clothing were at different places upon the road and in the woods, lying and perishing, for want of teams and proper management." [4]

Nevertheless, the army staggered on and came at last to Valley Forge, too tired, too hungry, and too weak to do more than huddle again around the campfires on its icy heights.

The place took its name from an ancient forge at the side of Valley Creek, which flows north into the Schuylkill, whose own course there is east-west, Valley Forge being on its southern side. From the creek the land rises steeply, over 250 feet in two-fifths of a mile, to an undulating plateau about two miles long and a mile and a quarter wide. The slopes on the west and on the north to the Schuylkill are less steep. This elevation was heavily forested with a variety of trees.

Along its southern edge was drawn an irregular line of entrenchments. Its western end was guarded by similar entrenchments and an abatis, running roughly north-south, also by certain redoubts and redans, forming a sort of inner stronghold. The western or creek side was thought to be sufficiently defended by the abruptness of approach from that quarter, and the north side by the width of the Schuylkill.

Throughout this space the various brigades were posted, each having its little village of huts drawn up in lines facing each other with streets between. Washington refused to seek other shelter for himself than that afforded by his marquee of coarse homespun linen, until his men were at least partly sheltered. He lived in it for a week, then established his headquarters at the western end of the camp in a large stone house. The general officers, although by the original plan each of them was to occupy a hut, soon distributed themselves in neighboring houses, mostly outside the camp.

The first requirement of the army on its arrival was shelter more suitable for winter than canvas tents. It was proposed that the troops build themselves log huts. Washington's general orders prescribed the plans and specifications. They were to be fourteen feet by sixteen in size, with log walls six and a half feet high, the interstices between the logs stopped with clay, the fireplaces and chimneys of clay-daubed wood, the steep-pitched roofs of planks or slabs. Twelve men were to occupy each hut. All this material had, of course, to be got out of standing timber.

Stirred to emulation by a prize of twelve dollars offered to the group which should finish its hut "in the quickest and most workmanlike manner," as well as driven by their necessities, the men went to work. Trees fell before their axes, were sawn into lengths, dragged through the snow by the men themselves, and notched to fit together at the corners of the huts. Others were split or sawn into rude boards for roofs and doors. Within two days the prize had been won by the most efficient group, but it was not until after Christmas that all the 9,000 men were housed. Even then their shelters were but apologies for dwelling places. They were far from weatherproof. The cold winter winds blew through their crevices. The ill designed fireplaces filled them with eye-stinging, throat-choking smoke. Few had wooden floors. For the most part the men lay on the damp earth, padded by a thin coating of scarce straw. Yet there was some warmth within them and shelter from snow and rain.

Shelter they had, of a sort; but in clothing there was a desperate lack. Lafayette wrote: "The unfortunate soldiers were in want of everything; they had neither coats, hats, shirts nor shoes; their feet and legs froze until they became black and it was often necessary to amputate them." [5] Dr. Albigence Waldo, surgeon of a Connecticut regiment, pictured a typical incident:

There comes a Soldier, his bare feet are seen thro' his worn-out shoes, his legs nearly naked from the tattered remains of an only pair of stockings, his Breeches not sufficient to cover his nakedness, his Shirt hanging in Strings, his hair dishevell'd, his face meagre; his whole appearance pictures a person forsaken & discouraged. He comes and crys with an air of wretchedness & despair, I am Sick, my feet lame, my legs are sore, my body covered with this tormenting Itch [a disease common in the camp].[6]

The lack of clothing was hardship enough; the lack of food was added torture. On December 20 General Varnum reported that his division had been two days without meat and three days without bread.[7] Three days later Washington informed the Congress that, the day before, lack of food had caused "a dangerous mutiny" which was suppressed with difficulty, and that there was in the camp "not a single hoof of any kind to slaughter and not more than twenty-five barrels of flour," nor did the commissary know when any more would arrive.[8] Salted beef and pork were almost as scarce as fresh meat. The lack was to some extent supplied by salted herring, which, however, were often found to be decayed when the barrels were opened. The common diet was flour-and-water paste baked in thin cakes on hot stones. "Fire-cake," the men called it. "Fire-cake and water for breakfast!" cried Dr. Waldo. "Fire-cake and water for dinner! Fire-cake and water for supper! The Lord send that our Commissary for Purchases may have to live on fire-cake and water!"

Even of water there was a lack. The high hills were barren of springs. Every drop the men got had to be carried in buckets from Valley Creek or the Schuylkill, or from a brook half a mile from the camp. "The warter we had to Drink," wrote one of them, "and to mix our flower with was out of a brook that run along by the Camps, and so many a dippin and washin it which maid it very Dirty and muddy." [9]

That in such conditions disease should be prevalent was to be expected. Smallpox was frequent, but not so frequent as the "putrid fever," typhus. There was no knowledge of the proper means of treating that dreadful ailment, or of preventing its spread; nor was there an adequate force of physicians, or a supply of even such medicines as they would have prescribed, or proper food for the men that came down with the fever that winter. A large hospital was established at Yellow Springs at which 1,300 cases were treated according to the limited knowledge and skill of the surgeons. Other cases were submitted to the care of the Adventist Sisters in their community at Ephrata, the Moravian Brethren at Bethlehem, and to "hospitals" in other near-by towns.

These hospitals were already crowded with sick and wounded men from the battlefields of Brandywine and Germantown—500 from Brandywine alone at Ephrata. Part of them had to be lodged in tents. Their beds were bundles of straw laid on the floors and used over and over again, without change, by successive invalids. Dr. William Smith said he had "known from four to five patients die on the same straw before it was changed." The typhus patients that came from Valley Forge were put in with the wounded men in the condition in which they arrived, not only ill with that contagious disease, but also "attired in rags swarming with vermin." That deadly fever became epidemic in the hospitals themselves. Doctors and nurses came down with it. At Bethlehem "not an orderly man or nurse escaped, and but a few of the surgeons." At Lititz there were 250 invalids cared for by two doctors. Both of them fell ill of typhus.[10] Of 1,500 patients received there, 500 died. Of 40 men of one Virginia regiment, only three survived. Those "hospitals" were but way stations on the road to the grave. It was not until spring that the spread of the disease abated at Valley Forge and the convalescents began to return to duty.

Foraging parties did what they could to supply food. Wayne harried New Jersey and secured some cattle, thereby earning the sobriquet of "The Drover." [11] Henry Lee (Light-Horse Harry) made forays into Delaware and brought up cattle that had been fattening on the marsh meadows along the river for the British army.[12] But Allen McLane was "the most dashing of all the raiders." [13] The whole territory outside the British lines was his playground. He foraged from the farmers, but had more joy in cutting off British expeditions and taking their cattle from them. Captain of an independent corps, now a small troop of horsemen, now a hundred men, mounted and on foot, including sometimes a contingent of Oneida Indians, he was at once forager, scout, and raider everywhere about Philadelphia and even, at times, in that city in disguise. "He became known to everybody as the constant hero of surprise and daring." [14]

To counteract Wayne's successful forays in New Jersey and to procure forage for their own army, the British sent similar parties into that state. One of these, commanded by Colonel Mawhood, the gallant leader of the British troops defeated at Princeton, was made up of the 17th, 27th, and 46th British regiments, the Queen's Rangers, a mixed force of 300 Tory foot and horse under Colonel John G. Simcoe, and the Tory New Jersey Volunteers. On March 12, 1778, it crossed the Delaware to Salem in New Jersey. There the 30 cavalrymen—"hussars"—of the Rangers "borrowed" horses from the inhabitants and mounted them.

About three miles southeast of Salem, Colonel Asher Holmes held Quintin's Bridge, spanning Alloway Creek, with a small force of New Jersey militia in some slight earthworks on the eastern side of the creek. For further security they had taken up the planks of the bridge. To mask this force and allow the foraging to proceed unmolested, another Colonel Holmes of the 17th British regiment with 70 men took post at a tavern on the west side. To strengthen this party Colonel Mawhood concealed the Rangers, part of them under Captain Stephenson in the tavern, part under Captain Saunders behind a fence in its rear, and the rest, with Simcoe, in the woods farther behind. The masking party of the 17th, in full view of the Americans, then began to retreat from the creek with apparent precipitation. Deceived, the Americans relaid the bridge planks and crossed the creek. Part of them took post on high ground near the bridge; the rest, 200 in number, pushed on in pursuit of the retreating British. Suddenly and unexpectedly they came upon the Rangers behind the fence. Their leader ordered a retreat. He was wounded and captured. The Rangers in the tavern issued forth and cut off the way to the bridge. Caught between two fires, the unfortunate militiamen broke and fled to the right to cross the stream above the bridge. "Captain Stephenson drove them across the fields. Captain Saunders pursued them, the Huzzars were let loose" upon them, "and afterwards the battalion, Colonel Mawhood leading them." Many of them were shot, others cut down by the hussars of the Rangers, and more were driven into the creek and drowned. There is no record of the American losses, but, though the party that had taken post on the high ground near the bridge appears to have escaped across it, the death toll was heavy. The British lost one hussar, mortally wounded.

In New Jersey this affair was called a massacre. It aroused strong feelings, particularly because of the presence of the New Jersey Tories and their participation in the ruthless pursuit and slaughter of fleeing men of their own state.[15]

Mawhood, after returning to Salem, decided to attack another party of American militia posted at Hancock's Bridge across Alloway Creek about five miles from Salem. He sent Simcoe with his Rangers and the New Jersey Volunteers in boats down the Delaware to a point below the mouth of the Alloway. Thence they marched two miles through knee-deep swamps before they reached fast ground near the bridge. At the same time, the 27th Regiment was approaching it in front, cooperating with Simcoe.

The attack was elaborately planned to entrap the 400 militia at the bridge, detachments being sent here and there to occupy different houses in the village, including Hancock's house near the bridge, which was supposed to be the headquarters of the militia.

But all except 20 of the 400 militia that had been holding the bridge had been withdrawn the day before. Simcoe's men approaching the village came first upon two sentries, whom they bayoneted. They then entered Hancock's house, in which the few remaining militia were sleeping. Aroused, these few made no opposition but, recognizing some of the New Jersey Volunteers, offered to shake hands with them. The answer was the bayonet. Every occupant of the house was killed, including Hancock and his brother, both Tories.

Meanwhile, a detachment of the Rangers had come upon a patrol of seven of the militia and shot down all but one. No prisoners were taken. This exploit, so typical of the ruthlessness of Simcoe's operations, most certainly was a "massacre," in the exact meaning of the word.[16]

To organize the effort to secure food and forage for the troops at Valley Forge and to push it to every extremity, Washington had appointed Nathanael Greene. A kind-hearted man, Greene undertook the "very disagreeable" job with reluctance; but, having undertaken it, he laid down rules for executing it which lacked nothing of thoroughness. His subordinates were to harden their hearts and "despatch the business as fast as possible." He bade them "search the country through and through," take all horses, cattle, sheep, hogs, all forage of every sort, all the wagons to carry it in. If distance or lack of wagons prevented the bringing of hay, corn, and such, they were to be burned; for an object secondary to feeding the Americans was starving the British. The motto was, "Forage the country naked!" [17] Receipts were given for the things taken, with promise of future payment.

But the country, he found, was already "very much drained." It was "strongly marked with poverty and distress." The cattle and horses had been largely taken into Philadelphia by the British. "The country has been so much gleaned that there is little left in it." [18] Not unnaturally, what was left was carefully concealed by the owners. All that Greene and his men could get was not enough.

Conditions in the camp grew steadily worse. The horses starved to death, 500 of them. For want of burial in the frozen ground their carcasses rotted about the camp in such numbers as to endanger the health of the men.[19] The soldiers themselves were not much better off than the horses. On February 16, 1778, Washington wrote: "For some days past there has been little less than a famine in the camp. A part of the army has been a week without any kind of flesh and the rest three or four days. Naked and starving as they are, we cannot enough admire the incomparable patience and fidelity of the soldiery, that they have not been ere this excited by their suffering to a general mutiny and dispersion." [20] Lafayette wrote in his memoirs, "The army frequently remained whole days without provisions, and the patient endurance of both soldiers and officers was a miracle which each moment seemed to renew." [21]

Fortunately, before the army could starve to death the combined efforts of Greene, now quartermaster general, and of Jeremiah Wadsworth of Connecticut, commissary general, gradually bettered conditions. Wadsworth applied himself to the collection of foodstuffs and clothing; Greene, to their transportation, gathering wagons and horses, repairing bridges, mending roads, organizing a corps of wagoners, so that much that once had had to be destroyed for want of transport could now be brought to the camp. By the arrival of spring there was a regular daily allowance to each man of a pound and a half of bread, a pound of beef or fish or pork and beans, and a gill of whisky. This was supplemented by fresh, sweet food that came to the army like manna from Heaven. The regular spring run of shad up the Schuylkill to spawn brought thousands upon thousands of those succulent fish to the nets of those accustomed to harvest them. The soldiers ate to repletion, and hundreds of barrels of the fat fish were salted down for future use.[22] "The cheeks of the young soldiers filled out, their arms recovered muscle and their step regained its spring; while the invalids who had survived the winter came back to the ranks by hundreds." [23]

But before the spring and its betterment of conditions there was a sad diminution of the army's strength. Not only death but desertion had reduced its numbers. Unable to endure the physical hardships, the weaker men, especially the foreign-born, went off "ten to fifty at a time." "In great numbers and even by companies," [24] they repaired to Philadelphia either to sell their arms for food or, in some cases, to seek service in the well fed, warmly clothed British army. Joseph Galloway, civilian governor of the town, whose duty it was to investigate the character of newcomers, testified that 2,300 of these deserters had reported to his office. Of these, one-half were Irish, one-fourth English or Scottitsh, the rest Americans.[25] The patriots were quoted as saying, "Our men depreciate as fast as our money." By these means, Washington's force was finally reduced to five or six thousand, of whom probably not more than half were really fit for duty. As the spring came on, efforts were made with some success to build up the enrollment by new enlistments; but it was hard to induce new men to submit themselves to the hardships of that sink of misery.

Yet more than restoration to health and increase of numbers was needed to turn that ragged horde into an army effective in the field. It had gone into camp a body of men experienced in a year, in many cases two years, of hard service. Its members knew how to shoot and how to stand being shot at—even, in a few cases, how to withstand the bayonet. But of the school of the soldier, of the manual of arms, of the facings, of forming column, of deploying in line of battle, of all the other military practices by which a soldier or a body of soldiers is exercised, moved, and maneuvered in camp, on the march, and on the field, they had only a slight and fumbling knowledge. Instruction in such practices was now the greatest need of the Americans, and it was miraculously supplied.

In February there came to the camp a forty-seven-year-old German soldier, a man of middle height, solidly built, heavy-featured, with a high forehead, a long nose, a strong chin, a full-lipped mouth, more often smiling than not. His light brown hair had somewhat thinned; but his brown-gray eyes, under heavy brows, were keenly alive, and his broad, full cheeks were ruddy with health.[26]

He called himself Frederick William Augustus Henry Ferdinand, Baron von Steuben. His letters of introduction to the Congress from Benjamin Franklin and Silas Deane in Paris stated that he had been a lieutenant general in the army of Frederick the Great and that monarch's aide-de-camp and quartermaster general. He himself spoke casually of his estate in Swabia. All that was simply eyewash. In fact, his Christian name was not Frederick William Augustus Henry Ferdinand, but something quite different; his family name was not Steuben, but Steube; he had no claim to the "von"; he had never been a lieutenant general, nor a general of any sort, in Frederick's army, nor his aide. His highest rank in Germany had been captain, and he had no estate in Swabia, nor anywhere else.[27]

He had, in fact, come to America a simple soldier of fortune looking for a job, and so closely resembled the typical specimen in fiction, with his easy disregard of truth in his accounts of himself, as to sound fictitious. But he was not a fiction, and all his fanciful fabrications were and are no matter at all. Baron von (or de, as he preferred it) Steuben deserves all the honor and praise he has since received from a grateful people. He was one of God's best gifts to America in its struggle for liberty.

Doubtless he was aware of the temper of the Congress towards foreign aspirants for office in the army and had sufficiently well justified confidence in his own ability to climb by his own merits, if he could only get a foot on the ladder of preferment, for he told a committee of the Congress that "he did not seek any rank or pay. He wished only to join the war as a volunteer and render such services as General Washington might think him capable of." [28] He would ask only that his necessary expenses while in the service should be defrayed. That seemed fair enough. The committee applauded his generosity, and the Congress accepted his services.[29]

Washington received him cordially, recognized his military ability, and asked him to serve as a volunteer acting inspector general in charge of the training of the troops. Steuben accepted the position and took a look at them. With his idea of an army, what he saw was shocking.

"The men," Steuben wrote, "were literally naked, some of them in the fullest extent of the word. The officers who had coats had them of every color and make. I saw officers . . . mounting guard in a sort of dressing-gown made of an old blanket or woollen bed-cover. With regard to military discipline, I may safely say no such thing existed. . . . There was no regular formation. A so-called regiment was found of three platoons, another of five, eight, nine and the Canadian regiment of twenty-one. The formation of the regiments was as varied as their mode of drill, which consisted only of the manual exercise. Each colonel had a system of his own, the one according to the English, the other according to the Prussian or the French style. . . . The greater part of the captains had no roll of their companies and had no idea how many men they had. . . . When I asked a colonel of the strength of his regiment, the usual reply was 'Something between two and three hundred men.' " He found one regiment of 30 men, one company consisting of one corporal. "The arms were in a horrible condition, covered with rust, half of them without bayonets, many from which a single shot could not be fired . . . muskets, carbines, fowling-pieces and rifles were seen in the same company." [30] The other equipment was equally varied.

Yet Steuben recognized the quality of the material he had to deal with, the fortitude of the soldiers, and their devotion to their cause. He told Washington that no European army would have held together under such deprivations of food, clothing, and shelter.[31]

The German officer's first task was to devise a uniform system of drill regulations. He based it on the Prussian system, with such adaptations as were required by American conditions. As he knew no English, but only French and German, he wrote it in French from which it was translated by his aide, Pierre Duponceau, and then polished by John Laurens and Alexander Hamilton. When the English version was presented to him he could not understand a word of it. He had to memorize the English form of each of its commands and rehearse them before his young American assistants.[32]

There was no printing press with the army. Hundreds of copies of the regulations had to be written in longhand for distribution to the officers and then copied into their orderly books. Speed was important as there was little time left before the year's campaign would open. Day by day the composition and translation of the original went on. The first lesson, written on a Monday night would be translated, copied, and in the hands of the drill-masters by Wednesday.[33]

Though, in accordance with the English practice, drilling the men in the American army had been left to the sergeants, Steuben would not have it that way. He would drill the men himself. His method was first to organize a model company of a hundred men selected from various regiments. When it was drawn up, he took from it a small squad and started at the beginning with "the position of the soldier." To explain that, he relied upon pantomime, himself assuming the proper attitude and calling on each man to imitate him, correcting each man's faults by indicating them. He taught them how to dress their line. He marched them forward in slow step, himself calling the time—over and over again. So he went on, teaching them to halt, to about-face, to march to the rear, and so on.[34]

While he drilled the squad the rest of the model company looked on, as did also hundreds of officers and thousands of men. He then split the whole company into similar squads and had an officer take over each one, while he watched and corrected errors. Then he drilled the company as a whole. This went on for three days, beginning always with the squads and ending with the full company, and always he exacted the strictest precision in their movements.[35]

Then Steuben took up the manual of arms, taught the men by his own example a simplified form of the Prussian manual, how to carry the musket, load it, fire it, how to fix the bayonet, and to charge. The men of the model company, all veterans, were interested and eager to acquire proficiency. They quickly learned the new movements, while the onlookers, practically the whole army, were instructed by observation.[36]

But his lack of English was a handicap. Once he gave an order which, because of his pronunciation, was misunderstood. Some of the men went one way, some another. He shouted it in French, then in German, but the model company was in complete confusion. He tried the sign language with no success. Then he blew up and cursed them vigorously in French and German, with an occasional "Goddam" for emphasis. Everybody laughed uproariously. A young American officer, Captain Benjamin Walker of New York, came to his aid, addressed him in French, and offered to interpret the command to the troops. Steuben said later that he was like an angel from heaven. The company was re-formed, the command given, and the maneuver executed. Steuben made Walker one of his permanent aides. It needed only such a bit of comedy, which was repeated more than once, to make the baron one of the most popular officers in the camp.[37]

A general drill program for the whole army was instituted on March 24. From that time on, the camp was busy. Each regiment was divided into squads of 20 men, to which the lessons were given in the same manner as to the original squad. The use of the bayonet was emphasized for the first time in the army of the Revolution. Under Steuben's instructions the men, who had shrunk from the bright steel of the British, became the "fierce bayonet fighters" that displayed their new ability a few weeks later at Monmouth and after that in the capture of Stony Point with that weapon alone and without firing a shot.[38]

The most important lesson the army learned was to march "in compact masses with steadiness and without losing distance." [39] Until then they had generally marched in Indian file, so that their column reached four times the distance needed for columns of fours, making it impossible to enforce discipline and prevent straggling as well as lengthening the time needed to form in line and front the enemy. This defect had been felt at Brandywine and at Germantown, where the heads of columns had arrived in time, but their tails came too late.[40] In April, Washington issued an order against marching in single file.[41]

Within a month Steuben "had the Satisfaction . . . to see not only a regular Step introduced in the Army, but I also made maneuvers with ten and twelve Battalions, with as much precision as the Evolution of a Single Company." He made a penetrating comment on the characteristics of the American in a letter to his friend Baron von Gaudy: "The genius of this nation is not in the least to be compared with that of the Prussians, Austrians or French. You say to your soldier 'Do this' and he doeth it; but I am obliged to say 'This is the reason why you ought to do that'; and then he does it." [42]

A letter from an officer at Valley Forge published in May said: "The Army grows stronger every day. It increases in numbers . . . and there is a spirit of discipline among the troops that is better than numbers. Each brigade is on parade almost every day for several hours. You would be charmed to see the regularity and exactness with which they march and perform their maneuvers. . . . Last year . . . it was almost impossible to advance or retire in the presence of the enemy without disordering the line and falling into confusion. That misfortune, I believe, will seldom happen again . . . for the troops are instructed in a new and so happy a method of marching that they soon will be able to advance with the utmost regularity, even without musick and on the roughest grounds." [43]

As they became more skilful, their soldierly pride increased and "a new morale, never more to be extinguished, soon pervaded the ranks of the Continental Army."

In May there was a grand review to celebrate the treaty of alliance with France. "The several brigades marched by their right to their posts in order of battle and the line was formed with admirable rapidity and precision." The artillery gave three salutes of thirteen guns each, and the troops fired a *feu de joie*, a fire of musketry commencing at the right of the front line and running, shot by shot, to its left and then back again along the second line to its right, which was "executed to perfection" and "gave a sensible pleasure to every one present." [44] Washington, in general orders, acknowledged "the highest satisfaction" with the spectacle. "The exactness and order with which their movements were performed," he wrote, "is a pleasing evidence of the progress they are making in Military Improvements." And he thanked "Baron Steuben & the gentlemen under him for their Indefatigable Exertions . . . the good effects of which are already so apparent." [45]

The Congress also took notice and on May 5, appointed Steuben inspector general of the army with the rank and pay of major general, the pay to commence from the time of his first joining the army.[46]

The exercises and training continued throughout May and until the middle of June, when the evacuation of Philadelphia called for active operations by the Americans. Then the troops took the field a real army at last, thanks in large part to the "baron."

Before the American army left the Forge, there occurred an affair very like those at Quintin's Bridge and Hancock's Bridge in March. General John Lacey with a body of Pennsylvania militia numbering 456 had been stationed at the Crooked Billet Tavern and village in Montgomery County, Pennsylvania. But the expiration of their terms of service had reduced their number by the end of April to 53 fit for duty, though some small reenforcements may have arrived. The purpose of this post was the interruption of supplies intended for Philadelphia.

Annoyed by this interference, Lieutenant Colonel Balfour sent Lieutenant Colonel Abercrombie with 400 light infantry, part of them mounted, a party of light dragoons, and Major Simcoe with 300 Queen's Rangers infantry, to attack Lacey. Abercrombie took a direct road; Simcoe made a circuit to get behind the Crooked Billet. By a night march on May 1 they enveloped Lacey in front and rear. A sentinel alarmed the camp, and Lacey marched his men towards a near-by wood, where they made a stand and exchanged fire with the enemy. Seeing that he was overpowered, he abandoned his baggage and retreated rapidly, keeping up his fire as best he could against the enemy on both his flanks and his rear during a two-mile retreat. Then he "made a sudden turn to the left, through a wood, which entirely extricated" him. He reported 30 of his men killed and 17 wounded, but changed this later to 26 killed and 8 or 10 severely wounded. The British had 9 wounded.[47]

Barren Hill

This narrative must now revert to the middle of the period of greatest destitution, the winter at Valley Forge. When the fortunes of the American cause and the strength of its military forces were at almost their lowest ebb, the Board of War conceived and the Congress approved one of the maddest of all mad projects. It was nothing less than, as expressed in the Congressional resolution of January 22, 1778, "an irruption . . . into Canada." [1] In spite of the lessons which should have been learned from the fate of Arnold's and Montgomery's expeditions and from the defeat at Trois Rivières, the Board and the Congress lightheartedly proposed this new venture, to be undertaken by some force or other not yet provided nor even reasonably in prospect. No plan of possibly successful operations was devised. Apparently that was left entirely to the ingenuity of the officers selected to lead the expedition, of whom the chief was a twenty-year-old Frenchman, who had had the very slightest military experience, his only qualifications being his nationality and his religion, Roman Catholic, to whose standard the French Canadians were hopefully expected to flock on those two accounts in an uprising against the British government.

That French youth was Marie Joseph Paul Yves Roch Gilbert du Motier, Marquis de Lafayette. Although a scion of an ancient and noble family, a typical aristocrat, and a favorite of the French court, young Lafayette had developed, as he later said, "an ardent love of liberty." When therefore, in 1776, he heard of the rebellion in America, knowing as little as possible of that country and of the reasons and causes of its revolt, "my heart espoused warmly the cause of liberty and I thought of nothing but of adding also the aid of my banner." [2] Actually he did not become a republican until later

His real reasons for joining the Americans were a youthful desire for glory and an equally youthful hatred of Britain.

He made no secret of his project of going to help the colonists. It was discussed by all Paris as the gallant idea of a romantic boy. "Of course," Madame du Deffand wrote to Horace Walpole, "it is a piece of folly; but it does him no discredit. He receives more praise than blame." It became known in London, too. "We talk chiefly," wrote Gibbon, the historian, "of the Marquis de la Fayette. He is about twenty, with 130,000 Livres a year. . . . The [French] Court *appears* to be angry with him." [3]

It was not really angry with him. Marie Antoinette herself favored his enterprise. But, being yet technically at peace with England, France had to preserve appearances. The Count de Broglie at first tried to dissuade him out of regard and affection for his family, but at last promised to help him and did so in one respect, that is, by introducing to him an experienced, able, and judicious soldier, a man of fifty years, the so-called Baron de Kalb, who was then seeking an engagement in the American army for himself and might, to some extent, act as guardian for the inexperienced, youthful enthusiast.

With his own money Lafayette purchased a ship and outfitted it. From Silas Deane, the American agent in Paris, he obtained a promise of major generals' commissions for himself and De Kalb and lesser offices for eleven other Frenchmen whom he proposed to take with him. [4] But at the last moment Viscount Stormont, the British ambassador, remonstrated strongly against such a breach of neutrality, and the French government, discouraged as to American prospects by Washington's successive defeats at Long Island, White Plains, and Fort Washington and his desperate retreat across the Jerseys, [5] intimated a purpose to arrest the young adventurer and wreck his plans. His own family, as well as the government, forbade his departure. Even Deane and Benjamin Franklin discouraged him. [6] But he persisted. Disguised as a postboy, he made his way to Bordeaux, where he found De Kalb and the others awaiting him and, on March 26, 1777, his ship, the *Victoire*, set sail. It was met in a Spanish port by two French officers with a *lettre de cachet* commanding him to return to France. Release from this entanglement was not effected until April 20, and even then only by Lafayette's audacious assumption that the government's failure to answer his request that it "relax in its determination" to stop him was "a tacit consent" to his departure. So again he set sail and landed, June 13, on an island off the South Carolina coast. Rowing to the mainland, he and some members of his party came at midnight to the house of Major Benjamin Huger, who received them with gracious hospitality. [7]

Carriages were procured, and Lafayette with six of his companions started on a journey of nine hundred miles through a country that impressed him with its "youth and majesty," to arrive in Philadelphia on July 27. His reception by the Congress was anything but gracious. In justice it must be observed that the Congress had been fairly overwhelmed by great numbers of adventurers seeking office in the American army. Silas Deane had been responsible for many reckless promises of commissions to men who, when commissioned, proved to be entirely unfit. In the case of Philippe du Coudray the demand was for the rank of major general, second in command of the whole army under Washington, and commander in chief of the artillery, the position already held by Henry Knox. This demand had resulted in threats to resign not only by Knox, but also by Greene and Sullivan. Coudray got the commission he asked for, but was not made second in command, nor chief of the artillery.

Lafayette's group was looked upon with disfavor. An appointment was made to meet them at the door of the State House. There, on the sidewalk, they were confronted by James Lovell, a delegate from Massachusetts and one of the few congressmen that could speak French. He very curtly asked for their credentials and complained to them of the quality of the French officers that had preceded them. "It seems," he said, "that French officers have a great fancy to enter our service without being invited. It is true we were in need of officers last year, but now we have experienced men and plenty of them." "It would be impossible," wrote Buysson, one of the group, "for anyone to be more stupefied than we were at such a reception." [8]

But Lafayette was not to be gainsaid by this representative of the Congress. He asked him to return to that body and read to it a short note: "After the sacrifices I have made, I have the right to expect two favours; one is to serve at my own expense,—the other is to serve, at first, as volunteer," that is to say, without a command. [9]

No pay, no command, merely the honor of a commission—those were novel terms. The Congress sent a second embassy to the applicants on the sidewalk, Lovell with another, "more skilful as well as more polite," says Buysson. The result of that conference was a resolution, adopted on July 31, recognizing Lafayette's "great zeal to the cause of liberty," accepting his services, and making him a major general on his own terms. [10] But the others of his party were yet uncared for and in an uncomfortable position.

De Kalb, a veteran soldier, was especially chagrined that so young a man as Lafayette, with practically no military experience, should be taken while he was left. He wrote a sharp and bitter letter to the Congress, setting forth his claims and inveighing against Deane's making engagements that the Congress would not fulfill. He closed by asking either the promised appointment or reimbursement of his expense in coming to America.[11] The Congress, on September 8, thanked him and the Viscount de Mornay, "with the officers that accompany them, for their zeal," declined their services, and ordered that "their expences to this continent and on their way home be paid." [12]

De Kalb, with Buysson and two others, was on a leisurely excursion to Bethlehem preparatory to departure from a southern port when he was overtaken by a messenger from the Congress, who informed him that he had been commissioned a major general. Buysson was later made a lieutenant colonel. Six others of Lafayette's party of eleven were also commissioned in accordance with Deane's agreement.[13]

Lafayette's first contact with Washington occurred at a dinner in Philadelphia. He was impressed by the "majestic figure and deportment" of the commander in chief and no less by "the noble affability of his manner." [14] Washington seems to have taken to the tall, slender, handsome, blond youth from the first. In him he saw the gentleman, as well as the ardent young seeker of glory. Gentility was always grateful to the Virginia aristocrat. He invited the boy to become one of his own military "family"—his staff—and there grew up between them an affectionate relationship which, Lafayette wrote to his wife, was like that of "attached brothers, with mutual confidence and cordiality," [15] but which would be more accurately described as that existing between father and son. Perhaps the childless Washington saw in this lad a son such as he would have liked to have.

The youth, accustomed to the uniform appearance of the pipe-clayed European armies, was less favorably impressed by the army in its camp on the Neshaminy. That army of "about eleven thousand men, ill armed and still worse clothed," he wrote in his memoirs, "presented a strange spectacle to the eye of the young Frenchman; their clothes were parti-colored, and many of them were almost naked; the best clad wore *hunting-shirts*, large grey linen coats." Their military tactics, too, were strange to him, awkward, and ill managed. Yet he thought "the soldiers were fine and their officers zealous; virtue stood in place of science and each day added to both experience and discipline." [16]

To this inexperienced though gallant young man the sapient Board of War and the compliant Congress confided the leadership of the proposed

March-hare "irruption" into Canada, naming as second in command Major General Thomas Conway.

Conway, a French Irishman, a capable, experienced soldier, was brave in battle, but of a discontented disposition. His name was given to the probably mythical "Conway Cabal." The other members, it has been said, were Horatio Gates, Richard Henry Lee and Francis Lightfoot Lee of Virginia, Benjamin Rush and Thomas Mifflin of Pennsylvania, Samuel Adams, John Adams, and James Lovell of Massachusetts; their object, the displacement of Washington and the succession of Gates in the chief command of the army.

That there was actually a conspiracy among those men, an organized effort worthy the appellation of "cabal" is very unlikely. Certainly no sufficient evidence of its existence has ever been discovered. But just as certainly some of them at least, notably Lovell, Conway, and Mifflin, were bitterly hostile to Washington as a military leader and laudatory of Gates, the conqueror of Burgoyne.[17]

The actual existence of such a conspiracy is of little importance in comparison with the general belief in its existence, which prevailed among Washington's friends in the army and elsewhere. Lafayette asserted it was a fact. When the Board of War, then composed of Gates as president, Mifflin, William Duer, Francis Lightfoot Lee, and Richard Peters (three of them reputed to be members of the supposed Cabal it will be observed) proposed this new Canadian expedition, and the Congress authorized it, the action was taken without consulting the commander in chief, without even giving him notice of it. With the same disregard of him, the officers to conduct the "irruption" were named by the Congress, Lafayette, Conway, and John Stark.[18] The first knowledge Washington had of it was conveyed in a letter from Gates advising him that the scheme had been adopted, asking him to spare Hazen's regiment as a part of the force to be sent, and enclosing instructions to be handed to Lafayette. Washington swallowed the insult, ordered Hazen's regiment detached for the purpose, and gave Lafayette the letter of instructions. But that high-spirited youth, though desirous of a command and a chance to win glory in the field, thought he saw in the proposal a scheme "to intoxicate" him with a prospect of military fame and thus to seduce him from his allegiance to Washington. He understood the offer to be of a command independent of the commander in chief, thus belittling Washington and weakening his position. Moreover, he objected to Conway, the conspirator, as his second in command. Although he regarded him as "a very brave and very good officer," yet he considered him as "an ambitious and dangerous man." He had already written to Washington that

Conway had "done all in his power, by cunning manoeuvres, to take off my confidence and affection for you." [19] He, therefore, wrote to the Congress that he must decline the commission, unless it was understood that he should remain subject to Washington's orders and report directly to him. He also went to York, where the Congress was in session and, as Henry Laurens, its president, put it, "discovered a noble resentment for the affront offered to his Commander Genl. Washington" and "said he would not go without a General Officer of the Rank of Major General in whom he could put confidence and therefore demanded Genl. McDougal or Baron Kalb and that their appointment should be through his General."

When the Congress and the Board of War hesitated to comply with these demands, Lafayette threatened to return to France and take all the foreign officers with him. "A good deal of struggle," says Laurens, "was made to elude the Marquis's demands, [but] he was firm and succeeded." [20] He also succeeded in obtaining from a now completely submissive Congress commissions for six of his fellow travelers from France, who should go with him to Canada. He went back to obtain Washington's orders detaching either McDougall or Kalb for the expedition.

The young commander's instructions called for the assemblage of a force of 2,500 rank and file, including Nixon's brigade, five other regiments, and "Capt. Whitcomb's Rangers." At Albany he was to be provided with ammunition, provisions, stores, and woolen clothing for the troops. If unable to raise a general revolt of the Canadians he was merely to destroy the works and vessels at St. Johns, Chambly, and Ile aux Noix and then retire to the Hudson River country; but if the Canadians responded to his seductions he was to invite them to send delegates to the Congress, and then he was to take Montreal.[21]

Lafayette undertook this mad project in good faith and with an enthusiasm that carried him uncomplainingly through the difficult journey of four hundred miles to Albany on horseback in midwinter. But there he was promptly disillusioned. Instead of the promised 2,500 men he found only 1,200 fit for duty; and the "most part of those very men are naked, even for a summer's campaign." Their pay was far in arrears, and all of them, quite naturally, "disgusted and reluctant to the last degree to begin a winter campaign in a so cold country." He had been assured by Gates that Stark would have cleared the way for him by burning the British fleet on the Lake "before your arrival." He found that Stark had not even been informed "what number of men, from whence, for what time, for what rendezvous I desire him to raise." He found that Conway, who had preceded him, had received letters from Schuyler, Lincoln, and Arnold, men who knew what they were talking about, declaring "in the most expressive terms that, in our present circumstances, there was no possibility to begin now an enterprise into Canada." The deputy quartermaster, the deputy commissary, and the deputy clothier-general, who were to have furnished the supplies and the warm clothing for the troops, were "entirely of the same opinion." The one who was "most desirous of getting there," Hazen, the Canadian, confessed that they were "not strong enough to think of the expedition at this moment." Everybody whom Lafayette consulted told him "it would be madness to undertake this operation." [22]

The ambitious young commander was chagrined at the failure of his enterprise before it had even begun, chagrined and angry. "I have been deceived by the board of War," he wrote to Washington. He was concerned about his reputation. He saw himself in a "distressing, ridiculous, foolish and indeed, nameless situation. . . . I am sure I will be very ridiculous and laughed at." [23] But the thing was plainly impossible. It was a fraud and a foreordained fiasco from the beginning. Even the Congress at last realized its absurdity. On March 2 it ordered that the "intended irruption be suspended for the present," at the same time recognizing the "prudence, activity and zeal" of its leader, being "persuaded nothing has or would have been wanting on his part." And belatedly, on March 13, it called the whole thing off by authorizing Washington to recall him and De Kalb.[24]

Lafayette had not long been established again in the camp at Valley Forge, and had, perhaps, not yet recovered from his chagrin on account of the Canadian fiasco, when he entered upon another adventure that came within a hairbreadth of plunging him into far deeper humiliataion, indeed of ruining his military career, and not only that but also placing the entire American army in dire jeopardy.

On May 18 Washington issued an order placing under Lafayette's command a division of about 2,200 men, one-third of the whole then much diminished American army,[25] and directing him to "march towards the enemy's lines" for the purpose of "being a security to this camp and a cover to the country between the Delaware and the Schuylkill, to obstruct the incursions of the enemy's parties and to obtain intelligence of their motions and designs. This last a matter of very interesting moment and ought to claim your particular attention." At the same time, he should remember that his detachment "is a very valuable one and that any accident happening to it would be a very severe blow to this army." He should therefore use every precaution "to guard against a surprise." [26]

That this expedition was as useless as it was perilous is manifest. The

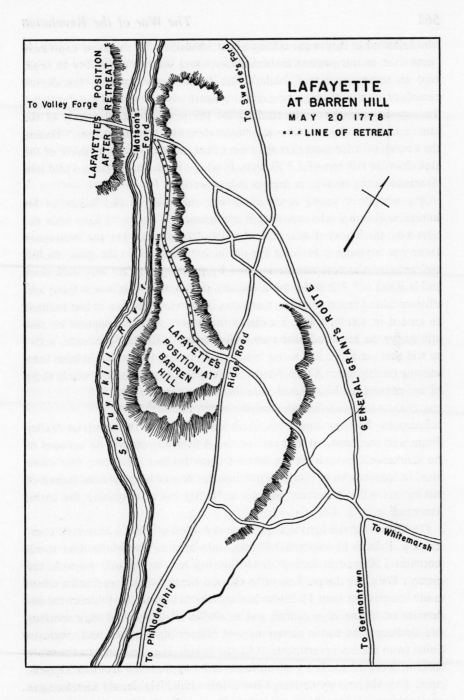

To Valley Forge

Matson's Ford

LAFAYETTE'S POSITION AFTER RETREAT

To Swede's Ford

LAFAYETTE
AT BARREN HILL
MAY 20 1778
× × × LINE OF RETREAT

Schuylkill River

GENERAL GRANT'S ROUTE

Ridge Road

LAFAYETTE'S POSITION AT BARREN HILL

To Whitemarsh

To Philadelphia

To Germantown

force allotted to it was too small to be a security to the American camp, to "cover the country between the Delaware and the Schuylkill and to interrupt communication with Philadelphia"; and it was far larger than was necessary or useful in gaining information as to the enemy's movements. The scouts already employed for that purpose, acting in small, swiftly mobile bodies, could obtain such information and watch the movements of the enemy with far better results than could be achieved by a conspicuous, slow-moving column of 2,200 men. Endangering a full third of the whole American army in such a useless enterprise calls for some explanation. It may probably be found in the character and ambition of the young man himself and in his relations with Washington.

A commission as major general without command was far from satisfactory to a young man eager for distinction. He had, in the previous fall, embarrassed the commander in chief by pressing for "a Command equal to his Rank." [27] He had secured this by the allotment to him of Stephen's division after the Battle of Germantown, but, so far, had had no opportunity to lead it in action. While his discomfiture over the Canadian failure was still heavy on his mind, one may well imagine a strong desire on his part to win the spurs that had so far eluded him, in an independent exploit. One may justifiably assume that Washington's desire to gratify the wishes of his young protégé led him to authorize this new enterprise, that it was his heart rather than his head that dictated the order, although some weight must be allowed to the commander in chief's estimate of the value of Lafayette's French connections, so valuable to the American cause, which would be complimented by such an important assignment to their young representative. Indeed, the Chevalier de Pontgibaud, one of Lafayette's aides, says in his memoirs that the order was made "partly out of friendship and partly from policy." [28]

The force chosen for the expedition consisted of Poor's New Hampshire brigade, Potter's Pennsylvania Militia, and Captain Allen McLane's partisan corps of 150 men including 50 Oneida Indians. It was allowed five fieldpieces. With this force, Lafayette crossed the Schuylkill at Swede's Ford and took post on May 18 below Matson's Ford at Barren Hill, a crossroads hamlet consisting of a church and a handful of houses twelve miles from Valley Forge and within eleven miles of Philadelphia, but no more than two miles from the British outposts at Chestnut Hill. His position was the center of a network of roads by which it could be approached from every direction. The Manatawny or Ridge Road from Philadelphia, via Germantown, passed through it on its way north to Swede's Ford. From the east came a road from Whitemarsh and Chestnut Hill to cross that other in the village, and still another led from Germantown to cross the first at a point a mile or so north of the Hill and run finally to Matson's Ford.[29]

Lafayette disposed Poor's brigade in a good position on a small elevation south of the church. The line faced the south, its right defended by the steep declivity to the Schuylkill, its left resting on two or three stout stone houses. In advance of the line he placed his five guns. Potter's 600 Pennsylvanians were detached to take post, at a distance, on the road from Whitemarsh to guard against surprise from that quarter. McLane's irregulars were stationed about a mile to the south on the Ridge Road and pickets were thrown out a mile farther on that road. Thus apparently secure from surprise, Lafayette rested that night.[30]

Of course the movement of such a column could be no secret. Clinton, who was about to supersede Howe in command in Philadelphia, knew about it immediately. To him it seemed simply a wonderful opportunity to capture the young Frenchman and so humiliate him and his country, America's new ally by a treaty made in February. He regarded it as a sure thing. Howe invited a party for dinner on the next night "to meet the Marquis de La Fayette." To make good this boast, he turned out almost the whole British army.[31]

General Grant, with 5,000 men and fifteen guns, marched from Philadelphia at half past ten in the evening of the 19th, taking a circuitous route which would bring him to that point where the road from Whitemarsh crossed the Ridge Road about a mile and a half north of Barren Hill. There he could cut the Americans off from a retreat by the Ridge Road to either Matson's or Swede's Ford and so to Valley Forge.

Grey was to lead another column, of 2,000 grenadiers and a small troop of dragoons, by way of Germantown on the road direct to the Hill with intent to attack Lafayette's left flank. Clinton, accompanied by Howe, was to bring a strong force up the Ridge Road from the south and establish himself not far below the American front. Thus the Americans would be boxed in on three sides, and the river was the fourth; and in the face of such overwhelming numbers, they could only surrender. The trap was to be sprung the next morning.[32]

Grant made good progress along the Whitemarsh road. Potter and his Pennsylvania militia, who had been ordered to hold that road, seem to have disappeared without trace. Lafayette says Potter had "thought proper to retire" from his post.[33] At all events, he offered no hindrance to Grant, who gained his desired position; nor did he give any warning to Lafayette. Grey got to his post on Lafayette's left flank. But the case of Clinton and Howe, coming up the Ridge Road, was different.

Captain Allen McLane, "a vigilant partisan of great merit," was on duty there. "In the course of the night," says John Marshall, "he fell in with two British grenadiers at Three Mile Run" and, presumably, captured them. They "informed him of the movement made by Grant and also that a large body of Germans was getting ready to march up the Schuylkill." That would be Clinton's column. McLane guessed what was afoot. He detached Captain Parr with a company of riflemen to meet Clinton's force and to "oppose and retard" it, while he hurried to the camp. He got there at daybreak and told Lafayette about Grant and Clinton. His news was confirmed by the sound of shots from Parr's company and by the arrival of a local patriot who had seen redcoats on the Whitemarsh road.[34]

The situation seemed desperate. Grant and Clinton, in great force, held the roads to the nearest fords, Swede's, Bevin's, and Matson's. It was a test for the young general, but he met it fairly. He put his men in a posture of defense and sent out scouts in all directions. One brought him good news; there was another road from the Hill to Matson's Ford by which Grant could be eluded, although his post was actually nearer the ford than was Lafayette's. It ran from Barren Hill down the steep ground to the riverside and then along it to the ford. It dropped down so suddenly and was so concealed by the height above that a marching army would be immediately out of sight from Grant's position and from Grey's as well.[35]

Lafayette arranged for a small rear guard to make demonstrations about the church and to throw out false heads of columns towards the north, so as to make it appear to Grant that he was about to be attacked. Grant's attention was arrested, and he prepared to oppose this apparent advance. While he was thus amused Lafayette sent Poor and the rest of his brigade down the sloping path. He himself remained behind to carry off the rear guard. The whole force reached and crossed the ford, with all its guns, before Grant was aware of the evasion. On some heights on the west side of the river, Lafayette drew up his men to contest the passage of the enemy; but no such crossing was attempted.[36]

Clinton, marching against the abandoned American post, was disgusted at meeting some of Grant's column coming down from the north and finding no Americans anywhere in sight. Without any further effort, the whole British force marched back to Philadelphia "much fatigued, and ashamed and . . . laughed at for their ill success," as Lafayette exultantly says in his memoirs.[37]

A ludicrous incident of the affair occurred when Clinton's dragoons, in advance of his column, came suddenly upon McLane's Indians, who were on picket duty on the Ridge Road. The Oneidas, unused to mounted troops, sprang up with such terrified and terrifying whoops and yells as to frighten the horses and the dragoons themselves. Both parties fled the scene in equal disorder and in opposite directions.[38]

McLane and his men got much honor for their service and were officially thanked for their "vigilancy," which had enabled the marquis to make "a glorious retreat as well as a safe one." [39]

At Howe's own request, preferred as early as the middle of November, 1777, the King graciously allowed him to resign his command in February, 1778. On May 8 Sir Henry Clinton came to Philadelphia from New York, with orders to take over from Howe, and more besides—no less than an order that the long sought, much desired, dearly bought capital of the rebels should be immediately evacuated.[40]

The truth is that Howe's entire campaign, from its beginning when he first proposed to himself the capture of Philadelphia, had been a sheer waste of time, of money, and of men. His thought all along had been to wear down American resistance by occupying places and winning battles without too great expenditure of man power. He had never thought it advisable to take large risks for decisive victories. His policy would have required large numbers of men and much time. Certainly the taking of Philadelphia could never have destroyed American resistance. In the countries of Europe, where not only the administrative and executive functions, including the nerve centers of the military forces, but also a large part of the commercial and industrial operations were concentrated in the capital cities, the capture of one of these would result both in a loss of prestige and usually also in a sort of paralysis of all national functions; wherefore the government would be compelled to ask for terms of peace. Philadelphia was in no degree such a capital. The governmental machinery did not center there, for the very good reason that the Americans had little governmental machinery; they had nothing but a Congress, which could sit in Baltimore or in York—or not sit at all, for that matter—without fatal harm to the country. The nerve center of the military forces, if the Board of War might be called that, could operate as well, or as badly, in any town as in Philadelphia. It is plain that, by capturing Philadelphia, Howe got nothing at all, and that the only result from Clinton's keeping it would be the strain of dividing his forces, maintaining a garrison there as well as in New York and keeping open the communications with New York across the contested territory of New Jersey or over more than 300 miles of river and ocean. The evacuation was a tardy confession of the costly error of its acquisition.

But all that afforded no consolation to thousands of Philadelphians, to whom the news of the intended evacuation was but little less terrible than a death sentence. The avowed Loyalists, who had fled to New York when the town was held by the American army, had hurried home on Howe's arrival. Other Tories, theretofore secret, had come out into the open. The Quakers, pacifists, nonresisters, had been more than suspected of aiding the royal cause. What was going to happen to all these when the American army came back to the city? They did not know, but they feared mightily.

Conspicuous among the repatriated Tories were the Allens, Andrew, John, and William; and even more conspicuous, dreadfully more so, Joseph Galloway. Widely enough known before, he had attained a peak of notoriety by personally guiding Howe's army along the road to those unguarded fords above the Forks of the Brandywine. No one in all the American army would ever forget that, nor could Galloway.

When the news of the intended evacuation was released, Galloway called on Ambrose Serle, secretary to Admiral Howe, with whom he had been on confidential terms for the last three months. He was filled "with Horror & melancholy," says Serle, "on the view of his deplorable Situation; exposed to the Rage of his bitter Enemies, deprived of a Fortune of about £70,000, and now left to wander like Cain upon the Earth, without Home & without Property. Many others are involved in the like dismal Case." [41]

Though not in the same kind of "deplorable Situation," certain gentlemen from England, arriving soon after the news became current, were almost equally disgusted. The British government, faced by the Franco-American alliance, had suddenly resolved to attempt conciliation of the rebellious colonies. It had proposed and carried through measures repealing the tea tax, the Boston Port Act, the restraints on the fisheries and on trade with Britain, and so on, wiped out practically every law that had been objected to by the colonists, and offered to give them a large measure of self-government, with free pardon to all the individual rebels. The Earl of Carlisle, William Eden, and George Johnstone, together with the two Howes, were appointed as a royal commission to settle details in America.[42]

The three commissioners from England landed in Philadelphia on the 8th of June to open negotiations with the Congress. They were horrified to find that their victorious army was in the midst of hurried preparations for the evacuation of the conquered capital, was, in fact, about to scuttle back to New York. The attempted reconciliation came to nothing; the Congress would not treat for peace unless the King would first acknowledge complete American independence or withdraw his troops from the country.[43] Later Congress refused to deal with the commission, partly because Johnstone tried to bribe influential Americans.

The officers of the British army were loath to lose General Howe. He had glaring faults, but when he set his mind to the business and stirred his sluggish disposition to activity, he was a strategist of great ability, a skillful tactician, and a bold and resourceful fighter in the field. They gave him a farewell party that outshone every celebration ever before seen in America. It was "a fantastic exhibition of sham chivalry," called the *Mischianza,* combining a tournament in which the Knights of the Burning Mountain and the Knights of the Blended Rose contended for the favor of the ladies, a ball, a banquet, a show of fireworks—all on a ridiculously elaborate and expensive scale.

CHAPTER 46

The Race Across the Jerseys

Washington's intelligence service informed him late in May that the British were "preparing for a general movement" of some sort. He was apprehensive that it might be "of an offensive kind," [1] perhaps against the post at Wilmington in Delaware, which had been held all winter by Smallwood's brigade of Maryland and Delaware regiments. On the other hand, it might be of an entirely different character: the evacuation of Philadelphia, of which there had been rumors, and a march across the Jerseys to New York. To provide for that contingency, he called on General Philemon Dickinson to arouse the New Jersey militia, and sent Maxwell's New Jersey Continental brigade to Mount Holly in that state. These two forces were to be ready to "give the Enemy some annoyance" by cutting away bridges and obstructing roads. [2]

But if Clinton evacuated the capital he might go by water, and go on up the Hudson to possess that important valley. To be ready for that, Washington laid out in full detail an "Arrangement of Army and Route to March to the North River." When even with "the most diligent pains" he could not find out which way Clinton was going or whether he was going at all, he came to believe that lack of transport vessels would compel him to go by land across the Jerseys. [3] To plan his own movements and to prepare for a possible attack on Clinton in New Jersey, he studied a map. [4]

He saw that the most direct route to New York from Gloucester in New Jersey, opposite Philadelphia, would be by way of Haddonfield, Mount Holly, Crosswicks, Allentown, Cranbury, New Brunswick, and Staten Island. It would be through country offering no important natural defensive

570

positions until the enemy got to Cranbury; but in the hills above that village there was a position that might easily block further progress.

He hardly needed to study the map to lay out his own course; it was all too familiar to him. From Valley Forge he could cross the Schuylkill at Swede's Ford, go on eastward to the Crooked Billet Tavern (now Hatboro), turn north to Doylestown, then east and across the Delaware at Coryell's Ferry. After that, by way of Hopewell and Kingston, he would come to Cranbury. Could he wait until Clinton had actually started and then beat him to that point? The distance was against him; it would be seven or eight miles, a good half-day's march, longer for him than for Clinton. But Clinton would be dragging an immensely heavy baggage train, while his own would necessarily be very light, and the road from Coryell's Ferry was somewhat better than that from Gloucester. It looked like a fair race.

By June 16 Washington's guess as to Clinton's plan seemed good, for on that day all the redoubts about Philadelphia having been stripped of their artillery before daybreak, several British and Hessian regiments passed over the Delaware at Cooper's Point.[5] That evacuation was a ticklish business. It involved the withdrawal of vast quantities of provisions and supplies, wagons, horses, and artillery, as well as 10,000 men [6] under the eyes of an enemy, now strengthened, refreshed, and drilled into a real army, a trained and disciplined fighting force. A vigorous attack, while Clinton's army was astride of the river, would probably result in a catastrophic defeat for him.

There was also another element to be considered. Three thousand Loyalists, men, women, and children, dared not remain in Philadelphia and submit themselves to the mercies of the incoming Americans. They and their portable possessions had to be carried away in ships, using cargo space that might have taken in a considerable part of the baggage that must now be carried overland. To evacuate that town was no light task, but it was successfully accomplished.

On the 18th the rest of the army left Philadelphia,[7] marched four miles to Gloucester Point and crossed to Gloucester in flat-bottomed boats, after which the last of the war vessels and the fleet of transports dropped down the river. "No shot was fired, nor did an Enemy appear until the whole were on the opposite shore," says André [8]—which is not exactly true.

In the interval between the withdrawal of the last defenders from the line of redoubts and the complete evacuation of the town, Allen McLane and his corps went in "by way of Bush Hill . . . between the 9th and 10th redoubts." At Second Street they came upon "the last patrol" and, having exchanged shots with it, cut off and captured a captain, a provost marshal, a guide, and 30 privates, with no loss on their own part.[9]

In the next night "the gallant Captain McLane" crossed the river and, in disguise, made his way through the British camp at Haddonfield.[10] The next day he reported his observations to General Benedict Arnold, who had been appointed to the command of the evacuated town.

A certain George Roberts had hastened to Valley Forge, and, at half past eleven of the morning of the 18th, told Washington that the evacuation was complete. This was confirmed by a courier coming immediately after from McLane with the same news.[11] Washington at once put his army in motion for Coryell's Ferry. Charles Lee had been released from captivity by exchange in March, had come to Valley Forge in May, and been reinstated in command of a division of three brigades: Hunterdon's, Poor's and Varnum's. It was immediately on its way. Wayne, in command of Mifflin's 2nd Division, composed of the 1st and 2nd Pennsylvania brigades and Conway's, got away at three in the afternoon. Lafayette's, De Kalb's, and Stirling's divisions, with the artillery, were to start at five the next morning. However, a rearrangement of the troops for the march across New Jersey was proposed. Lee was to command the right wing, six brigades, and Lafayette the second column, made up of the 1st and 2nd Maryland brigades and Weedon's and Muhlenberg's divisions.[12]

The number of men in Washington's army at this time has been variously estimated. The official returns on June 12 showed that the army had been increased—miraculously, it must seem—to a total of 13,503 officers and men. There were perhaps 1,300 in Maxwell's brigade at Mount Holly and 800 New Jersey militiamen under Philemon Dickinson also in that state. There may have been, on the march from Valley Forge from 11,000 to 12,000 of all ranks—a large force for that war, in excellent condition. The good work of Nathanael Greene as quartermaster general and of Jeremiah Wadsworth as commissary general showed in the clothing and equipment of the men and in their improved physical condition. Steuben's efforts had been so effective that they now performed "manoeuvres with great exactness and dispatch" and were "well disciplined." [13]

By the 23rd the entire army had crossed the Delaware at Coryell's Ferry, and the next night it was encamped at Hopewell, about fifteen miles west of Cranbury. The British army was then in camp at Allentown, about fifteen miles southeast of the Americans and ten miles south of Cranbury.[14] This was satisfactory progress for Washington's troops. But what use were they going to make of their effort?

On June 17, before leaving Valley Forge, Washington had called a council of war and told it that he believed Clinton would evacuate Philadelphia with a force of about 10,000; that he himself had about 11,000 fit for duty and there were 800 in New Jersey (which does not seem to take into account either Maxwell's or Dickinson's troops); that he wanted advice as to the conduct of the campaign in the immediate future. Two members of the council were for attacking the British on their march, if they crossed New Jersey, in order to make an "impression." Six were for following and annoying them, without bringing on a general action. The rest seem to have agreed with Charles Lee that it was advisable to let them get away. Now, at Hopewell, another council was called: Should they now "hazard a general action"? If not, what? Lee was "passionately opposed to strong measures." He said it would be "criminal" to hazard an engagement. Let Clinton get on to New York and good riddance to him. The majority, "still under Lee's spell," voted with him.[15] What then? Why, strengthen the troops hanging on Clinton's left flank, Maxwell's and Dickinson's, and keep the main army in hand until the situation developed further.

Maxwell with his 1,300 Continentals, and Dickinson with his 800 New Jersey militia, had been obeying their original orders, advancing before Clinton's left flank, destroying bridges and obstructing roads. John Cadwalader with about 300 Continentals and a few militia was hanging on the British rear. Now Morgan was detached with 600 riflemen to annoy the enemy's right flank, and Scott, with "a very respectable Body of Troops" was to hang on their rear and left flank. All this contemplated no more than annoyance and harassment of Clinton's march, with no idea of a general engagement.[16]

At Allentown the British army was nearer the key town of Cranbury than the Americans were. On paper Clinton could win a race to it; but not in reality. All the way from Philadelphia his army had been subject to an alternation of burning sun and soaking rain. Heavily clothed as his troops were, especially the Hessians, they were drenched first with sweat, then with rain. They either trudged through ankle-deep dry sand or slopped through puddles of water. The bridges were demolished; new ones had to be built. The roads were obstructed with felled trees; they had to be cleaned. Causeways had to be built over bogs so that the heavy artillery and wagons could get across. They had 1,500 wagons in their train, subject to all the delays and accidents that happen to wagons in a rough country. Because of these circumstances and perhaps because Clinton was in no hurry anyway, they had taken six days to make the thirty-four miles to Allentown. The heat and the rain bore heavily on the Americans too; but their clothing was light, very light, and the packs they carried weighed almost nothing compared with those of the British and the Hessians—60 to 100 pounds of clothing and equipment.[17] Their bridges and roads had been left unmolested; their wagon train was small and light. In the same six days they had made forty-seven miles.[18] Clinton would not be at Cranbury before Washington.

And if Clinton were now to follow the road he was on, leading to New Brunswick and Staten Island, Washington, being several miles nearer New Brunswick, might reach that place first and fall upon him while he was crossing the Raritan. Worse still, perhaps, would be an attack in force on his left flank, while he was dragging his heavy column between swamps and streams on the way to New Brunswick. That might result in a crushing defeat. As he had no knowledge of the Americans' intention not to attack him in full force, he had to act on the assumption that they would. It was time now for him again to consult a map.

Yes, there was a way to avoid the New Brunswick route. At Allentown a road forked to the right from the one he was following. It ran in a north-easterly direction past Monmouth Court House to Sandy Hook, whence his army might be carried in ships to New York. And it would take his army constantly farther from the Americans instead of always nearer, like the road to New Brunswick. He decided to take it, for it was most important to get his army to New York—far more important than a victory over the Americans, unless it should be a crushing one.

For this new route a complete rearrangement of the British army was necessary. Hitherto it had been able to move for the most part in two columns on parallel roads, thus keeping a compact, strong formation. But from Allentown to Sandy Hook there was only a single road. Clinton divided his army into two bodies and put Knyphausen in advance with one. After it came the baggage train, twelve miles long, and then the second half of the army with Cornwallis in immediate command, Clinton over him. Early in the morning of June 25 this interminable serpent of soldiery, guns, horses, wagons, and camp followers set out on a march of nineteen miles to Monmouth Court House.[19]

The road was deep with sand, the atmosphere heavily humid, and the heat terrific—exceeding 100° in the sun. On the march nearly a third of the Hessians, struggling along under clothing and equipment enough for three times as many men, were overcome by the heat and fell by the roadside. Many of the troops died of sunstroke.[20] In the afternoon of the 26th they went into camp at Monmouth Court House, and all that night a furious thunderstorm poured upon them. The exhaustion of the men and the continued intense heat made it impossible to go on, the next day.[21]

On the 25th Washington, leaving his tents and heavy baggage at Hope-well, moved his army about seven miles to Rocky Hill and Kingston. He was not too well satisfied with the cautious decision of the last council of war. He rather inclined to the opinion held by Greene and Wayne and Lafayette, favoring an attack by a strong force on the enemy's rear. In anticipation of such action, he had detached Wayne, with Poor's New Hampshire Continental brigade, 1,000 men, to join the advance guards under Scott, Maxwell, Morgan, Dickinson, and the others. The advance contingent was thus built up to the respectable total of more than 4,000.[22] But it needed unified command.

Charles Lee, who as the senior major general had first claim to this separate command, declared when Washington offered it to him that it was "a more proper business of a young volunteering general, than of the second in command of the army," thereby pointing directly at Lafayette, who was eager for it. Washington gave it to Lafayette, and he set out to take the job.[23] Then Lee learned that the advance force was to include nearly half the army and asked for the command.

The shift of command from Lafayette to Lee was the fundamental error of the campaign. It is, or should be, a military axiom that the execution of any intended operation should never be committed to an officer that disapproves of the plan. "That," says Jomini in his *Art of War*, "is to employ but one-third of the man; his heart and his head are against you; you have command only of his hands. . . . An unwilling commander is half beaten before the battle begins." [24] Lafayette, strongly in favor of attack, should have been left to carry it out.

When the commander in chief, with his unaccountably persistent blindness to Lee's real character, consented to his superseding Lafayette he arranged the transfer with as little injury to Lafayette's feelings as possible.[25] With Lee went Varnum's brigade and the rest of Scott's, bringing the force under his command up to more than 5,000 men. If Morgan's 600 riflemen and Dickinson's 800 militia, both properly subject to Lee's orders, be added, his available force should be 6,400.[26] Morgan actually was operating independently. Lafayette had been ordered to Englishtown, about five miles west of Monmouth Court House. Lee joined him there and took command of all the advance troops, including Dickinson's men, who were on the left flank of the British army. Morgan was on the right.

On the night of the 25th Washington marched the rest of his men from Kingston to Cranbury. There he was halted by a heavy rainstorm followed by intense heat, but at sunrise he pushed on along the Cranbury road within five miles of his advance at Englishtown. The British army still lay in a good defensive position, centering on Monmouth. Such was the situation of the two armies in the evening of June 27, 1778.[27]

Monmouth

In spite of the reluctance of the council of war at Valley Forge to advise any sort of attack upon the retreating British army, Washington decided upon an attack in some force. On June 27 he called Lee to his headquarters and, in the presence of Lafayette, Wayne, Maxwell, and Scott, told him his intention and directed him to carry it out by engaging Cornwallis's grand division as soon as it was in motion the next morning, promising to support him, if necessary, with the rest of the army. He prescribed no particular plan, but requested Lee to call together that afternoon the general officers of his division and arrange the details of the attack. He also asked the other generals to waive their respective claims to precedence of rank, to submit themselves to Lee's orders and to fight wherever he directed them.

Lee appointed a conference at five o'clock. When the generals attended he merely said that, as the numbers and exact situation of the enemy were not definitely known and the terrain had not been carefully examined, he would make no plan, but would move cautiously and rely upon his officers and men to act according to circumstances. During that night he made no effort to secure the information, the lack of which he had urged as preventing the adoption of a plan.

Late that evening Washington sent an order, directing Lee to detach a party of observation to lie near the enemy's camp and give notice of its moving off or of any movement that might portend a night attack. The order was received about one o'clock in the morning; but it was six o'clock before a detachment of 600 men, composed of Grayson's Virginia regiment, Scott's brigade, and part of Varnum's. with four guns, all under command of Colonel William Grayson, started from Englishtown, five miles from the British camp.

To an understanding of the extraordinarily confused and confusing battle now imminent, a clear comprehension of its terrain is essential. The road from Englishtown to Monmouth Court House came first to Freehold Meeting House. Thence it continued in a southeasterly direction to the Court House, where it stopped at a right angle against a road which ran northeast to Middletown and Sandy Hook and was the route of the British retreat. Another road from the Court House ran north to Amboy. The principal points otherwise to be noted are three "ravines." The first of these, the west "ravine," a morass through which ran a branch of Wemrock Brook, was crossed by a bridge on the Freehold-Monmouth road about two and a half miles from the Meeting House. A mile to the southeast on that road was the middle ravine, another morass through which ran the main stream of Wemrock Brook. A causeway crossed it. These morasses, it must be noted, were on the road by which the American troops advanced to Monmouth. The third morass, the east "ravine," was parallel to the road from Monmouth to Middletown and Sandy Hook and some distance west of that road. No road crossed it, but it played a part early in the battle.

The camp of the British army stretched in a line along the road from Allentown, which continued past Monmouth through Middletown to Sandy Hook. It therefore formed a right angle with the road from Englishtown to Monmouth by which the Americans were advancing.

Clinton was convinced that Washington's purpose was not simply to capture the British baggage train. He therefore started Knyphausen, with a part of the army and the wagons, forward on the Middletown road at four o'clock the next morning, while he himself and Cornwallis, with a larger force, prepared to follow. Cornwallis's command was composed of the 3rd, 4th, and 5th British infantry brigades, the 1st and 2nd battalions of British grenadiers, all the Hessian grenadiers, the British Guards, the 1st and 2nd battalions of British light infantry, the 16th Light Dragoons, and Simcoe's Tory Queen's Rangers, all together comprising the élite of the British army.

General Dickinson with his New Jersey militia had been on the alert all through the previous night. He discovered the movement of Knyphausen's grand division and sent word of it to Lee and to Washington. He was then on a hill just east of the west ravine. There he came into contact with a party of the enemy with whom he exchanged fire. Thinking that it was the advance guard of the second division of the British army, he retreated across the ravine, just as an American detachment came up. It was, in fact, merely a flanking party thrown out by Cornwallis, and when the Americans advanced across the bridge over the ravine, it withdrew. This was the first skirmish of the battle.

On receiving Dickinson's message, Washington is reported to have sent word to Lee that he "desired he would bring on an engagement, or attack the enemy as soon as possible, unless some very powerful circumstance forbid it, and that he would very soon be up to his aid." He is also reported to have ordered Lee to attack so as to make an impression upon the enemy, but to be careful not to be drawn into a scrape.

Lee's column moved from Englishtown about seven o'clock in the morning, Colonel Richard Butler with 200 men in the van, followed by Colonel Henry Jackson with an equal number, then part of General Woodford's brigade, 600 men with two guns, then General Varnum's, about as many with two guns, General Wayne's command of 1,000 men and four guns, General Scott's "detachment" of 1,400 with four guns, and General Maxwell's 1,000 men and two guns.

At some time after eight, before he arrived at the Meeting House, Lee halted the column for half an hour. There was some excuse for this delay, because Captain Benjamin Walker, aide to Steuben, had come up with word that the British had not yet marched. This of course referred to Cornwallis's division, Knyphausen's then being well on its way. When Dickinson came up Lee, petulant as ever, accused him of sending false information, to which Dickinson replied with spirit. This altercation was not calculated to steady the mind of so unstable a man as Charles Lee.

There was another halt in this march—the column's advance seems to have been marked by a spirit of hesitation—and Lee sent Wayne forward to take over command of the advanced detachment, which had been under Colonel Grayson.

This advance guard came into contact with the enemy when it met a small body of cavalry and infantry, a covering party sent out by Clinton. It was attacked, and retreated. This was the "second skirmish."

From that time onwards the conduct and disposition of the various elements of Lee's force, their movements to and fro, before Washington came up and the real battle began, make this preliminary part of the affair "the most confusing in its movements and the most difficult to present or follow in detail of any of the battles of the Revolutionary War." [1] In broad terms, it may be stated that Lee's troops were brought into the part of the field that lay between the east ravine and the road to Middletown, facing that road.

They were not drawn up in formal line of battle. The various brigades and detachments were, in general, disposed in an irregular pattern and shifted about in kaleidoscopic arrangements and rearrangements. There were skirmishes here and skirmishes there, advances and withdrawals, shifts of this and that brigade or regiment to this point and that. Orders were given and promptly countermanded. Lee certainly had no plan and no grasp of the situation as a whole. He gave orders, and so did Wayne and the other generals; the field officers gave orders to one another, and those to whom orders were given obeyed or disobeyed as they pleased. The field must have looked like a great anthill, with those bodies of soldiery hurrying hither and thither and back again. It would serve no useful purpose to describe it all in detail, as no clear understanding of so many simultaneous movements could be conveyed in words; nor is it important that they should be. The one fact that emerges clearly from that welter of maneuvers is that Lee had no plan of attack.

Clinton had started to follow Knyphausen about eight o'clock, leaving a rear guard or covering party at Monmouth. Lee conceived the idea of cutting off this covering party and had even sent word to Washington that "the rear of the enemy was composed of 1,500 or 2,000 men; that he expected to fall in with them and had great certainty of cutting them off." One of his aides, imbued with his general's confidence, said to Lafayette, "The rear guard of the enemy is ours," and Lee himself made a similar statement. He began to move his troops with that in view, but without telling any of his officers what his plan was, nor how these movements contributed to it. Having no idea of what they were doing, and receiving, in most cases, only brief orders in general terms, the officers made ineffective and uncoordinated dispositions of their men.

But there had been some hot fighting between various individual elements of the Americans and the British rear guard, with successes and repulses about evenly divided. Clinton saw that they were not merely such attacks as were to be expected from Dickinson and Morgan, but seemed to be the preliminaries of an attack in force. He therefore sent for a brigade of British foot and the 17th Light Dragoons from Knyphausen's division, to cover his right flank, then faced about and marched back to the scene of action. There he disposed his troops in line facing the Americans and prepared to receive their attack. Lee saw his plan of cutting off the rear guard fade into impossibility.

He ordered Lafayette, with three regiments of Wayne's detachment and some artillery, to march against and attack the British left. Lafayette, having gained a proper position for that purpose, believed that he could not attack, indeed that his troops were exposed to a British thrust. He began to move to a new position. Scott and Maxwell observed his movement. To them it looked like a retreat that would leave them cut off from the main body. They therefore fell back. So did Colonels Grayson and Jackson with other troops. Lafayette also began to pull back, probably without orders. Then came an order from Lee for him to retire. Similar orders were given and were not given to others. And that is how the retreat began.

It became general. By regiments in good order, by disorganized regiments in no order at all, the retreating mass swelled until it included Lee's entire division. In sweltering heat—the thermometer stood at 96° in the shade— 5,000 weary, sweating, thirsty men tramped along the road back towards Englishtown, and Lee rode along with them. He seemed altogether self-possessed. The descriptions of his conduct by some officers would lead one to believe that he was enjoying a quiet satisfaction in the defeat of an attempt that he had disapproved and voted against, a sort of I-told-you-so satisfaction. Other officers later said the retrograde movement was carried out in good order, that Lee covered it with rear-guard actions, and that the movement was necessary to avert a crushing blow from Clinton.

Washington, with the main army, a little larger than Lee's advance force, had been on the march to his support ever since he got word of Clinton's movement from Monmouth. He stopped at a house on the way for a late breakfast, while his men went on. He had received Lee's message about cutting off Clinton's rear guard. Comparing the number of Lee's troops with Lee's estimate of the size of the Brititsh rear guard, he had no reason to doubt that all was going well with the advance. He was therefore incredulous of news given him by a gentleman of the vicinity that Lee's force was retreating. His informant said he had got this from an American fifer, who was then at hand. Washington indignantly ordered the fifer under arrest for spreading false alarms. He was again on his way when he met several other men who told the same story. Still he would not believe it.

Pushing on, he met an indubitably retreating party, then a whole regiment in disorder, the men apparently exhausted with the heat, then another regiment and another, then Maxwell's brigade, and Ogden's regiment. Why were they retreating? Maxwell didn't know. They were just going along until he got further orders. Ogden said angrily they were all flying from a shadow. At last Washington met Lee.

Of what happened then there are half a dozen different accounts. Washington certainly challenged him with some such question as "I desire to know, sir, what is the reason—whence arises this disorder and confusion." Disconcerted by his chief's angry manner, Lee stammered out, "Sir? Sir?" "What's all this confusion for?" Washington demanded. "And what is the cause of this retreat?" Of the rest of the interview, there are several versions. Washington Irving offers a full page of dubious dialogue. Lafayette, who was not on the spot, said many years later that Washingtton called Lee "a damned poltroon" and ordered him to the rear. Others report his language as "strongly expletive," as "a terrific eloquence of unprintable scorn." But the most thoroughly satisfying, though probably apocryphal, account came from General Scott in reply to the question whether he had ever heard Washington swear. "Yes, sir, he did once; it was at Monmouth and on a day that would have made any man swear. Yes, sir, he swore that day till the leaves shook on the trees. Charming! Delightful! Never have I enjoyed such swearing before or since. Sir, on that memorable day he swore like an angel from heaven!" But whatever turn the conversation took, whatever Lee's answer was, one thing is certain, the retreat was stopped.

Washington, who as an equestrian was always impressive, was mounted on a great white horse, a gift that day from Governor William Livingston of New Jersey. Lafayette described the effect of his arrival upon the tired, discouraged men: "His presence stopped the retreat . . . his fine appearance on horseback, his calm courage, roused to animation by the vexations of the morning, gave him the air best calculated to excite enthusiasm." Lafayette also recalled how, later, he rode "all along the lines amid the shouts of the soldiers, cheering them by his voice and example and restoring to our standard the fortunes of the fight. I thought then, as now, that never had I beheld so superb a man." [2]

The retreat having been halted and the troops turned back towards the scene of action, Washington galloped along the road to Monmouth Court House. He had crossed the bridge over the west ravine when he met Colonel Walter Stewart's 13th Pennsylvania Regiment and Lieutenant Colonel Nathaniel Ramsay, with the 3rd Maryland. They were the last in the retreat, with the British coming after them and not more than 200 yards in their rear. Washington called on them to face about and hold the enemy back until he could form a new line behind them. Wayne was at hand; he undertook to form these two regiments on the north side of the road, while Washington went about organizing the new line.

The two regiments were immediately attacked by a party of Light Dragoons. Stewart was badly wounded and was carried off the field, Lieutenant Colonel Lewis Farmer taking his place. The heavy pressure of the dragoons was strongly resisted, but the Marylanders were slowly driven back. Ramsay, the last to withdraw, was wounded in a hand-to-hand fight with one of the dragoons, overpowered and taken prisoner.

Washington sent Varnum's brigade and Lieutenant Colonel Eleazer Oswald, with six guns, to reenforce the two hard-pressed regiments. Four more guns were soon after brought up, and Knox took charge of the artillery. Colonel Henry Beekman Livingston's 4th New York Regiment was added to the defenders. In all these movements while under sharp attack, there was much confusion. There was confusion also on the road to the west, along which many men, not having been checked by any orders, were still in full retreat. But there was heavy fighting between the now stationary American defenders and an attacking force of dragoons and grenadiers.

Meanwhile, Washington was drawing up his fresh force on a rise of ground just west of the westerly ravine. Greene's division was on the right, Washington in the center, Stirling's division on the left. Lafayette commanded the second line. Artillery was well posted on both wings, particularly well on the right, where it was so placed on Comb's Hill as to enfilade an attacking force. Varnum's brigade, which had been heavily engaged, was withdrawn to the rear to be refreshed. Wayne, with the 3rd, 7th, and 13th Pennsylvania Continentals, the 3rd Maryland, and one regiment from Virginia, was posted along a hedge by an orchard in front of the American center.

A British attack was aimed at Stirling's wing. The British light infantry, the 42nd Foot, and the famous Black Watch pressed forward and were met by a heavy fire from the guns of Lieutenant Colonel Edward Carrington's battery. British fieldpieces were brought up, and a smart artillery duel ensued. Volley after volley of musketry came from both sides. Stirling, with Washington and Steuben, passed along the American line, encouraging the men. For nearly an hour the guns on both sides pounded their opponents, the muskets rained lead without cessation. The fighting was terrific. The American regiments in that line had been brought up to their positions under the eye of Steuben. Under fire they had wheeled into line "with as much precision as on an ordinary parade and with the coolness and intrepidity of veteran troops." Alexander Hamilton afterwards said that never, until he saw those troops deploy and fight as they did, had he "known or conceived the value of military discipline." [3] It was Steuben's reward to see those results of his teaching.

The pressure on Stirling's wing was relieved when the 1st and 3rd New Hampshire regiments and the 1st Virginia moved out to the left through

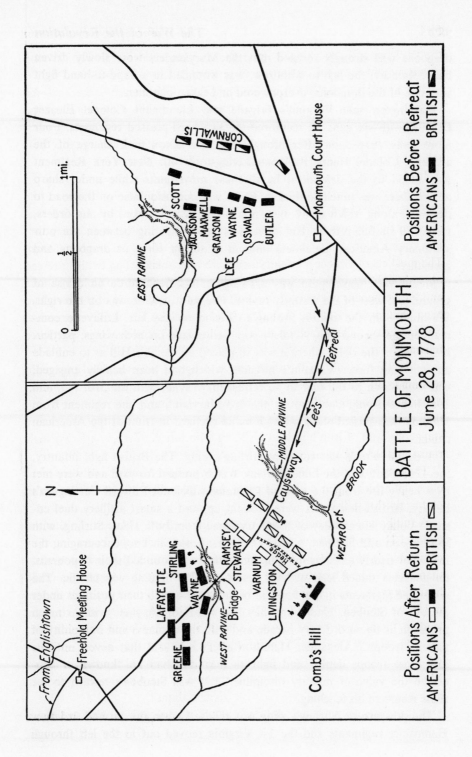

BATTLE OF MONMOUTH
June 28, 1778

Positions Before Retreat
AMERICANS ■ BRITISH ◣

Positions After Return
AMERICANS ◤ BRITISH ◻

CORNWALLIS

Monmouth Court House

EAST RAVINE

SCOTT
JACKSON
MAXWELL
GRAYSON
LEE
WAYNE
OSWALD
BUTLER

Retreat

Lee's

MIDDLE RAVINE

Causeway

WEMROCK BROOK

Comb's Hill

LIVINGSTON
Hedge
VARNUM
STEWART
RAMSEY

Bridge
WEST RAVINE

WAYNE
STIRLING
LAFAYETTE
GREENE

Freehold Meeting House

From Englishtown

N

1 mi.

½

0

the thick woods and charged upon the extreme right of the British, who gave way and fell back out of fire to re-form.

The attack on the left wing having failed, Clinton sent another force against Greene on the right. It was composed of "the very flower of the rear division and of the army," [4] English and Hessian grenadiers, light infantry, the 37th and 44th regiments, the Coldstreamers, and another battalion of the Guards. Cornwallis in person directed the attack.

In the usual formal fashion, they came forward in line and under an enfilading fire from the six-gun battery on Comb's Hill in charge of the Chevalier de Mauduit du Plessis, Knox's brigade adjutant. Its fire was directed right across the front line of the attackers, with such accuracy that one round shot struck the muskets from the hands of an entire platoon. The muskets of Greene's infantrymen were also ablaze. The British pressed on, although five of their officers, including the colonel of the Coldstreamers and the lieutenant colonels of the 37th and 44th, and many of the men had been shot down. But the American fire, especially the artillery crossfire, was too heavy. The attack on the right wing failed, and the attacking force fell back.

While this assault on the right was in progress, a determined onslaught was made on Wayne's position, behind that hedge, by light infantry, grenadiers, and dragoons. They came on with such intrepidity and dash that they were close to the American line before they met the first volley. Then a staggering rain of iron and lead hit them with terrific force, shattering their ranks and driving them back.

They re-formed and charged again. Wayne held his fire until they were close upon him. Then a blast of grapeshot and bullets stopped them again, and again they fell back.

A full hour passed before they made a third effort. This time Lieutenant Colonel Henry Monckton of the 45th Foot, the Sherwood Foresters, now commanding the 2nd Battalion of grenadiers, formed his line not more than five hundred feet from the hedge, so close that the Americans could hear him talking to his men. He gave the command "Forward to the charge, my brave grenadiers!" and on they came. With Monckton at their right leading them, they dashed forward at top speed. Wayne held his fire: "Steady, steady! Wait for the word, then pick out the king-birds!" At forty yards' distance, he gave the word, and a volley crumpled the British ranks. Monckton fell so close to the hedge that some of the Americans leaped out and seized his body and the colors of his battalion.

Still the British persisted. A fourth attack was organized with so large a body of troops that the line along the hedge was outflanked on both ends. No further resistance was possible. Wayne drew off his men in good order. They had served their purpose well, for the principal American line, from Greene to Stirling, was now too firmly posted to be endangered by the withdrawal. There was no further attempt to take the position by assault. Cannonading on both sides continued for a while, until the British withdrew about six o'clock to a strong position east of the middle ravine.

But Washington was not satisfied with having beaten off these attacks; he wanted a victory. Fresh troops—if any troops that had borne the burden and heat of that day could be called "fresh"—were brought forward, General Woodford's Virginians, Colonel Thomas Clark's North Carolina Continentals. They were to attack the British on both flanks simultaneously. But by the time they were organized and had got within striking distance of the enemy, it was too dark to risk an engagement.

The Americans lay on their arms that night, Washington beneath the branches of an oak with his cloak for covering, Lafayette beside him. Every man was ready to renew the fight in the morning, but when morning came there was no enemy to fight. As noiselessly as Washington had slipped away from Cornwallis at Trenton, now Clinton had eluded Washington. Having started at midnight, he caught up with Knyphausen's division by daybreak and was in Middletown by ten o'clock. On the 30th his whole army was at Sandy Hook, and by July 5 it was in New York.

The casualties reported by the Americans were 8 officers and 61 privates killed, 19 officers and 142 privates wounded, 130 privates missing. The British admitted 4 officers and 61 enlisted men killed, 15 officers and 155 men wounded, 64 missing; and then there is an unusual entry, "3 sergeants, 56 rank and file died with fatigue." That means, of course, by sunstroke or heat prostration, to which may also be ascribed the deaths of at least 37 of the "missing" Americans.[5] The British had also lost 136 men by desertion while on the march from Philadelphia; and the Hessians, 440.

Monmouth might be claimed as a victory by both sides with equal justice. Both sides occupied the field, which is the usual criterion of victory. Clinton did not want the field; he wanted to get to New York, which he did. The Americans had repulsed all the attacks on their main position, but that was only a matter of defense, while their real intention was offensive. On the whole, one can see little gained by that toilsome march across New Jersey in pursuit of the British army, except the kudos of having fought a drawn battle with the formidable professional soldiers of England and Germany. The battle is, however, notable for the courage displayed by both armies, as well as for the fact that it was the longest of the whole war and the last important engagement in the North.

But for General Charles Lee it had the most serious consequences. He had been publicly rebuked on the battlefield by the commander in chief, and the talk of some in the camp was bitter against him; he writhed under the double injury to his self-respect. On the 29th he wrote Washington a letter which began mildly enough, but grew bitter as it went on to accuse him of "an act of cruel injustice" and to "demand some reparation." With this Lee coupled a threat of resigning "from a service, at the head of which is placed a man capable of offering such injuries." He was confident, he said, of justifying himself, "to the Army, to the Congress, to America and to the World in general."

Washington replied that he would soon have an opportunity of justifying himself or of being found guilty of a breach of orders, of misbehavior before the army, and of "making an unnecessary disorderly and shameful retreat." To this Lee replied in equally strong terms and asked for a court martial. It was granted; he was found guilty of disobedience of orders, making "an unnecessary and, in some few instances, a disorderly retreat," and disrespect for the commander in chief, and sentenced to be suspended from the army for twelve months. This verdict went to the Congress for its approval, and was approved by a close vote. Many months later Lee wrote an insulting letter to the Congress, and it finished the affair by resolving that it had "no further occasion for his services in the army of the United States." [6]

Newport

The American army lay at Englishtown two days for rest and refreshment. On the second day the men were under orders "to wash themselves
this afternoon and appear as decent as possible," so that at seven o'clock in
the evening they might, in seemly fashion, "publicly unite in thanksgiving
to the supreme Disposer of human Events for the Victory which was obtained on Sunday over the Flower of the British Troops." [1]

On the 1st of July they began a series of marches northward through
New Brunswick, Scotch Plains, Aquackanock, and so on, that familiar road
so often trod by them either in retreat or in advance, through Paramus
(now Ridgewood) and Kakiat (now West New Hempstead) to Haverstraw, where they encamped on July 15.[2] On that day Washington called
on the Commissary Department for "Fifty of your best Bullocks and . . .
two hundred Sheep, if to be procured, and a quantity of poultry" to be presented to Charles Henri Théodat, Comte d'Estaing, "Admiral of the French
Fleet now laying off Sandy Hook," [3] for the French had come. The treaty
of alliance had blossomed and borne fruit. Twelve ships of the line and four
frigates, mounting 834 guns and carrying 4,000 soldiers, had arrived at
the Delaware capes on July 8, just ten days too late to catch Admiral Howe's
fleet, retreating from Philadelphia, and bottle him up in Delaware Bay.
D'Estaing had then turned northward to Sandy Hook, across which he could
see the English fleet at anchor in the bight formed by the Hook and the
Jersey shore. Howe had only nine ships of the line to d'Estaing's twelve and
only 534 guns to the Frenchman's 834.[4] D'Estaing had but to get across

the bar, extending from Staten Island to the Hook, to get at the British fleet, and the odds against Howe would do the rest.

But he could not cross the bar; the water was too shallow for the deep-draft French ships. Try as he would, using pilots sent by Washington, offering 50,000 crowns to anyone that would take him over, he could not get at the Britishers. He lay in that tantalizing position for eleven days, then gave it up and, in agreement with Washington,[5] sailed north to Rhode Island, where Newport had been held by the British ever since Howe had sent Clinton with 6,000 men and many ships to occupy it in December, 1776. It was now under the command of Sir Robert Pigot with 3,000 men.

General John Sullivan had been in command at Providence with a force of about 1,000 Continentals since the middle of March. Anticipating d'Estaing's movement, Washington had directed Sullivan to apply "in the most urgent manner" to the states of Rhode Island, Massachusetts, and Connecticut to raise "a Body of 5,000 men inclusive of what you already have," also to collect boats, engage pilots and in general get ready for a descent on Newport in conjunction with the French fleet and troops.[6] Six thousand of the New England militia had turned out, with Major General John Hancock at their head. Washington had sent Lafayette to Providence, with two of the best brigades in the army, Varnum's Rhode Islanders and Glover's from Marblehead. He also sent Greene to assist Sullivan in the enterprise. Sullivan's force was thus raised to 10,000 men.[7]

The part of Rhode Island occupied by the British was that island cut off from the mainland by Seaconnet Passage on the east, Middle or Narragansett Passage on the west, and narrow straits on the north. Newport was at its southern end, from which two roads, the east and west, ran to the island's northern extremity.

D'Estaing's fleet arrived off Point Judith, close to Newport, on July 29, but Sullivan's army was not collected and ready for cooperation until August 5. It had been agreed that d'Estaing should send troops up the Middle Passage and land them on the west side of the island, while Sullivan's men were to come down from Providence, cross over by the ferry at Tiverton, and so possess the east side.[8]

In accordance with this arrangement, d'Estaing sent two ships of the line up the Middle Passage and two frigates up the Seaconnet Passage.[9] The British frigate *Cerberus*, 32 guns, lying on the western side of the island, tried to get down into Newport harbor, but ran aground, and was set on fire by her captain and blown up. The frigates *Juno, Orpheus,* and *Lark*, each carrying 32 guns, the *Kingfisher*, 16, and the *Pigot* galley met a like ignominious fate. The *Flora*, 32 guns, and the *Falcon*, of 18, also

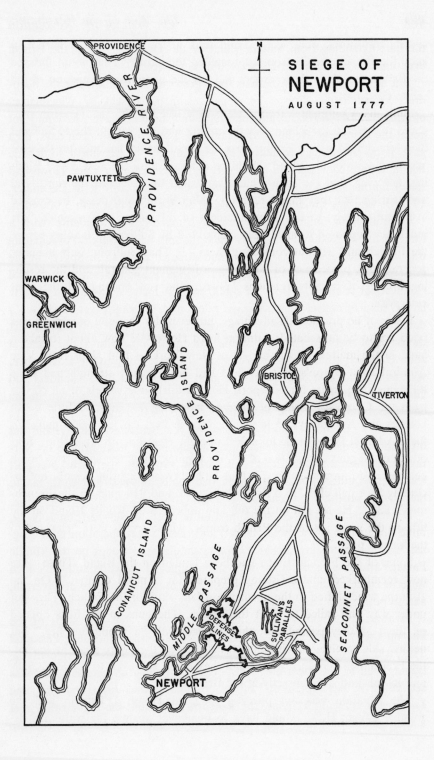

SIEGE OF
NEWPORT
AUGUST 1777

PROVIDENCE

PROVIDENCE RIVER

PAWTUXTET

WARWICK

GREENWICH

PROVIDENCE ISLAND

BRISTOL

TIVERTON

CONANICUT ISLAND

MIDDLE PASSAGE

SEACONNET PASSAGE

SULLIVAN'S PARALLELS

DEFENSE LINES

NEWPORT

several transports, were scuttled and sunk in front of Newport harbor to keep the French vessels from approaching too close.[10] That about finished the British vessels in those waters and left the unopposed command of the sea to the French.

Sullivan's Continental troops were now, on the 8th, at Tiverton prepared to cross to the island; but the militia had not yet got there. Sullivan therefore agreed with d'Estaing that the simultaneous landings on the east and west sides of the island should be deferred until the next day.[11] Finding, however, that the enemy had abandoned the works at the north end and fearing that they might reoccupy them during that delay, he crossed over immediately, to the disgruntlement of d'Estaing, who resented "the indelicacy supposed to have been committed by Sullivan in landing before the French and without consulting them." [12] Thus Sullivan, only a major general, took precedence of d'Estaing, a lieutenant general; and the resulting breach of friendly relations between the two endangered the joint enterprise.

It was of no practical disadvantage, however, for the joint enterprise was fated not to be prosecuted; Admiral Lord Howe was now about to take a hand in the matter. By the arrival at New York of four ships from Vice Admiral John Byron's fleet his fleet had been greatly strengthened since d'Estaing's departure for Newport. He had thirty-one vessels of all classes from the *Cornwall*, a ship of the line mounting 74 guns, to little bomb ketches and row galleys; [13] in all, the British fleet carried 1,064 guns. Of these Admiral Howe made up a fleet of eight great line-of-battle ships, four others of 50 guns each,[14] two of 44, six frigates, three fire ships, two bomb ketches, and four row galleys; [15] thus he had twenty fighting vessels, not including his small craft, to d'Estaing's sixteen, and 914 guns to the Frenchman's 834.[16] He set sail on the 6th and appeared off Rhode Island on the 9th, to the great joy of the British troops, whose spirits were "elevated to the highest pitch." [17]

Some of the French troops had been landed on the island. These were now reembarked, and d'Estaing prepared for a naval combat.[18] On the 10th the wind shifted to the northeast, a fair wind for the French. They got under way and sailed to meet the British. The guns in the forts opened on them as they passed out; they replied with "a prodigious fire," but neither side received much damage. As soon as they were past the harbor, the Frenchmen "crouded all the sail they could set, even to Studding Sails and Royals and stood directly at the British fleet." [19]

The situation was not pleasing to Lord Howe. D'Estaing had the weather gauge; Howe would have to maneuver against the wind. He declined the offered engagement and stood off to the southward, hoping for a turn of the wind that would give him the windward position.[20] For two days the fleets maneuvered within sight of each other, and then Nature intervened. A great gale blew up and scattered both fleets. A result of this dispersal was the meeting of single ships in combat. The French line-of-battle ship *Languedoc*, 84 guns, engaged the British *Renown*, 50 guns, in a brief battle, without decisive result. The French *Marseillais*, 80 guns, met the British *Preston* of 50 and fought until darkness put an end to the conflict, again without result. The French *César*, 74 guns, encountered the British *Isis*, 50, and was somewhat worsted, but not put out of action.[21] But the ships of both nations had been much damaged by the storm. The British frigate *Apollo* was dismasted and most of the rest were in unseaworthy condition. Howe's fleet bore away for New York to refit, the French returned to Rhode Island.

In the meantime, on the 15th, Sullivan with about 10,000 men including the lately arrived militia, though unsupported by his allies, had moved down towards the enemy. General Pigot withdrew his outposts into the lines about Newport and set about strengthening them with a new breastwork and an abatis.[22] Sullivan broke ground for entrenchments, mounted two batteries, and began a line of approach by parallels. There was heavy cannonading by both sides with no substantial damage to either.[23] The British were surprised that he confined his works to the eastern side of the island and made no move against their western flank, whereby he might have compelled Pigot to defend two fronts at once;[24] but the western side appears to have been left, out of politeness, for the French to care for in accordance with the original agreement. Both sides kept on with their labors on the offensive and defensive works until the 20th, when d'Estaing's fleet reappeared.

Sullivan then applied to d'Estaing for the promised aid. But that thin-skinned gentleman was still nursing his injured pride and was in no way mollified by Sullivan's forwardness since his departure. He said that the orders of his King and the advice of his officers constrained him to retire to Boston at once for refitment of his vessels. Sullivan and Lafayette joined in a personal appeal for only two days cooperation, within which time they were sure Newport could be taken.[25] D'Estaing was obdurate. At midnight of the 21st he sailed away, taking his 4,000 troops.

Discouraged by the defection of the allies in whom they had placed their greatest trust, the militia deserted in droves; 5,000 went off within a few days,[26] so weakening Sullivan's force that there was no more thought of attacking Pigot. Sullivan's job now was to get out with a whole army.

During the night of the 28th the retreat began. Pigot followed, sending General Prescott with the 38th and 54th British regiments against Sullivan's left, General Smith with the 22nd and 43rd regiments and the flank companies of the 38th and 54th up the east road of the island, also against Sullivan's left, and General Baron von Lossberg with Hessian jägers and two Anspach battalions up the west road.[27] Sullivan had posted his light infantry under Colonel Henry B. Livingston on the east road and Colonel John Laurens on the west, each being about three miles in advance. Both made contact with their respective opponents, but were too few to withstand them. Both were reenforced and repulsed the enemy.

Pigot then sent the 54th Regiment and Brown's Provincial corps, Tories, to Smith, and Huyne's Hessians and Fanning's New York Provincials to Lossberg. The Americans were driven back. Sullivan drew up his men in two lines. Smith's corps attempted the American left, but was repulsed by General John Glover's brigade and retired to a piece of high ground.[28] Lossberg took two small redoubts and set up batteries from which he cannonaded the American right. Sullivan's artillery replied.[29] The *Sphynx* and *Vigilant*, sloops of war, the *Spitfire* galley, and the brig *Privateer* came up close to that wing and brought their guns to bear on it. Aided by this fire, Smith sought to turn the Americans' right; but it was reenforced, and after he had made three assaults its musketry broke the British ranks and sent them back in confusion.[30] Though only 1,500 of Sullivan's men had ever been under fire, their spirit and resolution were without fault. A newly raised Rhode Island all-Negro regiment under Colonel Christopher Greene especially distinguished itself by "desperate valor," repelling three successive "furious onsets" of the Hessians.[31]

The cannonading from both sides was heavy for an hour; that of the Americans so discouraged Pigot's troops that they failed to come to grips with Sullivan's. Desultory musketry continued between the two sides for six hours until it faded out at dark. In the night Sullivan resumed his retreat as secretly as possible. John Glover's amphibious Marblehead regiment again proved its special worth in carrying the army across Howland's ferry to Tiverton, where it was landed safely with its guns and baggage by the next morning. Sullivan dismissed the remaining militia and took his Continentals back to Providence where they remained throughout the winter.[32]

In these various encounters the Americans are reported to have lost 30 killed, 137 wounded, and 44 missing, the British 38 killed, 210 wounded, and 12 missing.[33]

It was a most fortunate escape, for the very next day a British fleet brought to Newport eight regiments, a battalion of grenadiers, and one of light infantry, 5,000 men under command of Sir Henry Clinton and Major General Grey, who would, without fail, have demolished Sullivan's force, if it had not withdrawn.[34] Having nothing to do at Newport, Grey conducted an expedition along the Massachusetts coast in the course of which he burned a number of privateers and merchant vessels, also a part of the towns of New Bedford and Fairhaven.[35]

Success in this enterprise against Newport had been confidently expected throughout the country. Anticipations of brilliant results in the capture of the British garrison had been universal. The disappointment of these expectations was equally great and widespread, and the blame for the failure was generally laid at d'Estaing's door. In general orders Sullivan indiscreetly censured the Frenchman for not having remained to help the Americans. This was resented by the French officers. D'Estaing explained and justified his movements to the Congress in a letter in which "his chagrin and irritation" at the censure "were but ill-conceived." [36]

Washington was disturbed by the situation. Writing that it had given him "very singular uneasiness," he reminded Sullivan that the French were "a people old in war, very strict in military etiquette and apt to take fire where others are scarcely warmed." He recommended, "in the most particular manner, the cultivation of harmony and good agreement and your endeavors to destroy that ill humour which may have got into the officers" and urged that "the misunderstandings" be kept from the soldiers. He addressed similar letters to Greene, Heath, and other persons of prominence in New England.[37]

But "the discontent in New England generally, and in Boston particularly, was so great as to inspire fears that the means of repairing the French ships would not be supplied" [38] at Boston. Hancock and Lafayette exerted themselves to allay it. The Congress resolved that "Count d'Estaing hath behaved as a brave and wise officer and that his Excellency and the officers and men under his command have rendered every benefit to these states, which the circumstances and nature of the service would admit of and are fully entitled to the regards of the friends of America." [39] Thus d'Estaing was appeased, and harmony was restored. His ships were refitted, and in due course he sailed away to Martinique, taking his 4,000 troops.

While these futile operations were being carried on, Washington had moved his army from Haverstraw to King's Ferry, thence across the Hudson and down to White Plains. He was pleased by the fact that "after two years of Manoeuvring and undergoing the strangest vicissitudes" he was now again at the place from which he had been driven after the retreat from Long Island, and that his enemy, then on the offensive, was now in New York "reduced to the use of the spade and pick axe for defence." [40]

The inactivity of Clinton's army puzzled Washington; he did not know whether it stayed quiet in New York from choice. The fact, of course, was that the war between Britain and France had developed into a conflict whose field was the high seas, its seat being the West Indies; the war in America had become a subsidiary element of that larger war. When Clinton took over the command of the British armies in America, in May, it had already been decided to desist from offensive operations in the North.[41] In November, besides sending General Grant and 5,000 men to St. Lucia, Clinton dispatched Lieutenant Colonel Archibald Campbell of the 71st Regiment with a force of 3,500 made up of British, Hessians, and New York Tories to Georgia. Under such conditions, he was satisfied to rest for the time being in his strongholds at New York and Newport.

During the summer of 1778 Washington's army was "the largest body of regular troops ever assembled under the American banner." [42] A return made in July showed 16,782 rank and file fit for duty; of these between 11,000 and 12,000 were in and about White Plains.[43] In September the army was rearranged; Putnam, Gates, Stirling, Lincoln, De Kalb, and McDougall each commanded a division.[44] Putnam was sent to West Point, De Kalb to Fredericksburg (now Patterson), New York, Gates and McDougall to Danbury, Connecticut, Stirling to a point between Fredericksburg and West Point.[45]

There was good news in October: a large shipment of clothing and shoes had arrived from France. The waistcoats and breeches were all alike, but some of the coats were blue, others brown, both kinds faced with red. They were assigned to the different states by lot: North Carolina, Maryland, New Jersey, and New York drew the blue; Virginia, Delaware, Pennsylvania, Massachusetts, New Hampshire, and Hazen's Canadians got the brown. But, as there were more of the blue than were needed for the first four states a second drawing was made, by which Massachusetts, Virginia, and Delaware got in the blue.[46] This was the first time that anything like uniform dress for the whole army had been possible.

In November the army went into winter quarters at several different places. At Middlebrook, Elizabeth, and Ramapo, New Jersey, at West Point and Fishkill, New York, and at Danbury, Connecticut, camps were established; thus a semicircle with a forty-mile radius was drawn about New York, and the vital points of the Hudson Highlands, through which the more southerly states communicated with New England, were guarded.[47]

The soldiers were to be sheltered that winter in log cabins like those built at Valley Forge; these they were, of course, to build for themselves. While building them they lived in canvas tents, and, although the winter was "remarkably mild and temperate" they "suffered extremely from exposure to cold and storms." [48] They were "better clad" than they had been at Valley Forge, but "exceedingly deficient in the articles of Blankets and Hats and soon will be of Shoes," said Washington, "as the call for them is incessant." There was almost always "a scarcity of food and forage." [49]

The difficulty was not a shortage of money; there was plenty of that, bushels of it, to be had of the Congress for the asking, plenty of Continental paper money. The trouble was that there was too much of it. It had sunk steadily during the past two years in real value, in purchasing power; and it was still sinking, faster and faster, month by month all that winter. By April, 1779, it was so depressed that, as Washington wrote, "a waggon load of money will scarcely purchase a waggon load of provision." [50] Nobody wanted to exchange good beef for vanishing paper.

CHAPTER 49

Stony Point

There were no military operations in the north during the winter of 1778, nor in the spring of 1779. Both armies lay in their winter quarters until summer was almost at hand. Then Clinton made the first move. On May 28 he assembled at Kingsbridge 6,000 of his best troops, British and Hessian grenadiers, light infantry, dragoons, Hessian jägers, and Provincial (that is to say, Tory) regiments including Simcoe's Queen's Rangers and Ferguson's corps, a very formidable force. On the 30th they embarked in a fleet of seventy sailing vessels and one hundred and fifty flat-bottomed boats, and on June 1 they landed on both sides of the Hudson, at Stony Point and Verplanck's Point, just below Peekskill.[1]

Washington had been apprehensive of a movement up the Hudson for the capture of West Point, and had ordered St. Clair's division up to Springfield, Stirling's and De Kalb's divisions to Pompton. McDougall was already posted in the Highlands with five brigades of Continental troops and two North Carolina regiments.[2]

There was a small, unfinished fort on Stony Point, occupied by a handful of Americans; on Verplanck's Point, across the river, was Fort Lafayette, held by a captain and seventy North Carolinians. Stony Point was taken by the British without opposition, the garrison having burnt a blockhouse before fleeing at the approach of the enemy. Fort Lafayette was a small but complete work, palisaded and surrounded by a double ditch and an abatis; suffering because of heavy cannon fire from Stony Point and from the ships, and surrounded by British troops on the land side, it was forced to surrender.[3] The British at once set about completing the works on Stony Point, a strong natural position.

Washington interposed his army between Stony Point and West Point, and Clinton made no further move up the Hudson. The principal position of the Americans was in Smith's Clove on "a fine level plain of rich land situated at the foot of the high mountains on the west side of Hudson river." [4] Though West Point seemed to be adequately protected for the moment, Stony Point and the opposite headland, Verplanck's, formed the gateway to the Hudson. Washington Irving likens them to the Pillars of Hercules, the gateway to the Mediterranean, Stony Point being the Gibraltar. Their possession by the enemy menaced West Point, "the key to the Continent." [5] They also effectively commanded King's Ferry, which ran from one point to the other and was a link in the principal highway from the New England states to the south.

Stony Point was "a defiant promontory" thrust out into the Hudson more than half a mile and rising 150 feet from the water, which washed three-fourths of its perimeter. To the river it presented a bold front, steep, rugged, and rocky. On the westerly, or inland, side it fell off irregularly to a wide and deep morass, which curved around from the river above to the river below. At high tide, this marsh was drowned and could be crossed on dry feet only by a bridge and a causeway from which ran a road to the King's Ferry landing on the northerly side of the Point, and another road to the fort.[6] Thus, for military purposes, the Point was virtually an island.

Clinton erected there two series of works. On the summit of the Point seven or eight detached batteries, connected in part by trenches, made a sort of semienclosed fort. To the west of it, but still on the height, a curved line of abatis was swung around from one side of the Point to the other. Farther down the landward slope were three small works protected by another line of abatis, also stretching from shore to shore; and all the woods thereabout had been felled. The garrison established there consisted of the 17th British regiment, the grenadier company of the 71st (or Fraser's Highlanders), a body of Loyal Americans, and certain detachments of artillerymen, something over 600 men in all, commanded by Lieutenant Colonel Henry Johnson.[7]

Washington had been much disturbed by the loss of the two points to the British, but felt that "an attempt to dislodge them, from the natural strength of the positions, would require a greater force and apparatus than we are masters of. All we can do is to lament what we cannot remedy." But after a little while he began to hope for the accomplishment of that difficult task.[8]

On June 28 he wrote to Anthony Wayne asking him to employ a trust-worthy and intelligent man to go into the British works, if possible, or other-wise to find out their nature and the strength of their garrison.[9] Allen McLane's partisan corps had, shortly before that, been detached from the Delaware Regiment and attached to Henry Lee's corps of similar troops,[10] which was operating in the country near Washington's camp. The task set by Washington was given to Lee's "most active officer," McLane, an astute and experienced scout.

On July 2, in company with a Mrs. Smith who wished to see her sons, presumably members of the garrison, he approached the fort with a flag of truce and was admitted. Wearing a hunting shirt and assuming the air of a simple countryman, he was allowed to look about the fort and obtain the desired information. He noted particularly that the entrenchments intended to connect the several batteries of the inner fort were incomplete.[11]

Covered by McLane's men, Washington himself spent a day in examining the vicinity. Colonel Rufus Putnam, Major Henry Lee, and Major Thomas Posey made reconnaissances under similar protection. On the basis of McLane's report and these other examinations, Washington made a plan for the attack and gave it to Wayne. Lee was ordered to patrol the region about the Point, and for nearly two weeks his men were scattered around, spying out all the approaches to the Point. McLane and his company were especially active, lying in the woods at night and picking up information by day from British deserters and the farmers that carried food to the fort.[12]

The force to be employed was the brigade of light infantry recently organized under the command of Wayne. This was made up of hardy and active veterans chosen for alertness, daring, and military efficiency from all the regiments in Washington's army. It was composed of four regiments of two battalions each.

Lieutenant Colonel Christian Febiger, a Dane from Virginia, commanded the 1st Regiment, made up of Virginians and Pennsylvanians, his battalion leaders being Lieutenant Colonel François Louis de Fleury, a distinguished French soldier, and Major Thomas Posey of Virginia. Colonel Richard Butler of Pennsylvania led the 2nd Regiment, with Lieutenant Colonel Samuel Hay of Pennsylvania and Major John Stewart of Maryland as bat-talion commanders. This regiment comprised men from Pennsylvania, Delaware, and Maryland. The 3rd Regiment, all Connecticut men, was led by Colonel Return Jonathan Meigs of that state, with Lieutenant Colonel Isaac Sherman and Captain Henry Champion. The 4th was but partially organized. It comprised men from Massachusetts and North Carolina under

Major William Hull of the former state and Major Hardy Murfree of the other. Captain James Pendleton of Virginia and Captain Thomas Barr, with 24 gunners, were to go along taking two small fieldpieces, more for ornament than for use, the plan of attack having no place for artillery. The whole force numbered about 1,350 of all ranks.[13]

In the morning of July 15, Wayne's men were drawn up at Sandy Beach, five miles below West Point, presenting themselves by command, in accordance with his customary attention to their appearance, "fresh shaved and well powdered." At noon they set out on a thirteen-mile march by a circuitous route "over rugged roads, across mountains, morasses and narrow defiles in the skirts of Dunderberg, where frequently it was necessary to proceed in single file." [14] At eight o'clock they arrived a mile and a half back of the Point where they were out of sight of the enemy. Up to this time none of the enlisted men and few of the officers had been informed of their objective, though most of them must have guessed it.

Here Wayne gave them their instructions. They were to form two columns: on the right, Febiger's regiment followed by that of Meigs and by Hull's battalion; on the left, Butler's regiment, Murfree's battalion following it. In advance of the right column, Fleury was to lead 150 "determined and picked men"; in advance of the left, a similar body was to be led by Stewart. These two detachments were to sling their muskets and carry axes to cut through the abatis. But accompanying each body of axmen there was to be a forlorn hope (in modern language, a "suicide squad"), an officer and 20 daredevils to rush through the openings they made and engage hand to hand with the enemy; Lieutenant George Knox was to lead the group on the right, Lieutenant James Gibbons that on the left. Each man of the whole force was to wear a piece of white paper in his hat, as was customary in night attacks, to distinguish him from the enemy.

Except in Major Murfree's battalion, not a musket was loaded; the bayonet was to be the only weapon. They were all to march to the attack with their pieces shouldered and in solid ranks. Any soldier that took his musket from his shoulder on the march or attempted to fire it or to "begin the Battle until ordered by his proper officer," and any one "so lost to every feeling of Honor as to attempt to Retreat one single foot or Skulk in the face of danger," was to be "instantly put to Death by his proper Officer." The strictest silence was to be observed on the march; but when they entered the works they were to shout and keep on shouting, "The fort's our own!" Rewards ranging from $500 to $100 were to be given the first five successively entering the works.

The two columns were to attack at different points; the right, which was the stronger, to make the main attack on the southerly side; the left, on the northerly. Murfree's men, with their loaded muskets, were to diverge from the route of the left column and approach the center of the outside abatis. As soon as they heard the sound of the attack on the right, "they were to begin and keep up a perpetual and gauling fire" to make the garrison believe the real attack was on front.[15]

At half past eleven the two columns advanced. The right column was to pass around the morass at its lower end, where a sand bar offered a fair crossing at lower tides. But the tide was high, and the bar was covered with water waist-deep. Keeping their close-ranked formation, the men started to wade across. At that moment the enemy's pickets discovered them, opened fire, and gave the general alarm. From the fort's guns and the garrison's muskets, round shot, grape, and bullets poured down upon them. There was no response from the Americans. Inspired by the courage and dash of Fleury and Knox, leaders of the van, they pressed forward the faster, reached solid ground and then the first abatis. The axmen swung at it. Their swift, biting strokes made an opening. The forlorn hope scrambled through. The main body followed, clambering over tree trunks, formed again, and pushed up the rough ascent towards the fort, now all alive with defenders and ablaze with gunfire. Wayne was struck down by a bullet that made a flesh wound in his head. He was stunned, but soon revived and continued to direct the assault. Captain Selden was hit; Captain Phelps, Lieutenant Palmer, and Ensign Hale fell. Men were dropping all around, but the column kept on. At the second abatis the axmen were already at work.

Meanwhile, off to the left, the other column was doing as well. Lieutenant Colonel Hay was wounded. Colonel Febiger received a slight wound. Lieutenant Colonel Hall's hat was shot through, his boots pierced. Many a man felt the impact of the bullets that rained upon their ranks as they pressed on to the fort. Signaled by the sound of the axes, Murfree's men, midway between two attacking forces, were keeping up a continuous fire.

The left column was through the second abatis now, Major Stewart at its head. He turned Lieutenant Gibbons and his forlorn hope off to the right towards the main works. Gibbons, his clothes "muddy to the neck" from crossing the morass and "almost torn to rags" by the sharp branches of the abatis, attacked the fort. Of his 20 men, 17 were shot down.

The right column had reached the fort first, near the flag bastion, and rushed through the sally port or climbed over the parapet. Fleury was the first man in. He tore down the flag. Behind him came Knox, then Sergeant Baker of Virginia, already four times wounded, then two other sergeants, Spencer of Virginia and Donlop of Pennsylvania, who earned the fourth

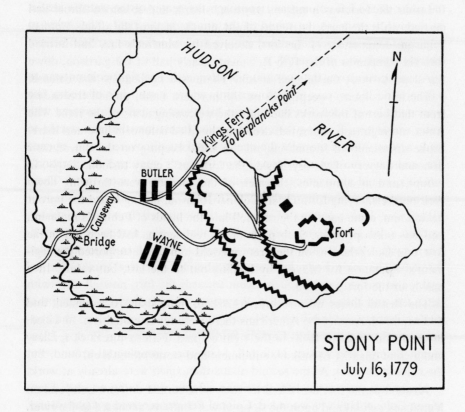

The War of the Revolution

STONY POINT
July 16, 1779

and fifth prizes. Behind them were many others, shouting, "The fort's our own!"

Inside the fort was a mêlée. Bayonet, sword, and spontoon thrust and parried, while the harried defenders fired into the mass of the attack. Colonel Johnson, commander of the fort, deceived by Murfree's fire, had hurried with six companies of the 17th Regiment, nearly half of the garrison, down the slope to meet the feigned attack. There was no head to the defense.

The left column, sweeping in on the northern flank, pushed the enemy from that part of the works back into the welcoming arms of the right. The American regiments separated, drove the huddled defenders here and there, broke up attempted formations, all the while keeping up the din of their disconcerting cry of victory. Inside the fort was a crazy turmoil. Singly, in groups, and in companies, the men of the garrison were throwing down their muskets, crying for quarter. Colonel Johnson, having heard the uproar behind him, came back on the run, fell into the hands of Febiger's regiment, and was taken prisoner. Such parts of his regiment as had been left in the fort, and such others as on their return could join them, supported the regiment's reputation for bravery by holding out to the last, but vainly. In a half-hour the fort was won.

The British losses were severe: 63 killed, more than 70 wounded, and 543 captured. Among the Americans there were fewer casualties: 15 killed, 80 wounded, most of these in the right column. Fifteen pieces of artillery and a great quantity of military equipment and stores were taken.

As soon as the fort was taken its guns were turned on Fort Lafayette on Verplanck's Point and upon the sloop of war *Vulture*, anchored in the river. The sloop dropped downstream. The commander of the Verplanck fort, receiving, in the language of Clinton, "the heavy fire of the Enemy," did not deign "to return a single shot, being sensible that it would have been of no material effect." [16]—of no more effect than the fire from Stony Point, which seems to have been no effect at all.

An attack on Fort Lafayette had been planned to follow the capture of the other, but whether as a determined effort to take it or merely as a distracting feint there is some doubt. At all events the attack was not made, owing to the failure of some of the troops detailed for that purpose to appear.

Washington inspected the captured fort and concluded that "it would require more men to maintain it than we can afford." He therefore ordered the removal of its guns and stores and the destruction of the works. Clinton reoccupied the Point, rebuilt the works, and installed a stronger garrison.

The American light infantry brigade was soon after disestablished, and its members returned to their proper regiments.[17]

No military advantage was gained by this exploit, beyond the capture of so many of the enemy and the guns and stores; but it had an inspiriting effect upon the American army and upon the people in general. A successful attack upon British regulars in a fortified position, with the bayonet alone, was an achievement unparalleled up to that time. The Congress hailed the news with enthusiasm, unanimously thanked Wayne for "his brave, prudent and soldierly conduct" and gave him a gold medal, commended Fleury and Stewart for their "personal achievements" and gave them silver medals. It praised Gibbons and Knox for "their cool determined spirit," and made them captains by brevet. It also ordered the captured military stores valued, and an equivalent sum of money divided among the troops.[18]

That the capture of Stony Point was a signal achievement, ably planned and gallantly executed, has been universally recognized. Charles Stedman, the English historian, wrote, "It was an enterprise of difficulty and danger, and the American general, Wayne, who conducted it, deserved great praise for his gallantry . . . as did the troops . . . for their bravery." [19] A gratifying element of the reports by the British officers is their recognition of the clemency displayed by the Americans towards their foes. General Pattison wrote that it must be allowed to Wayne's credit, "as well as to all acting under his orders, that no instance of Inhumanity was shown to any of the unhappy Captives. No one was unnecessarily put to the sword or wantonly wounded." Commodore George Collier wrote: "The laws of war gave a right to the assailants of putting all to death who are found in arms. . . . The rebels had made the attack with a bravery never before exhibited, and they showed at this moment a generosity and clemency, which during the course of the rebellion had no parallel." [20]

Paulus Hook

Major Henry Lee, Jr., was an active and daring officer, high-spirited and mettlesome. His sobriquet, Light-Horse Harry, has in it more than a suggestion of the romantic kind of valor that is also implied in the nickname of his colleague, Mad Anthony Wayne, and neither of them was averse to public recognition of his own gallantry and dash. Now, in July, 1779, Mad Anthony was basking in the glory of his achievement at Stony Point—in which Lee and his corps had been unnoticed and inactive participants in the reserve—with the thanks of the Congress ringing in his ears and, what was more important, in the ears of everyone else. Light-Horse Harry took notice; "Stony Point had piqued his emulation." [1]

While scouting in the country west of the Hudson he had observed an outlying British post at Paulus—or Powles—Hook. It was not in such a romantic position as that other perched on its rugged eminence, but in many respects it was not unlike Wayne's prize. Here then was an opportunity to match his rival. He suggested to Washington an enterprise against it. [2]

After some hesitation, on the score of the number of men proposed by Lee to be risked and of the advisability of a plan of attack differing in some respects from Lee's, Washington approved the scheme. [3]

Paulus Hook was a low-lying, blunt point of sandy land projecting into the Hudson directly opposite New York City; it is now a part of Jersey City. It was backed by wide boggy salt meadows, across which ran a single marshy road from the fast land beyond. A creek, fordable in only two places, cut it off from the main, and a deep ditch that ran entirely across the peninsula made it an island. This could be crossed only at low tide; access to the works was by a drawbridge across the ditch, closed on the land side by a heavy gate. Beyond the ditch a double row of abatis extended from the water above the Hook to the water below; this formed the wall of the position on the land side. The water side was defended by a continuation of the abatis and by certain breastworks. It was thus, except for its low-lying position, a sort of second edition of Stony Point.

On a slight elevation in the middle of the enclosure was a circular redoubt, about 150 feet in diameter, surrounded by a ditch and a line of abatis; it mounted six heavy guns. Near it, to the northeast, was another redoubt oblong in plan, 250 feet long, 150 wide, mounting three 12-pounders and one 18. The entrance to the works, by the drawbridge, was well defended by a substantial blockhouse and breastworks. There was another blockhouse by the riverside, and scattered about were barracks and other buildings. Its natural position and these artificial works made Paulus Hook a position of considerable strength.[4]

The garrison had been composed of a part of the 64th British infantry, a part of the Invalid Battalion, a regiment of Skinner's Provincials, and a detachment of Van Buskirk's New Jersey Volunteers; but Van Buskirk's men went out on a marauding expedition in the morning of July 28, and were replaced by a company of 48 Hessians and Captain Dundas's light infantry company, making its total strength on the night of the attack something over 200 rank and file. There were also within the works a number of artificers and other noncombatants. Major William Sutherland was in command.[5]

McLane and his company had been scouting all up and down the country from Stony Point to the Hook for two months, traveling light, fast, and incessantly and sending information to Lee's headquarters near Paramus. As the time for the attack on the Hook drew near, McLane concentrated his attention on its near neighborhood. From a deserter, he obtained precise information as to its garrison. He arranged a rendezvous with Lee "in order to conduct him to attack Powles Hook." [6]

The attacking force was to consist of 100 men from Woodford's Virginia brigade under Major Jonathan Clark; these were to form the right; two Maryland companies commanded by Captain Levin Handy were to compose the center; 100 of Muhlenberg's Virginians and McLane's troop of dismounted dragoons were to make up the left, which was to be led by Lee in person. After the fashion of the Stony Point enterprise, there were three forlorn hopes, "desperadoes led by officers of distinguished merit," to lead the van and cut through the abatis. Their leaders were Lieutenant Mark

Vanduval of the 1st Virginia on the right, Lieutenant Philip Reid of the 5th Maryland in the center, and Lieutenant James Armstrong of Lee's dragoons on the left. There was also a reserve under Captain Nathan Reid of the 10th Virginia.[7] But this arrangement became somewhat disordered and had to be altered to meet certain exigencies before the attack was actually begun, as will appear.

At half past ten in the morning of August 18, Lee left Paramus with Handy's two Maryland companies, taking a number of wagons to make the enemy think this was an ordinary foraging party. At the New Bridge across the Hackensack he met the Virginia contingent and McLane's troop. He was then fourteen miles from the Hook and should have been able to reach it by half an hour after midnight, the time set for the assault; but a number of delaying difficulties soon arose.

From the New Bridge the combined forces set out at four o'clock on the direct Bergen road; but when they came near some enemy outposts they filed off on a road to the left. Their principal guide, either from timidity or from treachery, misled them, and what should have been a short march was prolonged to three hours. "By this means the troops were exceedingly harassed." To regain the right way, they had to penetrate the "deep mountainous woods." [8]

Dissatisfaction rent the party. Major Clark was aggrieved at having been put under the command of Major Lee, whose commission was of later date than his own, and had some words with him about it. Perhaps because of that or perhaps because of disgust with the conduct of the enterprise, discontent spread through the ranks of the Virginians; and half of them abandoned the expedition. Thus Lee lost a substantial part of his force and, although Clark stayed with him and "exerted himself," the efforts of the rest of the Virginians "to second his endeavours were not the most vigorous." [9]

In spite of this defection, in spite of the fact that he could now rely only upon the Marylanders, half of the Virginians, and McLane's troop for the necessary vigor and élan of the assault, Lee pushed on; but it was four o'clock in the morning when he came to the edge of the marshy meadows behind the Hook. The coming dawn menaced his success, and a rising tide would soon make the ditch impassable.

Undiscovered by the enemy's sentries, Lee sent Lieutenant Michael Rudulph of McLane's troop forward to reconnoiter the approaches. He reported all quiet within the works and the ditch still fordable. The troops were then set in motion.[10]

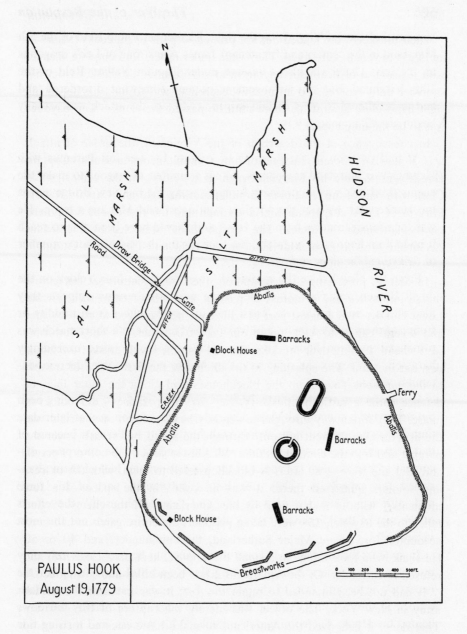

N

HUDSON

SALT
MARSH

SALT MARSH

SALT MARSH

RIVER

Road

Draw Bridge

DITCH

Gate

DITCH

CREEK

Abatis

Abatis

Abatis

Abatis

Ferry

Block House

Barracks

Barracks

Barracks

Block House

Breastworks

0   100   200   300   400   500 FT.

PAULUS HOOK
August 19, 1779

Their muskets were loaded but not primed—"pans open, cocks fallen"—and their bayonets were fixed. They were under orders for complete silence, with a promise of death for anyone who should take his musket from his shoulder until ordered. To insure this, each man was to hold his hat in his right hand close against his thigh until he passed the canal. "The bayonet was to be the only appeal." [11]

In consequence of the desertion of the Virginians, the order of attack was somewhat altered. Instead of three simultaneous assaults, Captain Handy was to hold his Maryland men as a reserve in the center, while Clark with part of the remaining Virginians on the right and Captain Robert Forsyth of Lee's corps with McLane's men and the rest of the Virginians on the left made the attack. The "desperadoes" were led by Lieutenant Archibald McAllister of Maryland on the right and Lieutenant Rudulph, also of Maryland, on the left.[12]

In silence, preserving their formation, the three columns set out across the swamp. "We had a morass to pass of upwards of two miles," wrote Levin Handy, "the greatest part of which we were obliged to pass by files and several canals to wade up to our breast in water." [13] The "forlorns" were ahead, trailing their muskets; the rest marched with musket on shoulder, hat in hand. The splashing in the ditch was the first notice of trouble to the garrison. Then from the blockhouses and along the outer lines of defence came a rattle of musketry; but the "desperadoes" did not even pause. They tore a way through the abatis. Clark's column on the right was the first through. It went not only through the abatis but actually over the parapet and into the circular redoubt. McAllister struck the colors. Forsyth and McLane were close after. A blockhouse fell to them, with the officers and soldiers quartered there. It was all over "in the space of a few moments," without a shot fired by the Americans. Of the enemy 50 had fallen to the bayonet, 158 were taken prisoner; the entire garrison had been accounted for, except Major Sutherland, the commander, and 40 or 50 Hessians, who took refuge in a small blockhouse, kept up a close fire, and refused to surrender. Of the Americans 2 had been killed and 3 wounded.[14]

It had not been intended to retain the fort; it was too near the British army in New York. The object was merely the capture of the garrison. That done, it behooved the Americans to make haste back to their camp with their prisoners before the enemy could cross over from New York, cut off their retreat to the north, and hem them in the narrow strip of land between the Hudson and the Hackensack. Already the alarm guns in New York were arousing the British. There was no time to take Sutherland and his Hessians in the blockhouse, no time, as it seems, even to spike the guns, not to mention packing up any booty. Lee had intended to burn the barracks, but, learning that there were a number of sick soldiers, women, and children in them, he forbore. Without delay the columns were re-formed, and the retreat began.

It is probable that only then did Lee realize the precariousness of his situation. He had arranged to have boats collected at Douwc's Ferry across the Hackensack below New Bridge and nearer the Hook. Stirling was holding 300 men at the bridge as a covering party. But Lee's troops were greatly fatigued; all their ammunition had been wet when they crossed the ditch, and Colonel Van Buskirk's strong foraging party might be coming back to the Hook by this time. An attack by them would probably result in disaster to the Americans. The situation was hazardous indeed. Lee detached Forsyth with a party of the least fatigued men to occupy Bergen Heights behind the Hook and cover the retreat. With the rest he made the best speed he could, hampered as he was by his reluctant prisoners, who obviously hung back in hope of a rescue.

The tired men pushed on to the rendezvous with the boats—and found no boats there. Captain Henry Peyton, with the first company of Lee's Legion, had been entrusted with that important element of the enterprise. He had expected the expedition to arrive hours earlier. When it did not he assumed that the enterprise had been abandoned and so took the boats back to Newark. Lee's men had marched thirty miles "through mountains, swamps and deep morasses, without the least refreshment," fought a battle, and now were fourteen miles from the New Bridge and without a single dry cartridge. Their situation was worse than hazardous; it was desperate.

Lee took it in hand. He ordered his troops "to regain the Bergen road and shove on to the New Bridge," and sent an express to Stirling to come down to meet him. At a point opposite Weehawken, he split his force in three, sending Handy with one part on the road over the hills. Clark with another along the Bergen road. With the rest he himself took "the centre route." The prisoners were divided among the three detachments. At that moment Captain Thomas Catlett and 50 of the recalcitrant Virginians appeared, equipped with dry ammunition. Lee gave some of them to each column to act as rear guards. Not long afterwards, Colonel Ball arrived with a detachment from Stirling, and none too soon, for just before the column reached the Liberty Pole (Englewood) Van Buskirk and his raiders fell on its right flank. Lee's rear guard faced about, Rudulph threw a party of the Legion into a stone house—and Van Buskirk retired. So, at one o'clock in the afternoon of the 19th, the entire command forgathered at the New Bridge, all safe and with all their prisoners.[15]

This enterprise, like that against Stony Point, had no military value except the prisoners taken and the inspiration derived by the army in general. But to Lee it was valuable indeed: "The country resounded with his praise." The Congress responded with a vote of thanks and a gold medal to match Wayne's. McAllister and Rudulph were brevetted captains. The sum of $15,000—Continental paper, of course—was appropriated to be divided among the soldiery. Another resolution commending the conduct of Clark, Handy, Reed, McLane, and half a dozen others was rejected, even though it carried no appropriation.[16]

But there was an unpleasant aftermath for Lee. The difficulty with the Virginians blossomed into charges against him of various minor acts of misconduct, chiefly based on his having taken precedence over senior officers in the expedition—which he had done by direct command of Washington. He was tried by court-martial and acquitted with honor.

Paulus Hook ended the active military operations of the armies of Washington and Clinton for the year 1779. Washington kept his men busy fortifying West Point and drilling under Steuben. Clinton, anticipating an intensification of the British effort in the south, abandoned Newport. Cornwallis arrived from England with reinforcements. These, added to the troops from Newport, brought the New York garrison up to 28,756 men, of whom 13,848 were British regulars, 10,836 were Hessians, and 4,072 Provincials.[17]

Washington's "whole force including *all sorts of troops*" amounted, in November, on paper to 27,099; but it had been dwindling, and it continued to dwindle. Only 14,998 were enlisted for three years or the duration of the war; the terms of the rest were expiring month by month. Also, as Washington wrote to the Congress on November 18, it could not be "supposed that the whole of the Troops borne on the Muster Rolls, were either in service, or really in existence, for it will ever be found for obvious reasons, that the amount of an army on Paper will greatly exceed its real strength." [18] But all the ordinary allowances were not enough to account for the diminution of the American forces, which actually occurred during the following winter. By April, 1780, the whole army under Washington's command amounted to no more than 10,400 rank and file, again on paper, of whom 2,800 were to complete their term of service in May.[19]

CHAPTER 51

The Hard Winter at Morristown

Washington kept his army about West Point until November in the hope that, in combination with the French fleet under d'Estaing "something important and interesting, if not decisive might have been attempted against the Enemy in this Quarter, with a good prospect of success." [1] But d'Estaing had taken his thirty-seven ships, his 2,000 guns, and his 4,000 men to besiege Savannah, Georgia. When his final attack there was beaten off he raised the siege, sent some of his ships to the West Indies, and, with the rest, sailed for France—on the same day that Washington wrote to Lafayette, "we have been in hourly expectation, for the last fifteen days, of seeing Count d'Estaing off Sandy Hook." A month later, he received this disappointing news. [2]

He immediately began to arrange for retirement of his troops into winter quarters. Poor's brigade was ordered to Danbury, Connecticut, to have "an eye to the Sound towards Norwalk, Fairfield &ca," all the cavalry to be quartered near by. Four Massachusetts brigades were to remain at West Point. The North Carolina brigade and Pawling's New York State corps were sent to a point in New Jersey near Suffern. Lee's Legion was posted at Monmouth in the same state. For the main army's cantonment, Morristown was again chosen. [3]

The movement of the army to Morristown exposed it to great hardships. De Kalb, for example, marched his division of two brigades of Maryland and Delaware troops, 2,030 in all, in six days to the new camp. It was a toilsome march. He wrote: "Our march lasted six days and traversed a country almost entirely unpeopled; it proved fatal to many of the soldiers, in

611

consequence of the cold, the bad weather, the horrid roads, the necessity of spending the night in the open air and our want of protection from snow and rain." [4]

James Thacher, a surgeon in the army, was marching down from Danbury about the same time. His journal is eloquent of similar hardships, without baggage or tentage:

It snowed all the afternoon and we took shelter in the woods. . . .

Marched the next day through deep snow . . . marched again early . . . twenty miles it being late at night before our men could all find accomodations in the scattering houses and barns along the road . . . on the 14th reached this wilderness, about three miles from Morristown, where we are to build log-huts for winter-quarters. Our baggage is left in the rear for want of wagons to transport it. The snow on the ground is about two feet deep and the weather extremely cold; the soldiers are destitute of both tents and blankets and some of them are actually barefooted and almost naked. Our only defence against the inclemency of the weather consists of brushwood thrown together. Our lodging the last night was on the frozen ground.[5]

The huts and barracks were then to be got out of standing timber, chiefly oak and walnut. They were weeks at this hard work. On February 1, 1780, one of the Connecticut officers wrote, "Completed our Hutts which destroyed our cloathing still more & we had to my certain knowledge not more than Fifty Men in the Reg[ts] return[d] fit for duty." [6]

The winter before, at Middlebrook, had been "remarkably mild and moderate." [7] This one was of another sort. It has been described truthfully as the worst during the war: "Though Valley Forge is fixed forever in the popular imagination, it deserves forgetfulness in comparison with the second stay at Morristown. . . . Very early that winter the cold came. And such cold! There had been nothing like it in the memory of the oldest inhabitant. Roads disappeared under snow four feet deep. New York harbor was frozen over." [8]

In January the men were still under canvas, "a miserable security from storms of rain and snow." Thacher relates that on the 3rd tents were torn asunder in

one of the most tremendous snowstorms ever remembered: no man could endure its violence many minutes without danger to his life. . . . Some of the soldiers were actually covered while in their tents and buried like sheep under the snow. . . . The sufferings of the poor wretches can scarcely be described, while on duty they are unavoidably exposed to all the inclemency of storms and severe cold; at night they now have but a bed of straw on the ground and a single blanket to each man; they are badly clad and some are destitute of shoes. . . . The snow is now from four to six feet deep.[9]

In February, De Kalb wrote: "It is so cold that the ink freezes on my pen, while I am sitting close to the fire. The roads are piled with snow until, at some places they are elevated twelve feet above their ordinary level." And all through March this "most severe and distressing weather" continued; "an immense body of snow" still lay on the ground.[10]

It was not only the piercing, petrifying cold, the four-foot snow, the nights of shelterless misery that the half-clad army at Morristown had to endure; there were the pangs of hunger as well. On December 18 Washington wrote to the governors of several neighboring states:

> The situation of the army in respect to supplies is beyond description alarming. It has been five or six weeks past on half allowance and we have not more than three days bread at a Third allowance on hand, nor any where within reach. . . . Our magazines are absolutely empty everywhere and our commissaries entirely destitute of money or credit to replenish them. We have never experienced a like extremity at any period of the war. . . . Unless some extraordinary and immediate exertions are made by the States from which we draw our supplies, there is every appearance that the army will infallibly disband in a fortnight.[11]

Major Patten of the Delaware Regiment wrote on January 17, "The Army has been reduced to the most Extreme want of provisions, having subsist[d] five days on half a pound of salt Beef and half a pint of Rice without any other kind of support whatever." [12]

Whatever supplies were furnished by the states appealed to, they were not enough. In the three weeks after Washington's appeal the situation grew steadily worse. By the first week in January, the army was "almost perishing." The soldiers then took the matter into their own hands. Washington wrote on January 9:

> They have borne their distress . . . with as much fortitude as human nature is capable of; but they have been at last brought to such dreadful extremity that no authority or influence of the officers could any longer restrain them from obeying the dictates of their own sufferings. The Soldiery have in several instances plundered the neighbouring Inhabitants even of their necessary subsistence.[13]

The state of affairs was unbearable. When Washington wrote that letter, he had already planned a stern remedy. He divided the state of New Jersey into eleven districts, fixed a contribution of grain and cattle to be supplied by each, allotted an officer to each district, and gave orders to go and get it. Bergen County, for example, was to supply 600 bushels of grain and 200 beef cattle, and Colonel Matthias Ogden was sent after them. Other counties were to furnish less or more, in accordance with their circumstances.

Major Henry Lee was to take care of Salem, Cumberland, and Cape May—
750 bushels and 200 cattle from Salem, while Cape May was let off with
only 50 head of horned beasts.

The officers were first to apply to the magistrates of their respective districts and solicit their aid. "You will at the same Time delicately let them
know that you are instructed, in case they do not take up the business immediately, to begin to impress the Articles called for. . . . This you will
do with as much tenderness as possible to the Inhabitants." The provisions
seized were to be valued, to be paid for at some indefinite future time.[14]

The scheme was effective. By January 27 Washington could write to the
Congress, "The situation of the Army for the present is, and has been for
some days past, comfortable and easy on the score of provisions." It is
pleasant to read in the same letter that the Jerseymen "gave the earliest
and most chearful attention to my requisitions and exerted themselves for
the Army's relief in a manner that did them the highest honour. They more
than complied with the requisitions in many instances." [15]

But 10,000 half-starved men can eat a large quantity of bread and
meat. By the first days of March the Board of War was writing to the
states the same story of empty magazines of provisions and predicting the
disbanding of the army if relief were not afforded.[16] The difficulty was not
the lack of food in the country; it was the lack of money with which to buy
it, the lack of money that had unquestioned purchasing power.

The value of the Continental paper dollar had been sinking during three
years past, as steadily and as irresistibly as the passage of time itself. In
March, 1777, it was but a little below par. In March, 1779, it took $1,000
Continental to buy $100 in specie. In May, 1780, De Kalb, for "a bad
supper and grog" and a night's lodging for himself, three others, and three
servants, without breakfast, paid $850. "An ordinary horse is worth
$20,000; I say twenty thousand dollars!" [17] At that time the pay and sub-
sistence for a captain of one certain regiment, $480, was worth about
$13, and a lieutenant's $126.60 was worth about $3.30. In January, 1781,
the paper dollar was rated at 75 for one of hard money. In that month
Allen McLane paid $600 for a pair of boots, $900 for six yards of chintz;
and none too soon did he make his purchases, for within three months the
paper dollar was quoted at zero.[18]

There was very little diversion, in active duty, for the army during that
dreary winter. In January, Stirling carried 2,500 men in five hundred
sleighs over the snow and across the ice to Staten Island for a surprise attack
on the enemy's camp. But the enemy were not surprised; they retired to
their strongholds, and nothing came of the effort beyond the capture of a

handful of prisoners, some tents, arms, and other loot. Against that profit, he had to charge a loss of 6 men killed and 500 "slightly frozen." [19] There were a few other unimportant forays on both sides, which accomplished nothing of consequence. In the spring of 1780 the war in the north was practically at an end. The south had become and continued to be the nation's principal battlefield.

CHAPTER 52

Some Minor Conflicts in the North,
1778-1781

Although Monmouth was the last important battle in the north, it will be well for the sake of clarity to pursue the other minor operations of the war in that sector, some occurring before and some long after the opening of the major conflict in the south.

The first of these took place in September, 1778. Early in that month it appeared to Washington that preparations were being made in New York for some major activities. He thought these might be intended either against the Highlands or against the French fleet then being refitted in Boston. As it finally appeared, there was nothing more serious afoot than two foraging expeditions, one on each side of the Hudson; but they were both conducted in considerable force. Cornwallis with 5,000 men was out on the west side of the river; Knyphausen with 3,000, in Westchester County on the east side.

Recognizing their purpose, Washington did not attempt to meet them in force. He merely sent small bodies of his troops to annoy them and check their movements as far as possible. One of these, composed of New Jersey militia and Lieutenant Colonel George Baylor's 3rd Continental Light Dragoons (otherwise known as "Mrs. Washington's Guards") under command of Wayne, took a position in front of Cornwallis. The militia under General William Winds were posted at New Tappan, in Rockland County, New York, the light horse at Old Tappan two and a half miles from the others. Cornwallis proposed to himself to cut them off.

The 71st Regiment and Simcoe's Queen's Rangers were detached from Knyphausen and ordered, under Lieutenant Colonel Campbell, across the

Hudson to go against Wayne at New Tappan. General Grey of Paoli fame, with the 2nd Light Infantry, the 2nd Grenadiers, the 33rd and 64th regiments, was sent against Baylor at Old Tappan.

But the boats for Campbell's contingent failed to arrive, and that part of the entreprise was abandoned. General Winds, having learned of the proposed attack on his troops, withdrew from his post without notifying Baylor. Grey approached Old Tappan at night unobserved until he met a sergeant's guard of a dozen men posted near Baylor's headquarters. They were all bayoneted. He then silently surrounded three barns in which Baylor's dragoons were asleep, fell upon them, and bayoneted 36 of the defenseless men, capturing 40 more. Only 37 managed to escape. Baylor was wounded and captured; his major, Alexander Clough, was mortally wounded. The escape from death of the 40 prisoners, the whole 4th Troop, has been attributed to the intervention of one of Grey's captains to save them.[1]

This savage exploit was soon followed by another of like character. The American privateers had been giving British ships a good deal of trouble. One of their favorite ports was Little Egg Harbor in New Jersey. In October, 1778, the British sloops of war *Zebra*, *Vigilant*, and *Nautilus*, two row galleys, and four small armed vessels were sent against that place, while Captain Patrick Ferguson with 300 men of the 70th Regiment and the Tory 3rd New Jersey Volunteers also marched against it.

Several privateers had left that port a few days before, but ten large vessels were caught and, with a dozen houses and several magazines of stores, were burned. A deserter—a French captain in Count Casimir Pulaski's Legion, an independent corps—told Ferguson that the Legion, consisting of three incomplete companies of light infantry, three troops of light dragoons, and a company of artillery, with one fieldpiece, which had been sent to cover Little Egg Harbor, was encamped eight or ten miles distant.

Late in the evening of October 14, Ferguson embarked 250 of his men in small boats, in which they rowed ten miles to Mincock Island. Leaving 50 men to occupy a defile through which Pulaski's post was approachable, Ferguson marched to a spot where the Americans, infantry of the Legion, were cantoned in three houses; and, at a little after four in the morning, he surprised them. The bayonet again did its deadly work. Fifty of the Legion were killed, including Lieutenant Colonel the Baron de Boze and Lieutenant de La Borderie, French officers. Pulaski had, on the first alarm, brought up his dragoons and, with the aid of the surviving infantry, drove Ferguson from the scene of slaughter. By taking up the planks of a bridge, Ferguson stopped the dragoons and escaped to his boats in much confusion. Pulaski's infantry followed, firing upon the retreating men and taking a few prisoners.

Ferguson made no bones of having been merciless in his murder of the unarmed men in the houses. "It being a night attack," he reported to Clinton, "little quarter could, of course, be given, so that there are only five prisoners." He also said he learned from the French deserter that Pulaski had "lately directed no quarter to be given and it was therefore with particular satisfaction that the detachment marched against a man capable of issuing an order so unworthy of a gentleman and a soldier"—as pretty a piece of self-indictment as one could hope to find.[2]

In the village of Poundridge, twenty miles northeast of White Plains, dwelt Major Ebenezer Lockwood, an active patriot, for whose arrest the British command had offered a reward. Colonel Elisha Sheldon with 90 of the 2nd Continental Dragoons was encamped in that vicinity. Lieutenant Colonel Banastre Tarleton undertook the double task of arresting Lockwood and defeating Sheldon. He took with him 70 of the 17th light Light Dragoons, part of his own Legion of foot and horse, all mounted, Simcoe's Queen's Rangers, a detachment of hussars, and some mounted jägers, about 360 in all. His approach was discovered by an American spy, and Lockwood and Sheldon were informed of it.

Sheldon formed his men a little above Poundridge church. Tarleton advanced in a narrow column because of the nature of the ground. His dragoons, in the van, drove Sheldon's small force from its position. Tarleton followed him for two miles, pressing heavily on his rear, both parties keeping up a scattering fire. But the militia of the neighborhood turned out and, from fences and farm buildings, began to fire on Tarleton's flanks. He took warning of his danger, faced about, and retreated, Sheldon and the gathering militia pursuing him. Part of his force, left at Poundridge, burned the church and several dwellings, Lockwood's among them. They also found in one of the houses Sheldon's colors and some officers' baggage and carried them off.

Tarleton made his escape, having lost only one man killed and one wounded. In his report to Clinton he gloried in the rather inglorious capture of Sheldon's standard and the baggage. The Americans' loss was 10 wounded, 8 missing.[3]

It was, as in the Little Egg Harbor case, the annoyance of small vessels and whaleboats that had been attacking British commerce in Long Island

Sound, as well as the activity of the Connecticut people in supplying the Continental army, that prompted Clinton to undertake a punitive incursion in that state. On July 3, 1779, a fleet of transports, to be convoyed by the frigate *Camilla,* the sloop of war *Scorpion,* the brig *Halifax,* and the row galley *Hussar,* was assembled at Whitestone, and the troops for the expedition embarked. They comprised the 54th Regiment, a regiment of fusiliers, the flank companies of the Guards, and a detachment of jägers, as a first division, under Brigadier General Garth, also the 23rd, or Royal Welch Fusiliers, the Landgrave's Regiment of Hessians, and the "King's Americans," a Tory regiment, as a second division under General William Tryon, former royal governor of New York—about 2,600 men in all.

Early in the morning of the 5th, the fleet anchored off West Haven, in New Haven harbor. The first division, accompanied by four fieldpieces, landed and marched against New Haven. There was little opposition. Twenty-five young men stood against them for a brief space of time and drove the Guards' light infantry back upon the main body, but without greatly delaying the advance. The planks of a bridge across West River were taken up, and two guns were mounted in some slight earthworks there. A skirmish ensued, and the invaders were forced to turn to another bridge. The militia opposed them in the usual style, firing from behind fences and buildings and causing some loss.

In the meantime, the second division had landed at East Haven, overcoming some opposition. These were joined the next day by Garth's detachment. Garth had expressed an intention of burning New Haven, but contented himself with general plunder of its inhabitants and with carrying off thirty or forty prisoners when on the 6th he reembarked all his troops and proceeded to Fairfield. Landing there on the 8th, the British force occupied the village. Its inhabitants having fled, there was no resistance to the plundering of their houses and the burning of two churches, eighty-three dwellings, fifty-four barns, forty-seven storehouses, two schoolhouses, the jail, and the courthouse. From that place, private property of great value was carried off. The next outrage was perpetrated upon the village of Green's Farms, where the church, fourteen dwellings, thirteen barns, and a store were burned and much valuable property was looted.

On the 11th, Norwalk was attacked. A body of fifty militia opposed the invaders for several hours with fire from houses but was, of course, unable to do more than delay them. Looting was general, to the value of over $150,000, and fire consumed the saltworks, some magazines, two churches, one hundred thirty dwellings, eighty-seven barns, twenty-two stores. seventeen shops, four mills, and five vessels.

The loss of life in these barbaric attacks was slight on both sides. The result was chiefly the arousing of intense indignation throughout the country and the strengthening of opposition to a government whose emissaries would so ravage undefended towns and so wantonly pillage the effects of their unresisting inhabitants.[4]

In February, 1780, an American force was posted in and about "Young's House," a dwelling in the town of Mount Pleasant in the turbulent county of Westchester, New York. It consisted of five companies of Connecticut troops under Lieutenant Colonel Joseph Thompson of Massachusetts, Captain Abraham Watson's company of the 3rd Massachusetts, Captain Moses Roberts's company of the 15th Massachusetts, Captain-Lieutenant Michael Farley's company of the 9th Massachusetts, and Captain James Cooper's of the 14th Massachusetts, perhaps 450 men in all.

In the night of February 2 a British force composed of the four flank companies of the 1st and 2nd regiments of the Guards, a hundred Hessians, a party of jägers, some of them mounted, and 40 mounted Westchester Tories of Colonel James De Lancey's regiment, 450 foot soldiers and 100 horsemen in all, commanded by Colonel Norton of the Guards, set out from near Fort Knyphausen (formerly Fort Washington) to attack the post at Young's House. An American sergeant's guard on picket duty fired upon the van of the enemy, but were all captured. Colonel Thompson, having been advised of the enemy's approach, formed his own force in front of the house to withstand them, placing the four other companies on his flanks. When the British came within gunshot, there was a hot exchange of fire for about fifteen minutes. But Norton flanked the American left and occupied an orchard behind the house. Thus surrounded, the Americans gave way; some took refuge in the house; the rest retreated, pursued by the mounted Tories. The grenadiers of the Guards forced the house, killed or captured all its occupants, and burned it.

The American loss was 14 killed, among whom was Captain Roberts, 37 wounded, and 76 taken prisoner, including Joseph Young, the owner of the house, Colonel Thompson, Captain Watson and Captain-Lieutenant Farley, two lieutenants, and two ensigns. The British lost but 5 killed and 18 wounded.[5]

The spring of 1780 was for the Americans one of the most doubtful seasons of the whole war; for the British it was one of the most hopeful. They were convinced that the American cause was on the verge of collapse. And that was not far from the truth, especially in New Jersey. Several causes operated to bring about this state of affairs. By the expiration of enlistments and the lag in recruiting new men, Washington's army, still in camp at Morristown, had been reduced to fewer than 4,000 men fit for duty; and the pay of this remainder was five months in arrears. Even if the arrears were made up, the soldiers knew that the paper money they would receive would be almost valueless. Meanwhile, on less than half-rations, they were always hungry.

The depreciation of the Continental currency struck a hard blow at the morale of the New Jersey civilians, too. Throughout that state, food had been taken from them upon promises to pay. But they knew that, if and when payment was made, it would be in worthless paper.

These causes created, among both soldiery and civilians, discontent, discouragement, and doubt as to the success of the cause. Among the soldiers, the feelings culminated on May 25 in open mutiny. Two regiments of the Connecticut line assembled, under arms, on parade at beat of drum and declared their intention of going home, "or, at best, to gain subsistence at the point of the bayonet." It was with the greatest difficulty that they were persuaded by their officers to return to their huts.

Under such conditions it is not surprising that Clinton thought that, by a demonstration of British strength, he could prevail upon the American soldiers to desert in large numbers, and upon the civilian population of the state to return to allegiance to the King. Accordingly, he assembled a force of 5,000 men under command of General Knyphausen and Brigadiers Mathews, Tryon, and Sterling, and sent it over from Staten Island to Elizabethtown. Washington was too weak to attack them in force, but the militia turned out to disappoint the enemy in the belief that the people were completely disaffected from the American cause. Twelve of them dared oppose the British advance, firing upon it and wounding General Sterling, who led the van. They were of course swept aside without difficulty, and the invaders marched on to the village of Connecticut Farms, being "annoyed by parties of militia the whole way." While passing through Connecticut Farms, one of the British soldiers fired through a window of the house of the Reverend James Caldwell and killed Mrs. Caldwell, who was sitting with her small children about her. Her body was removed from the house, and it was fired. The church and every other house in the village, save one, were also burned after they had been looted of everything portable. General William Tryon is said to have given the incendiary orders.

The American militia assembled, with a few Continental troops, at Springfield near by. On the way to that town Knyphausen was checked at a bridge across the Rahway River "by a detachment from that army which was represented to be mutinous . . . drawn up in force, ready to dispute his passage." Other detachments of the Continental army arrived from Morristown and took up a threatening position in support of the men at the bridge.

Knyphausen now perceived that "the information upon which the expedition had been undertaken was not to be depended upon." He therefore faced about and returned to Elizabethtown. But, upon reflection, he concluded "for the credit of the British arms" he would "remain some days longer in New Jersey, lest their precipitate retreat should be represented as a flight."

On June 23, he marched back toward Springfield, harassed on the way by a body of militia under General Maxwell. General Greene, with 1,000 Continentals and a force of militia under General Philemon Dickinson, proceeded from Morristown to Springfield, having detached Major Henry Lee and Colonel Elias Dayton with small parties of Continentals to delay the British advance. Greene and Dickinson posted their men behind the bridge at Springfield.

Approaching that town, Knyphausen divided his force into two columns. General Mathews, with half of the troops, went forward on the direct road to the town to amuse Greene, while the other column went to the right towards Vauxhall bridge, with intent to turn the American left and gain its rear.

Greene sent Henry Lee's cavalry and a Continental regiment to the Vauxhall bridge. They made a good stand there, inflicting "very considerable injury" on Mathews's troops, but were driven back towards Greene's force and made a new stand, still on the Vauxhall road. Knyphausen then attacked the main position, coming first upon Colonel Israel Angell's Rhode Island Regiment, which offered a spirited resistance for forty minutes, then fell back to a new position with Colonel William Shreve's New Jersey militia. Greene recalled both of them to the main body. Being so outnumbered, his left flank threatened with encirclement, Greene withdrew all his troops to certain heights in his rear. His force being now concentrated and holding a good position, he sent Colonel Henry Jackson's Massachusetts Continental regiment and Colonel Webb's of Connecticut to support Lee's contingent on the Vauxhall road. There the British right column was stopped.

Knyphausen hesitated to attack Greene in his new position. He realized that "every mile of his future march . . . through a country naturally difficult . . . would be no less obstinately resisted." He, therefore, decided to abandon his enterprise. He set fire to nearly fifty dwellings in Springfield, leaving only four unburnt, then took the road back to Elizabethtown, pursued by Captain Davis with a small party of Continentals and a number of militia, who fired on his flanks and rear and inflicted considerable damage.

The loss of the British in this expedition seems not to have been reported. Of the Americans, 13 were killed, 61 wounded, and 9 were missing. The success of Greene with a thousand Continentals, and of Dickinson with his untrained militia, in checking the advance of 5,000 enemy infantry supported by several guns and a substantial number of horsemen, and turning them back from Morristown, was highly creditable. The barbarous incendiarism, with the wanton murder of Mrs. Caldwell, increased the animosity of the Jerseymen and instilled a new spirit of resistance in the American troops. There was no further attempt at hostile operations by the enemy in that state.[6]

A little before Knyphausen's incursion into New Jersey, Clinton had embarked some troops on transports and made a feint of ascending the Hudson. To counter this threat, Washington had started the greater part of his troops north towards Ramapo and the Clove, leaving Greene in command at Morristown, with two Continental brigades and the Jersey militia. He continued to move north, to Peekskill and finally to West Point, of which post Benedict Arnold was in command.

On September 22 an affair that shocked the army and the American people as nothing had done since the beginning of the war, culminated at West Point. It was the effort of Benedict Arnold to deliver that post to the enemy. The well known story of Arnold's treason has been fully and so ably covered in Carl Van Doren's *Secret History of the American Revolution*, and no effort will be made to tell it in this narrative, which seeks to confine itself to a description of the armed conflicts between the British and American land forces. We therefore proceed to the next and to the last engagement of the war in the North.

In the fall of 1780 a party of Tory refugees from Rhode Island was established in St. George's manor house in the town of Brookhaven on Long Island, which had been turned into a sort of fort.

To this enemy post Major Benjamin Tallmadge of the 2nd Continental Dragoons turned his attention. With two companies of dismounted dragoons, about eighty men, he embarked in eight boats at Fairfield, Connecticut, in the afternoon of November 21, 1780. Having landed on Long Island at nine o'clock in the evening, he detailed Captain Sutton, with twenty men, to guard the boats and started across the island with the rest of his force. But so heavy a storm of wind and rain blew up that he realized he could not recross the Sound that night. He therefore returned to the boats and lay hid until it abated in the evening of the 22nd, when he again set out.

The fort, though small, was formidable. The original house was protected by two strong stockades, twelve feet high, diverging at angles to its front, on its right and left. That on the right terminated at a strongly barricaded house; that on the left at a strong little fort close to the shore, surrounded by a deep ditch and an abatis. It mounted two guns. Another line of stockade connected the extremities of the other two, making the whole a triangle.

Tallmadge divided his men into three parties, so as to move against all sides of the triangle at the same time. Their muskets were unloaded, their bayonets fixed. At dawn his own party approached the east front of the fort, undiscovered by the enemy until they had got within forty yards of the stockade. When a sentinel fired on them, all three parties rushed to the attack. Tallmadge's pioneers cut through the stockade on the east front. The others scaled their respective sides, shouting "Washington and Glory!" The manor house was carried "with the bayonet in less than ten minutes." But a part of the garrison took refuge in the other house, from which it directed its fire upon the attackers. It was answered, and the house was stormed. A door was burst in, and the occupants were seized and thrown out the windows. The entire garrison was captured, and the works with a quantity of stores were destroyed.

Tallmadge got back to his boats, having as his only casualty one man wounded. Of the Tories seven were killed or wounded, and fifty-four officers and privates, "with a host of others in the garrison," presumably noncombatants, were captured. The whole party reached Fairfield in safety that night. For this exploit Major Tallmadge was thanked by Washington and by a resolution of the Congress.[7]

During the winter of 1780–1781 Washington's army was cantoned at various points from Morristown through the Hudson Highlands to Connecticut. Its physical condition was, as in its former winter camps, distressing in the extreme. Food was lacking, shelter was inadequate, clothing was scanty, and pay was always in arrears.

The soldiers of the Pennsylvania line had an additional reason for discontent. Their enlistment papers bound them to serve "for three years or during the war." They construed this as limiting their service to whichever event should first ensue, either the expiration of three years or the end of the war. As the three-year period had expired, they claimed their discharge; but the military authorities held that they must serve to the war's end, even if it was postponed beyond three years. That dubious statement in the enlistment papers, capable of either interpretation, was a cause of trouble in other cases also; but, coupled with their physical hardships at this time, it aroused strong resentment among Wayne's brigade of Pennsylvanians now in camp near Morristown.

In the evening of January 1, 1781, there was a deal of disorder in their camp. The men, who should have been in their huts, were out on the parade ground, muskets in hand, running about, shouting to one another, and occasionally firing their muskets. The officers strove to quiet the tumult and get the men back into their huts. The efforts were partially successful for a time, but at midnight the men again broke out. Shots were fired here and there. One officer was killed, and two were wounded. The mutineers took possession of the artillery park, killing a soldier on guard there.

Wayne, Colonel Walter Stewart, and Colonel Richard Butler attempted to control the situation; but Sergeant William Bouzar, the ringleader, boldly demanded payment of the arrears in pay and discharges for all that had served three years, saying the men were determined to present their grievances to the Congress in Philadelphia. Wayne faced them intrepidly, but without avail. At beat of drum six regiments formed in column in good order, under command of their sergeants, and set off on the road to Trenton.

Unable to control them, Wayne, Stewart, and Butler followed. The men bivouacked first at Vealtown, then at Middlebrook, and finally at Princeton on January 3. Appeals to the Congress had been sent ahead, and at Princeton they awaited a reply. Lafayette and St. Clair, of whose division the Pennsylvanians were a part, met them there; but the mutineers ordered them out of the camp, saying that they would deal only with Wayne, Stewart, Butler, and the Congress.

In Philadelphia there was the greatest consternation, and it was even proposed that the Congress should leave town to avoid meeting the mutineers; but better advice prevailed. Joseph Reed, President of the Congress, with a committee of its members went to Princeton and, after protracted negotiations, obtained an agreement. Arrears of pay, with allowance for depreciation in value, were to be made up as soon as possible; certain articles of clothing, to which the men were entitled, were to be furnished; and every soldier that had enlisted "for three years or during the war," and had served three years, was to be discharged. If the enlistment papers could not be found, each man's oath was to determine his right to discharge. Nearly all of them were discharged, but a large proportion of them reenlisted. It was a complete victory for the mutineers, and one result was the encouragement of a similar revolt.

Three New Jersey regiments at Pompton marched off towards Trenton on January 20. But Washington was ready now to adopt sterner measures. He sent Major General Robert Howe of North Carolina with a detachment of New England Continentals, "to compel the mutineers to unconditional submission" and "instantly [to] execute a few of the most active and incendiary leaders." Howe surrounded the mutineers' camp at Pompton—to which place they had returned—and ordered them to assemble, without arms, which they did. He then selected one man from each of the three regiments, the most forward in the matter according to the officers' reports, and tried them by court martial. Having been found guilty, two of them were hanged; the third, not so vicious as the others, was reprieved. That broke the revolt. The body of mutineers submitted and returned to duty.

While the negotiations for settlement of the Pennsylvania revolt were in progress, Clinton, thinking he saw an opportunity to demoralize the American army, sent two Tory emissaries, James Ogden and John Mason, to Princeton with an offer to take the mutineers under his protection, give them free pardons and pay them what was due. The mutineers seized the two messengers and turned them over to Wayne. They were tried, condemned as spies, and hanged. Wayne offered a reward in gold to the mutineers for this indication of their fidelity. It was declined by Bouzar, their leader, who said his men agreed that they were not entitled "to any other reward but the love of our country." [8]

As a part of the reward for his treason Benedict Arnold received a commission as brigadier general in the British army, and was sent in December, 1780, on an incursion into Virginia, to be more fully described hereinafter. By June, 1781, he was back in New York. There he devised a plan for an expedition against Connecticut in the hope of diverting the attention of some part of Washington's army from the campaign in Virginia.

The troops assembled for this purpose were in two divisions. The first included the 40th and 54th British regiments, the 3rd battalion of New Jersey Volunteers, Tories, a detachment of Hessian jägers, and some artillery, Lieutenant Colonel Eyre in command. The second, led by Arnold in person, was made up of the 38th British regiment, two Tory battalions, called the Loyal Americans also the American Legion, a detachment of jägers, and some guns, about 1,700 in all.

New London, where a very considerable quantity of military stores had been accumulated by the Americans, was chosen for the first attack. It was defended by two forts, Trumbull and Griswold. Trumbull, on the west bank of the Thames River, was built to defend the harbor and was weak on the land side. Griswold was a square fortification. Its stone walls, twelve feet high, were surrounded by a ditch. It was fraised with pointed pickets and supported by outside earthworks. Trumbull's garrison was Captain Adam Shapley's company of 24 Connecticut State troops. Griswold contained about 140 militia under Lieutenant Colonel William Ledyard.

At nine o'clock in the morning of September 6, 1781, Arnold's force landed, one division on each side of the harbor. Arnold's corps marched towards the town, but four companies of the 38th, under Captain Millett, were detached against Fort Trumbull. On the way, Millett's troops were strengthened by the addition of a Tory company under Captain Frink. Shapley's tiny force could not hope to hold the fort. It fired a single volley of grape and musket bullets upon the invaders, striking down four or five of them, spiked the fort's guns, and retreated to Griswold.

Arnold, meanwhile, had gone on to take a small redoubt on Town Hill, commonly called "Fort Nonsense." It was held only by a small party of the townsmen, but they offered resistance with "a brisk fire" which inflicted some damage. Then Arnold formed his men for an assault, and the civilian garrison abandoned the redoubt. Arnold now ordered Eyre with his division to attack Griswold, leading his own corps on towards the town. A few of the citizenry with an old, iron six-pounder fired on him and fled. Eyre approached Griswold and summoned it to surrender. Shapley, its commander, knowing his garrison was too weak to resist successfully, was inclined to comply, but Colonel Nathan Gallup urged him not to do so, promising him a reinforcement of two or three hundred militia if he would hold out. Shapley then refused the demand. But Gallup was unable to bring in the promised aid.

Eyre divided his men into two parties and attacked two sides of the fort simultaneously. The garrison met them with a heavy fire. Eyre was mortally wounded, and his men were repulsed. They came on again, made a lodgment in the ditch and succeeded in tearing down a part of the fraising, but were again repulsed. A third attack was successful. Mounting on one another's shoulders, they swarmed over the parapet or climbed through the embrasures, in spite of an enfilading fire from a 9-pounder in the fort. The garrison offered a stubborn resistance. Major Montgomery was killed by a bayonet thrust at the hands of Captain Shapley. An ensign of the 40th was killed. Three officers of the 54th were wounded. But the works had been forced, and Ledyard offered to surrender. He tendered his sword to Lieutenant Colonel Van Buskirk of the New Jersey Volunteers, who received it and instantly plunged it into Ledyard's body. Some of the attackers finished him off with their bayonets.

Then began an indiscriminate slaughter of the garrison. Tories, Hessians, and British regulars alike joined in the butchery with musket shot and bayonet. They pursued men that had fled into the barracks and the magazine or crept under the gun platforms, shot them, cut them down with swords, bayoneted them without mercy, killing wounded men as they lay on the ground. The fort was a bloody shambles. Only 6 of the garrison had been killed while defending it and no more than 18 were wounded, but when the massacre ceased 85 lay dead in the fort and 60 wounded, many of them mortally. The remaining few were taken captive.

In the meantime Arnold's division entered the town and began its destruction. The torch was applied to building after building by detachments that proceeded systematically. The courthouse, the jail, churches, stores, shops, dwelling houses, warehouses, wharves, shipyards, and a dozen vessels small and large were burned. The little town of Groton met the same fate. In the two towns more than 140 buildings were consumed by fire.

The loss of the British in this expedition was more than might be expected, 48 killed and 145 wounded. The Americans lost, in all, about 240 killed, wounded, or taken captive. In matériel, their loss was heavy, including 71 cannon of various sizes and many muskets, besides a great quantity of stores of food.

Having thus visited upon the unoffending civil population of his own state this punishment for devotion to the cause that he himself had so long and so well defended and then so basely betrayed, General Arnold embarked his gallant troops and returned to New York. This was the last engagement of the war in the north.[9]

Wyoming

One of the more important operations of the war on the northern border took place not in Tryon County, but in a somewhat remote sector, the Wyoming Valley in Pennsylvania.

That valley was a particular part of the great valley of the north branch of the Susquehanna River, the greater part of it being in Luzerne County. Its length was about twenty-five miles; its width about three. Two ranges of hills, rising to a height of 800 to 1,000 feet, hemmed it in. Between them the valley was diversified by hill and dale, upland and lowland; its broad levels bordering the river to a width of one to two miles were conspicuous for beauty and fertility. In all its aspects it was a land formed by nature as a garden spot of peaceful fruitfulness as well as a delight to the eye. And yet, although its first settlers in 1742, Moravians led by Count Zinzendorf, enjoyed for a few years untroubled peace and plenty, it soon became and continued for thirty years to be a scene of tumultuous conflict between rival claimants. Pennsylvania claimed the Wyoming Valley as a part of Penn's grant from the King. Connecticut claimed the Valley as lying between lines extended westward from its own northern and southern boundaries, on the ground that its territory beyond New Jersey extended "from sea to sea," from the Atlantic Ocean to the Pacific.

Rival land companies were chartered by those two colonies that fought bloody battles for the Wyoming Valley, and each tried to dispossess the other's settlers. At the outbreak of the Revolution, Connecticut was in the ascendant, the inhabitants generally recognizing the authority of that state in all their affairs.

For protection from the Indians of the surrounding country the settlers had built a number of "forts," stockaded and entrenched blockhouses. Of these the most important were Fort Durkee on the left bank of the Susquehanna a little below the borough of Wilkes-Barre; Fort Wyoming in the borough; Ogden's Fort on the left bank three or more miles up the river; Forty Fort opposite Ogden's on the other bank; the Pittstown Redoubts five miles farther up on the left bank; Wintermoot's Fort opposite Pittstown; and Fort Jenkins a mile above Wintermoot's. These were, as usual in the border country, intended as places of refuge for the inhabitants in case of Indian attacks, rather than as permanent military posts. Although there were of course differences of political opinion among the settlers, the Tories seem to have been largely outnumbered by the patriots. Many of the Tories left the Valley and joined the forces of Sir Guy Johnson. The remaining patriots enrolled their militia to the number of 1,100, of whom 300 left to join the regular American army.

The headquarters of the Tory forces of Johnson and Colonel John Butler in the spring of 1778 was at Fort Niagara on Lake Ontario. At that time a decision was taken to launch an expedition against Wyoming. Colonel Butler set out near the end of June with 400 white men, including his Rangers, a detachment of Johnson's Royal Greens, and a miscellaneous contingent of unattached Tories from New York, Pennsylvania, and New Jersey, also perhaps 500 Indians, chiefly Senecas, the most ferocious of the Six Nations.

At Tioga Point on the river they embarked in canoes and bateaux and on rafts, to land about twenty miles above Wyoming; and they entered the Valley on June 30 through a notch in the mountains on the west. Their first contact with the settlers was with a party of seven men and a boy working in the fields near Fort Jenkins. Four of these were killed, three captured; the boy escaped. A little "fort" near by, called Exeter, occupied chiefly by Tories, surrendered without resistance. Fort Jenkins was also promptly surrendered, its tiny garrison having been weakened by loss of the seven mentioned. Wintermoot succumbed without fighting. It must be understood that the "garrisons" of those little places consisted of a few men in each, with the women and children of their families, who had taken refuge therein.

In the meantime, a very different Butler, the patriot Colonel Zebulon Butler, had taken command of the available armed forces of the Valley—a company of about 60 men, so-called "regulars," which had been authorized by the Congress to be enlisted for its defense; he had also assembled two or three hundred of the militia. These had been concentrated at Forty Fort. By the decision of a council of war the patriots marched against the invaders on July 3, intending to take them by surprise. Approaching Wintermoot, where John Butler maintained his headquarters, they were discovered by an Indian who gave the alarm. The Tory commander promptly took a position in a plain covered by trees and undergrowth and deployed his men in line of battle. His left, composed of his Rangers, rested on the fort; the Royal Greens held the center; and the Indians, the right.

Zebulon Butler's line was formed with militia on the right and left and the "regulars" in the center. At two hundred yards his men opened fire, continuing to advance until they were within half that distance. For half an hour the two sides kept up a heavy fire. Then a body of Indians gained unperceived a position on the Americans' left flank and opened fire which threw that wing into confusion. Its commander, Colonel Nathan Denison, ordered one company to wheel so as to face this flank attack. Some of his untrained men took the order for a command to retreat, and the whole wing was disordered. The savages seized the opportunity. Throwing down their muskets and yelling like madmen, they fell upon the confused mass with their tomahawks and knives. In a hand-to-hand encounter the Americans fought back; but the whole line was broken and was soon in full flight pursued by their savage enemies, who had regained their muskets and now shot down or tomahawked those they could come up with. The Americans, cut off from retreat to their fort, scattered to seek safety by swimming the river or fleeing to the mountains. Their losses were great; no more than 60 of the whole force escaped death or capture. Of those taken, many were subjected by the Indians to systematic torture ended only by lingering death after agonizing sufferings. John Butler said that 227 scalps were harvested in that fight. He reported his losses as one Indian and two Rangers killed, eight Indians wounded.

Colonel Denison with a few of his men succeeded in getting back to Forty Fort. Colonel Zebulon Butler, with such of the "regulars" as he could gather together, retired to Fort Wyoming and thence withdrew from the Valley. Both forts were surrendered under a promise by John Butler that the lives and property of the people should be preserved. But the promise was not made good. In spite of his orders, it is said, the whole Valley was given over to plunder and destruction and was soon entirely laid waste. Houses and mills were burned. John Butler reported 1,000 houses and "all their mills" so destroyed. Included in these was every house in Wilkes-Barre. A thousand horned cattle and countless sheep and swine were driven away. Personal property of all sorts was carried away or destroyed. The families of the inhabitants were broken up and individually dispersed in the mountain wilderness and in the great swamp in the Poconos, thereafter called "The Shades of Death," where they died of exhaustion and starvation. Many were carried into captivity by the Indians. Depopulated and devastated, the beautiful Wyoming Valley had become a scene of ruin and desolation.[1]

Mohawk Valley

German Flats, a village on the Mohawk River in perhaps the most fertile and beautiful part of the valley—where now stands the town of Herkimer—was the next to fall victim to the fury of the Indians. It contained sixty or seventy houses on both sides of the river, several mills, a massively built stone church, and the large stone mansion house of General Herkimer, which had been stockaded and was generally known as Fort Herkimer. There was also another small defensive work, a dilapidated blockhouse called Fort Dayton.

Late in August, 1778, Joseph Brant was at Unadilla, an Indian town about fifty miles southwest of the Flats. At the head of 300 Tories and 150 Indians, he marched against the ill-fated village early in September.[1] Its inhabitants had suspected an attack and had sent out four scouts towards Unadilla. They were met by Brant's Indians, and three of them were killed. The fourth got back to the town and spread the alarm.

Having this warning, the inhabitants gathered up their most valuable portable possessions and took refuge in the two forts and the church. Brant's marauders reached the Flats in the stormy night of September 12. At dawn, they swept into the town. Without making even a demonstration against the three little strongholds, they set fire to every house and barn. When the entire town was in flames, they collected all the horses, cattle, and sheep and drove them back to Unadilla. No lives were lost; but the prosperous little town was but a heap of ashes and its people were entirely bereft of their only livelihood.

In revenge the Americans struck at Unadilla. From Schoharie, early in

October, came Lieutenant Colonel William Butler. (The chronicles of the time are as full of Butlers as of Clintons; but William was no kin of Zebulon, nor of John, nor were they related to each other.) With him were his 4th Pennsylvania Continental regiment, a detachment of Morgan's riflemen, and a small corps of "rangers." On October 8 they entered the town without opposition, "the enemy having that day left it in the greatest confusion, leaving behind a large quantity of corn, their dogs, some cattle and a great part of their household furniture." Butler's troops "fared sumptuously, having poultry and vegetables in great abundance." [2]

Unadilla was not a savage village of huts and wigwams. It was a well built town of stone and frame houses, with brick chimneys and glazed windows. The troops first burned an outlying part consisting of "ten good frame houses, with a quantity of corn," then "set fire to all the town . . . burned all the houses" except one. They also reduced to ashes "a saw-mill and grist mill, the latter the only one in the country." [3] Having revenged German Flats, they marched back to Schoharie.

As German Flats had been followed by Unadilla, so now Unadilla invited reprisal. Cherry Valley was a village in Tryon County about fifty miles west of Albany. Its people were of more intelligence and a higher grade of morality than was common in these border settlements, scrupulous in the observance of their religious duties and industrious in a civilized manner. In the spring of 1778 Lafayette, then at Albany preparing for his "irruption" into Canada which never came off, visited the Mohawk Valley and directed the building of a fort at Cherry Valley, considering it as an important military outpost in its relation to Albany through the intermediate post at Schoharie. It appears to have been built in the form of a heavy stockade surrounding the village meetinghouse.

Apprehensive of an attack, the villagers called on the Continental army for aid. Colonel Peter Gansevoort, who had so well defended Fort Stanwix, solicited the command of the force to be sent; but his application was denied, and Colonel Ichabod Alden with the 7th Massachusetts Regiment, 250 men, was sent—unfortunately because neither he nor his men had had any experience in Indian warfare.

From Chemung, near Tioga, Captain Walter Butler, son of Colonel John, with 200 of his father's Rangers, set out late in October on a 150-mile march down the Chemung River to the Susquehanna, up that river to Otsego Lake, and so on toward Cherry Valley—a march not only long and toilsome, but also, as November drew on, of great hardship from cold weather and heavy rains and snows. At some point on the way, he met Joseph

Brant, with 500 Indians then on the way from the Susquehanna country to winter quarters at Fort Niagara, and induced him to join in the enterprise.

On November 8 Alden had word from Fort Stanwix (Fort Schuyler) that his post was in danger of attack. The people of the village were properly alarmed and asked permission to remove themselves and their valuables into the fort; but Alden refused their request, assuring them that he and his men would be vigilant against surprise and strong in defense.

On the 9th he dispatched scouts along two roads from the enemy country but, in his ignorance, overlooked an old Indian trail leading to the village. He was so careless as to permit his officers to quarter themselves in houses outside the fort. He himself and Lieutenant Colonel William Stacey lodged in the house of Robert Wells.

Captain Walter Butler approached the town in the early morning of November 11 by the unwatched trail, unseen in a heavy fog, and scattered his men in parties to attack the houses. One of the first was the Wells house. Alden and Stacey tried to escape to the fort; but Alden was overtaken, shot or tomahawked, and scalped, and Stacey was captured. The savage intruders burst into the house and massacred Wells, his mother, wife, brother, sister, three sons, and a daughter as well as the sixteen soldiers billeted there as a sort of headquarters company. Other houses were similarly attacked, and their inmates murdered or taken prisoners. In all more than 30 of the non-combatant inhabitants of the village were slaughtered. Many escaped into the surrounding forests.

Having no artillery, Butler could make no impression on the fort. He kept up a heavy musket fire upon it for several hours, but made no attempt to take it by assault. The town was given over to plunder and the torch. Every dwelling house, barn, and building in it was burned, and all the livestock were collected and driven off. With thirty to forty prisoners in his train, he marched away. But he had not gone far when he decided to release all the captive women and children except two women and their children, whom he retained as a punishment to their husbands, who had been especially active against the Tories and Indians. His motive for this apparently humane action was the desire to secure the release of his own mother, some of her young children, and some other members of his family, who had been detained in Albany when he and his father fled to Canada. General James Clinton agreed to the exchange.[4]

Although the towns in the border country were never free from casual attack and many of them suffered from the desire of the Indians for plunder and scalps, the next real battle in Tryon County did not come until the summer of 1779, when the Tories and Indians attacked Minisink, a village on the Neversink River in the Shawangunk Mountains. Count Pulaski and his cavalry command had been stationed there in the winter of 1778–1779, but were ordered south in February to join Benjamin Lincoln's army.

In July, Joseph Brant saw his chance. He detached 60 Indian warriors and 27 Tories disguised as Indians from a much larger body, which he left in the mountains between Minisink and the Delaware River, and stole into the sleeping town during the night of the 19th. Its inhabitants were awakened by the sound of crackling flames and the smell of smoke to find several of their houses already afire. The intruders seem to have been bent on plunder and destruction rather than on taking scalps, for few of the inhabitants were actually shot down as they attempted to escape, though many were taken prisoners. Then houses and twelve barns, a paltry stockade-fort, and two mills were plundered and burned before the invaders marched away with all the cattle, their other booty, and their captives, to Grassy Bank on the Delaware, where the main body lay.

When news of this outrage reached Goshen, Dr. Benjamin Tusten, lieutenant colonel of the militia, called on his regiment to repair at once to Minisink. On the next day 149 of the militiamen and volunteers met him there; and, in spite of his prudent reluctance to venture on a battle against so astute and subtle a warrior as Brant and in spite of the fact that Brant's strength was unknown, a majority voted to pursue the intruders. Major Meeker brought matters to a head by mounting his horse, flourishing his sword, and crying: "Let all the brave men follow me. The cowards may stay behind!" Everybody followed him.

That day they traveled seventeen miles and encamped. The next morning they were joined by a militia colonel, John Hathorn, with a few men. Hathorn, outranking Tusten, took command. The next day they came upon the camp occupied by Brant's force the night before. By the extent of it and the number of fires, it seemed that the enemy greatly outnumbered the pursuers. A second "council" outvoted the more prudent officers, including Tusten and Hathorn, and decided to go on.

A small scouting party, sent ahead, fell into an ambush, and its leader was shot down. Nevertheless, the whole body pushed recklessly onward until, at the edge of the Delaware River, near where Port Iervis now stands, they descried the Indians and Tories making towards a ford. Hathorn led his men to the right to intercept the enemy before they got to the ford, thus losing sight of them. Brant turned his course also to the right and took a position in the rear of Hathorn's party. Finding no Indians at the ford or on the road to it, the patriots turned back, met their enemies, and the firing began.

By "an ingenious movement" Brant contrived to cut off about 50 of his foes from their main body. The rest took a position on a hill, formed a square and, from the cover of its rocks and trees, engaged the Indians and Tories who surrounded them. It was then about ten o'clock in the morning; and from that time until late in the afternoon a battle of musketry was kept up. Then Brant saw that one man, holding a corner of the square behind a rock, had been shot down. He led his men in a charge through the opening and poured a deadly fire on all sides upon the patriots around him. Hathorn's little force was greatly outnumbered; the square was burst apart and a general flight ensued. The Indians followed the flying men and shot them down or tomahawked them relentlessly. Tusten had gathered 17 of those wounded in the battle in a sheltered place and was caring for them when the Indians found him. He and all of the wounded were massacred. Of those in the fight, 45 were killed in action. Of the whole number, including the 50 earlier separated from the rest, only 30 survived.

Brant went on his way and destroyed another small village in the Mohawk Valley. Other small towns in Pennsylvania near the New York boundary were ravaged by the Tories and Indians within the next few days.[5]

CHAPTER 55

Sullivan's Expedition

Petitions from the inhabitants of the frontiers in Pennsylvania and New York stirred the Congress to activity in their behalf. On February 25, 1779, it directed Washington to take effectual measures for their protection and for the "chastisement of the savages." [1] Washington had had the matter in mind long before that. In January he had considered an expedition against Fort Niagara, the British base on Lake Ontario, which he decided to lay "entirely aside for the present and content ourselves with some operation in a smaller scale against the savages," to be prosecuted in the spring.[2]

In February, Washington had sent to Schuyler and others for information as to the number of men needed for an expedition against the Six Nations and their British and Tory allies, the character of their country, the roads leading to it, and so on.[3] When he received the congressional resolution in March, he was able to reply that a plan for the purpose had been "some time since determined upon and preparations are making." [4] He immediately offered the leadership of the enterprise to Gates, at the same time writing to Major General John Sullivan that he wished him to take it if Gates declined. Gates did decline, prudently, on the ground that he had not the "youth and strength" requisite for such service; [5] and Sullivan accepted.

The country of the Six Nations extended from Lake Ontario on the north to the Susquehanna River in Pennsylvania and from the Catskill Mountains on the east to Lake Erie. These Indians had achieved a high degree of civilization, measured by their establishment of a constitution regulating their affairs, by their permanent settlements, and by their cultivation of the soil. The men were hunters and warriors, but the women were agriculturists of merit. Their villages and towns were composed of substantial log cabins or houses framed with hewn timbers, covered with bark or with sawn boards that were painted. A few of the houses were stoutly built of stone, and many had fireplaces, brick or stone chimneys, and glazed windows. Surrounding the villages were extensive fields and gardens which grew an abundance of corn, peas, beans, pumpkins, and other vegetables in wide variety. Most notable, as evidence of a culture of long standing and promised permanence, were the orchards of apple, pear, and peach trees of great extent and rich fruitfulness.

Washington's purposes, as communicated to Sullivan, were two, "the total destruction and devastation of their settlements and the capture of as many prisoners of every age and sex as possible" to be held as hostages—"the only kind of security to be depended on" for the good behavior of the Six Nations. The country, he wrote, was not to be "merely *overrun* but *destroyed*." [6] The first purpose, destruction and devastation, Sullivan achieved to his complete satisfaction; the second, seizure of hostages, Sullivan completely failed to achieve.

The plan of operations was twofold. Sullivan's grand division of the forces to be employed was to rendezvous at Easton in Pennsylvania and march north by Wyoming to meet at Tioga Brigadier General James Clinton's division coming from Canajoharie by Otsego Lake and the Susquehanna to that point, whence the combined forces were to march north into the Indian country. [7]

Sullivan's division was composed of three brigades. The first brigade, under General William Maxwell, comprised the 1st and 2nd New Jersey Continental regiments and Oliver Spencer's Regiment—one of the sixteen Additional Continental regiments. The second, under General Enoch Poor, consisted of the 1st, 2nd, and 3rd New Hampshire Continentals and the 7th Massachusetts. The third brigade, under General Edward Hand, included the 4th and 11th Pennsylvania Continentals, the "German Regiment" from Pennsylvania and Maryland, Colonel Thomas Proctor's 4th Artillery Regiment with four 3-pounders, two 6's, and two howitzers, a detachment of Morgan's Riflemen under Major James Parr, Captain Anthony Selin's Independent Rifle Company, and a corps of Wyoming militia. This division had, in all, 2,312 rank and file. Clinton's division was in one brigade, made up of the 2nd, 3rd, 4th, and 5th New York Continentals and a company of Lamb's 2nd Artillery, about 1,400 in all, with two small guns. [8]

Sullivan arrived at Easton on May 7, [9] and found part of his force already there, the rest on the way. He lingered for what seemed to Washington and

Clinton an unduly long time; but he himself laid the delay to the failure of the quartermaster's department and the commissariat to furnish the necessary supplies and clothing for his men, also to the fact that he had to cut twenty-three miles of road for the passage of his artillery, his pack-horses, and his herd of beef cattle to Wyoming.[10] He reached that place on June 23. Again there was a long delay while he waited for new provisions and ammunition, to replace what had been spoiled on the way, and for boats.

Meanwhile, Clinton at Canajoharie had been more expeditious. When he received his first instructions from Sullivan his preparations were well under way. More than two hundred bateaux were ready and a three months' supply of provisions was stored at Fort Stanwix (Schuyler). By June 17 the portage of his boats and supplies across the twenty miles of exceedingly bad, hilly roads between the Mohawk River and Otsego Lake was begun. Four horses were required to draw each boat. On June 30 he wrote Sullivan that his entire force, boats, and supplies were on Otsego Lake awaiting orders.[11] Sullivan was tarrying at Wyoming.

Washington was filled "with inexpressable concern" by the extent of Clinton's preparations in provisions and bateaux. He had expected him "to move rapidly . . . quite light" with provisions only to serve until he met Sullivan at Tioga. By such preparations, he wrote to Sullivan, "instead of having his design concealed till the moment of execution, and forming his junction with you in a manner by surprize, the design is announced; the enemy watching him and in place of moving light and rapidly, and as it were undiscovered, he goes incumbered with useless supplies" and "has his defence weakened by the attention he must pay to his convoy." [12]

Sullivan answered that he himself had not "the most Distant prospect of keeping that part of the Army which is with me from Starving Long Enough to Compleat the Expedition," so that it was necessary for Clinton to bring full supplies for his own division for the whole period.[13] Washington accepted the explanation, merely urging Sullivan to lighten his troops "to the greatest possible degree" and hasten his operations.[14]

It is difficult to understand how Washington could have expected Clinton to march 1,400 men through the Indian country, even traveling light and with a minimum of provisions and boats, and at the same time conceal his design and surprise the watchful savages ever on the alert and spying upon him every step of the way. Certainly Clinton entertained no delusions as to the possibility of preserving secrecy. On July 4, at Otsego Lake, he celebrated the day with a salute of thirteen guns and a *feu de joie* of "three Volleys of musketry one after another," which meant that thirteen cannon and more than four thousand muskets resounded through the forest. Sullivan was equally unconcerned about secrecy. When at last he moved from Wyoming his departure was signaled by cannon fire; and every morning on the march the sunrise gun gave the enemy notice of his position.

Clinton at the lower end of Otsego Lake impatiently awaited Sullivan's orders for seven weeks. He used some of the time in damming the outlet, thus raising the level of the lake two feet and storing water to give him good depth in the stream below when his boats should be on their way. At last, on July 31, Sullivan left Wyoming; 120 boats carried his artillery and stores, 1,200 pack-horses transported the baggage of the army, and 700 beef cattle promised it food. On August 11 he reached Tioga.[15]

Sullivan had not waited, however, for a junction with Clinton before beginning the devastation of the Indian villages. On the second day of his march he detached General Hand, with the light troops, and General Poor's brigade to take positions west and east of the town of Chemung, while Colonel Reid with two New Hampshire companies approached another side and the rest of the army yet another, so as to "prevent an Escape" of its inhabitants. But "the Enemy's Precaution defeated the intention of a Surprize,"[16] which is hardly to be wondered at, since "a few cannon" had been fired the night before and the army had marched in style—"drums were beating, fifes playing and colors flying." [17] All the inhabitants had left Chemung.

The town consisted of "between 30 & 40 Houses, some of them large and neatly finish'd; particularly a Chapel and Council House." Sullivan ordered it burned; he also "caus'd their Fields of Corn, which were of a considerable extent and all their gardens, which were replete with Herbage, to be destroy'd." "We had a glorious Bonfire of upwards of 30 Buildings at once," wrote Major James Norris in his journal.[18]

Clinton left Otsego Lake on August 9, his more than two hundred boats riding grandly on the flood caused by breaking down the dam. On the 22nd he met Sullivan at Tioga and was greeted by a salute of "13 Pieces of Cannon," [19] which contributed little more to the preservation of secrecy and surprise. Meanwhile, on August 14 the town of Onaquaga, "one of the Neatest of the Indian towns on the Susquehana . . . with good Log houses with Stone Chimneys and glass windows" and a "Church" had been burned and "a great number of apple trees" either girdled or cut down; on the 18th, another of twenty houses, with "plenty of Cucombars, Squashes, Turnips &c" was similarly destroyed.

On the 26th the combined forces, having left most of their heavy baggage and 250 men to hold Tioga, moved up the Chemung River with proper caution, light infantry well in advance and strong bodies of flankers thrown out on both sides of the main body. But William Rogers, the chaplain of Hand's Brigade, though not a military man, or perhaps because he was not a military man, expressed an opinion in his journal that "the great parade and regularity, which is observed, must unavoidably in the end . . . greatly defeat the purpose of the expedition"—the capture of Indians to be held as hostages—"considering the coyness and subtilty of the Indians." [20] The other purpose, however, was in part effected by the destruction of a hundred acres of "beans, cucumbers, Simblens, watermelons and pumpkins," also corn "such as cannot be equalled in Jersey." [21] In the course of the expedition one officer who kept a diary marveled at an ear of corn eighteen inches long; another measured an ear an inch short of two feet from butt to tip.

So far the enterprise had had only a slight brush with a party of Indians near Chemung. The Indians had abandoned their towns and had fled as the troops advanced. But on the 29th they made a stand on the left bank of the Chemung River, about six miles southeast of the present city of Elmira and close to the Indian village of Newtown.

On a height parallel with the river and not far back from its edge, the Iroquois and their British allies had erected a long breastwork of logs that they artfully concealed by planting green bushes along the front. Between it and the river was the trail Sullivan's troops were following. The breastwork was evidently intended as an ambuscade, rather than as a defensible position, the expectation being that an unexpected fire upon the flank of an unwary marching column would throw it into confusion. This was to be followed by attacks on its front and rear from both ends of the breastwork that would cause a panic among the men, a stampede of the horses and cattle, and a complete rout of the invaders. The position was held by Captain Walter N. Butler with two battalions of the Rangers, a small detachment of the 8th British regiment, and perhaps 200 Tories, and by Joseph Brant with about 500 Indians.

Fortunately for the Americans, their advance was led by Major James Parr with three companies of Morgan's riflemen who discovered the ambuscade before being endangered by it. The column was halted, and a plan for an attack was made. The artillery was posted on a height whence its fire could "enfilade the breastwork and sweep the ground in its rear." General Poor's brigade of three New Hampshire regiments and Alden's Massachusetts men, together with the riflemen, supported by Clinton's New Yorkers, were to make a circuit of the enemy's left and attack it in flank and rear, thus cutting off its retreat.

With considerable difficulty Poor's brigade mounted a steep hill covered by thick underbrush. He was opposed by "a loose scattering fire" from the

Indians on that side; but a bayonet charge forced them back, and he gained the top just as the artillery began its bombardment of the works. At this the enemy abandoned the breastwork and attacked the right of Poor's line, Colonel John Reid's 2nd New Hampshire, swarming about it in a half-circle of superior numbers. The 3rd New Hampshires under Colonel Henry Dearborn, who had gone ahead, turned at command and moved to the aid of the endangered regiment. Two regiments of Clinton's New Yorkers also came up from the support. There was a short but sharp conflict, the British regulars, Brant's Indians, and Butler's Greens fighting bravely. Meanwhile, Colonel Hand's Pennsylvanians and Colonel Ogden's New Jerseymen had worked their way along the river to the enemy's right. Thus menaced on all sides, Butler and Brant gave up the fight. The "retreat halloo" was sounded, and the defenders fled around Poor's right, "leaving their dead behind (amounting to eleven or twelve) which were scalped immediately." The light troops pursued them for a mile or two and took prisoners—one white man and one Negro, hardly important enough to serve as hostages. In this fight the Americans lost 3 killed and 39 wounded.[22]

Here was added to the chronicles of the expedition a pleasing touch. The bodies of two dead Indians were found after the battle and "skinned . . . from their hips down for boot legs; one pair for the Major the other for myself," says Lieutenant William Barton of the 1st New Jersey in his journal.[23]

The American army remained on the ground, sending the wounded and the heavier guns back to Tioga and destroying a near-by village and "150 acres of the best corn that Ever I saw (some of the stalks grew 16 feet high) besides great quantities of Beans, Potatoes, Pumpkins, Cucumbers, Squashes & Watermellons," says Lieutenant Beatty. Newtown was the next to go. "Good buildings of English construction" were burned there.[24] On the 31st Catherine's Town, thirty houses, another village of eight, and a third of twenty, with their cornfields and orchards, were destroyed.[25] Appletown was burned on the 4th of September, and Kindaia's thirty "neatly built & finished" houses made a fine bonfire on the 5th, while the army was employed in "destroying corn & fruit" trees, of which there was a great abundance. "Many of the trees appeared to be of great age." Two days later, one detachment burned the chief town of the Senecas, Kanadaseagea, eighty houses, and destroyed "a great number of fruit trees"; another put an end to Schoyere. Canandaigua, "a very pretty town," "very Compact & Neatly built" with thirty houses "much better built than any I have seen before" went up in flames.[26] Honeoye and Kanagha followed.

On the 13th Lieutenant Thomas Boyd of Morgan's rifles met with disaster. Sent out with a small party to reconnoiter Genesee, he was ambushed; 22 of his men were killed, and he was captured along with Sergeant Parker. Taken to Little Beard's town, they were subjected to the most ingeniously hideous tortures before being decapitated.

Genesee, an ancient town of 128 houses, "mostly very large and elegant," says Sullivan, was the next victim. The surrounding fields of corn and "every kind of vegetable that can be conceived" engaged the whole army in their destruction. The corn was cut and stuffed into the houses before they were set on fire.[27]

The expedition went no farther; but on the way back it mopped up what it had overlooked before. The towns around Cayuga Lake, including about a hundred "exceedingly large and well built" houses with two hundred acres of "excellent corn, [and] a number of orchards, one of which had in it 1500 fruit trees," were destroyed.[28] A squaw "so old as not to be able to be brought off" and an Indian boy "decrepid to such a degree that he could not walk" were captured. One house was left standing for them to stay in, but some practical jokers, soldiers of the army, fastened the door on the out-side and set the house afire. The old squaw and the crippled boy were burned to death in it.[29]

By September 30 the expedition was at Wyoming, and by October 15 at Easton. Sullivan summed up his achievements in a letter from Wyoming to John Jay, President of the Congress: "The number of Towns destroyed amounts to 40, besides scattering houses. The quantity of Corn destroyed . . . must amount to 160,000 bushels, with a vast quantity of vegetables of every kind. . . . Except one Town . . . about 80 miles from Genesee, there is not a single Town left in the Country of the five nations." He was congratulated by Washington on the success of his expedition, and the Congress voted its thanks to him.[30]

Although he had brought back no hostages, he had achieved "the total destruction and devastation" of the Indian towns. And yet there have been hostile criticisms of the whole affair. One historian calls it the "ruthless destruction of the greatest advance in civilization that the red men in this country have ever attained." Another declares: "A greater degree of bar-barity than Pontiac or Brant ever exercised—putting even Wyoming to the blush—was seen in the savage mutilation of the bodies of the fallen enemy, by scalping them and by flaying them for boot-tops; in the destruction with-out mercy of the growing crops and orchards which surrounded the dwell-ings; in the burning of cabins, [one] with the helpless and decrepit who had sought refuge therein." [31] The destruction of the growing crops and espe-cially the orchards, which was never before practiced by the Indians, has been especially disapproved. Against such destruction it is said that General Hand and Colonel Dearborn protested without avail.[32]

Entirely apart from such excesses, the expedition may be criticized on the ground that it failed to accomplish its real purpose, the protection of the border settlements from further ravages. The Indian and Tory forces were not destroyed, nor even crippled. True, they were driven from their towns, but only to be thrown back upon the British at Niagara for shelter and food during the terrible winter of 1779–1780 and thus welded more firmly than ever to the King's cause. From Niagara they returned, exasperated and revengeful to ravage the borders with even greater malignity than before. The enterprise may seem as futile as it was barbarous. Yet the Iroquois must have been daunted by the sight of the Americans marching through their country. A heavy blow had been dealt to their military prestige, which was fast diminishing.

In July, Washington had authorized a similar expedition, on a smaller scale, against the Mingos, Munsees, and Senecas in the Allegheny River valley.[33] On August 11 the 8th Pennsylvania Continentals under Colonel Daniel Brodhead accompanied by a number of militia and volunteers, in all about 600 men, set out up the river. On the 15th a party of 30 to 40 Indians coming down in canoes, after a sharp brush, were defeated with a loss of five dead on the ground and others carried away. The Indian town of Cannawago was found deserted and was destroyed, as were several others. In all, several hundred houses were burned and five hundred acres of corn were destroyed, without opposition and without loss, in a journey of four hundred miles, going and returning.[41] Brodhead also received the thanks of the Congress and the commendation of the commander in chief.[34] This expedition is subject to the same comment as Sullivan's.

C H A P T E R 5 6

The Indians Strike Back

Washington wrote to Lafayette on October 20, 1779, that he was well pleased with "the entire destruction of the Country of the Six Nations" and was convinced that the Indians were exceedingly "disconcerted" and "humbled." [1] But the Iroquois were not yet utterly helpless. In the following year the savages, aided by their British and Tory allies, struck back with a vigor increased and a ferocity intensified by their exasperation.

The prelude to these new operations was on a minor scale. In April, Brant led a small force of Indians and Tories against the little village of Harpersfield, which he surprised and destroyed, killing a few people and taking 19 prisoners. He intended to follow this by an attack on one of the Schoharie forts, but, being falsely informed that the fort had been reinforced by 300 Continental troops, he abandoned that enterprise and marched back to Fort Niagara. Other sporadic attacks, particularly upon the Dutch settlements along the base of the Catskill Mountains and farther north, with the usual tale of houses burned, people killed and captured, indicated that the borderers were not immune from further depredations; but all these were trifling compared with the foray which Sir John Johnson organized.

In May, 1780, Johnson sailed up Lake Champlain to Crown Point at the head of 400 of his Royal Greens and Butler's Rangers and 200 Indians. Thence he marched to the Sacandaga River and came entirely undiscovered in the night of May 21 to the Johnstown settlements, where he divided his force. Half of it swept westward up the Mohawk to the Dutch village of Caughnawaga, burning on the way "the houses and barns of the inhabitants, putting to death every male capable of bearing arms," [2] and finally laying the village in ashes.

With the remaining half, Sir John occupied Johnstown and then marched to the mouth of the Cayadutta, burning houses and killing or capturing the inhabitants, and to a junction with the other part of his force at Caughnawaga. He continued up the Mohawk valley for several miles, burning every house not owned by a Tory, slaughtering the cattle and sheep, and carrying off the horses. A number of persons were killed, and many prisoners were taken. Back at Johnstown, the invaders applied the torch to all its houses before they started on their return march.

Governor Clinton assembled the available militia and attempted to intercept Johnson at Ticonderoga; but Johnson got safely to his boats at Crown Point and so to St. Johns, with 40 prisoners. After that there was a lull in the hostilities until August, when Canajoharie felt the blows of the revengeful Indians and Tories.

The Canajoharie settlements were defended by Fort Plain, Fort Clyde, and Fort Plank. Plain, the most important, at the point where Oquaga Creek flows into the Mohawk, was an irregular quadrangle of earth and logs surrounding a three-story blockhouse of heavy hewn timbers. The upper stories were pierced for musketry, the lower one for three or four cannon. Smaller blockhouses strengthened the four bastions at the corners of the fort. Clyde was about two miles southwest of Plain; and Plank, an equal distance northwest.[3] There were lesser fortifications near these, simple stockades surrounding houses.

At the head of about 500 Indians and Tories, Brant approached Fort Plain on August 2. Disregarding the fort, into which most of the neighboring settlers had fled for protection, he burned the neighboring church, fifty-three dwelling houses, as many barns, and a gristmill. Sixteen persons were slain and fifty or sixty made captive. Three hundred cattle and horses were killed or driven away. Taking a leaf from Sullivan's book, the invaders burned the ripe grainfields. Thus, in one day, this fair settlement was reduced to ashes and left a desolation.

The Schoharie valley was next. Its main points of defense were Upper Fort, Middle, and Lower—stockades of logs and earth drawn around strong stone houses, the Lower Fort also enclosing a stone church.

In September, Sir John Johnson collected at Lachine, near Montreal, three companies of his Greens, a company of British regulars, a company of Hessian jägers, and 200 of Butler's Rangers, with two mortars and a "grasshopper." He ascended the St. Lawrence to Lake Ontario and Oswego and marched thence across country to Unadilla on the Susquehanna, where he was joined by Brant and a famous Seneca chief, Cornplanter, with a large body of Indians. The united forces have been variously estimated at 800 to 1,500 men. The plan of Johnson and Brant was to march along the east branch of the Susquehanna, thence to the head of Schoharie valley and sweep it from end to end clear down to Schenectady. They passed the Upper Fort in the night of October 15 without being observed and approached the Middle Fort early in the morning, setting fire to the intervening houses as they went along.

The Middle Fort was held by 150 state troops, "three months' men," and about 50 militia—all under command of Major Melanchthon Woolsey of the state troops. He sent out 40 men to reconnoiter; they were driven back by Johnson's advance guard. The invaders then completely invested the fort and sent a flag with a demand for surrender.

In the garrison was Tim Murphy, who had shot General Simon Fraser at Bemis Heights, as has been told. Murphy was a frontiersman and Indian fighter of note, and his remarkable double-barreled rifle had accounted for 40 of his pet foes. He knew that the Indians had kept a score against him and was sure that, no matter what promises of protection might be given the garrison upon its surrender, he would be marked by the Indians for vengeance. Moreover, he had no confidence in the steadfastness of Major Woolsey, who seems to have been generally regarded as a bit of a coward. He therefore decided to prevent negotiations for a surrender.

As the flag approached the fort, Murphy took a shot at it. He did not hit its bearer, who immediately retired to the enemy's lines. Sir John then opened on the fort with artillery and musketry, to little effect. In the middle of the morning another flag appeared, and Murphy prepared to receive it as before. Woolsey objected, drawing his sword and threatening to run him through if he attempted to fire. But the militia rallied about the rifleman, supporting his statement that Woolsey was a coward and intended to surrender. Murphy took another shot at the flag-bearer, fortunately without hitting him; the flag retreated, and the firing on the fort was resumed. The farce of the flag was enacted a third time, Murphy playing the same part as before.

Woolsey then ordered a white flag to be raised, but Murphy, backed by Captain Reghtmeyer of the militia, threatened to shoot anyone who tried to obey the order. Sir John then decided to raise the siege from a fort which he could not batter down. He drew off his forces and marched down the valley.

The Lower Fort was attacked in a feeble way, without success, and again the invaders went on down the valley, burning all the patriots' houses, barns, and standing crops and killing or carrying off all the domestic animals.

No buildings were left standing except those known to belong to Tories. On these the patriots later visited their vengeance by burning them.

Johnson then called at Caughnawaga again and destroyed the houses erected since his last visit. Marching up the Mohawk valley, he continued his ravages with torch and tomahawk on both sides of the river; everything combustible was burned.

Fort Paris, in the village of Stone Arabia, was held by Colonel John Brown, who will be remembered for his activities in connection with the capture of Saratoga by Ethan Allen and Benedict Arnold and in the Quebec campaign. He had only 130 men, all militia. General Robert Van Rensselaer, who had mustered a force of militia and marched to Caughnawaga, ordered Brown to sally out and attack the enemy, promising to fall upon their rear. Brown, a good soldier, obeyed, and marched his 130 men against Johnson's force, perhaps ten times as many. They met and engaged the enemy near an old ruined earthwork, Fort Keyser; but Van Rensselaer failed to come up. Outnumbered perhaps ten to one, Brown's men fought until a third of them, including the intrepid leader, had been killed. Not until then did the rest abandon the fight.

Stone Arabia was destroyed. After that Johnson sent out small bands to pillage and burn all the country for miles around. Having reassembled his men in the evening of October 19, he marched to Klock's Field on the north side of the Mohawk. Van Rensselaer with 1,500 men, including a number of Oneidas, followed him along the south side. While delayed in a search for a ford, Van Rensselaer received and accepted an invitation to dine with Governor Clinton at Fort Plain, some distance away. His departure at this critical moment angered his officers, the Oneida chief boldly denouncing him as a coward and a Tory. While he was gone, the baggage wagons were driven into the river in a line to serve as a sort of bridge, by the help of which the troops crossed in single file.

Johnson accepted the challenge and drew up his men in battle formation behind a hastily contrived breastwork. The British regulars, the Greens, and the Rangers held this, while Brant's Indians, supported by the Hessian jägers, were posted on the left in a concealing growth of shrub oaks. Van Rensselaer, on his return from the dinner, deployed his force in line, Colonel DuBois commanding the right, Colonel Cuyler the left, and Colonel Morgan Lewis the advance. Captain Robert McKean and his Oneidas were in the right wing. Thus arrayed, the whole line advanced upon the enemy. DuBois's wing charged upon Brant's Indians with such impetuosity that they broke and fled. Sir John is said to have left with them. The rest of Johnson's troops, however, stood fast, and there was a spirited encounter. The flight of the

Indians encouraged the attackers and greatly weakened Johnson's force. The Americans were eager to pursue the fugitives and to assault the feeble breastwork, but Van Rensselaer, with a decisive victory in sight, failed to push his advantage. He withdrew his troops three miles to a place suitable for a bivouac.

In the morning the Oneida chief Louis with his warriors and Captain McKean with his volunteers broke away from Van Rensselaer's command and started after Johnson's retreating men. Van Rensselaer and his main force followed as far as German Flats. Van Rensselaer then ordered McKean and Louis to push ahead, promising support. The advance party, the next day, came upon Johnson's camp-ground and found his fires still burning; but Louis, distrusting the general, refused to go any farther until assured of the promised support. He was proved to be right by the arrival of a messenger announcing that Van Rensselaer had given over the pursuit and was already on his return march. It seems to be certain that only his irresolution stood in the way of a complete victory, either in the battle or on the retreat. Johnson escaped to Canada by way of Oswego.

There was comparative peace in the valley for some two months. In January, 1781, Brant again took the warpath. The Oneida villages had been destroyed in 1780 by an expedition sent down from Canada by Sir Frederick Haldimand as a punishment for their adhesion to the American cause. Their inhabitants had been forced to flee to the white settlements near Schnectady for shelter and food. Even the slender barrier they had interposed between the marauders and the settlers in the valley was gone. Brant's Indians now dared openly to visit German Flats in small parties and carry on their work of destruction. In March fifteen men from Colonel Philip Van Cortlandt's 2nd New York Continentals convoying provisions for Fort Stanwix were cut off and captured. In April a similar party was taken.

To add to the terrors of the population, continually menaced by Indians and Tories, Fort Stanwix, the key post in the valley, was abandoned in May. It had been partly damaged by floods. Then it caught fire and was destroyed. When the garrison removed to Fort Dayton and Fort Plain the valley was struck by the deepest gloom. Its few remaining "forts" were feebly garrisoned and ill supplied with provisions and ammunition. The despondency was so great that Schuyler and General Clinton were apprehensive that in case of another invasion there would be wholesale defections among the troops, which were unable to defend the homes of the inhabitants of the border, and which seemed hopeless of final success.

In his trouble General Clinton appealed to Colonel Marinus Willett, who had so signally distinguished himself in the siege of Stanwix and upon other occasions and was then in command of the 5th New York Continental regiment, soliciting him to take command of the militia and state troops to be raised for the summer campaign. Willett accepted, and confidence in him revived the spirits of the people. He established headquarters at Fort Rensselaer (Canajoharie) and collected the remains of the companies engaged in the previous year's campaign—no more than 380 men. These were divided among German Flats, Schoharie, and other settlements. They soon found work to do.

On June 30, 1781, several hundred Indians and a few Tories led by Doxstader, a Tory, attacked Currytown, on the river below Canajoharie, killed several of its people, took others captive, and looted and burned the houses. Seeing the smoke, Willett at Fort Plain gathered 150 men and set out in the night against the invaders. Doxstader's force had taken a strong position for his camp. At six in the morning Willett approached it. He sent Lieutenant Jacob Sammons with ten men to give the enemy one fire and then retreat. The Indians were thus drawn from their position. Leaping forward, they pursued Sammons until they came upon the main force, which they attacked furiously. But a heavy fire drove them back. Willett called for bayonets and soon they were in full flight, leaving 40 dead on the field. The patriots' loss was 5 killed and 9 wounded or missing.

Willet was successful in giving some measure of protection to the settlers in the lower part of the valley; but the upper valley was still harassed. Shell's Bush, five miles north of Herkimer village, was attacked in August by a Scottish refugee from Johnstown, Donald McDonald, with 60 Indians and Tories. Shell's house was stockaded, and after most of the inhabitants of the settlement had fled to Fort Dayton he undertook, with two or three of his sons, to defend it. The attackers tried to fire it and then to force its door; but Shell and his boys, supplied with loaded muskets by Mrs. Shell, held them off for several hours, killing 11 and wounding 6. They finally gave up and withdrew.

A similar incursion that summer by Captain Caldwell of Butler's Rangers and 400 Indians and Tories from Niagara was repelled by Colonel Albert Pawling with a force of state troops and militia, with considerable enemy losses.

In October there was an invasion in force. Four companies of the Royal Greens, Butler's Rangers commanded by Colonel John's son Walter, and 200 Indians—in all, 1,000 men, under command of Major Ross—marched from Oswego. From the lower end of Oneida Lake they struck through the forest and, on October 24, came upon the village of Warrensbush, where

Schoharie Kill emptied into the Mohawk. Their coming was unobserved; they struck it "as suddenly as though they had sprung from the earth," [4] and committed the usual outrages, killing people, destroying property and burning houses. Willett was twenty miles away at his headquarters when he got the news. He marched all night with 400 men and found Ross's force at Johnstown, where great damage had been done. He sent Colonel Aaron Rowley with a body of state troops and militia to attack Ross on the flank and in the rear, and led his main body against the enemy's front, driving them back from an open field into the woods. There was a stubborn fight for some time, Willett's single fieldpiece being taken and retaken. In spite of the discrepancy in numbers, Willett seemed to be in a fair way to overcome Ross when his militia were seized with an unaccountable panic and the whole right wing turned and fled. Ross might then have had a complete victory; but as his men were confused in an effort to take prisoners and scalps, Rowley fell upon them in the rear and pressed the attack with vigor. Willett, with what men he could collect, kept up the fight in front, and the broken and tangled battle lasted until dark. The enemy then retreated precipitately to a height six miles distant. The loss was 40 killed on each side; but Willett's men took 50 prisoners.

In the morning Willett pushed the pursuit to Stone Arabia, whence he sent a detachment to destroy Ross's boats on Oneida Lake. This effort failed, but at German Flats he learned that the enemy had taken a northerly course. With 400 of his best men and 60 Oneidas who had joined him, he marched all day in a driving snowstorm and encamped in a wood in the Royal Grant. Jacob Sammons, sent forward with some Indians to reconnoiter, found the enemy's camp; but a night attack was deemed inadvisable.

The next day Willett overtook his quarry at Jerseyfield on Canada Creek, and the two forces engaged in a fight across the creek. After Walter Butler was shot down by an Oneida, the Indians broke and fled, followed by the rest of Ross's men. Willett kept after them until they were entirely routed and dispersed in the forest. He then led his troops in triumph back to Fort Dayton, having lost only one man in the pursuit and fight. The loss on the other side was never known. This expedition of Ross and Butler was the last invasion of the New York border during the war. Negotiations for peace were under way, and hostilities on the border ceased.

The War in the South

The Seat of War in the South

The war in the South may be considered under two heads: the campaigns in Virginia, and those in the Carolinas and the northern fringe of Georgia. Most of the earlier battles were fought in the more southern country and the later and final campaigns were conducted in Virginia, so that they may be taken up separately in that order. As the physical characteristics of the Carolinas' terrain and the racial characteristics of their inhabitants largely determined the military operations there, these may profitably be first considered.

The coastal region of the Carolinas extends, in general, eighty to one hundred miles inland—a level, sandy plain "without a hill and almost without a stone, but gradually rising, as you advance, to 190 feet above the level of the coast. Sixty miles of sandhills follow, with hollows between, like the waves of a stormy sea. . . . A fertile tract of highlands succeeds . . . beyond which . . . extends a region of hills and dales, well watered and well wooded." Back of all these rise the Blue Ridge Mountains, forming the western border of North Carolina and touching South Carolina on its northwestern corner.

The lower lands are in considerable part sandy pine barrens, monotonous and desolate, although healthy and valuable for their timber. Here and there in the barrens are treeless savannas, "vast natural lawns" of tall grasses affording pasture for cattle, sometimes surrounded by swamps. Along the rivers and at their mouths are swamps in which grow cypress, bay trees and loblolly pines. Interspersed in the low country and predominant in the higher back country are red earth, oak and hickory lands, fit for orchards, corn, small grains, tobacco, indigo, and other crops. The low lands have produced rice in abundance.

Most important in the two states are their river systems. Rising in the high hinterland, the principal rivers flow roughly parallel southeast to the sea, dividing the country into long, narrow districts. From north to south, important in this narrative because they were so influential over the military campaigns, the rivers begin with the Dan, which crosses into Virginia and empties into the Roanoke. South of that two small streams, Troublesome Creek and Reedy Fork, unite to form the Haw, which receives the Alamance and unites with the Deep River to form the Cape Fear River.

Southwest of that again is the Yadkin, which also changes its name about midway in its course to Pee Dee. This habit of name changing reaches its height in the next great river. It begins in the North Carolina mountains as the Catawba; below Camden, in South Carolina, it becomes the Wateree; after it receives the Congaree, which begins at the junction of the Broad and the Saluda, the Wateree becomes the Santee; and under that name it flows onward to the ocean.

South of the Wateree-Santee system are the little Edisto and the Combahee. Finally, there is the great Savannah River, the boundary between South Carolina and Georgia. All of which is highly confusing. The principal facts important to remember are that the river systems dividing the terrain into long, narrow districts were mostly bordered by swamps; that they were almost entirely unbridged and passable only at a few fords except by boats; that they were subject to sudden, high rises from unpredictable, torrential rains, which rendered crossing difficult, hazardous, or impossible; that they, therefore, largely controlled the movements of the contending armies and often determined the outcome of campaigns in that country.

In the two states there was only one considerable city, Charleston. This, one of the four principal American seaports, had fewer than 14,000 people, of whom more than a third were Negro slaves. Hillsboro and Salisbury, in North Carolina, had perhaps sixty to seventy houses each; Charlotte was but a village.[1]

The population of the Carolinas was most diverse in origin, race, and religious belief. The earliest settlers were English, coming largely after the restoration of the monarchy—Roundheads in flight from the new régime and Cavaliers seeking to mend broken fortunes. After the Revocation of the Edict of Nantes in 1685 French Huguenots flowed in. Dutchmen, dissatisfied with life in New Amsterdam after it became New York, Scotch-Irish, Scottish Highlanders, Catholic Irish, Swiss led by their compatriot John Peter Pury, foreign Protestants of various nations induced by bounties

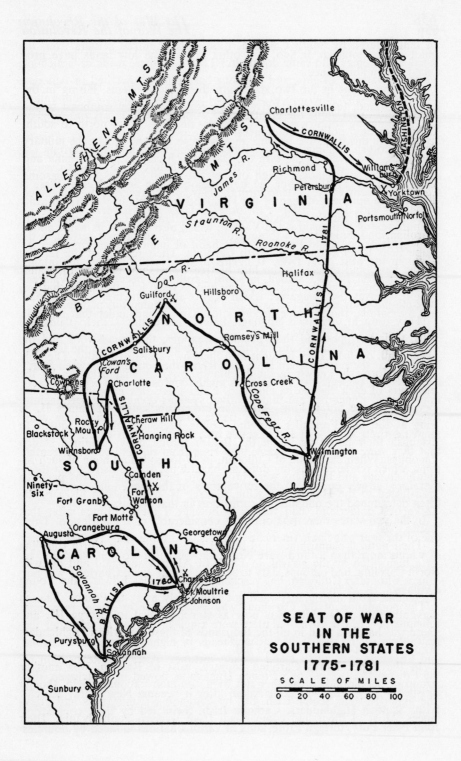

ALLEGHENY MTS
BLUE MTS
VIRGINIA
James R.
Charlottesville
CORNWALLIS
Richmond
Williamsburg
Petersburg
Yorktown X
Portsmouth Norfolk
Staunton R.
Roanoke R.
CORNWALLIS 1781
Halifax
Don R.
Guilford X
Hillsboro
NORTH CAROLINA
CORNWALLIS
Ramsey's Mill
Salisbury
Cowan's Ford
Cowpens
Charlotte
Cross Creek
Cape Fear R.
Rocky Mount
CORNWALLIS
Cheraw Hill X
Blackstock
Hanging Rock
Wilmington
Winnsboro
SOUTH
Camden
Fort Watson X
Ninety-six
Fort Granby
CAROLINA
Fort Motte
Orangeburg
Georgetown
Augusta
CAROLINA
1780
Charleston X
Savannah R.
BRITISH
Ft. Moultrie
Ft. Johnson
Purysburg X
Savannah
Sunbury

ATLANTIC

SEAT OF WAR
IN THE
SOUTHERN STATES
1775-1781

SCALE OF MILES
0 20 40 60 80 100

of land offered by South Carolina, thousands of mixed settlers from the northern colonies who came down after 1740—all these made up a mélange of races, national origins, and religions hardly to be matched in America. And the tendency of all was to segregate themselves in distinct communities, for the most part along the great rivers.² Among them, racial and religious differences bred political differences.

The Scottish Highlanders constituted an important and a disturbing element. Some of these settled in South Carolina before 1685; others came to Georgia in the 1730's. After the termination of the Seven Years' War, in 1763, large numbers of men of the Highland regiments in the British army were rewarded for their service by grants of land in Georgia and North Carolina, and emigrated to those provinces. The major part settled in the Cape Fear River country of North Carolina. Their reports of the fertility of the land, and especially the lure of free ownership, brought thousands of their people from the isles of Rasay and Skye to join them. By that immigration and by natural increase, they became a numerous people.

They brought their own language, habits, and customs, their plaids and kilts, their bagpipes and their peculiar weapons, the broadsword and the skean dhu, or dirk. They brought also their own spirit of loyalty. The only civic tie formerly known in the Highlands was personal devotion by the members of each clan to its chieftain. Later there was imposed upon that devotion to the Stuart king. After the forced abdication of James II, as long as the Old Pretender and the Young Pretender actively sought to establish their house again on the British throne, they remained stanch Jacobites. When the Battle of Culloden, in 1746, ended all hope of such reestablishment and the clans were broken up, their allegiance was perforce transferred to the Hanoverian King, George II, even though his son, the Duke of Cumberland, had ruthlessly butchered their kinsmen after that battle.

Their natural clannishness and solidarity was excited in North Carolina to a high pitch by the arrival, in 1774, of Allan Macdonald and his wife Flora, who, after Culloden, had rescued Prince Charles Edward, the Young Pretender, from his pursuers and got him safely away to France. She, so fervently then a Jacobite, was now as stanchly loyal to George III, and there was hardly a man in all the thousands of these American Highlanders who would not follow where she led.

In the upper North Carolina country, west of Raleigh, was another group of people linked together not by a common national origin, though the majority were Scotch-Irish, but by common circumstances and grievances. Most of them had come down from western Pennsylvania. Their contacts in trade and otherwise were with that province; they had few relationships with the Carolinians to the east and south, whom they grew to dislike and distrust. Their particular grievance was the impositions upon them of illegal fees and excessive taxes by dishonest court officials, sheriffs, and collectors of taxes appointed by the governor. This resulted in a group hatred of all the machinery of the law, which was displayed in many acts of violence by which they prevented the holding of courts in their district. They called themselves Regulators.

William Tryon, the royal governor, undertook to put down this inchoate rebellion. He gathered a force of 1,018 militia infantry and 30 light horse and marched against them, ravaging and looting their farms and homes. At the Alamance River, he found about 2,000 of them, only half armed and completely unorganized. On May 16, 1771, there was a battle. Though Tryon's force was completely equipped and provided with artillery, the Regulators held their ground for two hours before they were dispersed with a loss of 20 killed and a great many wounded, the attacking force having 9 killed and 61 wounded. On trial, 12 of the prisoners taken by Tryon were found guilty of treason; 6 were hanged.

Thousands left the now hated province, crossed the mountains and sought new homes in the valley of the upper Tennessee River, where they set up "a state, independent of the authority" of the British King. Most of these emigrants became patriots.

To 6,400 who remained, Tryon administered a British oath of allegiance; they swore "never to bear arms against the King, but to take up arms for him, if called upon." This oath, taken under circumstances amounting to duress, probably did not rest heavily upon their consciences. Because they hated the people of the low country who supported Tryon, and who became patriots, many of the regulators were Loyalists in the American struggle for independence, and could not be moved from their position even by the adjurations of their own Presbyterian ministers.

The Germans and the Scotch Irish, largely settled in the back country where there was no political organization, no representation in the legislature, no courts, had no use for stamps and did not drink tea; nor had they any interest in the abstract principles of the rights of men to be governed and taxed only by their own elected representatives. Quite comfortable under British rule, they were often passively, if not actively, disaffected to the American cause. In South Carolina the two groups made the area between the Broad and Saluda rivers, where they were especially strong, a territory inimical to the revolutionary movement.

Those are but samples of the wide and deep cleavages of sentiment toward the Revolution, splitting section from section, race from race, one family from another, and even dividing the individual persons in the same family. Nowhere else in the American colonies were the different opinions so often, so continuously, and so ferociously expressed in action.[3]

The bitterness of feeling between the two factions was carried to extremes beyond anything ever experienced in the northern colonies, except possibly in Tryon County, New York. In Massachusetts, for example, and pretty much in all the northern colonies, the revolutionists were in the majority or, at least, were so much better organized that the Loyalists were unable to make headway and were effectively oppressed and repressed. They wore tar and feathers, rode on rails; their farms and houses were ravaged, with occasional burning or complete wreckage of their buildings; and ordinarily in the North they were unable to retaliate. In the Carolinas there were barbarous outrages and bloody murders, shootings and hangings, and they were not all on one side. The Tories were strong enough and bitter enough to hold up their end in this kind of warfare, and the patriots responded in kind.

The country was mostly wild, and its inhabitants, outside the few towns, were largely lawless men, accustomed to asserting their own rights and avenging their own wrongs without intervention of law, and to carrying on their feuds with deadly weapons and ruthlessly. The encounters between Tories and patriots were therefore violent without restraint, to the extent of downright savagery on both sides.

Before the war began, the three most southern colonies had the usual militia regiments; but the militiamen were so divided in their political opinions that they could not be relied upon to act in favor of the cause of the Revolution. In August, 1775, the legislature of North Carolina responded to the request of the Continental Congress by authorizing the enlistment of two regiments; James Moore and Robert Howe were commissioned as colonels. In April, 1776, four additional regiments were raised, and Moore and Howe were appointed brigadier generals. Four more regiments were raised later. In 1775 South Carolina first raised two infantry battalions to serve principally in the eastern section of the state and one of Rangers, or mounted infantry, for the western part. In the next year a regiment of artillery and a regiment of riflemen were added. Georgia, though much smaller in population than either of the others, responded to the call of the Congress by raising three regiments in 1776. The colonels were Lachlan McIntosh, Samuel Elbert, and James Screven. In the next year a fourth was raised, Colonel John White commanding.

These regiments were supposed to conform in numbers to the Continental standard fixed by the Congress in November, 1775—eight companies of 91 men each, officers included; but their ranks were of course, not always full. For instance, in March, 1776, McIntosh's Georgia regiment numbered only 236 men and had only 100 present for duty.

But with such a background and with passions so rampant, organized partisan warfare flourished as nowhere else in the Thirteen States. Nowhere else did this war show its true character as a civil war so plainly. Among the leaders of partisan bands on the side of the revolutionaries, three were pre-eminent. Their names became household words throughout the country, and they typified the racial diversification of the people. Francis Marion was of French Huguenot stock, Thomas Sumter's parents were English-Welsh, Andrew Pickens was born of Irish parents. These three were of such outstanding importance in the southern conflict that they deserve individual notice.

Francis Marion was forty-three years old at the outbreak of the Revolution. He entered the war as a captain in one of South Carolina's first regiments in 1775, but became colonel of his own partisan regiment, a legion of combined horse and foot. Still later he had the title of brigadier general of state troops, but continued to act as a partisan leader. He was small of stature, healthy, hardy, and vigorous, brave in action but not foolhardy. His countenance, notably handsome in all its features, was impassive. He was sparing of words, abstemious in his habits, a strict disciplinarian, ever vigilant and active, fertile of stratagems and expedients that justified his nickname of Swamp Fox, quick in conception and equally swift in execution, unrelenting in the pursuit of his purposes, yet void of ruthlessness or cruelty to his victims. Henry Lee said of him that "calumny itself never charged him with violating the rights of person, property or humanity." [4] He was in all respects unexcelled as a partisan leader.

Thomas Sumter was forty-one years old in 1775, the year in which he entered the regular service as a captain in one of the South Carolina regiments, the Rangers. Later he commanded his own corps of irregulars as a brigadier general. He has been variously described: by one authority as "tall" and "vigorous"; by another as "a man of large frame, well fitted in strength of body to the toils of war"; and by a third as a small man possessed of great strength and agility.[5] In any case it is certain that he was dauntless and resolute. His bold, imperious countenance signified the arrogance of his decisions, the tenacity of his prejudices, his persistence in the execution of his own plans, and his unwillingness to subject himself to the control of another. Less scrupulous than Marion in the use of military force, "he was apt to make considerable allowances for a state of war. . . . He did not occupy his mind with a critical examination of the equity of his measures, but indiscriminately pressed forward to his end—the destruction of the enemy and the liberation of his country." [6] Not so cautious as Marion, not so much of a strategist, he was more inclined to take risks and trust to boldness of attack and the sheer fighting ability of his men. Lee likened him to "Ajax, relying more upon the fierceness of his courage than upon the results of unrelaxing vigilance and nicely adjusted combination." His fighting spirit and personal intrepidity gained for him the sobriquet of "Carolina Game Cock." [7]

Andrew Pickens was five years younger than Marion. Beginning as a captain he became a colonel and finally a brigadier general of South Carolina militia. His command, like those of the others, was always chiefly engaged in irregular operations. He was of medium height, lean, and healthy. His long, narrow face, with strongly marked features, was indicative of his strict religious character; he was an elder of the Presbyterian Church, devoted to its observances. It also indicated his rather dour habit of mind— it is said that he seldom smiled and never laughed. He was extremely guarded in conservation; "he would first take the words out of his mouth, between his fingers, and examine them before he uttered them." [8] His exploits were less spectacular than those of the other two, but his work as a partisan was not less vigorous, nor less successful.

The troops under command of these three varied from time to time. Now they were numbered in hundreds, horse and foot; now, but a dozen bold and hardy followers, white and black; sometimes they were all dragoons, fully armed and uniformed as such; sometimes they wore nondescript, even ragged, clothing and were haphazardly armed. At times they acted in concert with the Continental regulars, at others independently. They were always ready to attack a British outpost, cut off an enemy detachment, a foraging party or wagon train. If defeated, they scattered, took refuge in the swamps or forests, only to reassemble and carry on the fight as occasion served. It was such men as these that harassed the British and the Tories, encouraged the patriots, and kept the flame of resistance to tyranny alight in the South during the darkest days of the Revolution.

Among the Regulators and especially among the Highlanders, Josiah Martin, who had become governor of North Carolina after Tryon's transfer to New York, thought he saw excellent material for a force to resist the rebellious colonists and to assist an expedition under Sir Henry Clinton and Sir Peter Parker then on its way south. He obtained from the Earl of Dunmore a thousand stand of arms, which had been intended for Dunmore's proposed Indian and Ethiopian allies. On January 10, 1776, Martin issued from the sloop of war *Scorpion*, in which he had taken refuge, a flamboyant proclamation referring to the "most daring, horrid and unnatural Rebellion . . . exerted in the Province . . . by the base and insidious artifice of certain traitorous, wicked and designing men." To suppress it he proposed "to erect His Majesty's Royal standard," and did "hereby exhort, require and command . . . all His Majesty's faithful subjects . . . forthwith to repair" to it, pronouncing "all such Rebels as will not join the Royal banner, Rebels and Traitors, their lives and properties to be forfeited." [9]

On the same day he addressed a warrant to Allan Macdonald, Donald McDonald, and half a dozen McLeods, McLeans, Stewarts, Campbells, McArthurs, and sundry others not bearing Celtic names and living in the middle part of the province and in Rowan County, including former Regulators. It called on them to raise a force of Loyalists to resist the rebels and apprehend them. They were to assemble at Brunswick, opposite Wilmington, on February 15. Donald McDonald was named as brigadier general, Donald McLeod second in command. On February 5 McDonald called on all Loyalists to assemble immediately at Cross Creek (now Fayetteville) in the Scottish country, in accordance with Martin's command. All the nine Scots named in Martin's manifesto promptly appeared at Cross Creek, but only four of the 17 others. About 1,500, mostly Scots, also repaired to the standard. On the 18th they encamped four miles below Cross Creek.[10]

James Moore, colonel of the 1st North Carolina regiment, had brought his troops with five fieldpieces and a few militia to Rockfish, seven miles below Cross Creek, and entrenched his camp there. On the 18th he was joined by Colonel John Lillington, with 150 minutemen, Colonel Kennon with 200, and Colonel John Ashe with 100 volunteer rangers, making up a force of about 1,100.[11]

There ensued an odd exchange of communications. McDonald sent a flag with a copy of Martin's proclamation to Moore and called on the rebels "to join the royal standard." Moore replied with a copy of the patriots' Test Oath which, if signed by McDonald's men, would entitle them to join the Continental army. Neither accepted the other's invitation.[12]

Lieutenant Colonel Alexander Martin of the 2nd North Carolina and Lieutenant Colonel James Thackston of the 4th were on their way to join Moore. He sent them orders to possess Cross Creek, in the rear of McDonald's force. To Colonel Richard Caswell and his 800 Partisan Rangers, also on the march, he sent Lillington and Ashe as a reinforcement, with orders to hold Moore's Creek Bridge while he endeavored to circumvent the Scots and fall on their rear.[13]

There followed a series of small-scale movements complicated by the necessity of crossing several streams, the Loyalists trying to get through to the coast, the patriots trying to hold them back. On the 25th Lillington posted his men at the east end of Moore's Creek Bridge, for which the Tories were heading. The next day Caswell arrived on the west bank and threw up a small breastwork which he soon abandoned, joining the others on the east side. Lillington then took up the planks of the bridge, leaving only the log stringpieces. These two forces amounted to 1,000 men.

The Tories had decided not to avoid their opponents any longer, but to cut through them. Before dawn on February 27, they marched to the attack. General Donald McDonald had fallen ill, and Colonel Donald McLeod was in command. A picked company of 80 Scots under Captain John Campbell led the van, followed by about 1,400, and 300 riflemen brought up the rear. The Highlanders, many in plaids and kilts and others wearing homespun, were armed with rifles, broadswords, and dirks. The rifles were for the first fires, and were then to be thrown aside. The broadswords were to take the place of bayonets in the charge.

Coming to the bridge over the narrow but deep, stream, they discovered its almost impassable condition. Nevertheless, they attacked. Drums beat, bagpipes skirled, and Campbell shouted the battle-cry, "King George and the Broadswords!" Flinging away their useless rifles, grasping their swords, the vanguard started to cross. The stringers were round and slippery—the Scots afterwards said they had been greased—and many fell into the water. Others were struck down by the fire of the riflemen in the entrenchment. Campbell, McLeod, and some others got across, but the two officers and many of their followers were killed. The hot fire from the breastwork, bullets from the rifles and grape from the guns, stopped the oncoming columns. The rebels charged down the slope, some of them carrying the bridge planks, which they relaid, and started across. The Tories turned and fled in utter confusion. The next day Allan Mcdonald, some other officers, and 850 soldiers were captured. The chief officers were confined, the privates disarmed and dismissed. The wagon train, 1,500 rifles, 350 muskets, and 150 swords became the spoil of the victors.[14]

In this short fight no more than 30 of the Scots were killed or wounded and only 2 of the other side. It was a small affair, but important in that it prevented a considerable reenforcement from joining the 900 men General Clinton had landed in Brunswick County, and forced him to retire from the state. Also, it broke up the strongest united groups of Tories and forced him to at least temporary inactivity.

CHAPTER 5 8

Charleston

When Lord William Campbell, newly appointed royal governor of South Carolina, landed in Charleston on June 18, 1775, he was politely received, but not cordially welcomed. The militia were drawn up in formal order, but the customary *feu de joie* was lacking. When his commission was read to the populace there were no loyal cheers, nor any handclapping. "The citizens for the most part preserved a sullen silence . . . no private gentleman awaited his Excellency's landing, nor attended his parade along the streets." [1] His escort did not exceed fifteen persons, comprising his own officers and a few placemen. It was altogether a chilly affair.

His stay in Charleston lasted for three uncomfortable months, during which he had the dissatisfaction of observing continuous preparations for armed resistance to the government, the enlistment of new provincial troops, the arming of a provincial sloop, and its capture of a vessel with a cargo of gunpowder. A crisis was reached when the Council of Safety effected the seizure of Fort Johnson, on an island at the mouth of the harbor, and even discussed the capture of the governor himself. He thereupon, on September 15, took refuge on the sloop of war *Tamar*, and never again set foot on Carolina soil.

Josiah Martin, who underwent a similar mortification in North Carolina, culminating in a similar escape to the *Scorpion,* wrote from the gubernatorial mansion to the British ministry: "The people of South Carolina forget entirely their own weakness and are blustering treason; while Charleston, that is the head and heart of their boasted province, might be destroyed by a single frigate. In charity to them and in duty to my king and country,

665

I give it as my sincere opinion that the rod of correction cannot be spared." [2]
A little later Lord William made a similar suggestion. Now, aboard his ship
of refuge, he wrote: "Let it not be entirely forgot that the king has dominions
in this part of America. What defence can they make? Three regiments, a
proper detachment of artillery, with a couple of good frigates, some small
craft, and a bombketch, would do the whole business here." [3]

That suggestion was unnecessary, for the King himself showed before its
arrival that he had not forgot the southern provinces, and, "in charity to
them," was preparing the appropriate "rod of correction."

On January 8, 1776, Washington in Cambridge had "undoubted Intelligence of the fitting out of a Fleet at Boston and of the Imbarkation of
Troops from thence, which from the Season of the year and other Circumstances, must be destined for a Southern Expedition," very probably for
New York, though "some say Virginia but all in conjecture." [4] He, therefore, directed Major General Charles Lee—whom he esteemed to be "the
first Officer in Military knowledge and experience we have in the whole
Army" [5]—to repair to New York and "put that City into the best Posture
of Defence, which the Season and Circumstances will admit of" and disarm
such of the inhabitants of New York and Long Island as were "not only
Inemical to the Rights and Liberties of America" but also disposed to aid
"in the reduction of that Colony to Ministerial Tyranny." [6]

Charles Lee has already bulked large in our narratives. He was born in
England, probably in 1731, of a family in good social standing, his father
an officer in the army, his mother the daughter of a baronet. He was an
ensign at the age of sixteen, a captain at twenty-four, a major at thirty. He
was brevetted lieutenant colonel in 1772. He served with credit in America
in the French and Indian War under Abercromby and Amherst. In the same
conflict in Europe, the Seven Years' War, he performed a brilliant feat of
arms on October 5, 1762, when he led a night attack on a Spanish post in
Portugal, crossing the Tagus River and carrying his objective at the point
of the bayonet, with the assistance of a charge of dragoons. He was the
recipient of testimonials of bravery and good conduct from his commander
in chief, the Count de la Lippe, and from the King of Portugal.

At the close of that war he retired from the army on half-pay. Seeking
service elsewhere, he was well received by Frederick the Great and became
aide-de-camp to Stanislaus, King of Poland, in whose army he attained the
rank of major general. With the Russian army he fought the Turks in 1769.
For several years he led a restless life, wandering about Europe and becoming more and more cynical and irascible. His liberal predilections, including

an unconcealed hatred of King George III and his friends, played a part in his failure to secure advancement in the British army; and this added to the violence of his criticism of the King.

In 1773 Lee returned to America, visited various parts of the country, and vented his spleen against the ministry, taking the part of the colonists in the political agitations then prevalent. His clever wit, his caustic tongue, and his pungent oral and written attacks upon the British government gained him much favor among the American politicians. But, more especially, his military reputation was highly regarded. Military commanders of wide experience were scarce among the American opponents of the British government; indeed, there was none other than he. When the Congress on June 17 1775, appointed major generals for the army around Boston, it could not overlook the claims of Artemas Ward, in full command there until the arrival of Washington as commander in chief, and it made him first major general; then quite naturally it named Charles Lee as the second. By the resignation of Ward less than a year later, Lee obtained command next under Washington.

In person Lee was above middle height and very thin. A well known caricature of him, which depicts him in the extremest tenuity possible in a human being, is said to be the best likeness available. His countenance was not prepossessing. He had an enormous aquiline nose, a mouth whose drawn-down corners indicated a satirical, cynical, sarcastic disposition. His manner of speaking was positive and dogmatic. In the character of an experienced professional soldier amid the amateur Continental officers, he strutted unchallenged as the one general who knew what it was all about. His arrogance and pedantry in the constant use of technical military terms, of which his associates did not even know the meaning, put them all to the blush. He was careless, even slovenly, in his dress. It may be said that he was egotistic, vain, petulant, captious, ill mannered, profane, violently changeable in his opinions, excitable almost to the verge of madness, and ambitious. At this time and for long after, his adherence to the Cause was almost universally thought to be "a prodigious acquisition." [7]

Sir Henry Clinton had in fact sailed from Boston on January 20 in the 20-gun frigate *Mercury* accompanied by a transport carrying two companies of light infantry and "a few Highlanders." [8] When Lee reached New York on February 4, he found that this enemy force had come into the harbor less than two hours before, and had thrown the town "into such a convulsion as it never knew before." [9] The alarm and confusion were "truly distressing." "It is imbossable to Describ the Convusen that this City was in . . . pepel moving as fas as posseble . . . as if it was the Last Day," wrote Garish Harsin to a friend. Rev. Mr. Shewkirk noted in his diary: "There was nothing but Comotion & Confusion. Trade & publick business was at a stand. . . . A Panic & Fear seized the People." Wagons were hurriedly sought to evacuate the women and children. But Clinton assured the mayor that he did not intend to land a single soldier, that he was there merely to have a talk with Governor William Tryon, who had formerly been governor of North Carolina. He sailed on the 11th, taking with him Governors Campbell and Martin, who had in the meantime come north from their respective posts. The alarm and confusion subsided somewhat.[10]

Having now for the first time in the War of Independence a separate command, Lee entered upon his novel duties with characteristic gusto. On his way through Connecticut he had persuaded Governor Trumbull to allot to him two regiments of that province's troops, 1,200 men; and he brought them with him, much to the alarm of the would-be peaceful inhabitants of New York. They feared that such an incursion of armed men portended an attack on the British vessels then in the harbor that would provoke a general conflict, for which New York was unprepared in ammunition and defensive fortifications. Its Council of Safety, by letter to Lee then on his way, protested against the proposed intrusion.[11]

Lee assured the committee that he had no intention of attacking the British. "If the ships-of-war are quiet, I shall be quiet." He promised to leave the main body of his troops "on the western frontiers of Connecticut" and to bring into New York "a force just strong enough to secure it against any designs of the enemy" until the Continental Congress should "take measures for its permanent security." [12]

This matter having been amicably adjusted, Lee made his entrance into the town on the 4th of February, as has been stated. Acting in harmony with the committee, he planned and began to put into execution an elaborate series of defensive works on Long Island as well as Manhattan. He made a full and really excellent report to the Congress on fortifying the town and its environs, in which he took into account the difficulty, if not the actual impossibility, of permanently holding a post "almost environ'd by navigable waters . . . against a powerful sea armament" and promised no more than making it "a most advantageous field of Battle." [13] If the Congress had apprehended the full meaning of that report, and had not tried so soon after to do the impossible, one of the great disasters of the war would have been averted.

But Lee was not to complete the work thus begun. The Congress, after directing him on February 17 to repair to Canada and relieve Schuyler of his command, changed its mind and ordered him to take command of the newly erected Southern Department, comprising Virginia, the Carolinas, and Georgia.[14] His selection to take on the defense of the southern colonies, now seen to be menaced by Clinton, was generally approved; but he predicted the direst consequences for New York unless the Congress or Washington acted decisively: "The instant I leave it," he wrote to Washington, "I conclude the Provincial Congress and the inhabitants will relapse into their former hystericks; the men-of-war, and Mr. Tryon, will return to their old stations at the wharves, and the first regiments who arrive from England will take quiet possession of the town and Long-Island." [15]

On March 7, Lee left New York for Charleston. En route he stopped in the governor's palace at Williamsburg, Virginia, where he learned that Clinton had put in at Norfolk and was holding conferences with Dunmore, the evicted governor. Soon he learned also that Clinton's little force was not the "rod of correction" which the King had directed to be prepared for his recalcitrant subjects in the southern provinces, that it was to be a much bigger stick indeed.

The revelation came through an intercepted letter.

Captain James Barron, commanding a vessel fitted out at Hampton to prey upon enemy commerce in the Chesapeake, found in the mails aboard a seized vessel a letter dated December 23, 1775, from Lord George Germain to Governor Robert Eden of Maryland. It appeared that His Majesty, "being determined, in concurrence with Parliament, to pursue the most vigorous measures for reducing his rebellious subjects in North America to obedience," had organized "an armament, consisting of seven regiments and a fleet of frigates and small ships," which was at that time "in readiness to proceed to the Southern Colonies . . . in the first place to North Carolina, and from thence either to South Carolina or Virginia as circumstances . . . shall permit." [16]

As a result of this discovery "the curtain" was, in the words of Lee, "in a great measure, drawn up." Yet not altogether, for, while the destination of the hostile fleet was North Carolina and, without doubt, that colony's principal harbor, the mouth of the Cape Fear River, the point of actual attack was not disclosed. It might be in any one of the three southern provinces. This uncertainty held him momentarily at Williamsburg, since Virginia might be the objective.[17]

Although the intercepted letter said that the expedition was "in readiness to proceed," it did not actually proceed for almost two months. On February 13, 1776, an impressive armada put out from Cork under command of

Admiral Sir Peter Parker. It comprised the 50-gun flagship *Bristol*, the 28-gun frigates *Active*, *Actaeon*, *Solebay*, and *Syren*, the frigate *Sphynx* carrying 20 guns, the *Friendship* with 22, the sloop *Ranger* with 8, the schooner *St. Lawrence* with 6, and the bomb ketch *Thunder* mounting 6 guns and 2 mortars.[18] It convoyed a fleet of more than thirty transports carrying about 2,500 troops—the 15th, 28th, 33rd, 37th, 54th, and 57th regiments and seven companies of the 46th—besides the usual complement of marines and seamen. General Lord Cornwallis commanded the military. Five days out from Cork, the fleet met violent adverse gales and was scattered. Some of the vessels were driven back to Cork, others found refuge at Plymouth and Portsmouth. The first vessels arrived at Cape Fear on April 18, and it was not until May 3 that the whole fleet, minus a few of the smaller vessels, reassembled there.[19]

Then began a discussion as to the point of attack. The original purpose seems to have been to invade North Carolina, set up the King's standard at Cross Creek, invite the Loyalists of that region to repair to it, and reestablish the royal government there. But the decisive defeat of the North Carolina Tories at Moore's Creek Bridge on February 27 had so diminished their ardor that no reliance could be placed on them.[20] Governor Dunmore had pleaded with Clinton to recover Virginia for him, and Clinton was so inclined. But Governor Campbell was equally insistent that South Carolina deserved the honor. Charleston was the most important port south of Philadelphia. Its commerce was of great aid to the American cause in the South. Its defensive works were unfinished. These arguments prevailed, and on May 30 the fleet again put to sea.[21]

Meanwhile, Lee had left Williamsburg for Wilmington, North Carolina. From that town he wrote on June 1 that the fleet had sailed—whether northward or southward, he could not tell. The people in Wilmington were "all of the opinion that Charlestown was their object; for my own part I do not see on what they ground their opinion." He would set out for that town on the morrow, "but at the same time [I] confess I know not whether I shall go to or from the enemy." [22] On his arrival at Charleston early in June, he learned that he had come in the right direction. The fleet dropped anchor almost simultaneously a short distance off Charleston bar. Lee's "presence gave us great spirits," says Colonel William Moultrie in his memoirs, "as he was known to be an able, brave, and experienced officer, though hasty and rough in his manners, which the officers could not reconcile themselves to at first: it was thought by many that his coming among us was equal to a reinforcement of 1000 men, and I believe it was." [23]

Low, sandy islands fringe the South Carolina coast, separated from the mainland and from each other by narrow inlets or creeks lined with swamps which are interlaced with other small creeks. In 1776 they were largely covered with palmetto trees, thickets of myrtle and other low shrubs, interspersed with occasional live oaks. Between James Island on the south and Sullivan's on the north was the entrance to Charleston harbor, the city being about six miles within the entrance. On James Island was Fort Johnson, which had been seized by the troops of the province in September and held against the royal governor ever since. It mounted twenty guns, 18- and 25-pounders. On the same island, nearer the town, was a battery of twelve heavy guns.

Sullivan's Island was about four miles long; and at high tide, when the wide swamps towards the mainland were under water, the fast ground was less than a mile wide. North of it lay Long Island, and between them was a narrow inlet called the Breach. Long Island was not fortified; but a small battery had been set up at Haddrell's Point, on the mainland below the south end of Sullivan's Island.

There were other fortifications about the town—batteries, flèches, and "bastions," distributed along and behind the waterfront—which had no part in the battle and hence need not be particularly described. In the town stores and warehouses along the wharves were torn down to clear the way for the fire from some of the earthworks in their rear.

Near the southern end of Sullivan's Island, where it swung around parallel with the curving shore of the mainland, was the principal fortification guarding the entrance to the harbor. Fort Sullivan had been planned, and construction had been begun, in January; but it was yet no more than half built.

The plan was for a square redoubt with a long, pointed bastion at each angle. So far as it was completed, it was built of two parallel walls of palmetto logs laid upon one another, the two rows tied together at intervals with logs dovetailed and bolted at each end. The space between the lines of logs, sixteen feet wide, was filled with sand. There were proper embrasures for cannon all along its sides and in its bastions, the merlons, or spaces between them, being especially strengthened. Inside, platforms for the guns were supported on brick pillars, the walls rising ten feet above them.

At the time of the attack upon it, only the front wall, toward the sea, its two bastions, and the wall on the southerly side, with the gun platforms, had been finished. The other two walls and the two rear bastions had been built to a height of no more than seven feet. Thus it was practically open and undefended in the rear and on the northerly side.

Along the front were mounted six 24-pounders and three 18-pounders. Along the southerly side were six guns, 9- and 12-pounders. In each bastion were five guns, ranging from 9 to 26 pounds.

Somewhat to protect its undefended rear, a traverse—that is to say, a simple line of earthen breastworks—was drawn across from one side of the enclosure to the other, and epaulements, or similar earthworks, had been hastily erected outside the fort, extending from the rear bastions to right and left. Three 12-pounders were mounted in each of these. Thus the front, including the two breastworks and excluding four guns on the inner side of each bastion, showed twenty-one guns to an enemy directly before it, while the southerly side showed only nine—six in the wall and three in the breastwork on that side.

To hold these outer defenses and the town itself, there were certain regiments of provincial troops. These had been first raised in 1775 to give the province a force independent of the militia—who, as has been said, were so divided in their attitude towards the British government as to be unreliable in case of conflict with the King's troops. The new regiments were to be "officered by gentlemen"; the rank and file, "enlisted for hire." At this time, there were six such regiments: the 1st Regiment of Foot under Colonel Christopher Gadsden and Lieutenant Colonel Charles Cotesworth Pinckney; the 2nd under Colonel William Moultrie, Lieutenant Colonel Isaac Motte, and Major Francis Marion; the 3rd under Lieutenant Colonel William Thompson; a regiment of artillery commanded by Lieutenant Owen Roberts; the 1st Rifle Regiment under Colonel Isaac Huger, and the 2nd under Lieutenant Colonel Thomas Sumter. Three volunteer artillery companies, not on the regular establishment, served during the coming battle. In all these numbered about 2,000 men.[24]

To them were added three Continental regiments: two from North Carolina numbering 1,400 rank and file, and one of 500 from Virginia which had been ordered down by Lee. The Virginians were commanded by that gallant fighting man, Colonel Peter Muhlenberg. The Charleston militia numbered 700. The rural militia responded to a call by Governor John Rutledge to the number of nearly 2,000, making a total defensive force of more than 6,500. However, but a few hundreds had any part in the coming fight.

The principal defense, the redoubt known as Fort Sullivan, was manned by Colonel Moultrie's 2nd South Carolina Regiment, 413 men, and the 4th Artillery, 22 men. The 1st South Carolina, 380 men under Colonel Gadsden, and a small detachment of artillerists held Fort Johnson. In the other battery on James Island, Captain Thomas Pinckney with a company from Gadsden's regiment was stationed. The positions of the rest, except the 3rd South Carolina and certain other troops, need not be described as they were mere onlookers of the conflict.

Of all these troops, only those from Virginia and North Carolina were in the Continental army, and therefore rightly under Lee. The South Carolina regiments were commanded only by Governor John Rutledge until the following September, when they were taken into the Continental line. Lee immediately assumed command of all of them, and began to issue orders or requests. A difficult situation at once developed, for some South Carolinians refused to follow his directions. It might have had serious consequences had not the governor at once issued a general order vesting the command of "the Regular forces and Militia of this Colony . . . in Major General Lee, orders issued by him are to be obeyed." [25]

The British fleet arrived off Charleston on the 4th of June, but many days elapsed before it could go into action. It was first necessary to take soundings, and to find a channel past the bar and buoy it. By the 7th the frigates and most of the transports had got across and anchored in good ground at Five Fathom Hole. On the 9th Clinton landed 500 men on Long Island, menacing Sullivan's Island. Lee detached Lieutenant Colonel Thompson's 3rd Regiment of South Carolina Rangers (300 in number), about 200 North Carolina Continentals under Lieutenant Colonel Thomas Clark, 200 South Carolinians under Captain Daniel Horry, the Raccoon Company of 50 riflemen, and a small corps of militia—780 in all—and directed them to proceed to Long Island and attack. Soon afterward, however, he withdrew the order to attack. In the course of the battle Thompson was reenforced by Muhlenberg's Virginians.[26]

The Breach was a peculiar body of water. When in the course of the battle the 15th Regiment, the light infantry, and the grenadiers tried to cross it their boats ran aground on shallows only a foot and a half deep; but in wading they plumped into great holes seven feet deep. There was simply no practicable way for troops to get from Long Island to Sullivan's. So, though the British force on land had been increased on the 10th to upwards of 2,500 men, they could not get at Thompson, and Thompson could not get at them, except for a sporadic interchange of harmless gunfire between a battery of palmetto logs, erected by the Americans and armed with an 18-pounder and a 6-pounder fieldpiece, and two small British earthworks, one for mortars and the other for guns. These two forces simply held each other in check and had no other part in the battle. Clinton perforce left to Parker "the glory of being defeated alone." [27]

For more than two weeks, Admiral Parker was busy in getting his warships over the bar. He had to lighten the *Bristol* and another 50-gun ship. the *Experiment,* which had joined him, by removing their guns, before they could be got across. At last, on the 26th, they were all inside the bar and ready for action.[28]

On the morning of the 28th the bomb ketch *Thunder,* covered by the 22-gun *Friendship,* anchored a mile and a half from the fort and opened fire. The *Active,* the *Solebay,* the *Bristol,* and the *Experiment* came within four hundred yards of the shore opposite the fort and dropped anchor with springs on their cables, in line broadside to the fort, at wide intervals. Behind them in a second line, spaced opposite the intervals in the first, the *Syren,* the *Actaeon,* and the *Sphynx* were anchored. As each came into position, it began to fire. When all were at their stations more than a hundred guns poured their metal upon the half-built fort of palmetto logs and sand, while the *Thunder* rained 10-inch shells upon it. Twenty-one guns responded to that "furious and incessant cannonade." [29] There was but little powder in the fort, not more than thirty-five rounds for each of the twenty-one guns that could be brought to bear on the ships. The artillerists laid their guns with care and without haste, striving for accuracy of aim and economy of ammunition. "Their artillery was surprisingly well served," wrote a surgeon in the fleet. The fire "was slow, but decisive indeed; they were very cool and took care not to fire except their guns were exceedingly well directed." [30]

For an hour the terrific thunder of great guns and small in this unequal combat was unabated. Then the second line, the *Actaeon,* *Syren,* and *Sphynx,* lifted anchor and drew around the lower end of the island towards a position whence they could enfilade the gun platforms along the seaward face of the fort, and at the same time bring their guns to bear upon the Cove behind that end of the island across which was the garrison's only line of retreat. To escape the fort's guns in this maneuver, they stood away to the south towards a shoal, the Middle Ground. Their circuit was too wide, and all three ran aground. The *Actaeon* and the *Sphynx* fouled each other, the *Sphynx* losing her bowsprit. The *Syren* and the *Sphynx* finally got off and had to withdraw for repairs. The *Actaeon* was immovable.

Meanwhile, the bombardment continued, all through the afternoon. The *Thunder,* trying to fire effectively at too long range, overcharged her mortars and shattered their beds. She had to pull away, but her companion the *Friendship* joined the fighting line, and the *Syren* again went into action.

The amount of metal thrown against that flimsy fort apparently should have been enough to blast it to pieces; and it would have done so had the

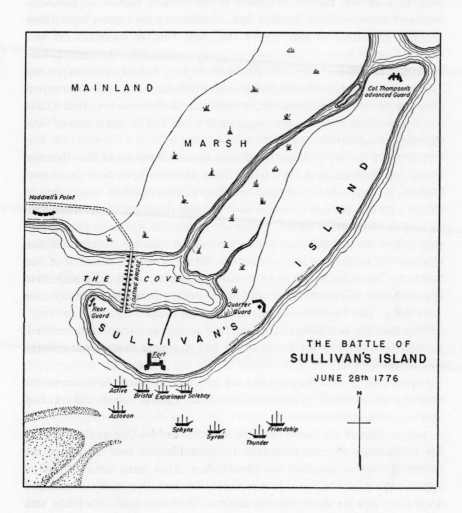

THE BATTLE OF
SULLIVAN'S ISLAND
JUNE 28th 1776

walls been of oak. But the substance of the palmetto tree is so porous, so soft, and so spongy that it offers little resistance to a cannon ball. There was no splintering, no shattering of the logs. The balls simply sank into them as into a sponge, and were as gently received by the sand behind the logs. Yet at times, when the broadsides of three or four of the ships were received at the same moment, the combined blows shook the whole super-structure. According to Moultrie, it "gave the merlons such a tremor, that I was apprehensive that a few more such would tumble them down." But the walls stood fast.[31]

The fire from the fort, on the contrary, did almost incredible damage. It was concentrated on the two larger ships, the *Bristol* and the *Experiment*. Early in the action the spring on the *Bristol*'s cable was shot away, and she swung with the tide end on to the fort. Its guns raked her decks from stern to bow with appalling effect. Twice her quarter-deck was swept clear of men except the admiral, and he was wounded.[32] The top of her mainmast was carried away. Her mizzenmast was hit by seven 32-pound shot and had to be cut away. Seventy of the fort's cannonballs hulled the ship. Had the sea been rough instead of still and smooth, she would probably have gone down. The *Experiment* suffered almost as much.

The fort did not escape damage. Its flagstaff was shot away and fell outside the wall. Sergeant Jasper of the 2nd Regiment climbed out through one of the embrasures and rescued it. He fixed it upon a sponge staff, mounted one of the bastions, and set it firmly in place. Once more the blue flag with a white crescent and the word "Liberty" showed the enemy that there was no surrender.[33]

In the midst of the battle Lee sent an order to Moultrie directing him if his ammunition became exhausted to spike his guns and retreat to the mainland. The ammunition was running low. After three o'clock Moultrie reduced the fire of his guns to ten-minute intervals. Gradually it dwindled to silence, and for more than an hour no shot was fired. Then Lee sent 700 pounds of powder to him, and a slow but steady fire was resumed.

Lee came over to see how things were going. He afterwards wrote: "The behaviour of the garrison, both men and officers, with Colonel Moultrie at their head, I confess astonished me. It was brave to the last degree. I had no idea that so much coolness and intrepidity could be displayed by a collec-tion of raw recruits." [34]

The bombardment of the fort continued until sunset, when it slackened. At half past nine the fire ceased on both sides. At eleven the ships "began to steal away—they made no piping, nor waited to heave up their anchors, but slipped their cables." [35] They anchored again at the Five Fathom Hole.

The morning found the *Actaeon* still aground. She was set afire by her crew, who rowed away to rejoin the fleet.

The losses in the British fleet were heavy, 64 men killed and 131 wounded. Of these casualties, 111 occurred on the *Bristol* and 79 on the *Experiment,* indicating the concentration of the Americans' fire on those two capital ships. Among the officers, Captain John Morris of the *Bristol* was killed, and Captain Alexander Scott of the *Experiment* lost his right arm. Lord William Campbell, who had volunteered to fight some of the *Bristol*'s guns, received a wound from which he died two years later. Among the Americans, 12 were killed, 5 died of their wounds, and 20 others were wounded. The weight of the fire from the fleet is indicated by the fact that 7,000 cannon balls were gathered on the island after the engagement. The British had expended 34,000 pounds of powder, the Americans 4,766 pounds.[36]

Clinton's troops lingered in their camp on Long Island for three weeks, entirely inactive, before they were embarked in transports for New York under the convoy of the *Solebay.* The rest of the fighting ships remained some time longer at anchor, repairing their damages.

From the first, Lee had been firmly of the opinion that the fort on Sullivan's Island was untenable. He declared that "it could not hold out half an hour and that the [gun] platform was but a slaughtering stage." He wanted to abandon the island entirely, and establish his main defenses on the mainland at Haddrell's Point. This would have left little Fort Johnson on James Island as the only defense against a close approach to the town by the ships, which, once it was silenced, could have taken a position close to that island, within half a mile of the town, and a full mile from Haddrell's Point. As Lee himself declared that four hundred yards was the maximum effective range for his guns, the ships would have then been quite safe from the Haddrell battery. He nevertheless would have effected the abandonment of Sullivan's Island if Governor Rutledge and his advisers had not insisted upon defending it.[37]

Lee had tried to provide a means of retreat from the fort to Haddrell's Point. He wanted a bridge built across the Cove between the two. As the Cove was a mile wide, there was neither time nor material to build such a bridge. Nevertheless, he stretched across the Cove a double line of planks, supported by boats and empty hogsheads. Two hundred men started to cross on it. It sank under them when they were halfway over. He was then obliged to rely on boats as a means of retreat.[38]

The stubborn insistence of Governor Rutledge and Colonel Moultrie upon holding the fort was responsible for the battle and the victory. Yet it must be said that Lee's judgment was not at fault, and that the governor and the colonel were probably in the wrong. No one could possibly have foreseen the accident that enabled the Americans to win—the grounding of the *Actaeon,* the *Syren,* and the *Sphynx* on the Middle Ground. There was plenty of water between that shoal and the southern end of Sullivan's Island to permit the three vessels to come to anchor in the undefended rear of the fort and then to blast the garrison out of its defenses. But for that accident, the whole tide of the battle might have been turned against the Americans. But that is the way with battles. In any case, the Americans had won a victory of the first importance that freed the entire lower south from the King's troops for more than two years. The credit belongs particularly to Rutledge, to Moultrie, and to Lee, who exhibited great energy in a situation where energy was badly needed. He saw to it that Fort Sullivan was in readiness. Had the British taken it, they would have had no easy task in capturing Charleston, for he was prepared to make an obstinate defense of the city.

While the fleet battered uselessly at Fort Sullivan the British were losing allies in the south, the Cherokee warriors. The Cherokees entered the war in 1776 because of long-standing grievances against the colonists. But their attacks on the frontiers of the Carolinas, injurious though they were, were not synchronized with British movements and had little bearing on the war in the south in general. Virginia, the Carolinas, and Georgia promptly sent militia and rangers into their country, which was laid waste. When the Cherokees resumed hostilities in 1779 their principal towns were again put to the torch. The Cherokees remained vexatious until the end of the war, but their power, weakened in the Cherokee War of 1760–1761, was now broken. Since the Catawba tribe aided the Americans, and since the warlike Creeks were mostly neutral until the last years of the war, the southern frontier did not suffer so much as Kentucky. When the Creeks did finally ally themselves with the British they were able to do little, especially since the appearance of the Spanish in strength at Mobile and Pensacola gave them much to think about. The forces of Bernardo de Gálvez on the shores of the Gulf of Mexico probably relieved the pressure upon the frontiers of Georgia and South Carolina in 1780 and thereafter. The entrance of Spain into the war in 1779 no doubt gave large indirect benefits to the American cause in the south.

C H A P T E R 5 9

Georgia

The gallant defense of Charleston, ending in a brilliant victory for the Americans, so discouraged the British government that no further serious military operations were attempted in the south until after the British reverses in the north of 1777–1778. Thirty-four Continental regiments, in all, were raised in the four southern states; many of them went north, joined Washington, and were of great service in the operations around Philadelphia. But the failure of the British efforts of 1777 and 1778 in the north to produce results that promised finality and permanence turned the attention of the government again to the south. When Clinton evacuated Philadelphia in June, 1778, he was under orders to discontinue offensive operations in the north, send 3,000 men to Georgia or Florida, and, in the following winter, to attempt the conquest of South Carolina, which would be "comparatively easy." [1]

On November 27, 1778, Lieutenant Colonel Archibald Campbell set sail from Sandy Hook with a fleet of transports convoyed by a squadron of war vessels under command of Commodore Hyde Parker; and on December 23 he arrived at Tybee Island at the mouth of the Savannah River, fifteen miles below the town of Savannah. General Augustine Prevost, commanding the British forces in East Florida, had orders to join in the reduction of the town; but he had not come up, and so Campbell undertook the task alone.

General Robert Howe, in command of an American southern army, was then at Sunbury, about thirty miles from Savannah. With 700 Continentals and 150 militia he marched to oppose the invaders.

Campbell brought his transports, guarded by the man-of-war *Vigilant,* the *Comet* galley, the armed brig *Keppel,* and the sloop of war *Greenwich* up the river to Girardeau's plantation, the first hard ground. He was opposed by fire from two small American galleys, but a single shot from the *Vigilant* drove them away, and he made an unopposed landing. His force comprised the 71st Regiment, the Hessian regiments of Woellwarth and Wissenbach, four Tory battalions, and a detachment of artillery—about 3,500 rank and file in all.

From the landing place a narrow causeway led through rice swamps to Girardeau's house and the main road to Savannah. Howe posted Captain John Carraway Smith with 50 South Carolina Continentals to oppose Campbell at that point. The British advance was led by Captain Cameron, with the light infantry, the New York Volunteers, and the first battalion of the 71st. Smith's men opened a smart fire of muskets, killing Cameron and two privates of the 71st and wounding five others; but the onward rush of the enemy's van drove them back, and they retired to the main American force.

Savannah had been fortified some twenty years before, but the defenses had fallen in ruins and were not tenable. Howe therefore stationed his troops on the road from Girardeau's, a half-mile east of the town. His right, composed of two South Carolina Continental regiments, the 1st Rifles under Colonel Isaac Huger, and the 3rd Rangers under Lieutenant Colonel William Thompson, extended from the road to a wooded swamp. It was supported by a hundred Georgia riflemen, militia, under Colonel George Walton in some buildings, and by one fieldpiece. The left was composed entirely of Georgia militia under Colonel Samuel Elbert. Its flank also rested on a swamp, and it had one fieldpiece. In the center, on the road, two guns were placed. A trench was dug across the road in front of the American line from one swamp to the other.

With the flanks of the line thus protected by swamps, it seemed that the British would have to make a frontal attack. But Campbell had picked up an aged Negro, one Quamino Dolly, and learned from him that there was a "private way" through the swamp on the American right by which its rear could be gained. He advanced to a point on the road where an intervening slight rise of the ground concealed his force from the Americans. He then proceeded to demonstrate against their left in a feint to cover his real purpose, which was to send Sir James Baird with his light infantry, followed by Turnbull's New York Volunteers, around their right by the way through the swamp.

Meanwhile the American artillery had been firing upon Campbell's main force, but had provoked no reply. The Americans learned of the enemy's intentions when Baird's force fell upon the rear of the Georgia militia on their extreme right and routed them. At the sound of the fire in that quarter Campbell ran his guns up on the concealing rise of ground and opened fire on Huger and Thompson. This was immediately followed by a charge of the whole British force. Attacked in front and rear, the American line broke and fled in confusion under heavy fire. The right managed to get away in large part over a causeway through the swamp, but the Georgia militia on the left had no such means of escape. Taking to the rice-swamp, they had to cross a deep creek, in which many were drowned.

The British pressed on into the town. Commodore Parker brought the *Comet* galley up to it and took possession of three ships, three brigs, and eight smaller vessels at its wharves. The houses of those regarded as rebels were looted, and many of the owners were captured. The American loss in this affair was heavy: 83 killed in the battle or drowned in the retreat; 453 captured, along with 48 cannon, 23 mortars, and 94 barrels of powder. On the British side only 3 were killed and 10 wounded.

The remains of Howe's disorganized force retreated eight miles to Cherokee Hill, and thence to South Carolina, leaving Georgia to its fate. Prevost, coming up from Florida, took the town of Sunbury, and Campbell took Augusta with little difficulty early in January. Between Campbell and Prevost, the state of Georgia was then in almost complete subjection. Campbell "acted with great policy, in securing the submission of the inhabitants." [2] They "flocked by hundreds to the King's officers, and made their peace at the expense of their patriotism." [3] "He not only extirpated military opposition, but subverted for some time every trace of republican government, and paved the way for the re-establishment of a royal legislature. Georgia . . . was the only state of the union, in which after the declaration of independence, a legislative body was convened under the authority of the crown of Great-Britain." [4] It "soon became one of the most loyal of His Majesty's possessions." [5]

Howe was greatly blamed for this defeat. It was charged that not only might he have made a successful stand on the bluff at Girardeau's plantation against the landing of the enemy, but he knew of that circumventing road through the swamp and neglected to guard it. A court of inquiry absolved him of blame, but "his military reputation never recovered from the shadow cast upon it by the loss of the capital of Georgia." [6]

Major General Benjamin Lincoln of Massachusetts had been appointed by the Congress in September, 1778, to command the Southern Department

and had taken post at Purysburg on the South Carolina side of the Savannah River about fifteen miles above Savannah. Having been joined by the
remains of Howe's force, he had 3,639 men, but only 1,121 were Continental troops; the rest were "inexperienced, undisciplined and restless
militia." Even among the Continentals few had seen service. Of his whole
force only 2,428 were reported fit for duty. Across the river, in Georgia,
General Prevost had perhaps 3,000 troops, besides an unknown number of
Tory irregulars.

Both sides desired to cross the river, but it was so wide and deep and
was bordered by such extensive swamps that neither dared attempt a crossing in force. With the aid of the navy, however, Prevost succeeded in sending Major Gardiner across with two companies of the 20th and one of the
16th, about 200 men, to take possession of Port Royal Island at the mouth
of the Broad River, about thirty miles behind Purysburg. Lincoln sent
General William Moultrie to arouse the militia in that district.

Moultrie was successful in his endeavor. With 300 of the Charleston
militia, 10 Continentals, and three fieldpieces, he occupied the town of
Beaufort on the island, on February 3, 1779. He formed his troops on
both sides of the road by which Gardiner was advancing, and their single
gun opened on Gardiner's troops with considerable effect. Although the
British had some shelter in a wood, while the American troops were on
open ground, the militia behaved well. The enemy's only gun, a howitzer,
was hit and dismounted early in the action, giving Moultrie an advantage.
For three-quarters of an hour the two forces fought a hot little battle. Then
the Americans' ammunition gave out, and Moultrie ordered a withdrawal,
only to discover that Gardiner's force was already in retreat. A small body
of American light horse pursued it and took a few prisoners.

The Americans lost 8 killed and 22 wounded. The British loss was un-
ascertained, but was comparatively heavy. A captured British lieutenant
was quoted as saying that it was not less than half of their whole number,
which is very improbable. This little affair sufficed for Prevost; he made
no further attempt upon South Carolina at the time.[7]

The complete subjection of Georgia had aroused the Tories in the back
country of that state and of South Carolina. Many were inclined to join
Campbell at Augusta. To stimulate such interest, he sent Lieutenant Colonel
John Hamilton with 200 mounted Tory partisans, to the back country of
Georgia. Hamilton was a man of worth, wealth, and high social position, a
typical Scottish Highlander and a veteran of Culloden, very influential
among his own people, yet highly respected by his opponents. Aroused by

his progress, in spite of well meant but ineffectual opposition, Colonel Boyd, a North Carolina Tory, raised a force of 700 adherents to the crown, chiefly Scotsmen, and started for Georgia to join him.

Boyd's men committed depredations upon the inhabitants of the country he passed through; "their general complexion was that of a plundering bandetti, more solicitous for booty than for the honour and interest of their royal master." [8] Colonel Andrew Pickens of South Carolina assembled a force of militia of that state and was joined by Captain John Dooley with a number of Georgians, making up about 300 men. They crossed into Georgia, leaving Captain Anderson with a small party at Cherokee Ford to oppose Boyd's crossing there.

Anderson was driven back, and Boyd's force crossed the river. Pickens thereupon set out in pursuit and took Boyd unawares at Kettle Creek, where his men were engaged in slaughtering a herd of stolen cattle. Their horses were turned out to graze, and their camp was in disorder when Pickens, having deployed his men in line, himself in the center, Dooley on the right, and Lieutenant Colonel Thomas Clark on the left, swept down upon it. The two wings swung around the camp and attacked it simultaneously with the center.

Boyd was an able soldier. He pulled his men together and fell back, disputing the approach with much obstinacy for nearly an hour. But, after he had been mortally wounded, more than 40 of his men killed, many more wounded, and 75 captured, his force broke and scattered—300 joining Campbell at Augusta and the rest fleeing to their homes. The patriots lost 9 killed and 23 wounded.

The prisoners were carried to South Carolina. There, they were tried on charges of treason, and 70 were condemned to death. All except five were pardoned, but these, deemed to be ringleaders, "to the shame of Southern justice and the horror of mankind, were hung." [9]

Beaufort and Kettle Creek raised the spirits of the rebels in the same degree as the conquest of Georgia had elevated those of the Tories. The militia flocked to Lincoln's camp at Purysburg in such numbers that his force was doubled, and he was emboldened to try to recover the lost state. For this purpose he sent General Andrew Williamson of Georgia with 1,200 men to the eastern bank of the Savannah River opposite Augusta, General Griffith Rutherford with 800 to the Black Swamp, and General John Ashe with 1,400 North Carolina militia and about 100 Georgia continentals, under Colonel Elbert, to Briar Creek in Georgia, south of Augusta.

When Ashe neared Williamson's post Campbell evacuated Augusta and started with its garrison towards Savannah. Ashe crossed the Savannah River and pursued the retreating enemy, but Campbell crossed Briar Creek and destroyed the bridge ahead of him. Ashe reached that stream on February 27, his force having been increased by 200 light-horse militia, and started to rebuild the bridge. General Prevost, disturbed by this incursion, devised a plan to defeat it.

He sent Major Macpherson with the 1st battalion of the 71st Regiment, some Tory irregulars, and two fieldpieces to the south bank of the creek facing the rebels, while Lieutenant Colonel Mark Prevost with the 2nd battalian of the 71st, Baird's light infantry, three companies of grenadiers of the 60th Regiment, a troop of Provincial light horse, and 150 Tory militia—about 900 in all—made a circuit of fifty miles to cross the creek above Ashe's camp and attack it in the rear.

Although reconnoitering parties of the enemy had been seen in the afternoon of March 2 and in the following morning, Ashe took no steps to meet the attack, except to form his troops in column with Colonel Elbert's Continentals in front. At Lieutenant Colonel Prevost's approach, Elbert advanced a hundred yards and opened fire. At this alarm, the militia faced about and ran without firing a shot. The Continentals continued firing for a few minutes. Then, finding themselves deserted, they also broke and fled in disorder. Most of the fugitives threw down their arms and plunged into the swamp. In trying to cross the river, many were drowned.

Between 150 and 200 having lost their lives, either in the brief action or by drowning, the catastrophe was completed by the capture of 11 officers including Elbert, and 162 noncommissioned officers and privates. Of those who escaped, not more than 450 rejoined the army; the rest returned to their homes.[10] Seven cannon, almost all the small-arms, the Americans' colors and all their ammunition and baggage were taken by General Prevost. The British lost 5 killed and 11 wounded. "This brilliant action by the British destroyed the possibility of recovering Georgia at that time."

The possession of Georgia by the British, and General Prevost's hostile activities, aroused apprehensions of imminent danger among the South Carolinians. Governor Rutledge received almost dictatorial power. He called out the militia in greater numbers than ever before. General Moultrie, now in command at Purysburg and the Black Swamp, was strengthened to 1,000 men. Lincoln's main army was also reenforced; he had in all about 4,000 men, besides those with Moultrie. With this force, he felt able to take the offensive.

On April 23, 1779, Lincoln crossed the Savannah River and marched towards Augusta. To counter this movement, Prevost crossed the river on April 29 into South Carolina, at Purysburg, with 2,500 men. Lieutenant Colonel Alexander McIntosh held that post with the 2nd and 5th South Carolina Continentals, about 220 men. At Prevost's approach he retired to join Moultrie at the Black Swamp. Prevost pursued him. Moultrie had withdrawn from the Swamp to Coosahatchie Bridge, a few miles in his rear. Thence, followed by Prevost, he retreated by successive stages marked by rear-guard skirmishes, to Charleston, where "he was received with open arms by the terrified inhabitants." [11] A number of militia from Orangeburg came in, and 300 light infantry sent back in haste by Lincoln were added to Moultrie's force, also the infantry of Pulaski's Legion, 80 men, while Lincoln, having occupied evacuated Augusta, was coming on with his main army by forced marches.

Prevost's plan had been merely to draw Lincoln back from Georgia, but now, encouraged by Moultrie's retreat and by the general panic among the inhabitants along his route, he decided to push on for Charleston. Leaving the larger part of his troops on the south side of the Ashley River, he crossed that stream and approached the town with 900 men.

Count Pulaski sallied out to meet him. Posting his men behind some slight earthworks, he rode forward to where a party of light horse was skirmishing with Prevost's advance. His intent was to draw the British van within range of his ambuscade. But his men, too eager for combat, left their works and followed him. The British van attacked them and drove them back into the town.

The neck of land between Charleston and the mainland, hitherto undefended, had been hastily but rather effectively fortified while Prevost was pursuing Moultrie, and all the houses that would afford cover for an attack on that side had been burnt. This presented an unexpected obstacle to Prevost, and he hesitated to attack. To gain time for Lincoln's army to arrive, Moultrie entered into correspondence with the British general, discussing terms for surrender, but, after two days' delay, notified him that he had decided to fight.

Prevost had intercepted a letter from Lincoln telling of his return to South Carolina. Fearful of being caught between two fires, he withdrew his troops in the night of May 12 to James Island, about two miles south of the town, then to the adjoining Johns Island. On the mainland at Stono Ferry, he erected fortifications—three strong redoubts with a heavy abatis in front. In their rear a bridge of boats connected the works with the island. Then, oddly enough, on June 16, he began to withdraw his troops in boats to Savannah, finally leaving only one battalion of the 71st, the Hessian von

Trumbach Regiment, a detachment of artillery, and some Tory militia, 900 in all, Lieutenant Colonel Maitland in command.

Lincoln had between 6,000 and 7,000 men in Charleston. He quite naturally saw his opportunity for a stroke. After midnight of the morning of June 20, with 1,200 men, he advanced against the enemy's lines. General Jethro Sumner commanded the right wing made up of North and South Carolina militia, with two fieldpieces; General Isaac Huger commanded the left, Continental troops with four guns; Colonel the Marquis de Malmedy and Lieutenant Colonel John Henderson with two companies of light infantry covered the flanks; and a force of Virginia militia with two guns was the reserve. Certain detachments of horsemen on the Virginian's right guarded the rear.

Advancing in line through a dense growth of pine saplings, the right wing was delayed, and Henderson's light infantry, covering the left wing, made the first contact with the enemy, two companies of the 71st Highlanders posted in advance of the British lines. Though greatly inferior in numbers, the Scotsmen stood fast. Henderson attacked with the bayonet, and a furious hand-to-hand fight ensued. With obstinate bravery the intrepid Highlanders maintained their ground until all but 11 of them had fallen.

Three hundred yards from the British lines, the main body of the Americans halted and for an hour exchanged cannon and musket fire with their opponents. The Hessian regiment gave way, and the Americans then pressed forward against the abatis. There their left was stopped by a shift of part of the 71st to that side. The Hessians were rallied and brought into action. Now Moultrie had word of British reenforcements coming over from Johns Island and thought it best to retire. The retreat, though pursued by the enemy, was made in good order, Colonel Andrew Pickens with some light infantry effectively covering the rear.

The American loss was heavy, 146 killed or wounded, and 155 missing. The British lost 3 officers and 23 men killed, 10 officers and 93 men wounded, one man missing. The extraordinary number of missing Americans suggests heavy desertions among the militia, for it does not appear that the British took any prisoners.

This affair reflected little credit upon Moultrie's generalship. To take only 1,200 men, largely militia, against 900 British and Hessian regulars strongly entrenched, when he had five or six times that number available, was certainly poor judgment. It did, however, hasten the departure of the British from the state. They withdrew in boats to Port Royal Island within a few days.

Prevost's incursion into South Carolina gave him no profit in a military sense, except that it drew Lincoln back from Georgia. But it is averred that, in another sense it was highly profitable to his force. Looting was widespread. The houses along the route were pillaged of valuables of every sort. Slaves in great numbers flocked to the invaders and disclosed to them the places where their owners had concealed their valuables. They were well received by the redcoats, but not so well treated. "It is supposed that the British carried out of the state about 3,000 slaves, many of whom were shipped off and sold in the West Indies." [12]

CHAPTER 60

Savannah

The summer of 1779 was a period of quiet in the south. After the affair at Stono Ferry, the British were content to hold their positions in Georgia and on Port Royal Island, and the Americans made no move against them. Port Royal was safe from attack as long as the British commanded the sea. But if such command could be overcome the separation of the British force between that post and Savannah would render both of them vulnerable, thought Governor Rutledge and General Moultrie.

With that in view, they sent messengers to Admiral Comte d'Estaing, whose fleet was operating in the West Indies, asking his aid. He accepted the invitation and sent two ships of the line and three frigates to Charleston to announce the coming of his fleet. With twenty ships of the line, two others of 50 guns, eleven frigates, and a number of transports carrying 6,000 soldiers, he arrived off Tybee Island at the mouth of the Savannah River on September 8, having first fallen in with and taken the British ship *Experiment* of 50 guns, the frigate *Ariel,* and two storeships conveying a large sum of money for the payment of troops in Georgia, also a quantity of naval stores.

The large ships of the fleet, which could not cross the bar, were anchored outside. The frigates *Truite* and *Chimère*, two armed American galleys, and the armed storeship *Bricole* were brought up into the river. The fleet had been sighted by the British frigate *Rose*, five days before it arrived, and a fast-sailing brig had been dispatched to New York to call on Clinton and Admiral Marriot Arbuthnot for aid. Prevost requested Maitland to bring his troops from Port Royal, and Lieutenant Colonel John Harris Cruger with a battalion of De Lancey's New Yorkers was called in from Sunbury. The war vessels *Vigilant, Fowey, Rose, Keppel,* and *Germain* had been stationed outside the harbor, but they retired up the river upon the approach of the French.

Savannah, as has been said, was surrounded only by indefensible ruined earthworks. The city stood on a bluff on the right or west bank of the river. On the north a broad, wooded morass extending to the river offered some protection, but on the south and west the land dropped from the bluff and there was open ground. Prevost set about rebuilding the old defenses and erecting new ones.

Four or five hundred Negroes were brought in from neighboring planta· tions to aid the garrison and the town dwellers in this effort. A curved line of earthworks, faced with a ditch and an abatis, was drawn around the town from the river below to the swamps above. On the north, or right, side three redoubts were built. The one on the left was the Spring Hill Redoubt. At the extreme right, beyond the first, or more northerly, redoubt, the Sailors' Battery of 9-pounders was erected, and another was placed between the second and third redoubts.

On the south side of the town two strong redoubts were framed of heavy logs, the spaces between the logs being filled with sand. The first redoubt on the north was held by a part of the King's Rangers, a Tory battalion under Captains Samuel Roworth and Alexander Wylly; the second was held by two companies of Georgia Tory militia and a regiment of the Tory North Carolina Volunteers, under Lieutenant Colonel John Hamilton; the third, the Spring Hill Redoubt, was commanded by Captain Tawes, who had a detachment of dismounted dragoons, with a South Carolina Tory regiment in support. The most northerly battery was manned by a company from the British Legion, a Tory corps, under Captain Patrick Stewart; the second battery was held by Captain Manby with the grenadiers of the 60th British regiment and marines from the British ships.

The great redoubts to the south were garrisoned, one by a body of the Georgia Volunteers under Major Sir James Wright, the royal governor of that state, the other by the 1st battalion of De Lancey's New Yorkers under Cruger. Both were supported by a battalion of the 71st Regiment, the 3rd battalion of Lieutenant Colonel Isaac Allen's New Jersey Volunteers, and detachments of Georgia militia.

A strong picket of British regulars, with a large body of armed Negroes, was stationed in the center, west of the town. Within the lines were sta· tioned, in order from south to north, the 1st battalion of the 71st Regiment under Major McArthur, the Hessian Regiment von Trumbach, the 2nd battalion of De Lancey's New Yorkers, the British light infantry under Major Graham of the 16th Regiment, the Hessian Regiment Wissenbach, the 2nd battalion of the 71st under Major McDonald, the 2nd battalion of the 71st, the grenadiers of the 60th and a company of marines, under Lieutenant Colonel Glasier, and a body of North Carolina Royalists. Exclusive of the Negroes, Prevost's force numbered 2,360 rank and file. It will be noticed that the great majority of the garrison was made up of American Loyalists, a fact emphasizing the character of the conflict in the South as a civil war.

To obstruct the river approach, the frigate *Rose*, the armed vessel *Savannah*, four transports, and several smaller vessels were sunk in the channel. To prevent the passage of fire rafts from the north down the river, a boom of logs was strung across it above the town. The armed brig *Germain* was stationed in the river off Yamacraw swamp.

On September 12, 1779, d'Estaing transferred 3,500 of his troops to small vessels which carried them up the river to Beaulieu plantation, about eight miles south of Savannah, and thence marched against that town. On the 15th Pulaski's Legion joined him, and on the 16th he summoned the garrison, in a rather flamboyant proclamation, to surrender "to the arms of the King of France." Prevost, in order to gain time for the arrival of Maitland's troops, applied Moultrie's method at Charleston: he asked a truce for twenty-four hours in which to consider the demand, and it was granted. Prevost used this interval in further strengthening his works.

Maitland's march from Port Royal has received the highest praise. Unable to proceed by sea because of the French fleet or by land because of Lincoln's intervening army, he was fortunate enough to discover a sort of inside channel through the swamps and, though himself ill of malaria, took his troops through a country that might have been deemed impassable. Wading waist-deep, they dragged their boats two miles through swamps, launched them again in creeks and rivers and so made their way to the Savannah River. Under cover of a fog they crossed it to the town, thus adding 800 men of the best fighting quality to Prevost's 2,400. Maitland himself was a most important acquisition for Prevost, who on his arrival replied to d'Estaing that he would defend the town.

Lincoln's army had left Charleston on September 8 and, after a tedious march delayed by broken bridges, joined d'Estaing on the 16th. He had only 600 Continental troops and 750 militia. The combined attacking force now numbered nearly 5,000 against the defenders' 3,200, but the garrison was strongly entrenched. If d'Estaing had attacked immediately upon landing, there is little doubt that he could have taken the town without difficulty—

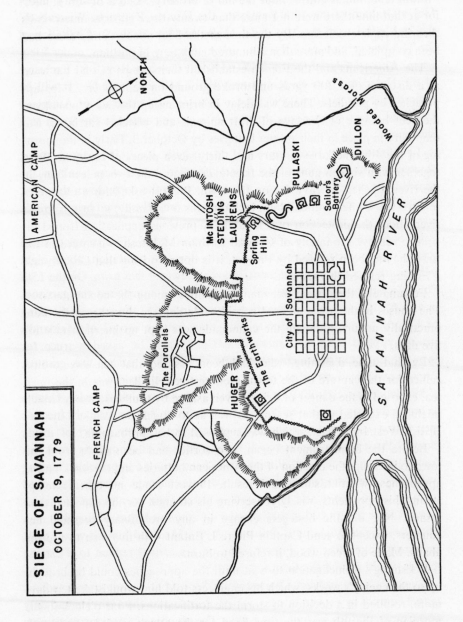

SIEGE OF SAVANNAH
OCTOBER 9, 1779

NORTH

AMERICAN CAMP

FRENCH CAMP

The Parallels

The Earthworks

HUGER

Spring Hill

McINTOSH
STEDING
LAURENS

City of Savannah

PULASKI

Sailor's Battery

DILLON

Wooded Morass

SAVANNAH RIVER

"within ten minutes and without the aid of artillery," said a British officer,[1] for at that time there were not more than twenty-three guns mounted on its then incomplete defenses. By the time of the final attack the defenses had been completed, and more than a hundred guns were in position.

The Americans and the French established their camps behind the town at a distance of 1,200 yards and broke ground on September 23 for approaches by parallels. There was delay in bringing up the heavy guns from the fleet because of shortage of draft animals and wheeled carriages. But they were in place in their proper batteries by October 3. Early in the morning of the 4th nine large mortars and thirty-seven pieces of heavy artillery, together with sixteen guns of the frigate *Truite* and the two galleys lying in the river, opened a heavy fire on the town. Prevost asked for a chance to remove the women and children, including his own family, to vessels in the river under the protection of d'Estaing. A previous application from Lincoln to remove the family of General Lachlan McIntosh, who were in the town, having been refused by Prevost, it is not surprising that Lincoln and d'Estaing refused this request.

Fortunately, there were not many casualties among the noncombatants. The houses in the town suffered considerable damage; but the works were practically unhurt, although the cannonade was kept up intermittently for five days.

By that time d'Estaing, who had been assured that ten days would suffice for the capture of the town, grew restive. His fleet was in the open sea, exposed to the danger of being driven ashore by southeast storms which might be expected at that season, as well as to attack by Admiral Byron's British West India fleet, which was supposed to be approaching.

Before the bombardment began, two sorties had been made from the town to interrupt the erection of the American batteries and the work on the approaches, without substantial result. Prevost made no other attempt against his opponents, wisely conserving his strength for the expected final assault. Nor did the besiegers engage in any preliminary personal encounters, except to send Captain Pierre L'Enfant with five men to fire the abatis. Made of green wood, it refused to burn.

D'Estaing's disinclination to wait until the approaches could be brought up to the enemy's works, which his engineers told him would take ten days more, resulted in a decision to storm the fortifications. Four o'clock in the morning of the 9th was the time fixed for the attack, and 3,500 French soldiers, 600 Continentals, 250 Charleston militia, and Pulaski's 200 horse were ordered to parade at one o'clock. They were formed in columns—the French in three, the first to be led by General Count Dillon, the second under Baron de Steding, a Swede in the French army, and the third a reserve under Colonel the Viscount de Noailles. The Americans were in two columns; the first being composed of the 2nd South Carolina Continentals and the 1st battalion of Charleston militia under Colonel John Laurens, and the second of the 1st and 5th South Carolina Continentals and some from Georgia, under General McIntosh.

Dillon's column was to march to the left and, by a hollow way between the bluff on the west side and the swamp, was to try, unobserved and hidden from the enemy's fire, to turn the British right between the Sailors' Battery and the town and so enter it. General Huger with an independent force of 500 militia was to proceed to the right against the east side of the enemy's works as a mask or feint to draw attention from the main attack and, if opportunity offered, to penetrate the defenses on that side.

The main attack was to be made by the forces of Laurens, Steding, and McIntosh, led by d'Estaing and Lincoln, against the Spring Hill Redoubt. Pulaski's cavalry was to precede Laurens's column, incline to the left, and enter the works when a breach should be made in the abatis on the left of the Spring Hill Redoubt.

Unfortunately, the discussion of the plan was overheard by Sergeant Major James Curry of the Charleston Grenadiers. He deserted to the enemy and informed them of the point of the main attack. A battalion of the 71st, one of the 60th, and a company of marines were added to its defenders, and that very able soldier Lieutenant Colonel Maitland was put in command of it.

As so often happened in these projected night attacks, the forward movement of the attacking force was delayed beyond the hour fixed. It was daylight before it began. Another misfortune occurred when Dillon's troops lost their way in the swamps west of the town and came out in the open instead of approaching secretly by the hollow way. They were discovered and were subjected to such a heavy fire that they never reached the enemy lines at all. Dillon ordered a retreat to the camp, and that was the end of that movement.

Huger on the right, after leading his men through some rice swamps, met such a heavy fire that he also withdrew. But the main force went on against the Spring Hill Redoubt. Laurens's force was the first to attack it. It climbed the bluff, crossed the ditch, cut through the abatis, and assaulted the redoubt with the utmost determination, in the face of a murderous fire of muskets and a devastating crossfire from adjoining batteries, which mowed them down rank by rank. The 2nd South Carolina Continentals, led by Lieutenant Colonel Francis Marion, reached the parapet first. Lieutenant John Bush and Lieutenant Homes planted the French standard and their regimental colors on it and were instantly shot down. Lieutenant Henry Gray replaced them and also fell. Sergeant Jasper, of Fort Sullivan fame, raised them again and was mortally wounded. But the parapet was too high to scale. The gallant South Carolinians were crowded together on the berm and in the ditch. They were forced back into and beyond the ditch just as McIntosh's troops came to their aid. Then Maitland turned loose the grenadiers of the 60th and a body of marines under Major Glasier.

The British left the redoubt and fell upon the mass of men in front of it with terrific effect in a hand-to-hand encounter, using bullets, bayonets, swords, pikes, feet, and fists. Captain Tawes, the former commander of the redoubt, himself killed three of the attackers with his sword before he was struck down. The fight at that point raged with unremitting fury for nearly an hour; but the crowded and confused allies were at last driven back, and retreated to their camp, leaving 80 dead in the ditch and 93 between it and the abatis.

While they were still fighting there, Pulaski, with his 200 horse, was attempting to force a passage between the Spring Hill Redoubt and the works west of it. At the abatis he encountered a crossfire which threw his men into confusion. He was hit in the body by a canister shot and mortally wounded. His men desisted from any further attempt and bore him from the field.

So the assault was beaten off at every point. The allies lost 16 officers and 228 men killed, 63 officers and 521 men wounded—a fifth of the whole number engaged and perhaps nearly half of those actually in the fight at the Spring Hill Redoubt. The British lost 40 killed, 63 wounded, and 52 missing. It had been the most severe fight of the war since Bunker's Hill—a magnificent attack and a superb defense.

After the battle Lincoln wanted to continue the siege operations; but d'Estaing would remain no longer. He returned his troops to their ships and sailed away. Lincoln marched back to Charleston. The south was sadly disheartened by this defeat, and much feeling against the French was aroused. Their defection at Newport in the previous year was remembered, and confidence in their value as allies was severely shaken. Throughout the country there was a great depression of spirits, and a corresponding depression in the already nearly worthless Continental money. Among the British and their American friends there was much elation. The southern Tories were emboldened to become more openly active against the American cause.

CHAPTER 61

Charleston Again

When Sir Henry Clinton heard of d'Estaing's arrival at the mouth of the Savannah River in September, 1779, he recalled to New York the 3,000 men that had been uselessly stationed at Newport for three years. When the French and Americans were defeated in their attempt upon Savannah and d'Estaing sailed away, leaving Georgia in the hands of the British, it seemed to Clinton that the time had arrived to attempt the subjugation of the southern states by a campaign that should begin in South Carolina and move through North Carolina into Virginia. He rather hoped that he could arouse the numerous Loyalists in the Carolinas, that they would flock to the King's standard and so reenforce him that he would be irresistible in his march to complete victory over the rebel forces in the south and that thus that great section would be restored to the crown. His plan was first to capture that most important city Charleston and establish a base there, and then to proceed inland.

Every circumstance seemed favorable to the project. Clinton's own army approximated 25,000 men, so that he could well spare a strong body of troops for this expedition. Washington's army, wintering in New Jersey, was so few in numbers that there seemed to be little prospect of his being able to send aid to the South. Lincoln's garrison in Charleston was desperately weak. The Carolinians generally were disheartened by the defeat at Savannah and the disappearance of the French. They were discouraged, moreover, by the fact that they had been left alone to oppose the enemy, with no aid from the North. Indeed, their forces had been drawn upon to help the North when, in 1777, all the Virginia and North Carolina Continentals had been sent up to reenforce Washington's army. The Tories had been so animated by the success of the British at Savannah that they might be expected to rise in numbers to aid the royal army. Then, too, the season was favorable. While operations in the north were extremely difficult in the winter, that was the best time for campaigning in the south. Altogether, Clinton's prospects were rosy.

On December 26, 1779, he turned over the command in New York to Knyphausen and sailed south with Cornwallis as second in command. His fleet of ninety transports carried eight British infantry regiments, five of Hessians, and five corps of Tories, besides detachments of artillery and cavalry—8,500 rank and file in all. It was convoyed by five ships of the line and nine frigates, with 650 guns, under command of Admiral Arbuthnot. The crews of all these vessels numbered about 5,000.

The voyage was stormy. Off Hatteras heavy gales came near to wrecking the expedition. Most of the cavalry and artillery horses perished; the stores were badly damaged; and the fleet was dispersed far and wide. One transport loaded with Hessians was driven clear across the Atlantic and went ashore on the coast of Cornwall. Thirty days had elapsed when the ships began to arrive off Tybee Island at the mouth of the Savannah River. After repairs to the rigging they sailed for Charleston on February 10, entered North Edisto Inlet on the 11th, and landed the troops on Johns Island, thirty miles south of Charleston.

The city of Charleston occupied the southern end of a narrow peninsula between the Ashley River on the west and the Cooper River on the east. Those two streams met at the tip of the peninsula and flowed into Charleston harbor, which was bounded on the south by James Island and Morris Island, on the north by the mainland and Sullivan's Island. Its defenses on the ocean side were two forts, Moultrie (formerly known as Sullivan's) on Sullivan's Island and Johnson on James Island. Moultrie, which had withstood the attack by Clinton and Admiral Parker in 1776, then being only partly built, had been allowed to fall into disrepair and was not now tenable. Johnson was in ruins. There was no defense against the intrusion of the enemy ships into the harbor.

On the land side Charleston was vulnerable. The broader part of the peninsula, on which the city was situated, was connected with the mainland by a long and narrow isthmus known as the Neck. It had been partially fortified in 1779, but these defenses were quite insufficient to repel a strong attack

Immediately upon landing on Johns Island, Clinton sent part of his fleet to blockade the harbor; but after that he moved with the leisureliness which so often marked the operations of the British army in the war and so often seemed inexplicable. He first seized Stono Ferry connecting Johns Island with the adjoining James Island; then he occupied James Island itself and bridged the creek or strait called Wappoo Cut that separated it from the mainland. Not until March 7 did he cross the Cut and erect batteries on the west bank of the Ashley opposite the town. March 29 had arrived before he crossed the Ashley, seven weeks after his landing on Johns Island.

His delay was deemed at the time to be a great advantage to the Americans, because it gave them time to strengthen their defenses. But it proved in the end to be their undoing, because, with reenforced defenses, they felt themselves strong enough "to hazard their lives and fortunes upon the event of a siege," [1] and this false sense of security induced Lincoln to draw all available troops into a town that was doomed to be captured and with it the whole American army in South Carolina—an event that any competent military man should have foreseen.

The legislature having invested Governor Rutledge with dictatorial powers, he impressed 600 slaves for work on the fortifications. The Neck was cut across by a ditch or small canal filled with water. Behind it were erected stout breastworks and redoubts well fraised and covered by a double abatis. One of the redoubts, a "horn-work" built of stone, stood in the center of the lines upon the main road to the north. It was known as the Citadel and was a work of considerable strength. On these lines, sixty-six guns were mounted, and a number of mortars.

At the town's southern extremity, a redoubt mounting sixteen guns was erected. Along the Ashley River side was strung a line of six small "forts," each mounting four to nine guns. On the Cooper River side there were seven of these little works, each mounting from three to seven guns. Fort Moultrie and Fort Johnson were repaired and armed.

To aid in the defense of the waterfront, there was a little fleet of armed vessels, several of which had been bought from d'Estaing. They were the *Bricole*, 44 guns, *Providence* and *Boston*, 32 guns each, *Queen of France*, 28, *Aventure* and *Truite*, 26 each, *Ranger* and *General Lincoln*, 20 each, and *Notre Dame*, 16. These were commanded by Commodore Whipple.

Within the town Lincoln had, at first, all 800 South Carolina Continentals, 400 Virginia Continentals, Horry's dragoons, the remains of Pulaski's Legion numbering about 380, and about 2,000 militia of both Carolinas. But in December, Washington had ordered south the Virginia and North Carolina Continentals that had been with him in the north.

Clinton had left 2,500 troops in Georgia, bringing 6,000 to Charleston. Feeling that he needed more men to take the town, he sent some of his transports to New York for reenforcements. He also called on General Patterson to bring up the Savannah garrison. In the middle of March, Patterson arrived with the 71st Regiment of Highlanders, the light infantry, the infantry of Tarleton's Tory British Legion, Ferguson's American Volunteers, Tory riflemen, and other Tory corps including Turnbull's New York Volunteers, Innes's South Carolina Royalists, and Hamilton's North Carolina Royalists, also a number of dragoons—in all about 1,500 men. In the middle of April, Lord Rawdon came from New York with 2,500 men. These additions brought the British force up to 10,000 men, exclusive of the 5,000 seamen.

To the aid of the garrison, Governor Rutledge called the South Carolina militia; but they failed to respond, declaring that they feared an outbreak of smallpox if they were cooped up in Charleston, which had indeed suffered from an epidemic of a peculiarly fatal character a few years before. He sent an emissary to Havana to ask for a Spanish fleet and an army to cooperate in the town's defense, Spain having lately declared war on Britain. But the Spaniards declined the invitation.

The reenforcements from the north did, however, arrive. On March 3 General James Hogun with 700 North Carolina Continentals finished a most arduous march of nearly three months through heavy snows and extreme cold. On April 6 General William Woodford appeared with 750 Virginia Continentals, who had marched five hundred miles in twenty-eight days.

To hold the fords of the Cooper River and keep open his communications with the northern part of the state, thus affording a way of retreat up the east bank, Lincoln stationed General Isaac Huger with about 500 men— Horry's horse, Pulaski's dragoons, Bland's, Baylor's and Moylan's horse, and about 100 men under Lieutenant Colonel William Washington—at Monck's Corner near the head of the Cooper and thirty miles north of Charleston. Thus, in the town, there were left about 2,650 Continentals and 2,500 militia to hold a circuit of about three miles of fortified lines.

In the meantime Clinton had been closing in. On March 20 there were indications of an intention to bring the warships into the harbor. The little American fleet could find no position there that offered a possibility of preventing or even delaying the entrance of the enemy vessels. It was therefore withdrawn into the mouth of the Cooper River, in the main channel between the town and the small island called Shute's Folly. Its guns were removed and four of the frigates with several merchant ships were sunk there and

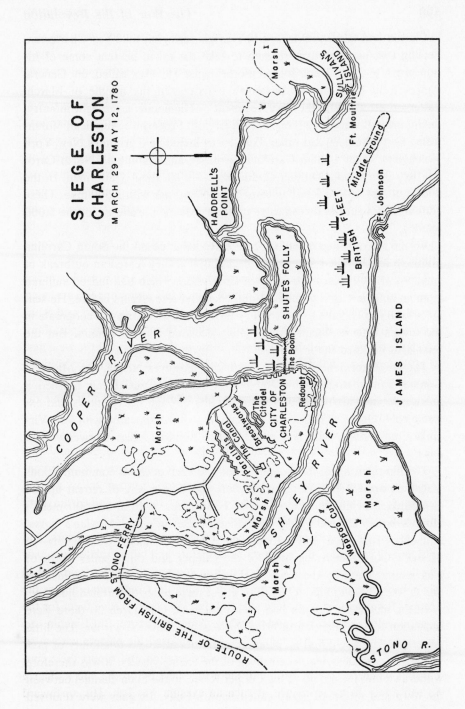

SIEGE OF
CHARLESTON
MARCH 29- MAY 12, 1780

HADDRELL'S
POINT

COOPER RIVER

SULLIVAN'S ISLAND

Ft. Moultrie

Marsh

Middle Ground

BRITISH FLEET

Ft. Johnson

SHUTE'S FOLLY

The Boom

The Citadel
CITY OF CHARLESTON
The Canal
The Breastworks
Parallels
Redoubt

Marsh

JAMES ISLAND

ASHLEY RIVER

Marsh

Marsh

STONO FERRY

Waddoo Cut

Marsh

ROUTE OF THE BRITISH FROM

STONO R.

in the channel on the far side of the island. They were made the basis of a log-and-chain boom to obstruct the passage up the Cooper, with the intention of preserving that means of access to the upper country and keeping open an avenue for reenforcement and possible retreat. The rest of the fleet, five warships and five galleys, were anchored in the river behind the boom.

On March 29 Clinton at last crossed the Ashley River in force and broke ground within 1,800 yards of the defenses on the Neck for regular approaches by parallels. On April 8 eight British frigates carrying 216 guns left their anchorage in Five Fathom Hole, ran by Fort Moultrie with an exchange of fire that did little damage on either side, and anchored between James Island and the town. Now Charleston was almost completely invested; the only way open was across the Cooper above Shute's Folly to the mainland east of the river and so north to the position at Monck's Corner still held by Huger.

Clinton completed the first parallel of his approaches and erected batteries there, and on the 10th he and Arbuthnot joined in a summons to surrender. Lincoln had failed to use his opportunity to abandon the town and withdraw his troops to the northward, thus saving them for future operations, which the disparity of his numbers with those of the enemy and the weakness of his defenses made advisable. The way for such a movement by Monck's Corner was indeed still open, risky though it might be, but so far he seems not even to have considered taking it. He refused to surrender, and the siege began in earnest.

In the morning of the 13th the enemy batteries on the Neck and James Island opened on the town a rain of bombs, red-hot round shot, and carcasses that lasted two hours. Fires broke out here and there that were controlled by the citizens with much trouble. They took to their cellars and, in general, escaped injury. The bombardment was renewed and lasted until midnight, inflicting much damage upon the buildings.

Then for the first time Lincoln called together his general officers, and told them he regarded the situation as desperate and contemplated evacuating the town. General Lachlan McIntosh, a courageous soldier, said that in his opinion not an hour should be lost in getting the Continentals across the Cooper River and up its eastern side to safety, in order to save them for the general welfare of the state and the whole American cause. But Lincoln was irresolute and preferred to temporize. He dismissed his officers with a request that they give the matter mature consideration and report their conclusions when he should again call them together. Before he had a chance to call upon them the chance of such an evasion was lost. His northward communications were severed by the destruction of the post at Monck's Corner.

The dragoons in Clinton's army were commanded by Lieutenant Colonel Banastre Tarleton, who was destined to achieve fame and merited obloquy in the south. Entering the British service at the outbreak of the war in America, he had proved himself an able soldier in Cornwallis's command throughout all the campaigns in the north, gaining some personal distinction. He was at this time twenty-six years old. In person he was short, stout and strongly built, muscular, and active. His countenance was handsome in feature, bold, insolent, and domineering in expression, revealing notable resolution, bravery, and pertinacity. In action, he was shrewd, sudden, and swift to strike. As a leader of cavalry, he was unmatched on either side for alertness and rapidity of movement, dash, daring, and vigor of attack. As a man, he was cold-hearted, vindictive, and utterly ruthless. He wrote his name in letters of blood all across the history of the war in the South. His command was the British Legion, made up of American Tories, a force of horse and foot, his infantry being usually mounted.

On the voyage of the British transports to Tybee, all his horses perished. He replaced them with horses impressed in the neighborhood, little tackies not strong enough for the heavy work of dragoons. His first desire was for better mounts, and he got a few in his first contact with the Americans, on February 23—a skirmish with a small body of militia, of whom he killed ten and took four prisoners. Three days later he encountered Lieutenant Colonel William Washington in command of the remains of Bland's, Baylor's, and Moylan's Virginia regiments of horse, who, as has been said, had been posted at Monck's Corner under General Huger, but were then operating along the Ashley. Washington drove Tarleton back and took several prisoners. But on April 14 Tarleton had his revenge.

His legion, reenforced by Major Patrick Ferguson's American Volunteers, a corps of riflemen, struck Huger's force at three o'clock in the morning, drove in the vedettes on the main road and followed them into their camp, charging upon the American cavalry with such suddenness and force that he routed it completely. His infantry instantly attacked with the bayonet a meetinghouse where Huger's militia was quartered, and dispersed all that were not cut down.

The Americans suffered heavy losses. Major Peter Vernie of Pulaski's Legion, four other officers, and fifteen privates were killed or wounded; seven officers and sixty men were captured. The rest, including General

Huger and Colonel Washington, fled to the swamps and escaped. In addition to forty-two loaded wagons, one hundred and two wagon horses and eighty-three dragoon horses were taken, affording qualified remounts for Tarleton's dragoons. The British lost only two men.

Lieutenant Colonel James Webster, with the 33rd and 64th British regiments, joined Tarleton the next day. Together with subsequent reenforcements, they possessed all the country east of the Cooper River and down to within six miles of Charleston, cutting that town's communications with the north and leaving Lincoln without a way of retreat.

By the 19th of April, Clinton's approaches were within two hundred and fifty yards of the lines on the Neck. At last convinced of the hopelessness of his situation, Lincoln called a council of war; and the possibility of evacuation and retreat or capitulation on favorable terms was discussed. Lieutenant Governor Christopher Gadsden was, somewhat irregularly, admitted to the council and strongly opposed the abandonment of the town. This dispute between the civil authorities and the military, who were convinced of the necessity of giving up the fight, caused an adjournment of the council to the next day. When it reconvened, Gadsden brought in the rest of the members of the Governor's Council, who stood with him against the evident intention of the officers to discontinue opposition to the enemy. One of the councillors even went so far as to say that, if the Continentals showed any sign of withdrawing, the townspeople would burn their boats, open the gates to the enemy, and assist them in attacking the American troops before they could get away. Gadsden and his supporters carried the day in the council of war, but on the 21st Lincoln took matters into his own hands. He proposed a capitulation on terms allowing the withdrawal of his force with the honors of war and with their arms and baggage and an unmolested march up the east side of the Cooper River to whatever destination they chose, also the unmolested withdrawal of the American ships. Clinton, of course, instantly and curtly refused the proposal. So the fight, such as it was, went on.

A sortie of 200 men with the bayonet only attacked the British lines on the Neck. A few of the enemy were killed, and a few captured. The British took a small work on Haddrell's Point on the mainland across the Cooper River opposite the town. Arbuthnot landed a body of seamen and marines on Sullivan's Island to take Fort Moultrie. The garrison, 200 men, surrendered without resistance. Tarleton attacked the remains of Huger's cavalry at Lenud's Ferry on the Santee, killed or captured 30 or 40 of them and dispersed the rest. By May 8 Clinton's approaches were close to the American lines, and a sap had drained the ditch across the Neck. All was in readiness for an assault when the British again demanded surrender.

Lincoln could not get away if he tried. He was hemmed in on every side by 14,000 of the enemy, including sailors from the fleet who had been landed to work the siege guns. But he still temporized, asking for a truce while terms were discussed. This was granted, and a correspondence with Clinton was prolonged until the evening of May 9. The two points on which agreement could not be reached were Lincoln's demand that the militia in the town should not be held as prisoners of war, and that upon surrender the garrison should march out with the honors of war, colors unfurled and drums beating a British march. Clinton and Arbuthnot denied both demands. They would not release the militia, nor would they allow the Continentals to march out with colors unfurled to the beating of either a British or an American march.

At eight o'clock in the evening of the 9th of May hostilities were renewed. The garrison fired the first gun, and then all the guns on the fortifications began a tremendous cannonade. Nearly 200 pieces of artillery were fired simultaneously, mortars threw shells in air that crossed one another and burst like meteors; "it appeared as if the stars were falling to the earth." [2] said Moultrie. The whole thing was aimless, a mere outburst of sound and fury, relieving the feelings of the garrison, but effecting nothing, yet it was kept up all night. The enemy, replying with everything they had, set many houses on fire. It was a night of horror that broke the spirit of the townsmen, who until now had resisted submission, and they petitioned for a surrender.

Lincoln then accepted Cornwallis's terms. The Continental troops were to be prisoners of war. The militia were to be allowed to go to their homes, being regarded with the armed citizens as prisoners on parole. At eleven o'clock [3] in the morning of May 12, all the Continentals marched out, [3] with colors cased and drums beating a Turkish march, and piled their arms beside the Citadel. The militia followed them later in the day and also gave up their arms. So Clinton took the town, 5,466 Continentals, militia, and armed citizens, 391 guns, 5,916 muskets, 15 regimental colors, 33,000 rounds of small-arms ammunition, over 8,000 round shot, 376 barrels of powder, all the remaining American vessels, and a great quantity of military stores, at a cost of only 76 men killed and 189 wounded. The American losses were also light, 89 Continentals killed and 138 wounded. Among the militia there were not more than a dozen casualties. The surrender was one of the greatest disasters suffered by the Americans during the whole war.

CHAPTER 62

Civil War in the South

Charleston having been captured, Clinton's next effort was to reduce the interior parts of the Carolinas to subjection to the crown. He sent out a series of detachments composed almost wholly of Tories, and for the next three months the Carolinas were the scene of the most furious and ferocious partisan warfare. Within that period, there were five engagements between the militia of the states favoring the American cause and their Tory opponents. British regulars had little part in any of them. It was a civil war, and it was marked by bitterness, violence, and malevolence such as only civil wars can engender.

Cornwallis proceeded first to occupy the interior parts of South Carolina. He sent Lord Rawdon with the 23rd and 33rd British regiments, the Volunteers of Ireland, a Tory corps raised by him in Philadelphia, Tarleton's Legion, Browne's and Hamilton's corps of Tories, and a detachment of artillery, about 2,500 men in all, to establish the principal post at Camden. Major McArthur with two battalions of the 71st Highlanders advanced to Cheraw to cover the country between Camden and Georgetown, where a Tory corps was posted. To connect Camden with Ninety-six, Lieutenant Colonel Turnbull with the New York Volunteers and some Tory militia was stationed at Rocky Mount. The remote post at Ninety-six was held by three battalions of Royal Provincials and some light infantry under Lieutenant Colonel Balfour. Lieutenant Colonel Browne with his own Florida Rangers and certain other detachments was posted at Augusta, Georgia. Major Ferguson with his American Volunteers was assigned to the country between the Catawba and the Saluda. The rest of the British troops were stationed at Charleston, Beaufort, and Savannah. Thus from Cheraw in the extreme northeast a strongly held line of posts ran across the northern part of the state through Camden to Ninety-six, while the posts at Georgetown, Charleston, Beaufort, and Savannah held the seacoast.

This unopposed occupation of such an extensive territory is eloquent evidence of the complete subjection of South Carolina at the time. After Lincoln's army had been captured there were no troops left in the state to oppose the enemy. The few small bodies of patriot militia coming to the relief of the besieged town had precipitately retreated to their homes to melt into the civil population as inconspicuously as possible.

A regiment of 350 Virginia Continentals and a small party of William Washington's horse led by Colonel Abraham Buford had advanced as far as Lenud's Ferry on the Santee, not more than forty miles from Charleston, when the town was surrendered. Huger sent them orders to retire to Hillsboro, North Carolina. Cornwallis sent Tarleton after them with 40 of the 17th British Dragoons, 130 of the cavalry of the British Legion, Tarleton's Tories, and 100 mounted infantry of the same corps. Both forces moved with great rapidity, and not until May 29 at the Waxhaws, a district near the North Carolina border now in Lancaster County, was Buford overtaken, after a march of 154 miles in fifty-four hours in which some of Tarleton's horses fell dead from the heat and were replaced by others taken from the inhabitants. Tarleton sent forward a flag, representing that he had 700 men, cavalry, infantry, and artillery, and that Cornwallis was close behind with nine British battalions. Under these falsely stated conditions, which made resistance seem vain, he called on Buford to surrender on the same terms as had been granted to the garrison at Charleston. Buford took counsel of his officers and decided to march on, maintaining the best rearguard action that was possible. He accordingly refused the offered terms and began to march.

But, in this short interval of truce, Tarleton had prepared for action. His right wing was composed of 60 of his own dragoons and as many of his mounted infantry, now on foot; his centre, of the 17th British dragoons and part of the Legion horse; his left, of 30 chosen horsemen and some infantry.

Immediately upon receiving the refusal of his terms, Tarleton's bugles sounded and his force swept down upon Buford's rear guard. They were cut down to a man. Buford, surprised by the suddenness of the attack, disposed his men to receive it; but, instead of throwing his wagons into a line across his front as a barricade peculiarly advantageous in opposing a cavalry attack, he drew the men up in open ground. He made another mistake in holding his fire until the enemy were within thirty feet of his line. That delay was fatal to him.

The shock of his volley came upon the enemy's horse too late to stop or even to confuse them. The impetus of their charge carried them against the Americans, broke their line, swept around both flanks, and left them a huddled defenseless mass. Buford hoisted a white flag and ordered his men to ground their arms. But Tarleton would not stay his troops. They fell upon the unarmed Americans with sword and bayonet. Cries for quarter were answered with slashing and stabbing steel. Men who had fallen wounded were bayoneted. Across the field and back the ferocious Tories raged seeking half-dead men to kill. Where one man lay on top of another, he was stabbed and then thrown off to expose the man underneath. The affair was a savage slaughter of helpless men.

A hundred of Buford's infantry, who had been in advance on the march, managed to get away. Buford himself with a few other mounted men escaped. Of the rest 113 were killed; 150 were so badly wounded that they could not be moved; 53, mostly wounded, were taken prisoners. Tarleton lost 5 killed and 12 wounded. Three regimental colors, four guns, a quantity of ammunition, and twenty-six wagons loaded with clothing and military stores fell into his hands. From that time on, "Tarleton's quarter" became a byword to describe relentless slaughter of surrendered men.

This little affair extinguished the last flickering flame of resistance in South Carolina. The British power throughout the state was thoroughly established. Clinton went back to New York with about a third of his troops, leaving Cornwallis and a mixed force of six British, one Hessian, and six Tory regiments, about 8,300 rank and file, in the South.[1]

With South Carolina and Georgia well under control, North Carolina was Cornwallis's next field for action. Its Loyalists gave glowing accounts of their strength and urged him to come over and conquer; but the extreme heat of the summer and the scarcity of provisions inclined him to remain in his camps until later in the year. There were, however, plenty of restless Tories in the Old North State who were disinclined to delay. One of these, John Moore of Ramsour's Mills, returning from service under Cornwallis early in June in a tattered suit of Provincial regimentals with a sword at his side, announced himself as lieutenant colonel of Hamilton's North Carolina Tory regiment. He raised a force of 200 Tories and encamped. Others flocked to his standard until, by June 20, he had 1,300 men, three-quarters of them armed.

In the meantime the North Carolina patriots were preparing to resist invasion. General Griffith Rutherford called on the militia, who responded to the number of 800 at a plantation near Charlotte. They were organized in three divisions: a body of 65 horse equipped as dragoons, under Major

William R. Davie; a battalion of 300 light infantry, under Colonel William L. Davidson, a Continental officer; and the remainder, infantry, under Rutherford. With this force, he decided to attack Moore's Tories. Colonel Francis Locke gathered another body of 400 patriot militia at Mountain Creek, not far from Ramsour's Mills, and also decided to go after Moore. With three small companies of mounted men in the van and the rest, an unorganized crowd of inexperienced, undisciplined, armed civilians, following in double file, Locke set out on June 19 to surprise Moore.

The Tories, equally irregular in organization and discipline, were encamped on a hill, with a picket guard of 12 men thrown out six hundred yards in front. At the approach of Locke's horse, this guard fired and fled to the camp, throwing it into confusion. The horsemen galloped after them up the hill, outstripping their own infantry. The unarmed Tories took flight, but the rest, seeing only the patriot horsemen, opened fire and drove them back down the hill until Locke's foot came in sight, formed a line at the foot of the slope, and opened fire. Responding to it, the Tories fell back to the top of the hill and over its brow. Their fire was renewed; and they came forward again, but when a small party of patriots gained their right flank and another their left, they again retreated to the hilltop. There was no concert in the movements of Locke's militia, no central command. Each captain led his men as he deemed proper at the moment. The simultaneous flanking of the Tories was purely accidental.

But Locke's force had, by these haphazard movements, gained the rear of the Tories and now fell upon them at close quarters. Neither side had any bayonets. Muskets were clubbed and fell upon heads vengefully. The Tories had green twigs in their hats; the rebels had pieces of white paper. These were the only distinctive equipment, and they lost their virtue when the hats fell off in the struggle and both forces were commingled. Doubtless many a patriot musket fell upon a patriot head, and many a Tory was struck down by a companion. For a while the combat was equal; but the Tories finally began to get the worst of it, broke through, and fled down the far side of the hill to a creek and across it, where they halted.

Thinking that his foe was about to renew the fight, Locke tried to re-form his men on the hilltop. Only 110 of the original 400 could be assembled, and he sent word to Rutherford, who was on the march, to hurry. But there was no fight left in Moore's men. They sent a flag to Locke asking for a truce to collect their wounded and bury their dead. While he was considering it, they ran off singly or in small parties. Moore got away with 30 men and joined Rawdon at Camden.

The affair sounds like a comic opera encounter, but it was far from playful. Of Locke's 400, not more than 250 were in the fight. Of these more than 150 were killed or wounded. Of the Tories, about 700 were engaged; and their casualties were equal in number to those of the patriots. The fight on the hilltop was a desperate hand-to-hand struggle, the crudity of the weapons equaled by the ferocity with which they were employed. The result was the crushing of the Tory element in that part of North Carolina.[2]

The downfall of Charleston and the activity of the British thereafter encouraged the South Carolina Tories to organize and join in repressing the rebels. On May 29 a party of Tories near Winnsboro was defeated and dispersed by Colonel William Bratton and Captain John McClure, leading a party of patriot militia. A similar group near Fishing Creek was similarly dealt with. To counteract these patriot successes, Lieutenant Colonel Turnbull, in camp at Rocky Mount, South Carolina, detached Captain Christian Houk (or Huck) with 30 or 40 dragoons, 20 mounted infantry of the New York Volunteers, and about 60 Tory militia, with orders to "collect all the royal militia on his march" and "push the rebels as far as he deemed convenient." Houk succeeded in increasing his force to about 400. With these he visited the house of Captain McClure, where Mrs. McClure, her son James, and her son-in-law Edward Martin were molding bullets. He plundered the house and took the two men prisoners, announcing that he would hang them the next day. Colonel Bratton's house was also looted, but no prisoners were taken. Houk then went on to Williamson's plantation, adjoining Bratton's, and camped for the night.

Bratton and McClure were thirty miles distant in camp with General Thomas Sumter's militia force when Mary McClure brought the news to her father. They led 150 mounted volunteers against Houk, and were joined by Captain Edward Lacey, Jr., Colonel William Hill, and Colonel Thomas Neal, militia officers, with 350 other volunteers. It was an entirely irregular force with no organization, led by officers with no authority. Every move was decided by vote of all the volunteers. In consequence, there was such misunderstanding of orders that 150 rode away from the rest and never stopped until they had reached Charlotte, North Carolina, forty miles distant. The remaining 350 went on to find Houk.

The division of sentiment in South Carolina is illustrated by an incident on this march. The little army had to pass the house of Edward Lacey, Sr., who was as much a Tory as his son was a patriot. To prevent him from alarming Houk, Captain Lacey set a guard about the house. But the old gentleman escaped and was on his way to Houk's camp, two miles distant, when he was recaptured and, by his son's orders, tied up in his bed.

By the time the patriots came near Williamson's plantation, 90 of them had fallen away. The remainder were divided into two parties to attack Houk's camp simultaneously on two sides. At dawn of July 12, they advanced from both directions, got between the camp and the picketed horses of the enemy, and opened fire from behind fences. Houk's force attempted resistance, but was overwhelmed by the fire from the fences. When Houk was shot from his horse and fell dead the patriots leaped the fences and charged upon the camp. The Tories threw down their arms and fled. They were pursued a dozen miles, and many were shot down in this pursuit. In all, Houk's force lost 30 to 40 killed and about 50 wounded. The rebels had one man killed. The two young men condemned to death were found tied up in a corncrib, and were of course released.[3]

Emboldened by the successful attack on Houk's force, many men in the neighborhood joined Sumter at Mecklenburg, in North Carolina about 35 miles north of the South Carolina line, building his force up to nearly 600. Sumter then decided to strike at Turnbull's post at Rocky Mount, the origin of Houk's expedition.

It was a strong position by nature and had been reenforced by art. On a high hill on the west bank of the Catawba, three log houses, perforated with loopholes and encircled by an open wood, were surrounded by a ditch and an abatis. They were garrisoned by 150 New York Volunteers and a detachment of South Carolina Loyalists. Sumter's attacking force consisted of Colonel Hill's and Colonel Lacey's South Carolina militia and Colonel John Irwin's Mecklenburgers, an unknown number. Turnbull had learned of their advance and was prepared to receive them.

"With all the impetuosity which characterized the movements of this gallant officer," Sumter attacked, but was repulsed three separate times by fire from the log houses. He then ordered an assault. Colonel Thomas Neal led the forlorn hope, which got through the abatis; but he and five of his men were killed in the attempt and many others were mortally wounded. Despairing of success, Sumter drew off his men and retired to Land's Ford on the Catawba. The Americans lost 14 men killed or wounded, the enemy about the same number.[4]

The actions at the Waxhaws, Ramsour's Mills, Williamson's plantation, and Rocky Mount were affairs of short duration, irregularly fought by small numbers of combatants. The next encounter between the patriots and Tories in South Carolina assumed the form and proportions of a real battle.

At Hanging Rock, twelve miles from Rocky Mount, Major Carden, with a detachment of infantry from the British Legion, Colonel Morgan Bryan's regiment of North Carolina Loyalists, a detachment from the Prince of Wales Loyal American Volunteers, and part of Colonel Thomas Browne's regiment of Rangers—in all, about 500 men—held a strong position on a high, rolling plain, its front covered by a deep ravine and a creek. Sumter, with 500 North Carolina militia under Colonel Irwin and Major William Davie, and 300 South Carolinians under Colonel Lacey and Colonel Hill, all being mounted infantry, marched from Land's Ford on the Catawba in the evening of August 5 to attack Carden.

In Carden's camp the Prince of Wales Loyal Americans were posted on the right, the Legionaries and Browne's Rangers held the center, and Bryan's Loyalists the left, which was separated from the others by a wood. Approaching the camp, Sumter split his force into three divisions: Major Davie on the right with his "dragoons" and a mixed corps of militia from both states, Irwin in the center with his Mecklenburg men, and Hill on the left with the South Carolinians. They were to ride to a point near the enemy's center and dismount. Then each division was to attack the corresponding part of the enemy's force. Misled by their guides, all three were brought opposite the enemy's left. Having dismounted, the entire corps fell upon Bryan's Loyalists. Attacked in front and on their flank, they were routed and with heavy losses fled in confusion to the center.

Pressing on, Sumter's men were met by a heavy fire from the Legionaries and the Rangers, and their advance was checked. Twice their opponents charged with the bayonet. While this part of the battle was being hotly fought, Carden took his Prince of Wales Loyalists on a circuit and gained the wood between his center and his left, thus bringing them down on Sumter's flank just as the Legionaries and the Rangers broke and retreated from their camp. This unexpected attack on their flank might have routed Sumter's men, confused as they were in the fight with the Legion and the Rangers. But they faced their new foes and, from behind trees, opened such a deadly fire that almost every officer was shot down and so many of the men fell that the rest threw down their arms and surrendered.

The camp was now open to plunder and, in great disorder, the victors seized their opportunity. The commissary's stores were ransacked. Liquor was found and disposed of on the spot. No thought was given to the still existing though scattered forces of the enemy, while an orgy of looting and drinking occupied the attention of nearly all the triumphant militiamen. In this state of affairs Carden saw a chance to retrieve his fortunes. A number of his Tories were got together near the center and formed into a hollow square. A larger body was collected in the wood. Sumter and his officers did their utmost to organize a new attack, but only about 200 men could be induced to leave their plundering and join Davie's dragoons for more fighting. These opened fire on the square, which was supported by two fieldpieces, but without much effect. Davie did, however, succeed in routing the other body in the wood.

A new danger now threatened Sumter in the shape of two companies of cavalry of the British Legion, which came into view. Davie's "dragoons" charged them and drove them into the woods. In this situation, Sumter decided that a retreat was necessary. Loaded with plunder, the disorganized militiamen, many of them intoxicated, left the scene of action, Davie's dragoons bringing up the rear and herding the stragglers forward.

The contest had lasted nearly four hours and had been fought with obstinacy and determination on both sides. Of the 500 Tories in the camp more than 200 were killed or wounded. The Prince of Wales detachment was wiped out, only nine escaping death or capture. The losses of the attacking party were never ascertained. It is noteworthy that the battle was fought entirely by Americans—patriots and Tories—not a single British soldier being present.[5]

De Kalb Marches Southward

As has been said, Washington in November, 1779, sent the North Carolina and Virginia Continentals south to reenforce Lincoln in Charleston. But when, in April, 1780, he learned that Rawdon was about to take 2,500 men down to join Clinton's army in South Carolina, he decided to "put the Maryland line and the Delaware Regiment, with the 1st Artillery of 18 field-pieces, under marching Orders immediately" to give "further succour to the Southern States." [1] Of these troops and this movement a military historian of the war has said: "It is just here that one fact in the struggle for American Independence should have specific notice. From 1776 before Boston and through the entire war, the states of Maryland and Delaware were represented on nearly every battlefield. Although their troops were few in numbers, they were distinguished for valor." [2] The Baron de Kalb was placed in command of the force sent southward.

Major General the Baron de Kalb was, in some particulars, a close parallel to General Steuben. Like Steuben a soldier of fortune, he also availed himself of fiction to support his pretensions to command in the American army. He called himself "Baron de Kalb," but he was not a baron nor had he a right to use the aristocratic particle "de." His name was simply Johann or Hans Kalb. He was the son of a Bavarian peasant. In 1737, at the age of sixteen, he left home. Nothing is known of his career until 1743, when he reappears as Jean de Kalb, a lieutenant in a French infantry regiment. The change in his Christian name and the assumption of "de" were intended to secure practical advantages. In the European armies of that period no commoner might hope for a commission; all such advancement was reserved for the aristocracy. Hans Kalb's merit as a soldier would have availed him not at all. Jean de Kalb might and did rise from the ranks.

For four years the young lieutenant fought in the European wars with credit. In 1747 he was a captain and regimental adjutant. At the outbreak of the Seven Years' War he was a major. Before long he became a lieutenant colonel. After the peace, in 1763, he married Anne van Robais, daughter of a wealthy French manufacturer. On the death of her parents four years later, she inherited the family homestead at Courbevoye, and with it a tidy fortune.

In 1767 the Duc de Choiseul sent De Kalb to America to "inquire into the intentions of the inhabitants," to report on their resources, "their plan of revolt," their strength and leadership—all, of course, to determine whether France should assist them in obtaining independence and thus injure Britain. De Kalb made an extended tour of the colonies and brought back a full report, but found Choiseul more interested in European than in American affairs. De Kalb remained inactive in civil life until 1776, when it became clear that a real war was on in America, and that there was a field for the military activities that he longed for. The Duc de Broglie recommended him to the American agent in Paris, Silas Deane, who engaged him, with a promise of a major general's commission. How he came to America with Lafayette and how he got his commission have already been told.

In person De Kalb had distinction. His aide-de-camp, Nicholas Rogers of Baltimore, described him as "a perfect Ariovistus, more than six feet tall." His countenance was engaging; he had a high forehead, keen hazel eyes, aquiline nose, strong chin, and an expression of good nature mixed with shrewdness. His physical endurance was extraordinary; he often made twenty to thirty miles in a day on foot, preferring "that exercise to riding." His "temperance, sobriety and prudence" were noteworthy. He would arise before day, work until nine, then take a slice of dry bread with a glass of water. After performing his morning duties, he partook of soup and a bit of meat, washed down with water, his only drink. His supper was as frugal as his breakfast. He bore the hardships of war with "patience, long-suffering, strength of constitution, endurance of hunger and thirst and a cheerful submission to every inconvenience in lodging," and would "arrange his portmanteau as a pillow and, wrapping his great horseman's cloak around him, stretch himself before the fire" and sleep soundly. Though ambitious for advancement in his calling, he was single-hearted and honest; energetic and enterprising, he yet tempered his actions with caution and common sense.

Brave to the point of temerity, he was an ideal leader of a combat force in action.[3]

There was some delay in getting started. When the quartermaster general reported that he was unable to make provision for the march Washington was disturbed; he wrote, on April 13, 1780: "How they will get on for want of Provisions, Transportation &ca., Heaven alone can tell, I cannot." [4] But the detachment broke camp at Morristown on the 16th, set out on its long journey, and somehow did get on. It numbered about 1,400 of all ranks.[5] The first brigade was composed of the 1st, 3rd, 5th, and 7th Maryland regiments under Brigadier General William Smallwood; the second, of the 2nd, 4th, and 6th Marylanders and the regiment of Delaware under Brigadier General Mordecai Gist. Their route was through Philadelphia to the Head of Elk in Maryland and thence by water to Petersburg, Virginia, the artillery following by land. De Kalb himself lingered in Philadelphia in an effort to procure wagons, of which he got only enough to carry his tentage; the soldiers were obliged "notwithstanding the heat of the season, to carry their own baggage." [6]

From Petersburg they marched at the rate of fifteen to eighteen miles a day into North Carolina.[7] Having news of the fall of Charleston, to the aid of which he was marching, De Kalb was somewhat at a loss as to his next move.[8] He held his men in camp at the plantation of General Parsons in Granville County on the border of that state. It had been Washington's idea that these Continentals would serve as a nucleus around which the patriot militia of the southern states could gather, making up a force sufficient "to check the progress of the British troops and prevent their getting intire possession" of South Carolina, also to encourage the rebels and depress the Tories.[9] De Kalb, accordingly, hoped for reenforcements while holding his troops in Granville County.

Reenforcements were disappointingly slow and few. There were no accessions of any importance. So he had to go on with his own troops. They marched on June 21, and arrived on the 22nd at Hillsboro,[10] thirty-five miles to the southwest. It was a hard journey. The soldiers, carrying all their baggage on their backs, suffered from the heat and from "the most voracious of insects of every hue and form," especially the ticks. "My whole body is covered with these stings," De Kalb wrote to his wife in France.[11]

At Hillsboro they rested a week, and then went on. With every mile they marched, their difficulties increased. North Carolina had been relied upon for provisions and transportation within its borders; but nothing was prepared. De Kalb sent requisitions and remonstrances to its governor without the slightest result.[12] Still they struggled forward for three days to Chatham Court House, thirty miles. There they rested three days; then on again one day to Deep River where they had to stop again, for they had no food at all.[13]

They had been living on the country, foraging as they went. The inhabitants had about exhausted the last year's crop of corn, and the new crop was not yet ripe. The foraging parties scraped the bottoms of the farmers' granaries and got little. For meat, they had only the lean, half-starved cattle that ran wild in the woods. They themselves were as lean as the cattle. One of them wrote of their hardships: "We marched from Hillsborough about the first of July, without an ounce of provision being laid up at any one point, often fasting for several days together, and subsisting frequently upon green apples and peaches; sometimes by detaching parties, we thought ourselves feasted, when by violence we seized a little fresh beef and cut and threshed out a little wheat; yet, under all these difficulties, we had to go forward." [14] But at Buffalo Ford on Deep River there was no going any farther. They lay there for two weeks.

Major General Richard Caswell was in the field with a numerous force of North Carolina militia. De Kalb had reason to believe that the state was taking care of its own, and that a junction with Caswell would not only strengthen his army but also relieve its wants. He called on Caswell to join him; but that gentleman preferred the personal distinction of an independent command and the glory of harrying Tories who had fled to the woods and swamps. He offered excuses and held aloof.[15]

Brigadier General Edward Stevens with some Virginia militia was supposed to join De Kalb, and Lieutenant Colonel Porterfield with a hundred other Virginians was somewhere about. But neither of these came to De Kalb's camp. With his unaided and uncared-for alien Continentals, many of them ill with dysentery induced by unwholesome food, and Colonel Charles Armand's Legion, formerly Pulaski's, of 60 horse and 60 foot, which had joined him, De Kalb was lying at Buffalo Ford when he received news of action of the Congress concerning the southern campaign.

Lincoln, formerly in command of the Southern Department, was in captivity. As De Kalb was the senior officer in the department, that command had devolved upon him. But he was a foreigner, and, though a thorough and widely experienced soldier and an officer of proved ability, he was little known in Philadelphia and had no influential friends or patrons to urge his merits upon the Congress. His continuance in the chief command was hardly considered.[16]

Washington's choice for the position was Nathanael Greene, undoubtedly the ablest of his major generals.[17] But the Congress had its own man in view, none other than Horatio Gates, the victor at Saratoga, about whose head hung an aureole of glory. Congress loved him; so "with almost unbecoming haste" and without asking Washington's advice, "though not ignorant of his opinion," it ordered Gates "to repair to and take command of the southern department." [18]

Gates Takes Command

Gates got word of his preferment at his plantation in Virginia and gladly accepted it. He received a sardonic warning from his friend and neighbor, Charles Lee: "Take care lest your Northern laurels turn to Southern willows." De Kalb received the news with no regrets. He wrote on July 16 that he was "happy to hear of Gates's coming." He also mentioned the difficulties he had encountered and his present condition: "Altho I have put the troops on short allowance for bread, we cannot get even that . . . no assistance from the legislature or executive power. . . . The design I had to move nearer the enemy to drive them from the Pedee River, a plentiful country, has been defeated by the impossibility of subsisting on the road. . . . I could hardly depend on any but the Maryland and Delaware regiments of my division and Col. Armand's legion and all those very much reduced by sickness, discharge and desertion." [1] He had been obliged to leave four pieces of artillery at the Roanoke River and six at Hillsboro for want of horses to draw them. He had now only eight guns. He intended to move up Deep River and join the recalcitrant Caswell, who had a considerable force of North Carolina militia.

De Kalb had marched to "Hollinsworth's Farm on Deep River" before Gates arrived on July 25. The meeting of the two generals was marked by proper ceremonies, including a salute of thirteen guns. Gates was polite; De Kalb was courteous and cheerful. While assuming command of the whole Southern Department, Gates confirmed De Kalb in command of his own division of "the grand army" (Gates's phrase); namely the Maryland and

Delaware troops. The rest of "the grand army" was but Armand's 120 and three small companies of artillery.[2]

Gates had now "an army without strength, a military chest without money."[3] Of the population around him, the patriots were depressed, the Tories elated and swarming everywhere. He faced a victorious enemy, strong, strongly posted, and planning to spread its conquests wider and wider. He might have been dismayed by the situation of affairs.

He took hold at once with all the vigor and decision to be expected from a great military genius. It had been De Kalb's intention to move southwest by way of Salisbury and Charlotte and so around to Camden, a circuitous route. But the forthright Gates would have none of that. The Grand Army must go at once, and by the most direct road, to Camden.[4]

Although the road De Kalb had intended to take was more circuitous, the country it traversed was fruitful, and the people were well affected towards the Revolution. Rowan and Mecklenburg counties, in which Salisbury and Charlotte lay, were chiefly inhabited by patriotic Scotch-Irish, and magazines of supplies and hospitals could be provided there. From Charlotte he could strike directly south to Camden and make an attempt upon it, with the comforting assurance of a friendly country behind his army in case of retreat.[5]

On the other hand the road Gates proposed to take, while fifty miles shorter, ran through thinly peopled and infertile pine barrens, a kind of wilderness in which deep sand alternated with swamps, presenting obstacles to the passage of the artillery and the few baggage wagons. Moreover, it was crossed by many watercourses, liable to be impassably swollen by a few hours' rain. More important was the fact that the scanty stores of food and forage had long since been gathered by the enemy. In addition to these disadvantages, the road traversed the Cross Creek country, the region of all the South most unfriendly to the American cause.[6]

When Gates gave the order to take this direct road "men and officers looked at each other with blank amazement." That they should march so precipitately, "with only a half-ration for today and not even a half-ration for tomorrow"[7] seemed hardship enough. But that they should be compelled to take the hard and hungry way was simply foolishly cruel.

Colonel Otho Holland Williams of the Maryland line was urged by De Kalb to persuade Gates to shift to the other road. Williams told the General about its advantages in the way of food and friendly inhabitants and that it was the old trading road from Philadelphia to Charleston, by which supplies from the north could reach the army. He pointed out, also, that they could increase their force by additions of the militia of the two well disposed counties, and advised orders to Caswell to join the army on the way, at the mouth of Rocky River on the Pee Dee.[8] To fortify his remonstrance, he presented a paper signed by the leading officers, advising the proposed change of plan. Gates listened, and promised to call a council of officers to discuss the matter, but never did call it. The order to march stood, and on July 27 the army set out by the hard way.

Day by day, the distress of the marching men grew more severe. Food was worse than scarce; there was none in the wagons. The men lived on green corn plucked from the few cultivated fields, and on peaches, with the usual physical results. Of pigs from farmers' pens, of chickens from their roosts, there were none. There were not even any farmers; they had fled and taken everything edible with them. Now and then stray cows were found running wild, miserable lean creatures; they were devoured. The officers made soup and thickened it with their hair powder. So they struggled on, plodding through deep sand, wading through swamps.[9]

At setting out on this journey Gates had tried to silence objections as to the lack of provender by asserting that there would soon be plenty, particularly rum; wagonloads were on the way and would catch up with them within two days at the latest.[10] Unless he had information that such wagons were coming from heaven, loaded with manna, there was, to put it mildly, no basis in fact for his statement; no wagons came, nor were there any on the way.

Having ceased to look behind with hope for these wagons, the men were told to look ahead: there was an abundance of corn growing on the banks of the Pee Dee. It was there, when they came to it, beautiful to see, but green, still green. They ate it ravenously, with the same results as before.[11]

Up to this time they had gathered no new adherents. Colonel Anthony White and Lieutenant William Washington, with the remains of Lincoln's cavalry, had retired into North Carolina after their disastrous experiences at Monck's Corner and Lenud's Ferry. They now solicited the aid of Gates's authority in their efforts to recruit their corps and offered to join him. He gave them no assistance. Indeed, "he did not conceal . . . that he held cavalry in no estimation in the southern field." [12] That, in the face of Tarleton's repeated successes, is a measure of Gates's military ability. By this neglect to aid Washington and White, he deprived himself of potential additions of great value to his army.

At the crossing of the Pee Dee, on August 3, Lieutenant Colonel Charles Porterfield, who as a captain of Virginia Continentals had fought so valiantly at Brandywine, joined Gates with a hundred Virginia state troops, a much needed reenforcement.[13]

Half starved, half sick, fatigued almost to exhaustion, still the men had to go on; and they did, seventeen or eighteen miles a day, though with no good grace. There were sullen murmurs among them, ominous glances at one another, black looks for the commander; mutiny seemed imminent and doubtless was, for they had almost reached the limit of their endurance. But the regimental and company officers went among them, praised them for their fortitude, reminded them of their past good conduct, showed them their own empty canteens and haversacks, and quieted them, at least for the time.[14] Sergeant Major William Seymour of the Delawares tells of their privations in his Journal: "At this time we were so much distressed for want of provisions, that we were fourteen days and drew but one half pound of flour. Sometimes we drew half a pound of beef per man and that so miserably poor that scarce any mortal could make use of it—living chiefly on green apples and peaches, which rendered our situation truly miserable, being in a weak and sickly condition, and surrounded on all sides by our enemies the Tories." [15]

At last, at Deep Creek, some beef and a little corn were brought in. The troops ground the corn in their little hand mills, making enough meal to give each man half a pound. The officers saw to it that the privates got their mush and their johnnycakes first.[16]

In the afternoon of August 5 came a letter from Caswell; he was going to attack an enemy post. Fearing that an injudicious action might result in the destruction of Caswell's force, upon which he relied to strengthen his own, Gates ordered his men forward to join the others. Discontent, arising from acute suffering, still prevailed in the ranks, and only the personal appeals of their officers induced the men to obey. They had marched five miles the next morning when another dispatch came from Caswell: instead of attacking the enemy, he was about to be attacked by Rawdon; he wanted help and wanted it at once.[17] Gates halted his men while he and Otho Williams pushed on to Caswell's camp for more information. They found the camp in the most complete confusion and disorder. But there seemed to be no lack of food; Caswell's table was furnished with "wine and other delicacies," such as the visitors had not seen for many a day.[18] North Carolina seemed to have cared for its own.

Rawdon made no attack. On the contrary, he intended to retire before the oncoming Americans; he had made a feint to scare Caswell and had then withdrawn from Lynch's Creek to Little Lynch's Creek, within a mile of Camden. The next day Gates joined Caswell, thus adding 2,100 North Carolina militia [19] to his "grand army," but greatly weakening it as the event proved. The combined forces then marched to Lynch's Creek.

What to do next might have puzzled an abler general than Horatio Gates.

He could not stay where he was; there was no food there. If he turned to the left, Camden would be in his rear, cutting off any help from the north. If he turned to the right, to the flourishing settlements of the Waxhaws, a two or three days' march, he would seem to be retreating and the North Carolina militia would desert him. So, without any plan or purpose, he went blindly straight ahead. He apprehended his insecurity sufficiently to order his heavy baggage, "as well as a part of the women and children following the camp" sent back to Charlotte. A futile order; there was no sufficient transport for the baggage, and "the women and children clung to their protectors." [20]

On the 11th he came to Little Lynch's Creek and found Rawdon at the other side of the stream on a commanding height, the approaches to which were difficult if not impossible in the face of a hostile force. The only road across the creek was by way of a wooden bridge, and even to reach that the attacking force would have to traverse a broad marsh in full view of the enemy.[21] But, difficult as the situation appeared to be, a really capable captain might have ordered a forced night march up the creek, crossed it above, flanked Rawdon, circumvented him, and entered Camden in his rear, almost unopposed, and thus taken the baggage, provisions, ammunition, and stores held there under a weak guard.[22] De Kalb is said to have advised such a movement, but Gates's sublime self-sufficiency was proof against all advice.

Yet he had to go on somehow, to some other place, so he turned to the right from the direct road he had been so persistently following, and marched away in broad daylight. Rawdon saw him go; he called in the small garrison at Rugeley's Mill, on Gates's route, and withdrew his own force to Logtown, a mile in advance of Camden, a position offering better opportunity for resistance than Camden itself.[23]

At Rugeley's, also called Clermont, on the 14th, Gates was joined by General Edward Stevens, with 700 Virginia militia.[24] He lay there two days.

CHAPTER 65

Camden

On the same day that Stevens added 700 men to the army, Sumter subtracted 400. He informed Gates that a number of South Carolina militia had joined him, and that he proposed to attack a British wagon train carrying clothing, ammunition, and other military stores from Charleston to Camden. He wanted reenforcements. The acquisition of such supplies would have gratified the Americans, but Gates's true objective was the destruction of Rawdon's force and the occupation of Camden. Those purposes accomplished, the wagon train would have fallen into his hands without much further effort. For their accomplishment he needed every man and every musket in his command and even more. The reasonable thing was to send for Sumter and add his troops to the main army. But Gates did the unreasonable thing. He detached a company of artillery, with two fieldpieces, 300 North Carolina militia, and, worst of all, 100 Maryland Continentals, and sent them to Sumter, under command of Lieutenant Colonel Thomas Woolford of the 5th Maryland.[1] For lack of horses, De Kalb had been obliged to deplete his artillery by leaving several pieces at the Roanoke and others at Hillsboro, as has been stated. The eight remaining were now reduced to six.[2]

In the meantime Cornwallis, disturbed by the approach of the Americans, whose numbers rumor multiplied by two, had hastened from Charleston to join Rawdon. Four companies of light infantry had also come to Camden from Ninety-six. There were now in the force opposing Gates a detachment of 17 men of the Royal Artillery, three companies of the 23rd Regiment (Royal Welch Fusiliers), numbering 282 rank and file, the 33rd (West

Riding) Regiment, 283 men, five companies of the 71st (Fraser's High-landers), 237 men, Tarleton's British Legion of horse and foot, 289 men, the Royal North Carolina (Tory) Regiment, 247 men, the Volunteers of Ireland, composed entirely of Irish deserters from the American army, 287 men, a company of 26 Pioneers, and more than 300 volunteer militiamen The rank and file numbered 1,944, the total of all ranks being 2,239.[3]

Gates had the Maryland and Delaware Continentals, reduced by the wear and tear of their long and difficult marches, by sickness, by desertion, and by the subtraction of the hundred sent to Sumter, to hardly more than 900 rank and file, Armand's 120 horse and foot, Porterfield's 100 Virginia light infantry, and the Virginia and North Carolina militia of Stevens and Caswell, nearly 2,800, Colonel Harrison's three companies of artillery, 100 men and six guns, and about 70 volunteer horsemen—4,100 rank and file in all, of whom 3,052 were reckoned fit for duty. Gates, therefore, outnumbered his enemy by 50 per cent, but, of the Americans, only the 900 Maryland and Delaware troops were disciplined and veteran regulars, while the British rank and file of regulars, including the Volunteers of Ireland, counted about 1,400 rank and file.[4]

Gates decided to march to a point on Sanders Creek about seven miles from Camden. He called his principal officers together and read to them his definite orders prescribing in detail the order of a night march. He did not ask for their advice as to the proposed move. The orders were simply read to them, "and all opinion seemed suppressed by the very positive and decisive terms in which they were expressed." Consequently, no one ventured to oppose them. But they "were no sooner promulgated than they became the subject of animadversion" among all the officers, who could not imagine "how it could be conceived that an army consisting of more than two-thirds militia and which had never been once exercised in arms together, could form columns and perform other manoeuvres in the night and in the face of an enemy." [5]

It had become apparent in the council of the officers that Gates counted his force at 7,000 men. Otho Williams, his deputy adjutant general, knew this was a gross error. He called on the regimental officers for instant returns of their strength; it proved to amount to 3,052 present and fit for duty. He showed the figures to Gates. But Gates wanted neither advice nor this information. "Sir," said he, "there are enough for our purpose." [6] Terse, epigrammatic, confident, that reply might have had a place in history along with Farragut's "Damn the torpedoes! Full speed ahead!" if only Gates had not been merely Gates.

The orders stood. They called for a march at ten o'clock that night.

Armand's horse were to lead the van with Porterfield's Virginians and Major John Armstrong's North Carolinians, both acting as light infantry, in Indian file on their right and left flanks, each two hundred yards from the road. Then an advance guard of infantry was to be followed by the 1st and 2nd Continental brigades, Caswell's North Carolina militia, Stevens's Virginians, and a rear guard of the volunteer horsemen flanking the baggage train. There were elaborate provisions for action, if attacked on the way, and for rearrangement, if necessary for any reason, and an injunction of the strictest silence on the march. Armand protested against placing the cavalry in the van for night service, because of the impossibility of its approaching the enemy unheard; Gates declined to see the point.[7] He was confident of victory. "I will breakfast to-morrow in Camden with Lord Cornwallis at my table," an incredible tradition makes him say.[8] He very nearly did, though as a guest of Cornwallis, instead of as host.

Some meat and corn meal had been secured and a full ration was served out to the men. Instead of the promised rum, the usual heart warmer and even more necessary stimulant for unusual exertion, Gates had the happy thought of issuing to each man a gill of molasses from the hospital store, brought down by Stevens from Virginia; it proved to be a medicine indeed, an untimely physic.[9] The men ate voraciously of half-cooked meat and half-baked bread with a dessert of corn meal mush mixed with the molasses. "Instead of enlivening our spirits," says Sergeant Major Seymour, it "served to purge us as well as if we had taken jallap." [10] On the march, Otho Williams tells us, the men were of necessity "breaking the ranks all night and were certainly much debilitated before the action commenced in the morning." [11]

So the already tired, worn-down men, now more than half sick, started at ten o'clock of the night of August 15 on a dreary, bewildering march. There was no moon. The air was sultry with the heat and humidity of a Carolina August. Starlight made the road dimly visible to the main column; but the way of the flanking parties, difficult enough to keep through the pine woods two hundred yards from the silently marching men on the road, was obscured by the trees. So for more than four weary hours they trudged through the deep sand and the frequent swamps to nobody knew what.[12]

Then, suddenly, the silence of the night was shattered by the rattle of musketry ahead. Without the least warning they had met the enemy. By an extraordinary coincidence, Cornwallis and Rawdon, intent on surprising Gates, had marched from Camden at exactly the same hour that he had chosen for his advance from Rugeley's Mills. To the astonishment of both, they had met. The fresh British soldiers had marched more than twice as far as the weary Americans, and the advance troops of Tarleton's British and Armand's American Legion had simultaneously opened fire.[13]

Tarleton immediately charged upon Armand's men; they fell back upon the infantry vanguard and then upon the 1st Continental Brigade, throwing it into confusion and spreading consternation throughout the whole American army. But Porterfield, ever stanch, and Armstrong threw in their flankers and poured upon Tarleton's men such a heavy fire that they in turn gave way.[14] The 23rd and 33rd British infantry deployed in line across the road and checked this attack. The Americans, somewhat recovered from the first shock of surprise, also hastily formed, and for fifteen minutes or so musket fire was kept up by both sides. Then, as if by common consent, the firing ceased. Neither side wanted to fight in the dark.[15]

There were a number of casualties. The greatest loss to the Americans was gallant Porterfield, who was mortally wounded in this first encounter.[16] Prisoners were taken by both sides, and from them each learned of the composition of the other. Gates's astonishment could not be concealed when he learned that both Cornwallis and Rawdon, with 3,000 men, lay opposite him at a distance of 600 yards.[17] He at once called together his general and regimental officers. There was still time to withdraw, and De Kalb thought that should be done. When Otho Williams summoned him to the conference, he disclosed his opinion by asking, "Well, has the General given you orders to retreat the army?" [18]

The council met. "You know our situation, gentlemen," said Gates. "What is best to be done?" Each man looked at the others, those who favored a retreat being naturally reluctant to be the first to suggest it. Then "the brave, but headlong" Stevens broke the painful silence: "We must fight! It is now too late to retreat. We can do nothing else. We must fight!" The other officers looked at him, at Gates, at each other, but no one spoke. "We must fight, then," said Gates. "To your commands, gentlemen." [19]

The two armies had met in an open forest of pines, thinly set—a narrow space flanked on both sides by wide swamps. Somewhat narrower where the British were, it widened behind the Americans. Thus, if they were driven back, their wings would be out of touch with the swamps and would be open to flank attacks. Otherwise, they had a slight advantage in that they were on higher ground with a clear way of retreat, while the British had the creek, two hundred feet wide, in their rear, a trap in case of defeat.[20]

The American line was formed before daybreak: Gist's 2nd brigade, composed of one Delaware and three Maryland regiments, on the right;

Caswell's North Carolina militia in the center; and Stevens's Virginians on the left, with Armand's corps on its left flank. Smallwood's 1st Maryland Brigade was held in reserve in the rear. The artillery was posted in front of the center. De Kalb, in command of the right wing, took his post with it in the line. Gates and his staff took a position six hundred yards back of the line.[21]

When the British line was formed its left, facing Gist's brigade and part of the American center, was composed of the Volunteers of Ireland, Tarleton's infantry, the Royal North Carolina Regiment, and Colonel Bryan's North Carolina Tory volunteers; Rawdon commanded that wing. The right wing comprised the 33rd Regiment, three companies of the 23rd, and a body of light infantry, Lieutenant Colonel James Webster commanding. There was a second line composed of the Highlanders, with two 6-pounders. Tarleton's British Legion cavalry was held in column behind the second line. Two 6-pounders and two 3's were in front of the British center. The flanks of both armies rested on the swamps.[22]

There had been desultory skirmishing during the night, with little effect except to prevent the militia from getting any sleep. In the gray dawn, Colonel Williams descried the British advance. They were coming on in columns. He hurried to Captain Anthony Singleton of the artillery.

"Yes," said Singleton. "I can distinguish the grounds of their uniforms. They're not more than two hundred yards off."

"Open on them at once!" replied Williams, and galloped away to report to Gates.[23] Singleton opened fire; the enemy's guns answered. The smoke settled in the hazy atmosphere, which was soon completely befogged. The British advanced steadily and began to deploy.

Williams found Gates at his post in the rear. "The enemy are deploying on the right, sir. There's a good chance for Stevens to attack before they're formed."

"Sir, that's right. Let it be done," said Gates, and that was the last order he gave in that battle or in any other to the end of the war.

Williams hurried to Stevens and gave the order to advance. The Virginians moved raggedly and reluctantly forward. But, even if they had moved with alacrity, it would have been too late for the intended purpose; the British were already in line.

While Stevens's men hung back, Williams called for volunteers to go forward with him and draw the enemy's fire. Forty or fifty responded and ran forward within forty yards of the British line.

"Take trees, men!" shouted Williams. "Choose your trees and give them an Indian charge!"[24]

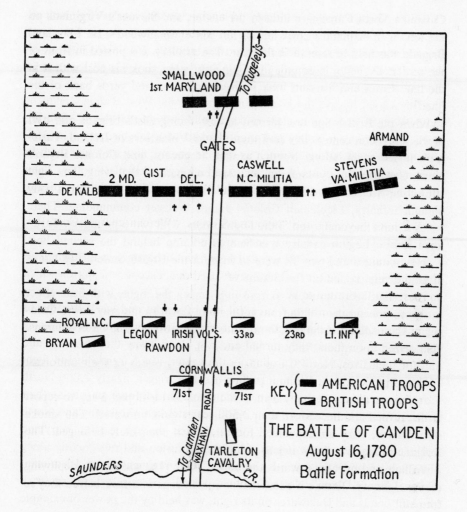

But the British line was already advancing, coming on steadily with no regard for Williams's efforts; he and his volunteers fell back to their own line. Cornwallis had seen the halting movement of the Virginians, their commander urging them forward, they hanging back. He ordered Webster to charge while the Americans were in disorder.

With a loud hurrah the Welch Fusiliers and the West Riding Regiment led by Webster came on in close ranks, a solid body of scarlet and glittering steel. They fired one volley and then charged with the bayonet. The Virginians had never before so much as seen an enemy; now they saw them in their most frightful guise. A few managed a ragged, harmless volley. Then all fell back in disorder, their leader and Williams striving mightily to rally them.

"We have bayonets, too!" shouted Stevens. "We can charge! Come on, men! Don't you know what bayonets are for?"

How could they know? They had never had a bayonet in all their lives until the very day before and had never used one, except as a spit on which to roast that last ration of beef.

They looked again at that dreadful line of scarlet and steel; they heard again the exulting cheers of those murderous Britishers. An overpowering fear seized upon them; they turned and ran, threw away their muskets and ran for their lives. North Carolina, in the center, saw Virginia in full flight and was panic-struck. Without pulling a single trigger, nearly 2,000 North Carolinians, almost as many men as the whole British force, cast away their arms, turned and fled. More than 2,500 fear-stricken Virginians and North Carolinians, "like an undamned torrent," burst through the 1st Maryland brigade in reserve, threw it into complete confusion and ran "raving along the roads and bypaths towards the north." One regiment alone, Lieutenant Colonel Henry Dixon's North Carolina, posted next to the steady ranks of the Marylands and Delawares on its right, was held by the power of example in its place.[25]

Now both the center and the left were gone, hopelessly gone. The right wing of Marylands and Delawares, under General Mordecai Gist and dauntless De Kalb, its own left wide open to the enemy, alone held the field against Rawdon's repeated attacks.

De Kalb called for the reserve, the 1st Maryland brigade. It had recovered from its confusion, but had so far had little part in the battle. His aide sought its commander, to give him the message; but Smallwood was not with his troops—he had, in fact, left the field.[26] Otho Williams took charge and brought the brigade forward in line with the American right wing. It was immediately hotly engaged. Williams tried to bring it up to the left of the

2nd Brigade, but the British were between them. In spite of his efforts, the enemy held open a gap of six hundred feet between the two.

Cornwallis saw his chance. He swung Webster's regulars against the front and flank of the 1st Maryland Brigade. The Marylanders gave ground, rallied, were driven back, rallied again, but at last were overcome and routed.[27]

Now there were only Gist's Marylands and Delawares left to fight or fly. They fought. "Firm as a rock the phalanx of de Kalb and Gist remained." [28] They had stood off Rawdon's Volunteers of Ireland, the Legion infantry, the Royal North Carolina Regiment, and Bryan's Tory volunteers, more than 1,000 men against their possibly 600—not only had held them off, but had driven them back. With one bayonet charge, they had broken through the ranks of their attackers and taken 50 prisoners. Then their left was turned, and they were forced back. De Kalb and Gist re-formed them. Again they charged, and again they were driven back. Yet once more they attacked.

It was at this point that their companion brigade was broken and swept away. The smoke and dust hung in clouds in the air, so thick that one could see but a little distance. De Kalb and Gist knew nothing of the retreat of the other brigade, were not aware of the fact that they and their few men stood alone on the field. They knew that *they* were winning their fight and thought the battle was going as well for the rest of the Americans; otherwise they would have seen that a further contest was hopeless and would have retreated as best they could, with no further sacrifice of their men. They had had no orders from Gates to retire. So they fought on, and "never did troops show greater courage than those men of Maryland and Delaware." [29] "With the same unflinching obstinacy, which they had shown at the Gowanus and on Chatterton's Hill, in 1776, the Delaware and Maryland troops contended with the superior force of the enemy for nearly an hour." [30]

De Kalb's horse was shot under him. "Long after the battle was lost in every other quarter, the gigantic form of De Kalb, unhorsed and fighting on foot, was seen directing the movements of his brave Maryland and Delaware troops." [31] His head had been laid open by a saber stroke. Captain Peter Jaquett, adjutant of the Delawares, fighting by his side, hastily bandaged the wound and begged him to retire. But no orders had come from Gates, now miles away in full flight. De Kalb still thought victory was in sight; he refused.[32]

The fighting was hand-to-hand, terrific in its fierceness. Sabers flashed and struck, bayonets lunged and found their meat, clubbed musket fell on cracked skulls. But Cornwallis, as vigilant as Gates was not, had now thrown his entire force on these last remaining foemen, 2,000 men on no more than 600.

Overwhelmed by numbers that almost entirely surrounded him, De Kalb called for the bayonet again. All together his men answered. De Kalb at their head, they crashed through the enemy's ranks, wheeled, and smote them from the rear. But ball after ball had struck their heroic leader. Blood was pouring from him; yet the old lion had it in him to cut down a British soldier, whose bayonet was at his breast. That was his last stroke. Bleeding from eleven wounds, he fell.[33]

The brigade had lost its leader, yet the worse than decimated ranks closed, advanced once more, repelled another charge—but that was all. Tarleton's cavalry, returned from pursuit of the fugitives, swept down upon them, broke their ranks, and the battle was over.

Major Archibald Anderson of Maryland rallied a few men of different companies of the Continentals; Colonel John Gunby, Lieutenant Colonel John Eager Howard, Captain Henry Dobson, all of Maryland, and Captain Robert Kirkwood of Delaware collected about 60 men. All these preserved a compact body in the retreat. Such of the rest as had not fallen or been captured scattered and fled to the swamps.[34]

Prostrate in the field lay De Kalb. It was only when the Chevalier du Buysson, his aide, threw himself on his general's body, crying out his name and rank, that the thirsty bayonets were withheld from further thrusts into his body.[35] Some of the enemy, British or Tory, carried him off and propped him against a wagon so that they might more easily appropriate his gold-laced coat. There he stood, gripping the wagon with both hands, his head in weakness bowed on his chest, bleeding to death from all his wounds, when Cornwallis came riding by, rescued him from the despoilers, and caused him to be cared for by the British surgeons. His great bodily vigor kept the life in him for three days before he died in Camden.

But where was Gates? From the time he gave that first order to Stevens, not a word of any sort had come from him to his fighting men. He had been "swept away" in that torrent of fleeing militia in the very first minutes of the battle, as some of the historians kindly describe his flight. "Swept away," he was—on the fastest horse in the army, a noted racer, "the son of Colonel Baylor's Fearnaught, own brother to His Grace of Kingston's famous Careless," [36] a fit charger for General Gates. And that gallant steed never stopped sweeping him away until he landed his master at Charlotte, sixty miles from the field of honor. There Gates slept that night.

CHAPTER 66

After Camden

"Never was victory more complete, or a defeat more total." It has been described as "the most disastrous defeat ever inflicted on an American army." [1] In the wildest disorder the beaten men were scattered everywhere; few could find their officers, who were as widely dispersed. In the swamps and the forests where their pursuers could not find them, but which separated them the more widely from one another, the fugitives found temporary refuge.

Colonel Tarleton and his horsemen pursued the fleeing Americans that kept to the road, picking up many prisoners, including General Rutherford of the North Carolina militia. At Rugeley's Mills be found Colonel Armand, with several other officers apparently trying to save and send off the baggage train, which, despite Gates's orders, had not left that camp; in fact, Americans were busy looting it. [2] They offered some resistance to Tarleton's horsemen on their approach, but were soon captured or driven away.

This chase went on for more than twenty miles; more and more of the fugitives were captured. Twenty ammunition wagons, and the entire baggage, stores, and camp equipage of the Americans, were taken. It was only when the British horses were too fatigued that Tarleton gave over the chase. [3]

Scattered in small groups or singly, looking vainly for their comrades and for leadership, the beaten men, though clear of their military foe, found themselves in a country swarming with civilian enemies. Most of them had thrown away or lost their arms and were unable to resist the Tories, "every day picking them up, taking everything from them which was of value." [4]

731

They had had no orders where to assemble in case of defeat. Those few that had retreated in more orderly fashion and escaped Tarleton, went on to Charlotte. The remains of Armand's horse and a few others also gathered there; Gist came in with only two or three men; Smallwood arrived with a handful. There was little food and no hope of defense in that open village, so they went on to Salisbury. Otho Williams has given an account of the miseries of the march to Salisbury of that "wretched remnant of the Southern army," followed by "a great number of distressed Whig families," 300 friendly Catawba Indians, wounded men from Buford's late "unfortunate affair . . . some in wagons, some in litters and some on horseback—their sufferings were indescribable . . . the disorder of the whole line of march . . . Compound wretchedness, care, anxiety, pain, poverty, hurry, confusion, humiliation and dejection would be characteristic traits in the mortifying picture." [5]

Sergeant Major Seymour of the Delawares wrote in his Journal, "We assembled at Salisbury the few that were left . . . this being the first place we made any halt. . . . From here we marched on the 24th under the command of Genl. Smallwood, directing our route for Hillsborough, which we reached with much difficulty on the 6th of September, 200 miles from Campden." [6]

Gates was already there. He had stopped only overnight at Charlotte on the 16th, the day of the battle, and had pushed on, the following morning, to Hillsboro as fast as fresh horses could carry him, arriving on the 19th, two hundred miles in three and a half days, a good record even for such a fast rider. [7]

"The fugitives from Camden came in daily, but in a deplorable condition, hungry, fatigued and almost naked" until about 700 had assembled, the meager relics of Gates's army of 4,000 men. There they must rest until they could be "completely refitted with clothes, tents and blankets"—also, most of them, with arms. [8]

The British army's casualties in the battle amounted to 324 of all ranks: 2 officers and 66 men killed, 18 officers and 227 wounded, 11 men missing. [9] Of the American loss there is no accurate record. It has been estimated that 650 of the Continentals were killed or captured, the wounded falling into the hands of the enemy. About 100 of the North Carolina militia were killed or wounded, and 300 were captured. Only 3 of the Virginians were wounded, [10] which proves the advantage of their more prompt departure from the scene. A heavy toll of Continental officers was taken in that battle: 3 were killed and 20 wounded, 14 of whom were captured—in all, 30 officers were taken. In this respect, the Delawares suffered most severely. Their commanding officer, a lieutenant colonel, their major, and 8 other officers were taken.

Gates's first job was to reorganize his shattered army. The North Carolina militia gave him no trouble; the survivors had "fled different ways as their hopes led or their fears drove them," and were so pursued and harried by the Tories that few, if any, turned up at Hillsboro. Many of the agile Virginians did appear at the camp, but their term of enlistment had so nearly expired that "all who had not deserted were soon afterward discharged." [11] It was only the Continentals that remained for reorganization.

The two brigades were compressed into one regiment of two battalions. The 1st, 3rd, 5th, and 7th Marylands became the 1st Battalion under command of Major Archibald Anderson of Maryland. The 2nd, 4th, and 6th Marylands and the Delawares became the 2nd Battalion under Major Henry Hardman of the same State. Colonel Otho Williams and Lieutenant Colonel John Eager Howard, both of Maryland, commanded the regiment.[12] In this rearrangement the Delaware Regiment became two companies of 96 men each of all ranks, under the two senior captains, Robert Kirkwood and Peter Jaquett.[13] The cavalry was embodied in one troop under Lieutenant Colonel William Washington of Virginia. The two brass fieldpieces left at Hillsboro, with a few iron pieces, composed the artillery.[14]

The initial losses of the army had been somewhat diminished by a gallant exploit of Colonel Francis Marion and 16 of his daredevils. On August 20 they fell upon a detachment of British and Tory troops escorting 160 American prisoners to Charleston. Rushing upon the guard at daybreak, before they had time to form, Marion took them all captive and released their prisoners, of whom fewer than half returned to the army. The rest were too much discouraged by their overwhelming defeat to continue in the service and left for their homes.[15]

There had been another momentary gleam of light on the otherwise dark horizon. Sumter with 300 of his own men and the 100 Continentals and 300 militia lent him by Gates, had made good his proposal to capture that British wagon train. On the 15th he took 100 British soldiers, 50 Tory militiamen, and 40 wagons laden with stores. But that gleam was quickly extinguished.

Hearing of Gates's defeat, Sumter began a retreat with his captives and wagons up the Wateree. At high noon of the 18th, while in camp on Fishing Creek, with all his arms stacked, some of his men bathing, others sleeping, himself asleep under a wagon, he was surprised by Tarleton, with 160 men. Charging on the unguarded camp, Tarleton cut Sumter's men off from their arms and routed them completely, killing 150 and capturing more than 300. All the recently taken British and Tory prisoners were released, and the wagon train recovered. In the little resistance the Americans were able to offer, one British officer was killed and 15 men either killed or wounded. Sumter himself escaped and rode into Charlotte two days later "without hat or saddle." [16]

Gates got news of this catastrophe while on his flight to Hillsboro, and it must have added gall and wormwood to his already bitter cup. Now he knew he was a hopelessly beaten man.

The reorganized American force at Hillsboro received some additions to its numbers. Colonel Abraham Buford, whose Virginia contingent had been cut to pieces by Tarleton's Legion at the Waxhaws in May, brought in its few remains and 200 new recruits. About 50 of Porterfield's light infantry also arrived. These were added to Buford's force, and they, with Colonel Otho Williams's newly formed regiment of Continentals, made up a brigade under General Smallwood, who was soon after superseded by Williams,[17] of whom some particular notice should now be taken.

He was a native of Maryland, thirty-one years old. His first military service had been with Captain Michael Cresap's Maryland Riflemen as ensign in 1775, marching with it to join Washington's army before Boston. In June, 1776, he became a major in a regiment of Maryland and Virginia riflemen which took part in the defense of Fort Washington, and he, with the rest of the garrison, was taken prisoner. Having been exchanged in January, 1778, he was appointed colonel of the 6th Maryland Continental Regiment, which became a part of De Kalb's division on his march to the south. His services in the Camden battle have been noted.

In person he was tall and "elegantly formed . . . his manner such as made friends of all who knew him." As a soldier and a man, he was highly valued by his companions in arms. His education was superior to that of most of his fellow officers.

On October 7 Gates made a new arrangement of his troops. Selected men were drawn from the Maryland and Delaware Continentals and from Buford's corps and made into three companies of light infantry. Those drafted from Buford made up the 1st Company, under Captain Peter Bruin of Virginia. The 2nd Company came from the lately formed 1st Battalion of Marylanders and was commanded by Captain Benjamin Brookes of that state. The 3rd was composed chiefly of Delawareans, with some addition of Marylanders; Captain Kirkwood of Delaware took command. To these were added 70 horsemen under Lieutenant Colonel Washington and Major Rose, also 60 Virginia riflemen. The infantry of this new *corps d'élite* were commanded by Lieutenant Colonel Howard of Maryland.[18]

Robert Kirkwood was born in New Castle County, Delaware, was educated at Newark Academy, and was engaged in farming when the war began. He was commissioned a lieutenant in Haslet's Delaware Regiment in January, 1776, and served in it until it was mustered out in December. He was a captain in Hall's regiment from its organization to the end of the war. His services in the southern campaigns will be described hereafter. Of the value of those services and his character as a soldier no better, more unbiased, more sincere estimate could be penned than the eulogium Henry Lee, a comrade in arms, included in his memoirs:

The remnant of that corps . . . from the Battle of Camden, was commanded by Captain Kirkwood who passed through the war with high reputation; and yet, as the line of Delaware consisted but of one regiment and that regiment was reduced to a captain's command, Kirkwood could never be promoted in regular routine. . . . The sequel is singularly hard. Kirkwood retired upon peace, a captain, and when the army under St. Clair was raised to defend the West from the Indian enemy, this veteran resumed his sword as the eldest captain in the oldest regiment.

In the decisive defeat on the 4th November [1791, the Battle of Miami] the gallant Kirkwood fell, bravely sustaining his point in the action. It was the thirty-third time he had risked his life for his country; and he died as he had lived, the brave, meritorious, unrewarded Kirkwood.

That gallant soldier Daniel Morgan, who had achieved fame by his splendid services at Quebec under Montgomery in 1776, and who, with his light troops, had contributed so much to the defeat of Burgoyne, had been neglected by the Congress. He had seen junior officers promoted over his head while his infinitely greater claim to rank as a general remained unrecognized. In justifiable resentment, he had resigned his colonel's commission in 1779 and retired to his home in Virginia.[19]

In June, 1780, the Congress "ordered" that he be called into service and "employed in the southern army as Major General Gates shall direct." No suggestion of even restoring him to his relative rank having accompanied the call, he declined to obey it. But after the Camden catastrophe he put aside his personal grievances and hastened to join Gates at Hillsboro, arriving late in September. On October 2 he was given general command of the newly formed corps of light infantry, and on the 13th the Congress belatedly gave him the deserved rank of brigadier general.[20]

The presence of a disorganized body of hungry soldiers made trouble in Hillsboro. The peaceful citizens complained to Gates, and he withdrew his men to a camp in the woodlands of an abandoned farm. Having no tents, they built wigwams of fence rails and poles thatched with brush and corn-stalks. Some food—not much, but more than they had had on their long march from Camden—was obtained, and gradually order was restored and discipline reestablished.[21]

But it was no picnic. Lieutenant Caleb Bennett of the Delawares wrote long afterward, "We found ourselves in a most deplorable situation, without arms, ammunition, baggage and [with] very little sustenance and for some time our situation was unenviable." [22] The light infantry corps fared some-what better than the rest of the army. The state of North Carolina, though its resources were well-nigh exhausted, managed "to collect a suit of com-fortable clothing for each one of Morgan's command before they entered upon the severe and active duties before them." Each man got one new shirt, a short coat, a pair of woolen overalls or trousers, a pair of shoes, and a hat or cap. The state also "supplied the other troops, but not so com-fortably as Morgan's." [23] There were not enough blankets to go around; what could be got were distributed to each regiment in proportion to its numbers.

C H A P T E R   6 7

King's Mountain

Sir Henry Clinton in New York was commander in chief of all His Majesty's forces in America. He had instructed Cornwallis to make the security of South Carolina, with its important port of Charleston, his main object, aiming to hold fast to what was won and not to risk it by bold and hazardous adventure. He had in mind as his next possible move the occupation of Delaware, perhaps during the following summer, with the considerable Tory element to render his army's subsistence there easy. But, even if this were not undertaken, he felt that, holding New York, South Carolina, and Georgia, he could carry on a war of attrition until the rebels were worn out and save for Britain at least a considerable part of her colonies, if not all.

After the destruction of Gates's army at Camden, Cornwallis was in practically undisputed possession of South Carolina and Georgia; a period of mere holding on to what he had would have fulfilled his duty to his superior. Clinton had, however, guardedly suggested that the conquest of North Carolina would be acceptable, provided that it could be accomplished without jeopardizing his hold on the other two states.

This suggestion gave Cornwallis a chance to do what he wanted; he was all for an aggressive war. Unless North Carolina were conquered and possessed, he said, it would endanger his posts to the southward; he might be compelled to abandon all he had gained and take refuge within the fortifications of Charleston. After North Carolina, he saw himself taking Virginia; then the rest of the south up to Pennsylvania "would fall without much resistance and be retained without much difficulty." [1] He had arranged with

737

Clinton to send his reports directly to the Ministry in London as well as to New York, thus in effect short-circuiting Clinton. The home government was induced to believe in his plans and later instructed Clinton to fall in with them. Now, it seemed to Cornwallis, was the opportune time to carry them out.

Cornwallis had concentrated his forces at Camden after Gates's defeat. There he had been reenforced by the arrival of the 7th British regiment (Royal Fusiliers) from Charleston and by some additions to his Tory regiments. From that point he now moved north in two divisions. The principal one, led by himself, comprised the 7th, 23rd, 33rd, and 71st regiments of infantry, the Volunteers of Ireland, Hamilton's and Bryan's North Carolina Tory regiments, and a detachment of horse, with four guns. It marched, on September 8, north up the left (east) side of the Wateree towards the Waxhaws. A secondary force led by Tarleton, comprising the British Legion cavalry and infantry and an additional detachment of light infantry with one small fieldpiece, marched parallel with the other up the right side of the river. At the Waxhaws, Cornwallis encamped on the left side of the river, there called the Catawba, its course at that point being from west to east. Tarleton's force made its camp on the right side at Wahab's plantation some distance away.

The American Colonel William Davie was in the neighborhood with 80 dragoons and two small companies of riflemen, commanded by Major George Davidson, the only regularly armed body of patriot troops in the whole state. Early in the morning of September 21, Davie approached Wahab's plantation. He found the cavalry of the Legion already in their saddles in a body near the house. He sent Davidson with most of the riflemen around through a cornfield, which would conceal their approach, to take the house in the rear. Leading his horsemen and the rest of the riflemen, he charged up the lane towards the front with such ardor and such a shouting that the whole enemy force gave way at once and fled, only to meet a sharp fire from Davidson's riflemen by which 60 were killed or wounded. Davie collected 96 fully equipped horses and 120 stand of arms and hastily retired to his camp at Providence before troops sent by Cornwallis could arrive on the scene. His loss was one man wounded. It may be noted that Tarleton himself at this time was ill and absent from his command.[2]

On September 25 Cornwallis resumed his northward march from the Waxhaws towards Charlotte in North Carolina, with Tarleton's Legion and light infantry in advance of the main body. Davie, with 20 horsemen, Davidson's two companies of riflemen, and a small body of Mecklenburg militia under Major Joseph Graham, was in Charlotte, a village of twenty dwelling houses and a courthouse, when Cornwallis's van approached.

Davie posted his 20 dragoons behind a stone wall near the courthouse, the rest of his men behind fences on both sides of the road to it. The infantry of the British Legion, commanded by Major George Hanger, and the light infantry deployed in line across that road and moved slowly up towards the courthouse, to be received with a close fire from the men behind the fences. From this they recoiled, though Cornwallis himself urged them on. Hanger ordered the Legion cavalry to dislodge Davie's dragoons behind the stone wall. They charged, but were stopped by the fire of the 20 men, and would not again go forward. As Stedman says, "The whole of the British army was actually kept at bay for some minutes by a few mounted Americans, not exceeding twenty in number."

Davidson's and Graham's troops abandoned their fences and joined the dragoons. Under the repeated orders of Cornwallis, the Legion infantry and the light infantry again attacked and succeeded in turning Davie's right flank. He ordered a retreat. He was pursued for several miles and lost 30 killed, wounded, or captured. The British lost 15 killed or wounded.[3]

It may be remembered that, in June, when Cornwallis was sending various expeditions to occupy posts throughout South Carolina, he had detached Major Patrick Ferguson with his American Volunteer regiment to cover the country between the Catawba and Saluda rivers. Ferguson went on to join Lieutenant Colonel Balfour, who was holding the post at Ninety-six. Thence he moved a few miles east and established his camp on Little River. It became a rallying post for large numbers of South Carolina Tories, whom he organized into seven regiments, about 4,000 men. With this strong force, Ferguson held the district of Ninety-six—the "upcountry"—in complete subjection, sending detachments in every direction to harass and plunder the rebels and making every effort to encourage the Tories to join the King's army.

At the time Cornwallis marched north from Camden, he sent orders to Ferguson to move from Ninety-six into North Carolina to spread the gospel of loyalism there and finally to join the main army at Charlotte.

Late in September, Ferguson was at Gilberttown in what is now Rutherford County, North Carolina. He had in mind the interception of a force of Carolinians and Georgians under Colonel Elijah Clark, which had made an unsuccessful attempt upon Augusta in Georgia, had been beaten off, and was now, with 300 men and 400 women and children, endeavoring to avoid the British forces in South Carolina and escape into the Old North State. But trouble was brewing for Ferguson behind the mountains to the west-ward.

Patrick Ferguson was a remarkable man. The son of a Scottish judge, he entered the British army as a cornet of horse at the age of fifteen and served in the wars on the continent of Europe until, as a captain, he came to America. He was ingenious enough to invent a breech-loading rifle which could be fired five or six times a minute, at least twenty-five times as fast as a muzzle-loading rifle when its barrel became fouled. It also used a pointed, instead of a spherical, bullet. A few such rifles were manufactured and were used with effect by the men in the British rifle corps he commanded at the Battle of the Brandywine; but for the most part his men were equipped with the muzzle-loader.

When Clinton sent the expedition south in 1779, Ferguson was allowed to raise his own corps of riflemen, American Tories, called the American Volunteers, of which he made effective use in independent operations until his death. He was a soldier of great merit, "a fit associate for Tarleton in hardy, scrambling, partisan enterprise; equally intrepid and determined, but cooler and more open to impulses of humanity." [4] Less bloodthirsty than the more famous Tarleton, he was yet a bitter foe of the rebels, whose homes he mercilessly plundered and destroyed.

Ferguson was at this time in the prime of life, thirty-six years of age, of "middle stature, slender make and possessing a serious countenance, yet it was his peculiar characteristic to gain the affections of the men under his command." [5] Though of slight build, he was strong and athletic. He was a dead shot with rifle and pistol, and, though his right arm had been disabled in battle, he was a formidable antagonist with the sword, wielded in his left hand.[6]

Beyond the mountains on the west, in what is now Tennessee, were the Watauga settlements inhabited by a hardy breed of frontiersmen, mostly Scotch-Irish, hunters, Indian fighters, expert shots with their long-barreled Deckhard rifles, weapons of precision. Their only other equipment was a horse, a blanket, a hunting knife, and a bag of ground, parched corn sweetened with maple syrup. When this gave out, they lived on the game that the country afforded. They were not only rebels, but bitter enemies of Ferguson himself, whose merciless plundering in the Carolinas had made his name infamous. To them he audaciously sent word that if they did not desist from opposition to the king he would march over the mountains, hang their leaders, and lay waste their country with fire and sword. This message was not well received.

The Watauga men had an idea that, if any fighting was to be done, it ought to be in the enemy's country rather than among their farms and homes and women and children. Colonel Isaac Shelby of Virginia and Colonel John Sevier accepted the challenge. They called on Colonel William Campbell of Virginia to join them. Campbell summoned Colonel Benjamin Cleveland of North Carolina. To Sycamore Flats on the Watauga River, by September 25, Colonel Charles McDowell of North Carolina brought 160 men, Sevier brought 240 "over-mountain men," Shelby brought 240 of the same, Campbell brought 400 Virginians. They were mostly mounted but, with their long rifles, would fight on foot. Ferguson called on Cornwallis for reenforcements; the over-mountain men called on Heaven, the Rev. Samuel Doak being their mouthpiece. In a service of prayer before they set out, he asked for the aid of "the sword of the Lord and of Gideon."

Ferguson started south towards Ninety-six. The "backwatermen," as Ferguson called them, followed. At the Catawba River Colonel Cleveland joined them with 350 North Carolinians. Ferguson eluded his pursuers, who thought he was for Ninety-six, by turning east towards King's Mountain. They came to the Cowpens, west and somewhat south of the mountain, on October 6. There Colonel James Williams with 100 North Carolinians and Colonel William Graham with 60 joined them, making their total force over 1,400. Having news of Ferguson's real route, they decided that 900 of the best mounted men should push after him as rapidly as possible, the rest to follow. On October 7 the forerunners came to the mountain on which Ferguson had established himself, with the announcement that "he defied God Almighty and all the rebels out of Hell to overcome him."

King's Mountain afforded a position of extraordinary natural strength. Its level summit was about 500 yards long and 70 to 80 yards wide, but broadened to 120 yards at its northeast end, where Ferguson had fixed his camp. Its steep, rocky, heavily wooded sides rose about 60 feet from the plain below. He had about 100 Rangers, picked men from the King's American Rangers, the New Jersey Volunteers, and the Queen's Rangers, also 1,000 Tory militia. The Rangers were men of a good class. The second in command was Captain Abraham de Peyster of New York. Another captain was Samuel Ryerson of New Jersey. The adjutant was Anthony Allaire of New York, and the surgeon was Dr. Uzal Johnson of New Jersey. These men were as well trained and experienced as regular soldiers. They were equipped with bayonets and well drilled in their use. The local Tory auxiliaries were provided with long blades to be fitted into the muzzles of their rifles or muskets and used as bayonets. It is a remarkable fact that Ferguson was the only British soldier in the ensuing battle, one of the most important of the war. On both sides, all the rest were Americans.

The patriots reached the mountain about noon of October 7, 1780, dismounted, fastened their blankets and coats to their saddles, tied their horses, and took positions in a line around its broader end and along the sides of its narrower part nearly to its southwestern extremity, Campbell's troops at the southwest end of the line on one side, Shelby's on the other. These two forces were to begin the attack, swarming up their respective sides and meeting so as to enclose Ferguson's at the broad end. A war whoop signaled the attack. The drums in the camp called their men to arms.

Shelby met the first fire. He restrained his men from replying until they had got nearer the top. Campbell could be heard shouting, as his men climbed the mountain: "Here they are, boys! Shout like hell and fight like devils!" Shelby's men were driven back by a bayonet charge part way down the height. Having no bayonets, they could only take trees and fire up at their enemy; and they did this with deadly effect.

Meanwhile, the rest of the rebels around the broad end of the mountain were climbing, taking cover, and firing. Cleveland's men gained the top, and Ferguson sent his bayonets at them, driving them back as he had driven Shelby's; but they, too, kept up their fire. Campbell and Shelby had again come on, and again Ferguson's bayonets repelled them. But Sevier's corps was now on the summit, and he had to turn to them. The bayonet was only a temporary resource. It might drive the attackers before it; it could not stop the bullets from the Deckhard rifles, aimed by dead-shot frontiersmen. All the rebel contingents came into the fight with unrestrained fury. Everywhere the Tories were surrounded by men, not in solid bodies to be attacked with the bayonet and driven back, but fighting each man on his own behind the trees fringing the open plateau. From every side came a hail of bullets.

The position of the Tories was hopeless, but Ferguson would not give up. He was everywhere on the field animating his men. Twice, when white flags were raised, he cut them down with his sword. To an officer who begged that the carnage might cease, he replied that he "would never surrender to such banditti." But at last he had to admit that the battle was lost. With a few others he tried to cut a way through the ring of his enemies. A rifle bullet stopped him. He fell from his horse and died with one foot caught in his stirrup.

His men, in terrified disorder, crowded behind their wagons and tried to keep up the fight. Cleveland brought up his force behind them. Completely surrounded, they fled to a hollow place. But there was no shelter there. They stood like a herd of deer in a corral, while the infuriated Whigs shot them down, crying, "Buford! Buford! Tarleton's quarter!" One of them rode out of the press showing a white flag. His saddle was emptied. Another met the

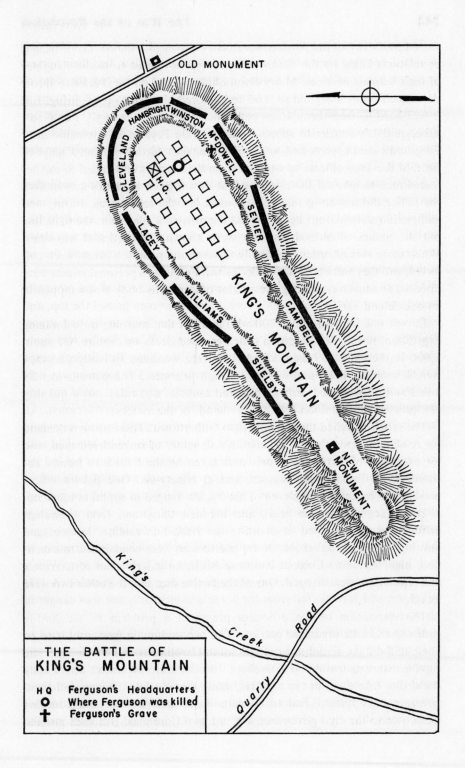

OLD MONUMENT

HAMBRIGHT WINSTON

CLEVELAND

McDOWELL

H.Q.

SEVER

LACEY

KING'S
MOUNTAIN

CAMPBELL

WILLIAMS

SHELBY

NEW
MONUMENT

King's

Creek

Road

Quarry

THE BATTLE OF
KING'S MOUNTAIN

H Q   Ferguson's Headquarters
○   Where Ferguson was killed
✝   Ferguson's Grave

same fate. Many of the patriots were bent on avenging the deaths of friends or relations killed by the Tories. They would not desist from the slaughter of their helpless enemies. Major Evan Shelby called on the Tories to throw down their arms. They did so, and he implored his men to cease firing. But it was hard to stop them. Campbell rode to the front crying: "For God's sake, quit! It's murder to shoot any more!" De Peyster, in command after Ferguson's death, protested to Campbell against further killing. Campbell ordered the Tory officers to separate from their troops and called to the defeated men to take off their hats and sit down. Even after this submission, the killing did not altogether cease; but at last the rebels ceased firing and gathered in a circle, four deep, around the prisoners, glaring at them, calling out the names of individuals who were known for particular atrocities. When some sort of order was finally restored the prisoners' arms were collected, and they were confined under guard. Ferguson's personal effects were divided, as souvenirs, among the patriot officers. His body was wrapped in an oxhide and buried.

Except one body of about 200 who had left that morning on a foraging expedition, not one of Ferguson's men escaped death or capture. Of about 1,000 in the fight, 157 were killed, 163 were wounded so badly that they were left on the field, and 698 were taken prisoners. The patriots lost 28 killed and 62 wounded. Fifteen hundred muskets and rifles and a quantity of stores and ammunition fell into the hands of the victors.

The rebels marched their prisoners to Gilberttown. There arose a demand for retaliation upon them for Tarleton's slaughter of surrendered men, and for execution of forty patriot prisoners taken by the British in former encounters, at Camden, at Augusta, and at Ninety-six. One patriot officer present had recently seen eleven of his friends hanged to suppress rebellion. A sort of court was convened, and between thirty and forty individual prisoners were convicted of assisting the British in raiding, looting, and burning houses of the rebels. Of the twelve who were condemned to execution, nine, including Colonal Ambrose Mills, an elderly man of character and reputation, were hanged. One of the twelve escaped; the other two were let off.

The disposition of the prisoners presented a problem to the hastily gathered and little organized patriots. The over-mountain men wanted to go home and did go, as did most of the South Carolinians and Virginians. The captives were entrusted to Cleveland's North Carolina men, who finally decided to take them to Gates at Hillsboro. Gates asked Thomas Jefferson, governor of Virginia, what to do with them. Jefferson suggested turning them over to the civil governments of the two Carolinas. But such governments hardly existed. In this impasse they were loosely guarded and within a few months all but sixty escaped.[7]

The effect of the victory at King's Mountain was instantaneous and of great importance. It turned the tide of the war in the south. On receipt of Ferguson's appeal for help, the very day of the battle, Cornwallis had sent Tarleton. Tarleton heard of the disaster on the way and returned in all haste to Cornwallis at Charlotte with the news. Rumor magnified the numbers of rebels to 3,000, and the British commander feared they would sweep around him into South Carolina and capture Ninety-six and Camden. Though the fear was baseless, it was true that the patriots of Mecklenburg and Rowan counties had been aroused and the partisan corps of Marion, Sumter, and Pickens were increasing in numbers and were more and more active. They did present an immediate danger to the British.

Cornwallis abandoned at once his project for the subjugation of North Carolina and, on October 14, started his troops on a hurried retreat. The rainy season had set in, and for several days rain fell incessantly. The roads were deep with mud, the swampy parts almost impassable. There was a lack of provision; for one five-day period the soldiers lived on corn gathered from the fields. Lacking tents, they spent the nights in the open, lying on wet ground. And always they were harassed by the American militia, hanging on their rear and cutting off baggage wagons. There was much sickness; Cornwallis himself, stricken with fever, lay in one of the wagons. After fifteen days of this wretched flight they reached Winnsboro, between Ninety-six and Camden, and encamped.[8]

For some time the two armies lay in camp, the Americans at Hillsboro, North Carolina, the British at Winnsboro, South Carolina. Morgan's newly organized light troops made an expedition to Salisbury and down into Mecklenburg County to cooperate with the local militia, but nothing "of consequence" happened.[9] Then, having heard of a Tory outpost at Rugeley's Mills, South Carolina, William Washington's horsemen marched against it.

Colonel Rugeley with 100 Tories occupied a log barn surrounded by an abatis. It was impregnable to bullets, the horsemen could do nothing with it, and Washington had no artillery. He fashioned a log into the semblance of a gun and propped it up on the stubs of three of its limbs. This "Quaker gun" was pushed boldly to the front by some of his dismounted men. The garrison was summoned to surrender or have their fortress blown to pieces. They surrendered, and Washington led the colonel, a major, and 107 privates back to Morgan's camp at New Providence, where Gates with his main force also came and established his camp.

Though there was no major activity on the part of the two armies at this time, Marion's irregulars were busy in South Carolina between the Pee Dee and the Santee River, arousing the people to revolt against the British, threatening the enemy's communications between Camden and Charleston, and cutting off supply trains. Cornwallis sent Tarleton after him. The Swamp Fox successfully eluded Tarleton's stronger force.

Sumter was active in the same country. Against him Cornwallis sent Major Wemyss with a part of the 63rd Regiment mounted and 40 of the British Legion horse. At Fish Dam Ford in what is now Chester County, Wemyss came upon Sumter's camp on November 9 and attempted a surprise; but he was on guard, and when Wemyss dashed upon the American pickets he was received with a volley. Two bullets hit and disabled him. His second in command pushed on, but Sumter from behind a fence poured upon the enemy such a fire that 28 of them were shot down. Further attempts were fruitless. Wemyss was captured, as were 25 of his men, and the rest retreated.[10]

Sumter then crossed the Broad River and, having received considerable additions to his force, threatened Ninety-six. Cornwallis was alarmed. He recalled Tarleton from his pursuit of Marion and ordered him to go after Sumter, taking the men of the 63rd who had been with Wemyss, along with his own Legion. Sumter was apprised of his danger by a British deserter. He crossed the Enoree River and marched to Blackstock's plantation on the south side of the Tiger. Tarleton followed so rapidly that his foot soldiers could not keep up. He pushed on with 170 of the Legion horse and 80 mounted men of the 63rd, leaving the footmen to follow.

Blackstock's was on high ground, the slope of the hill being quite abrupt and covered with brush and thickets. The Tiger River swung around the American rear and right flank. A road led past the buildings of the plantation, a house and a log barn, and Sumter posted part of his men in these, the rest along fences skirting the road. His whole force numbered 420 men.

Tarleton saw the strength of the American position and paused at the foot of the hill for his foot soldiers to come up, meanwhile dismounting the infantry of the 63rd to fight on foot. Sumter took advantage of the division of his enemy's force. He directed Colonel Elijah Clark with 100 men to pass Tarleton's flank and get between him and the infantry he was expecting. Sumter led a corps against the men of the 63rd. Under heavy fire, the British charged up the steep hill and drove Sumter back, Tarleton's horse following in support. But near the buildings they met a concentrated fire from the men posted in them and had to retire. Tarleton tried again, without success. He was finally obliged to retreat.

The Americans claimed that Tarleton's casualties amounted to 92 killed and 100 wounded, an impossible number if, as he claimed, only 250 of his men were actually in the fight. He admitted a loss of 51 killed and wounded. Of the Americans, 3 were killed and 4 wounded, one of them Sumter, who was shot in the right shoulder.

Sumter, fearing another attack by the 71st Regiment and the rest of the 63rd, who had been sent in support of Tarleton, withdrew across the Tiger River. This withdrawal seems to have been the basis of Tarleton's extraordinary claim of success in his attempt, in which he said 100 Americans had been killed and wounded and 50 captured. The prisoners appear to have been civilians picked up on his withdrawal to Winnsboro, one of whom he hanged. The only advantage actually gained by Tarleton was the temporary disablement of Sumter.[11]

C H A P T E R   6 8

Before Cowpens

The Congress had been unfortunate in the selection of commanders in the South. It had chosen Robert Howe, and he had lost Savannah and all Georgia. It had chosen Benjamin Lincoln, and he had lost Charleston and all South Carolina. It had chosen Horatio Gates, and he had lost all the rest of the south and his army. When his successor was to be chosen the Congress decided to entrust the choice to Washington. On October 5 it resolved "that the Commander-in-Chief be and is hereby directed to appoint an officer to command the southern army, in the room of Major General Gates." [1]

Washington delayed not at all in making his selection. On the day after he received a copy of the resolution, he wrote to Nathanael Greene at West Point, "It is my wish to appoint You." The Congress approved the appointment, gave Greene command over all troops from Delaware to Georgia with extraordinarily full powers, "subject to the control of the Commander-in-Chief"—Gates had reported to Congress only—and adopted Washington's suggestion that Steuben go south with Greene.[2] From the very beginning of the war, Greene had been Washington's right arm and had displayed indefatigable industry and strength and breadth of intelligence. Indeed, in the opinion of some well qualified judges he was Washington's superior, both as strategist and as tactician.

Whether his appointment was a misfortune, Greene was in doubt. Certainly, in the state of affairs in the south, there was little promise of an easy task or of a successful result of the best efforts he could put forth. Nevertheless, he was not "altogether without hopes of prescribing some bounds to the ravages of the enemy." [3] With that modest program he accepted the appointment and was soon on his way to his new command.

Henry Knox had promised him a company of artillery with four field-pieces and two light howitzers, and Quartermaster General Timothy Pickering was to send him two companies of artificers. In Philadelphia he asked Joseph Reed, president of Pennsylvania, for four or five thousand stand of arms. All Reed and the Board of War could furnish was fifteen hundred. He called on the Congress for clothing, but they had none to give him. He tried to get the Philadelphia merchants to furnish five thousand suits and take bills on France in payment, but they excused themselves. Reed promised him 100 "road-wagons"; and Pickering, 40 "covered wagons." From the Congress he got $180,000 in Continental currency, which was worth practically nothing in real money. Having begged Washington "to urge unceasingly the necessity of forwarding supplies for the southern army, as it will be impossible to carry on a winter campaign without clothing," [4] he went on his way.

At Annapolis, Greene pleaded with the Maryland Board of War for clothing; and he wrote to Caesar Rodney, president of Delaware, for "speedy reinforcements of men and supplies of every kind." He left General Mordecai Gist in Baltimore to arrange for forwarding whatever he could get from Maryland and Delaware, and Steuben in Richmond for a similar purpose. In Virginia, Governor Thomas Jefferson told him "The situation as to clothing is desperate." By letter, Greene called again and again on the Congress and everyone else he could think of for clothing. He got assurances of good will everywhere, but very little else. Virginia and Maryland pleaded poverty so great that they could not even furnish forage for his horses. Neither Delaware nor North Carolina took "any measures for giving effectual aid" to him. [5]

On November 27 he was at Hillsboro; and on December 2, at Charlotte. There he met Gates "with respectful sympathy and Gates, whose manners were those of a man of the world, returned his greeting with dignified politeness." Otho Williams wrote that their conduct was "an elegant lesson of propriety exhibited on a most delicate and interesting occasion." [6] On the next day, Gates issued his last orders, announcing the change of officers, and Greene found himself in command of the "grand army" of the Southern Department of the United States of America. It consisted of 90 cavalrymen, 60 artillerists, and 2,307 infantrymen on paper, of whom 1,482 were present and fit for duty. Only 949 of the paper infantry were Continentals; the rest were militia. And, for a final summing up, fewer than 800 of the whole force were properly clothed and equipped. [7] Greene wrote to Joseph Reed on January 9, 1781: "The appearance of the troops was wretched beyond description, and their distress, on account of [lack of] provisions was little less than their suffering for want of clothing and other necessaries."

The first task of the new commander was the establishment of order. The troops, he wrote to Reed, had lost "all their discipline" and were "so addicted to plundering that they were a terror to the inhabitants." He saw that it was necessary to establish "a camp of repose, for the purpose of repairing our wagons, recruiting our horses and disciplining the troops." [8]

There were but three days' provisions on hand when he arrived in Charlotte, and no promise of any more. The country round about had been stripped clean by the army and, more especially, by the North Carolina militia, who had ravaged it without any compensating military service.[9] It was plain that another place must be found for the camp of repose.

Greene sent General Thaddeus Kosciuszko, a Pole on whose sound judgment and engineering ability he greatly relied, on an exploring trip. Kosciuszko reported that on the Pee Dee River near Cheraw Hill, just south of the border between the Carolinas, there was a suitable location. To that point Greene decided to go.[10] But there was a still more important decision to be made; and, in making it, Greene determined the whole course of the ensuing campaign.

With such troops as he had, in such a wretched condition, Greene could not hope to offer battle to Cornwallis. He must wait until they were refitted and reenforced. Yet he must not appear to retreat before the expected advance of his opponent from Winnsboro, lest he increase the confidence of his enemy, lower the spirits of his own men, and dishearten the people of the country, who looked to him for defense and would be valuable to him if they believed in him. But, as Cheraw Hill was more distant from the enemy than Charlotte, a removal to that point would look like a retreat and hence have the undesirable effect he wished to avoid. He must carry on some encouraging operations that would not incur the danger of a general engagement. Such operations must, in short, be partisan in nature, threatening Cornwallis's flanks, interrupting his communications, cutting off his supplies, and at the same time animating Marion, Sumter, and Pickens with their partisan bands to similar enterprises.[11]

To meet the situation, Greene made a daring decision; he decided to divide his already insufficient army. The decision was opposed to the classic rules of warfare: to divide an inferior force in the face of a superior enemy was to invite that enemy to destroy first one and then the other of the parts. There had been examples enough of the impropriety of such a division in this very war: Washington splitting his army at New York and Long Island in August, 1776; Howe scattering his Hessians in New Jersey in December, 1776; Burgoyne sending his Hessians to defeat at Bennington in August, 1777; Washington allowing Lafayette to take post at Barren Hill in May, 1778. The most recent example was Ferguson at King's Mountain. Every one of these, except Barren Hill, had resulted in disaster; and Lafayette had escaped from Barren Hill only by the skin of his teeth. To divide so vastly inferior a force as Greene's at Charlotte might seem to be suicidal.[12]

On the other hand, there were excellent reasons, even compelling reasons, to disregard the classic rule and fit the strategy of the moment to the inescapable actual conditions. The ability to do that is the hallmark of a really great general.

Greene saw that, by separating his army into two parts, he made it easier for both to subsist on the country, living on the very regions from which the British drew their supplies; and that if Cornwallis later should take the natural route back into South Carolina he would find a fighting force on each of his flanks. If he turned against the left-hand American force, that on the right might attack Charleston; if against the right-hand force, Ninety-six and Augusta would be exposed to that on the left. If he made no movement, the intended harassment of his army could be better effected. As to the danger of either division being attacked and defeated, Greene relied upon the mobility of the Americans to escape from the more encumbered, slower British. So, with all those reasons to justify him, he carried out his plan, "the most audacious and ingenious piece of military strategy of the war." [13] The proof of its validity was that it worked.

Greene had confirmed Morgan in the command of the light infantry, now composed of 320 Maryland and Delaware Continentals, 200 Virginia riflemen under Captains Triplett and Tate, and "from 60 to 100" light dragoons under Lieutenant Colonel Washington, Major Howard being still in command of the infantry. This was to be one of the two divisions. The second division, about 1,100 Continentals and militia, was entrusted to General Isaac Huger of South Carolina, Greene remaining with it.[14]

Three great rivers traversed the country in which Greene expected to operate. A knowledge of the fords and ferries and of the roads leading to them was indispensable to his safety and success. He accordingly sent Lieutenant Colonel Edward Carrington, his quartermaster, to explore and map the Dan River, and Edward Stevens, major general of Virginia militia, and General Kosciuszko to the Yadkin and the Catawba for the same purpose. They were also to collect or build flatboats to be carried on wheels or in wagons from one river to another.[15] These precautionary measures proved to be of the utmost importance in the ensuing campaign.

On December 16 Greene directed Morgan to cross the Catawba to its western side, join the North Carolina militia under General William Davidson, and operate between the Broad and the Pacolet rivers, "either offensively or defensively, as your own prudence and discretion may direct—acting with caution and avoiding surprises by every possible precaution." The main objects of the detachment were to protect the people, to annoy the enemy, and to collect and store provisions and forage. If Cornwallis moved in force towards Greene's proposed camp at Cheraw Hill, Morgan was to rejoin the main army or to fall upon the enemy's flank and rear, as occasion served.[16]

An excessive rainfall that inundated the lowlands delayed Greene's departure; but on the 20th he was on his way. The march of his army was a desperate affair: the roads were deep with mud, the horses were too weak for want of food to drag the wagons without frequent halts, and the men were not much better off. But on the 26th he arrived at his destination, Cheraw Hill, and established the camp of badly needed repose.[17] There, with his 650 Continentals, 303 Virginia and 157 Maryland militia, he was in a position to support Marion or to threaten Camden, and he was nearer than Cornwallis to Charleston.[18] It was not a bad situation, though it was 140 miles from Morgan across the Catawba.

Morgan left Charlotte the day after Greene, "marched to Biggon Ferry on Catawba River, crossed the ferry," and marched, marched, marched, under the same hardships as the other part of the army. On Christmas Day he went into camp on the Pacolet River, after fifty-eight miles in all of "very difficult marching in crossing deep swamps and very steep hills which rendered our march very unpleasant." [19] While in this camp he was further reenforced by Davidson with 120 men, and by Major Joseph McDowell with 190 North Carolina riflemen.[20]

Two days after his arrival at the Pacolet, Morgan detached William Washington with his dragoons and 200 mounted militia and sent him against a party of 250 Tories who were ravaging the country along Fairfort Creek. They rode forty miles the next day, found their enemy near Ninety-six, killed or wounded 150 of them, and took 40 prisoners, without any loss to themselves.[21]

The two divisions of the army lay in their respective camps, with only routine activity, for three weeks. To Greene in this period came a desirable reenforcement. Lieutenant Colonel Henry Lee's Legion, sent down by

Washington, arrived on January 13. It comprised 100 horse and 180 foot. About the same time Colonel John Green of Virginia brought in 400 militia. The men of Lee's Legion were worth far more to Greene than their numbers would seem to indicate. They were "the most thoroughly disciplined and best equipped scouts and raiders in the Revolution" and one of the few corps of American troops that were maintained in uniform. Their short, green coats closely resembled those of Tarleton's men. Lee was "horse-proud," and the mounts of his horsemen were "powerful, well bred and kept in high condition." On the march, the horsemen frequently took up the foot soldiers behind them and thus expedited their progress.[22] Greene sent the Legion to Marion to assist him in a stroke against Georgetown. They had a brush with the garrison there and captured its commander by surprise, but, for want of artillery, were unable to breach the "fort," in which the rest had taken refuge. They paroled the captive officer and retired.[23]

Meanwhile, Cornwallis had rested at Winnsboro, with a secure hold on South Carolina and Georgia. He too had been reenforced. His dispatches and reports to London had convinced Germain that his plan for the conduct of the war should displace Clinton's; and Clinton had taken a decision to send substantial reinforcements to the south. He had accordingly sent Major General Leslie down with 2,500 men; 1,500 of these joined Cornwallis at Winnsboro, and the others remained at Wilmington. Cornwallis then had in his army a brigade of the Guards, the 7th or Royal Fusiliers Regiment, three companies of the 16th Regiment, the 23rd or Royal Welch Fusiliers, the 33rd, the 2nd battalion of the 71st or Fraser's Highlanders, the Hessian Regiment von Bose, 600 Hessian jägers, Tarleton's Legion, and 700 Provincials or Tories, a total of about 4,000 men.[24] It was a force so much greater in numbers, so much better trained, armed and equipped than Greene's whole army of 3,000 tatterdemalions that one would have supposed Cornwallis secure in his position and confident of the future. In fact, he was much disturbed in mind.

Greene's splitting of his army had astonished him, shocked his sense of the proprieties of warfare; it seemed to him audacious to the verge of recklessness. Tarleton could not believe Greene would have done it if he had known of Leslie's addition to the British army. It offered such a good opportunity for an advance from Winnsboro, "which, if executed with tolerable rapidity, might separate the two divisions of the American army and endanger their being totally dispersed or destroyed." [25] But Cornwallis saw the situation more clearly.

He saw what Greene had seen: that if he attacked Huger's force Morgan might strike at Ninety-six and Augusta; if he went for Morgan the way to Charleston would be open to Greene. He therefore saw he could only follow the unorthodox example of his opponent and divide his own army—not into two parts, but into three.[26]

He sent Leslie to hold Camden against an attack by Huger's division. He directed Tarleton to find and crush Morgan, while he himself, with his main army, moved cautiously and slowly up into North Carolina to intercept and destroy the remains of Morgan's force after its expected defeat by Tarleton.[27]

His orders to Tarleton, then posted at Ninety-six, were set forth, on January 2, in these terms: "If Morgan is still at Williams' or anywhere within your reach, I should wish you to push him to the utmost. . . . No time is to be lost." To which Tarleton replied: "I must either destroy Morgan's corps or push it before me over Broad river towards King's Mountain." Cornwallis answered that Tarleton had understood his intentions "perfectly."[28]

Cowpens

Tarleton's force comprised his own Legion, 550 horse and foot; a battalion of the 7th (Royal Fusiliers) Regiment numbering 200; a battalion of the 71st (Highlanders) Regiment, 200 men; 50 of the 17th Light Dragoons; a small detachment of the Royal Artillery, and a party of Tory militia of unknown number. The whole numbered about 1,100 rank and file, with two light fieldpieces, 3-pounders called "grasshoppers." [1] Morgan's corps, as has been noted, consisted of 320 Continentals, 200 Virginia militia riflemen, about 80 of Washington's dragoons, and Davidson's 140 and McDowell's 200 North Carolina and Georgia militia riflemen.[2] On the march, he was joined by Lieutenant Colonel James McCall with 30 mounted South Carolina and Georgia militia,[3] making his total force up to about 1,040, nearly equal in numbers to Tarleton's corps. In trained regulars Tarleton outnumbered him more than three to one.

Tarleton's first move was made on January 15, north across the Enoree and Tiger rivers towards Morgan, then on the south side of the Pacolet. Having news of this advance, Morgan crossed the Pacolet with the intention of defending the ford; but Tarleton, on the 16th, crossed the river six miles below him. Morgan then withdrew precipitately to Thicketty Creek, his adversary occupying the ground, on which he had lain the night before, a few hours after it had been vacated.[4] Early in the morning of the 17th, Tarleton resumed his pursuit of the Americans, who retired to the Cowpens, where "a certain prosperous Loyalist, named Saunders" [5] used to roundup his ranging cattle. At this place Morgan decided to stand.

His choice of battleground has been severely criticized. It was in "a wide plain covered with primeval pines, chestnut and oak," free from undergrowth and therefore open to Tarleton's horsemen, three times as many as his own and of the best quality. There were no swamps or thickets upon which to rest the flanks of a battle line or to offer a refuge from cavalry. At a short distance in the rear and around the left of such a line drawn up to face Tarleton's advance, the Broad River curved, cutting off a retreat to the north or east towards Greene and Huger.[6] Henry Lee has pointed out that beyond the Broad, near King's Mountain, there was a position disadvantageous to cavalry, convenient for riflemen, and affording means of retreat. The Cowpens position was a most unlikely place for a small force to choose for battle, presenting every opportunity for its wings to be turned and for complete destruction in case of defeat. Yet Morgan chose it and afterwards stoutly defended his decision:

I would not have had a swamp in view of my militia on any consideration; they would have made for it, and nothing could have detained them from it. And, as to covering my wings, I knew my adversary, and was perfectly sure I should have nothing but downright fighting. As to retreat, it was the very thing I wished to cut off all hope of. I would have thanked Tarleton had he surrounded me with his cavalry. It would have been better than placing my own men in the rear to shoot down those who broke from the ranks. When men are forced to fight they will sell their lives dearly and I knew that the dread of Tarleton's cavalry would give due weight to the protection of my bayonets and keep my troops from breaking as Buford's regiment did. Had I crossed the river, one half of my militia would immediately have abandoned me.[7]

The argument seems labored, to excuse an unmilitary decision. The truth seems to be that Morgan, a fighter by nature, was irked by being obliged to retreat before Tarleton, and turned on his foe because he wanted to give battle, disregarding the weakness of his position. Henry Lee thought that his choice of that field grew out of "irritation of temper" which "overruled his sound and discriminating judgment," and that "confiding in his long-tried fortune, conscious of his personal superiority in soldiership and relying on the skill and courage of his troops," [8] he simply decided to stop his backward movement and fight it out where he happened to be.

Whatever may be said of his choice of ground, there is no criticism of the disposition of his troops for the battle. It was novel, ingenious, and masterly.

Having been joined by Pickens with 70 North Carolina riflemen the evening before the battle, Morgan, who, though a general, was far from being a "brass hat," visited the campfires, talking and joking with his men in their own language, his voice cheerful, his manner confident and reassuring. He told them that "the Old Wagoner" (his nickname) would crack the whip over Ban Tarleton in the morning as sure as he lived. "Just hold up your heads, boys," he said to the militia, "give them two fires and you're free." They had a good night's rest and a full breakfast the next morning.[9]

After breakfast Morgan formed his battle line. Behind and to the north of the ground where his men had bivouacked was a slight eminence, rising gradually for about three hundred and fifty yards and then sloping northward into a swale. Behind that the ground ran to a lesser eminence, which in turn sloped northward to a plain, beyond which ran the river. The whole terrain was covered by an open wood.

His disposition of his men was as unorthodox as Greene's division of his army. On the southern and higher elevation, he formed his main line. Howard's light infantry of Maryland and Delaware Continentals held the center. On their right were Tate's Virginia militia and a small company of Georgians, and on their left Triplett's Virginians. These militiamen were mostly old Continental soldiers who had served their terms of enlistment and rejoined as volunteers. This line contained in all about 450 men. Howard commanded it.

About one hundred and fifty yards in front, 300 North and South Carolinia militia under Pickens were posted in open order in a thin line three hundred yards long. In front of them, at a similar interval, 150 picked riflemen, Georgians and North Carolinians under Major John Cunningham of Georgia and Major Charles McDowell of North Carolina were thrown out in line as sharpshooters. Back of all these, and behind the lesser rear eminence, Morgan posted as a reserve 80 of William Washington's dragoons and 45 of Lieutenant Colonel James McCall's Georgia mounted infantry armed with sabers to operate as cavalry.[10]

The formation was unusual in that it put the weakest contingents so far in front of the battle line to receive the first shock of the attack without immediate support from the regulars. But Morgan's plan was well considered as suitable to the character of his own troops and of his enemy, as was disclosed by his orders for the conduct of the battle.

The sharpshooters in the front line in irregular formation were to take cover behind trees. They were to withhold their fire until the advance of the enemy was within fifty yards, and then to take careful aim at "the men with the epaulets." After two volleys they were to retire slowly, firing at will, and fall into the spaces in the second line of militia.

The second line, thus reenforced, was to fire "low and deliberately," was not on any account to break, but, when too hard pressed, was to retire to the left and so around to the rear of the main formation, where they would, Morgan told them, be perfectly safe. There they were to rally, re-form, and be held in reserve. Those orders were not given to the officers only; every man was informed of the plan of action, and all in the second line were especially cautioned not to be alarmed by the falling back and apparent defeat of the men in front of them; it was all a part of the plan.[11] The baggage had been sent under suitable escort a few miles to the rear, and the horses of the militiamen in the first two lines (they were all mounted) were tied to trees behind the cavalry reserve, an arrangement very consoling to their owners as affording a means of swift retreat in case of disaster.

This disposition having been made, the men were told to "ease their joints"—that is, to sit down—until the enemy was sighted, but not break their formation. Morgan then rode along the lines, encouraging the men with homely exhortations. The disposition had been made without haste and in a confident and assured manner. As a consequence, the men were in good spirits and ready for a fight.

Tarleton, eager to fulfill his promise to destroy Morgan's corps or push it back towards King's Mountain, where Cornwallis would finish it off, had allowed his men little rest that night. At three in the morning they were afoot. For five hours, mostly in the dark, they marched on muddy roads, through swamps and creeks and over broken ground, covering eight very long miles, before they came in sight of the Americans.[12]

When he first perceived his enemies Tarleton, with a small party, rode forward to reconnoiter their position. A sight of the first line of riflemen checked him before he was near enough to observe satisfactorily the main battleline. He at once ordered his Legion cavalry forward to dislodge the sharpshooters. As the horsemen came on, they received a volley that emptied fifteen saddles. They recoiled, so convinced of the marksmanship of the always dreaded riflemen that they could not be induced afterwards to charge upon the Americans. The front-line men, still firing at will, then retired and took their places in the second line.

Tarleton thereupon deployed his troops in battle formation, his light infantry on the right, the infantry of the Legion in the center, and the 7th Regiment on the left, with 50 dragoons flanking each wing. The Highlanders and 200 cavalry formed the reserve. The "grasshoppers" were placed in the center and on the left. This disposition had hardly been effected when the impetuous Tarleton opened the battle with his guns and immediately sent his whole line forward.

The second line of the Americans, under Pickens, waited until the enemy were "within killing distance." Then, taking careful aim, they delivered their fire, reloaded, and fired again with deadly accuracy. A large proportion of

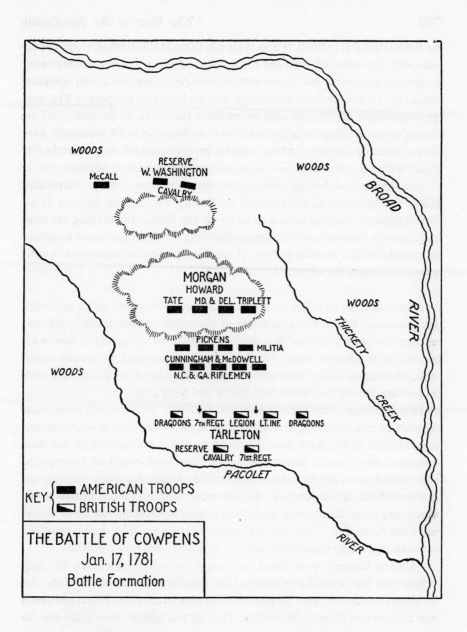

WOODS

McCALL

RESERVE
W. WASHINGTON
CAVALRY

WOODS

BROAD

MORGAN
HOWARD
TATE   MD. & DEL. TRIPLETT

WOODS

THICKETY

RIVER

WOODS

PICKENS
MILITIA
CUNNINGHAM & McDOWELL
N.C. & GA. RIFLEMEN

CREEK

DRAGOONS 7TH REGT. LEGION LT. INF. DRAGOONS
TARLETON
RESERVE
CAVALRY 71ST. REGT.

PACOLET

RIVER

KEY { ■ AMERICAN TROOPS
      ◧ BRITISH TROOPS }

THE BATTLE OF COWPENS
Jan. 17, 1781
Battle Formation

the British that fell in the battle were struck down at this time. The oncoming line checked, wavered, but came on again. Pickens's men, according to orders, turned about and ran across to the American left to seek shelter behind the Continentals. Those on the right had to make a long traverse, and the dragoons on the British right swept down on them.

Suddenly, to the astonishment of their enemies, Washington's and Mc-Call's horsemen appeared from behind the rear eminence, which had concealed them. Swords in hand—they had been ordered not to fire their pistols —they charged the pursuing British dragoons and routed them completely. Pickens's troops gained their desired refuge.

The flight of the first lines was taken by the British for the beginning of a retreat of Morgan's whole force. Shouting their triumph, they rushed against the main American line. Howard's Continentals and Tate's and Triplett's Virginians surprised them—they stood fast. Kneeling for greater accuracy and aiming low, they fired volley after volley. Checked, but advancing again, the equally courageous British line came on relentlessly. There was hot fighting in this phase of the battle for nearly half an hour.

Then Tarleton called on his reserve of Highlanders, extended them on his left, and sent them forward. His line now stretched beyond the American right. Howard saw that he would be outflanked. He ordered the company on his extreme right to face about in line and then wheel to the left so as to make a right angle with the others and repel the flankers. The order was misunderstood; they faced about, but instead of wheeling to the left, marched in good order towards the rear. Those on their left and then the whole line, thinking that a general retirement had been ordered, also faced about and without haste or disorder marched back with the others.

Howard was not displeased with this movement, because it extricated his whole line from the threatened outflanking. But Morgan, surprised at the withdrawal, hurried to him and challenged him with, "What is this retreat?"

"A change of position to save my right flank," answered Howard.

"Are you beaten?" asked Morgan.

"Do men who march like that look as though they were beaten?"

"Right!" said Morgan. "I'll choose you a second position. When you reach it, face about and fire." They went back over the hill and down into the depression behind it.

Seeing this withdrawal, Tarleton was sure of his victory. He ordered up his Legion cavalry and threw everything he had against the Americans. His men, each eager to outstrip the others, broke ranks and ran forward in tumultuous disorder. Washington, pursuing the British dragoons, had got in advance of the American line and seen the confusion in the British ranks, not visible to the others behind the hill. He sent word to Morgan: "They're coming on like a mob. Give them one fire, and I'll charge them."

Morgan received the message just as Pickens's riflemen, having made a complete circuit of the field, came up on his right. He gave the order to the Continentals: "Face about, give them one fire and the day is ours!" The British had followed the Americans over the hill first occupied. Coming down its rear slope in a mad rush, they were within fifty yards of their enemy when Morgan's order was obeyed. The whole line faced about and blazed with gunfire. The Americans fired from the hip, holding their muskets with bayonets ready. The shock was terrific. Howard seized the moment for the final order: "Give them the bayonet!" Into the tangled ranks of Tarleton's infantry and the Royal Fusiliers, the Maryland and Delaware Continentals drove with irresistible force. At the same time, Washington and McCall struck them on the flank and in the rear. Bayonet and saber split the throng of redcoats and tore it apart.

"Throw down your arms and we'll give you good quarter!" shouted Howard. Muskets clattered on the ground; some of the British ran, others stood, crying for mercy. The American officers were put to it to hold their men from giving the beaten foe what they called "Tarleton's quarters," which meant the bayonet to disarmed men, but they succeeded.

In the center the battle was over; but on the American right the Highlanders held out, and the British dragoons from their left wing were still active. Pickens's riflemen, re-formed and ready, opened upon these with such a destructive fire that the dragoons fled; but the stubborn Highlanders fought on. Not until the whole weight of the Americans fell upon them did they yield. Then their commander, Major McArthur, gave up his sword to Colonel Pickens.

Meanwhile Tarleton had been urging his reserve of 200 dragoons to go forward from their post in the rear. They refused to move. He tried to protect and remove his artillery. Washington attacked him and drove his men from the field, but the British artillerists stood to their guns. They were the last to be overcome; they never did surrender. Almost to a man they were struck down at their posts.

Washington followed Tarleton, who, with a few officers and about 140 horsemen, was in full retreat. In the ardor of the chase, Washington got well ahead of his troop. Seeing that, Tarleton and two of his officers turned and attacked him. One of them aimed a stroke at him; but an American sergeant who had come up caught the blow on his saber and wounded the assailant in the arm. Another officer was about to cut Washington down when a fourteen-year-old bugler shot him with his pistol. Tarleton thrust at the American colonel; when the blow was parried he fired, wounding Washington's horse, and galloped away. Washington kept up pursuit of the fugitive infantry and took many prisoners. The British baggage guard cut the horses loose, mounted them, abandoned the wagons, and got away.

The victory was complete in every particular. The British lost 100 killed, among them 39 officers. Prisoners were taken to the number of 229 wounded and 600 unhurt. In all, nearly nine-tenths of the entire British force were killed or captured. Of the Americans only 12 were killed and 60 wounded. The two British guns, 800 muskets, two stand of colors of the 7th Regiment, 35 baggage wagons, 100 dragoon horses, 60 Negro slaves, and a quantity of ammunition fell into American hands.[13]

News of the victory at Cowpens was received with delight throughout the country. In Greene's camp at Cheraw it was celebrated by a *feu de joie*. South Carolina made Pickens a brigadier. Virginia gave Morgan a horse and a sword. The Congress, in an enthusiastic resolution, praised and thanked him and his troops for obtaining "a complete and important victory" over Tarleton's "select and well appointed detachment," and gave him a gold medal. To William Washington and Howard it awarded silver medals and swords and to Pickens a sword. This battle again proved the value of militia properly handled. Also it gave a deathblow to Tarleton's reputation as a military leader.

It had other far more important results. Though "small in scale" it was "momentous in result." [14] In the opinion of John Marshall, "Seldom has a battle, in which greater numbers were not engaged, been so important in its consequences as that of Cowpens." [15] It gave Greene his chance to exercise his strategical genius in the conduct of a campaign of "dazzling shiftiness" that led his opponent by "an unbroken chain of consequences to the catastrophe at Yorktown which finally separated America from the British crown." [16]

C H A P T E R   7 0

Cornwallis Pursues Morgan

In the moment of his victory the cool-headed Morgan did not forget that his position was still precarious. Cornwallis's much greater army was in the field and might be near at hand. The British general had agreed with Tarleton to march his men to King's Mountain to cut off Morgan's retreat; but he seems to have been apprehensive of danger to his right flank from the army of Greene and Huger. He moved only a few miles from Camden and then waited a week, until Leslie, on the way to join him, had crossed the Wateree. On the day of the battle, instead of being at King's Mountain in Morgan's rear, he was twenty-five miles to the south.[1]

Nevertheless, he endangered Morgan. In five or six hours after the battle, Tarleton's fleeing cavalry would bring him news of the catastrophe at Cowpens; and, marching light and with speed, he might yet intercept Morgan's column, encumbered with a mass of prisoners nearly two-thirds of its own number. Moreover, the road Morgan had to travel to escape to the north met at Ramsour's Mills the road Cornwallis would take to cut him off, and the distance to that point from Cowpens was about the same as the distance from Turkey Creek, where Cornwallis had halted and still held his army. Even if the British general detached only a thousand infantry with a few pieces of light artillery, and sent them posthaste to Ramsour's Mills, he could without doubt hold Morgan until the rest came up to finish him off. It was plain that only the utmost expedition on Morgan's part would suffice, not only to save the fruits of his victory, but also to avoid disaster.[2]

Morgan's first duty was to his wounded men and to those of the enemy. He detached Pickens and a number of mounted militia to gather them up and care for them as best they could; after that they were to bury the dead. Of the enemy's baggage, he prepared to carry off as much as he could that might be useful, especially tents, of which he had none, and ammunition. The abandoned muskets were also collected. Though the battle was not over until about ten o'clock, the retreat was under way towards the east by a little after noon. Between Morgan and Greene ran four rivers: the Broad, the Catawba, Lynch's Creek, and the Pee Dee. Marching six miles, Morgan crossed the Broad and encamped. Pickens, having set up tents for the wounded on the battlefield and having left them in care of the surgeons under a flag of truce, joined him the next day.[3]

Early in the morning of the 18th, after sending out patrols to secure information as to the movements of Cornwallis's army, Morgan pushed on towards the fords of the Catawba. At Gilberttown he detached Pickens with the greater part of the militia and an escort of Washington's cavalry to conduct all the prisoners towards Island Ford on a branch of the Catawba, while he himself took the Continentals and the rest of the militia to Sherrill's Ford on the main stream.[4]

On the evening after the battle Cornwallis, in his camp at Turkey Creek twenty-five miles away, was still awaiting Leslie's reenforcement when a hard-riding courier on a well lathered horse brought him the news of Tarleton's defeat. Since he had been confident of the overthrow of Morgan, "it is not difficult to conceive of his embarrassment and mortification," says Fortescue. "He was now in exactly the same position as after Ferguson's defeat at King's Mountain, when, with Rawdon at his side, he had declared that the invasion of North Carolina must be abandoned." [5]

But now he was hopelessly committed to the projected invasion by the destruction of the fortifications of Charleston which he had ordered, and by his having brought up, under Leslie's escort, the whole matériel for the campaign. "Deeply as his lordship was affected with the weight of this misfortune, and greatly as he saw his difficulties increased by it, he was nevertheless resolved to prosecute the original plan . . . as the only means of maintaining the British interest in the southern colonies." However, perhaps necessarily in making preparations, he delayed his departure from Turkey Creek until the 19th, and thereby let his prey escape.[6]

Even when he did start, he went in the wrong direction. Thinking that Morgan, dazzled by his success, would hold his ground near the Broad River or perhaps make an attempt on Ninety-six, Cornwallis marched northwestward toward the Little Broad River to cut him off. But Morgan, as has been said, had headed straight for Sherrill's Ford by way of Ramsour's Mills, where Cornwallis by marching due north with equal celerity might have met and destroyed his depleted and much inferior army.[7] Having learned of Morgan's actual movement, Cornwallis shifted his march towards the north and arrived at Ramsour's Mills on the 25th, to find that the Americans had not only passed that point two days before, but had now crossed the Catawba, thus putting two rivers between themselves and him.[8]

In contrast to the slow movement of the British army was the rapidity of Morgan's march. In less than five whole days he crossed two rivers and covered one hundred miles, under conditions that were not particularly favorable. Seymour's restrained statement, "On our way thither we had very difficult marching, being very mountainous," [9] hardly even suggests the hardships they endured, duplicated soon after by those of Huger's division on the march to join Morgan.

At Ramsour's Mills, Cornwallis again paused. If he was to catch up with the fast-moving Americans he must travel even more rapidly than they did. He had lost all his light troops at Cowpens; now, therefore, he must transform his whole force into light troops by relieving it of its cumbersome impedimenta.

He spent two days in destroying his superfluous baggage. He set an example to his men by drastically reducing his own, and his officers did likewise. Except the wagons needed to carry ammunition, salt, and hospital stores and four others for the transport of the sick and wounded, every wagon and all its contents were burned. All the tents went into the fire; all the store of provisions, except as much as the men could carry in their haversacks, went up in smoke. And last, the greatest sacrifice of all, the rum casks were stove in and the precious liquor was poured out on the ground. "The men," says Trevelyan, "looked on sadly, but passively." They could not do otherwise, of course; but it may have been largely because of this disheartening and ill-boding destruction that during those two days at Ramsour's many Hessians and some few British soldiers deserted, perhaps 250 in all. It was a magnificent gesture, but in the event it proved to be "vain and useless and finally fatal" to Cornwallis and his army.[10]

Meanwhile, on the east side of the Catawba, Morgan was resting and refreshing his troops while he waited the return of the detachment he had sent off with the captives. Pickens, having delivered them to a commissary for prisoners at Island Ford to be sent into Virginia, crossed the stream there and rejoined Morgan at his camp, where the whole command lay until February 1.[11]

For a whole week after the battle Greene and Huger, with their division, waited at Cheraw for news of Morgan; on the 25th it came. Overjoyed though he was, Greene could not fail to see that the situation of Morgan and the best of the American army was precarious and might soon become desperate; he took measures accordingly. He sent orders to the commissaries at Salisbury and Hillsboro to get ready to move their prisoners and their stores to Virginia. He directed Carrington, his quartermaster general, to assemble boats on the Dan River at the boundary between North Carolina and Virginia, against the possible necessity of a retreat, and he ordered Huger to get his division ready to march and ultimately join forces with Morgan. Then, with a guide, one aide, and a sergeant's guard of dragoons, he set out on the 28th to ride through a country infested with Tories the hundred and twenty-five miles that lay between the Cheraw and Morgan's camp on the Catawba. It was an imprudent act, its only justification being success; he arrived in a little over two days.[12]

Huger's orders were to march up the Pee Dee and the Yadkin (really the same river) to Salisbury, North Carolina, whither Greene expected to direct Morgan's force. Huger sent off the least necessary baggage, the poorest horses, and the worst wagons to Hillsboro, and on the 28th started a march of one hundred and twenty-five miles to Salisbury. It was a hard march. His men were sometimes without meat, often without flour, always without rum. It was cold; they had little clothing, few blankets, no tents. Every day they had to ford deep creeks of icy water and march on until the heat of their bodies dried their rags. Rain fell on them. The roads froze in rough ruts at night and were slippery with mud by noonday. Over them many marched on naked feet. Yet, in all that march, Huger lost not even "a single sentinel" by desertion.[13]

Greene reached Morgan's camp on the 30th. In conference, a difference of opinion arose. Morgan was for a quick retreat into the western mountains beyond probable, or even possible, pursuit—a prudent move if nothing but the army's safety were desired. But Greene had larger, more far-reaching plans. As soon as he heard from Morgan that Cornwallis had destroyed his baggage and seemed resolved to march on towards the north, he exclaimed, "Then, he is ours!" He immediately wrote to Huger that he hoped to ruin Cornwallis, if he persisted in the "mad scheme of pushing through the country," and urged him to effect a junction of the two divisions as soon as possible; also to recall Lee's Legion from Marion at Georgetown. "Here is a fine field and great glory ahead." [14]

Greene's plan was to retreat due north—not into the mountains, difficult if not inaccessible to Cornwallis's army, but through a country where the

British general not only could but would follow. Day by day, he would keep just far enough ahead of his pursuer to avoid being caught, but near enough to keep alive in Cornwallis a hope, even an expectation, of bringing him to battle. He would tease his opponent along farther and farther from his supply bases, while he himself would be drawing nearer and nearer his own in Virginia and the north. It was a bold, a hazardous plan, subject to all the accidents of such a march, which might force him to stop and give battle under difficult conditions. Morgan saw in it the danger of disaster and opposed it, declaring that he would not be answerable for the consequences if it were tried. "Neither will you, for I shall take the measure upon myself," Greene replied, and issued orders accordingly.[15]

On the 28th Cornwallis, having completed the destruction of his baggage, marched towards Beattie's Ford on the Catawba, beyond which was Morgan's camp. Finding the river so swollen by rains that it could not be passed, he halted within four miles of the ford and waited two full days for the flood to subside.[16]

General William Davidson had called on the North Carolina militia to guard the fords in the neighborhood of Morgan's camp. He had collected 800, including 56 mounted riflemen, and posted them on the eastern bank at four crossings along thirty miles of the river, the largest number, about 300, at Beattie's Ford.[17]

The river having fallen to a practicable depth by January 31, Cornwallis moved to cross it. He had left Rawdon with 700 men to hold Camden, and now had nearly 3,000. His plan was his favorite, an outflanking movement. One division of his army under Lieutenant Colonel Webster, comprising the 33rd Regiment, the 2nd battalion of the 71st, the Royal North Carolina Regiment of Tories, the Hessian jägers, the artillery, and the wagons, was to approach Beattie's Ford as if to cross there. This movement was made at one o'clock in the morning of February 1. It was, however, merely a feint. Cornwallis himself and General O'Hara, with the brigade of Guards, the Hessian Regiment von Bose, the Royal Welch Fusiliers, 200 cavalry, and two light fieldpieces, started at the same time for Cowan's—or Mc-Cowan's—private ford six miles below Beattie's.[18] This was the real movement, a crossing which, without the opposition expected from Morgan at Beattie's, would outflank the Americans.

Cowan's Ford was about five hundred yards wide, with a rocky bottom over which the river was still three to four feet deep, running with swift turbulence. The ford had a certain peculiarity; about halfway across it split in two. The straight course, used by wagons, was deeper and rougher. That which diverged to the right was longer but shallower and had a smoother bottom; it was more used by horsemen. It reached the east bank about a quarter of a mile below the other. At its point of emergence, Davidson had posted most of his guard, leaving only a picket of 25 men at the wagon ford.[19]

. It was near dawn of a dark and rainy morning when O'Hara's division reached the west end of the ford and saw the fires of the militia on the opposite bank. He formed the Guards in column of fours and ordered them to cross. With cartridge boxes high on their shoulders and bayonets fixed on unloaded muskets, they marched into the waist-deep water led by a Tory guide; the rest of the division followed. The roaring of the water drowned the sound of their approach, and it was too dark for the American sentinel on the opposite bank to see them before the head of the column was a hundred yards advanced in the river. Then he gave the alarm, and the small body of militia opened fire. The first three ranks were visibly thinned by the rifle bullets. The column halted, only to come on again, the men and horses struggling against the current, stumbling over rocks, losing their footing, and being swept downstream, but nevertheless steadily advancing.

In mid-stream the guide took fright and got away, without telling the officer leading the advance that he should break off to the right and take the horse ford to its landing below. So the column kept on, straight across on the wagon ford. In its rougher, deeper waters, men and horses were swept off their feet. Colonel Hall's horse was shot under him and he sank under the water, but was caught and saved from drowning. Cornwallis's own horse was shot, but did not fall until it reached the other bank. General O'Hara and General Leslie were both overthrown and so were many of the cavalry. But still the column pressed forward.

General Davidson down at the horse ford had heard the firing and hurried his men up to the scene of action. Before he got there the light infantry of the Guards had reached the bank, loaded their muskets, and opened fire, driving back the few riflemen and covering the landing of the rest of the British. Davidson withdrew his men from the river's edge and tried to beat back the oncoming enemy, who formed, as soon as they were out of the water, loaded, and fired. A bullet struck him in the left breast; he fell dead, and his men broke and scattered. Colonel Hall, who had so courageously led the British across, was shot dead just after he set foot on the bank.

This brave exploit accomplished nothing save the crossing of one contingent. Morgan was not outflanked; his troops had left their camp the evening before. General Webster with the other division of the British crossed at Beattie's Ford later in the day without opposition. By the time Cornwallis's whole force was across, Morgan's troops, who had marched all night and part of the next day, were thirty miles away on the road to Trading Ford on the Yadkin, the next river. Their march, says Seymour, was "very unpleasant . . . it having rained incessantly all night, which rendered the roads almost inaccessible." [20]

Morgan and his men had departed, but Greene with two or three aides had stayed behind to arrange for Davidson's militia to rendezvous at a certain point and to join Morgan's force, after their duty at the fords was done. His aides were sent here and there on this business. Greene went on alone and narrowly escaped capture. He was but a few miles beyond Tarrant's Tavern, where many of Davidson's militia had assembled, when Tarleton's cavalry came clattering up in pursuit of them. The militiamen delivered a hasty fire, ran to their horses, and made off with some loss. [21]

At the point of rendezvous Greene waited vainly for the militia until midnight. Then came a messenger to tell him that Davidson was dead, the militia dispersed, and Cornwallis across the river. He rode on alone to Salisbury. At Steele's Tavern in that village he dismounted, stiff and sore, to be greeted by a friend. "What? Alone, Greene?" "Yes," he answered, "alone, tired, hungry and penniless." Mrs. Steele heard him. After getting him a breakfast she brought two little bags of hard money and gave them to him. "You need them more than I do," she said. [22] The contents of those two little bags constituted the entire military chest of the Grand Army of the Southern Department of the United States of America.

CHAPTER 71

The Retreat to the Dan

With the crossing of the Catawba by both armies began the famous Retreat to the Dan, "one of the most memorable in the annals of war."[1] From the numbers of men engaged in it—about 2,000 in the American army and less than 3,000 in the British—it may seem to have been a trifling affair; but its consequences were great. It led—indeed, forced—Cornwallis to Yorktown, where the power of Britain in the American states was shattered.

There had been four unbridged rivers, besides innumerable tributaries, after Morgan had passed the Broad. One, the Catawba, was now behind both, but there yet remained the Yadkin, the Deep River, and finally the Dan. At any of these, the mischance of high water at the fords or lack of boats elsewhere might stop either army, forcing the pursued to stand and fight or balking the pursuer of his quarry.

The Dan was the ultimate goal of the Americans. Once across it and in Virginia, Greene could call on reenforcements and supplies; there was safety. It could be crossed on its upper reaches at fords; lower, ferriage in boats would be necessary. These had been provided for the Americans by the foresight of Greene and the skill and energy of Carrington. Towards them Greene must make his way, but in such manner as to deceive his opponent into believing that he was for the fords above. That was the strategic problem which Greene solved in such masterly fashion as to extort from Tarleton the admission that "every measure of the Americans during their march from the Catawba to Virginia was judiciously planned and vigourously executed."[2]

Greene wrote to General Washington[3] that "heavy rains, deep creeks, bad roads, poor horses and broken harriers, as well as delays for want of provisions," had prevented Huger's division from reaching Salisbury in time to join him and Morgan there. With Cornwallis at his heels he knew he could not await Huger's arrival. So, from Steele's Tavern that night, he sent a message to Huger to change course to the northeastward and meet Morgan's column at Guilford Court House. He then rode on to catch up with Morgan.

Morgan had passed through Salisbury and reached Trading Ford on the Yadkin, about seven miles east of the town. It was usually a good fording place, but the long continued rains had raised it above fording depth. Boats were necessary, and, by Greene's foresight and Kosciuszko's energy, they were there. In the night of the 2nd and 3rd of February, the cavalry swam their horses across, the infantry took to the boats.

After passing the Catawba, the two temporary divisions of the British army had joined on the road to Salisbury. Cornwallis had then added O'Hara's mounted infantry to his own cavalry and sent the combined force to catch Greene before he crossed the Yadkin, while he himself burned more baggage so as to double his teams and get the few remaining wagons out of the mud, in which they were sunk to the hubs.

The Americans had been followed by many of the country people fleeing from the British advance. A few of their wagons, guarded by some of the militia, were still on the west bank of the Yadkin when O'Hara's van came up. There was an exchange of shots before the guard was dispersed. O'Hara got the wagons, but nothing more. The American army was on the other side, and so were all the boats. O'Hara could not cross.[4]

Despite the continued rain and the almost impassable roads Cornwallis, by doubling his teams, succeeded in reaching Salisbury by three o'clock in the afternoon of February 3. He was then only seven miles from Trading Ford, beyond which were the Americans. O'Hara had sent his cavalry back from the ford to Salisbury, but held his infantry on high ground overlooking the river. Cornwallis sent him some fieldpieces, and he attempted to bombard Greene's camp across the river. Greene had sent away with his prisoners his only artillery, the two little "grasshoppers" captured at Cowpens, and could not reply. But his camp was behind a high, rocky ridge that paralleled the stream, and the bombardment did no damage, except to knock the roof off a cabin in which he was busy with correspondence.[5]

The river was still rising and was now too deep even for horses; but Shallow Ford, ten miles up the river, was always passable. Taking it involved a wide swing to the west from Greene; but Cornwallis was encouraged to make this departure by the receipt of information that the lower fords on the Dan were impassable at this season of the year, and that there were not enough boats at the ferries to take the Americans across within a reasonable time. He was therefore convinced that Greene would have to use the upper fords. A swing to the west would give the British army a shorter road to them. Accordingly he gave up trying to catch Greene and Morgan before they could join with Huger, and decided to intercept their combined forces before they could reach the upper fords. With this in view, he lay at Salisbury four days, collecting food. On the 8th he crossed the Yadkin at Shallow Ford.[6]

Greene and Morgan marched from Trading Ford on the evening of February 4 in a northerly direction, which must have confirmed Cornwallis's belief as to their destination. They halted at Abbott's Creek, a few miles from the Moravian settlement at Salem, to obtain definite information as to Cornwallis's course and then turned due east to Guilford Court House, which they reached on the 6th. In forty-eight hours, including all hours of rest, they marched forty-seven miles.[7] Considering the weather, continuously rainy, the state of the roads, the shortage of food, and the condition of the men, that was excellent progress. Seymour describes Huger's division, which met them there. The men were "in a most dismal condition for the want of clothing, especially shoes, being obliged to march, the chief part of them, barefoot from Chiraw Hills. Here, however, the men were supplied with some shoes, but not half enough." [8]

By this time Cornwallis had reached Salem, twenty-five miles west of Guilford, and had encamped. Greene's primary purpose had been to draw him farther and farther from his base of supplies, to wear down his army and to add to his own force enough militia to turn on his pursuer at the proper time and give him a battle, which would be decisive. Retreating as far as the Dan and into Virginia was the alternative to that major purpose, to be adopted only if necessary. Now, at Guilford, he considered whether it was not time to stand and invite his opponent to fight. He studied the ground; it seemed to offer a good defensive position. Lee's Legion had joined him. He had called for the militia and sent to Hillsboro for a supply of ammunition. He expected reenforcements from Virginia. If the new troops and supplies would come, a stand at this point seemed possible.

But only 200 militia from the neighborhood joined him. The expected Virginia reenforcements and the ammunition failed to arrive. His whole army numbered only 2,036 men, of whom no more than 1,426 were reliable Continentals. Cornwallis had from 2,500 to 3,000 excellent troops. The addition of 1,500 militia would probably have decided the question in favor of fighting, because Greene dreaded continued retreat for its depression of the militia and its encouragement of the Tories to rise. A council of war decided against making a stand, and arrangements were made accordingly.[9]

Pickens was sent back to try to arouse the militia to intercept the British foragers and to cut off their intelligence service. Greene then detached 700 of the élite of his army, including all the cavalry, 240 men under William Washington, a battalion of 280 of the Continental infantry under Colonel Howard, the infantry of Lee's Legion, and 60 Virginia riflemen under Major Campbell. They were to act as a light corps covering the retreat of the main army, interposing themselves between it and the British, keeping as near the pursuers as possible, breaking down bridges and in every way harassing and delaying them, and leading them towards the upper fords of the Dan, while Greene and Huger made for Boyd's and Irwin's ferries on its lower reach.

The command of this corps was offered to Morgan; but he was so ill with ague and rheumatism that he was unable to continue in the campaign. It was then given to Colonel Otho Holland Williams of Maryland, and Morgan retired to his home in Virginia, to appear in arms no more.[10]

The stage was now set for a contest between Greene and Cornwallis, the result of which would be of vast importance to the American cause. If Greene's little army were overtaken and destroyed, Cornwallis would find his way open to join forces with the British in Virginia. He would be able to release all the Burgoyne prisoners and those recently taken at Cowpens, fortify Richmond, and establish strong posts at Hillsboro and elsewhere in the Carolinas. In short, the war in the south would virtually be at an end; except for partisan operations, the whole region would be completely and perhaps finally subjugated and permanently held by the British crown. So far as the four great southern states were concerned, the fate of the war hung in large part upon this contest.

For a month or more Americans throughout the country had realized how much was at stake, and had watched with fearful concern the movements of these two armies. Never since Burgoyne's invasion had their feelings been so wrought up; and in France as well as Britain interest in this fateful game was at a high pitch.[11]

In the evening of February 8 the light troops under Williams left Guilford and turned west towards Salem to take a road running north between the British army and the roads on which respectively the main American force was traveling. Two days later Greene and Huger, with the main army, started directly to the Dan's lower crossings.[12] Cornwallis, in an effort to alarm

Greene for the safety of his stores at Hillsboro and thus cause him to turn still farther east, made a demonstration towards the Americans with a part of his troops. But becoming aware of the intervening light troops, which he took to be the advance guard of the whole American army, he desisted and directed his march towards the upper fords of the Dan, thus, as he thought, fending off Greene from his objective.[13]

The race for the Dan was now on. The distance from Guilford was only seventy miles, but the season was still midwinter; it still rained and snowed intermittently. The roads, in a red-clay country, were frozen into a rough and broken surface at night, but by day softened into deep mud that clung to the wheels of the wagons, the hooves of the horses, and the feet of the men, so that yard after yard was gained only by an exhausting struggle.[14]

Williams and Cornwallis were on parallel roads, not far apart. At one time, when the British army had stretched out to the dangerous length of four miles, Cornwallis halted his van to bring up his rear and then pushed on with all possible speed, moving at times thirty miles a day, an almost inconceivable speed under the existing conditions. Williams had to travel as fast to keep ahead of the British. To guard against Cornwallis's making a detour and getting between the light troops and Greene's army, as well as to protect his own force from surprise, Williams had to send out such numerous patrols and establish such strong pickets that half of his force was always on night duty. He halted for only six hours each night; each man got only six hours rest in every forty-eight. They never set up a tent. "The heat of the fires was the only protection from rain and sometimes snow." [15] They started each day at three in the morning and hastened forward to gain a distance ahead of their pursuers that would give them time for breakfast— breakfast, dinner, and supper in one, because this was their only meal for the day. Cornwallis came on with equal speed.

In the afternoon of the 13th Cornwallis diverged from his line of march, taking a causeway that led him into the road that Williams's troops were following. According to custom, they had made their early morning march and were trying to roast their meat and bake their corn bread at fires dampened by the falling rain, when a countryman on a jaded, little pony came to tell them that the enemy was right behind, only four miles away.

Lee's Legion formed the rear guard of the light troops. Williams sent Lee back along the road to verify this information. The result was a clash with a troop of Tarleton's horse, in which eighteen of the enemy were slain and the rest put to flight. In this affair Lee's bugler, a lad of fourteen years, was cut down and killed in a manner that seems to have been wanton. In reprisal he declared his intention of hanging one of his prisoners, Captain

Miller, and was deterred only by the near approach of the British van, which compelled him to hasten to rejoin Williams.

But Williams had decided that by now the British had been sufficiently misled as to the route taken by the main American army, and that Greene and Huger had had time to reach the Dan. Therefore, while Lee was engaging Tarleton's troop, he had taken a right-hand road leading to Irwin's Ferry, where he expected to find the main army. Lee's men, having missed their one meal of the day, took a byroad that would lead them to Williams and meanwhile give time to refresh themselves at a farmhouse. The byway was somewhat obscure, and Lee felt safe from immediate pursuit; but while the men and his horses were in the midst of their meal they heard shots in their rear. Cornwallis had discovered the short cut, and Lee's vedettes were signaling the near approach of the enemy's van.

Horses were hastily saddled. The infantry were sent on the run to cross a bridge over a swollen creek, while Lee, with the horse, rode back to support his vedettes. He checked the British advance long enough for the foot soldiers to cross the bridge, and then turned and galloped after them. The enemy's cavalry followed fast, but Lee's horses were superior. They got over the bridge, and there was a hot chase across a mile-wide plain before the fugitives gained a height along which ran the Irwin's Ferry road, and the pursuit ceased.

Cornwallis still hoped to catch them before they crossed the Dan. He followed fast. More than once O'Hara in the van was within musket shot of Lee's rear guard. More than once it seemed that the light troops must stand and fight. When they came to a creek or a ravine, the British cavalry would rush forward to attack them in the confusion of crossing, but they always got across in time. At last Lee caught up with Williams. It was growing dark, and the Americans hoped that the enemy would halt for the night; but Cornwallis still came on, determined to run them down. Night fell and they could not see the rough and rutted road they traveled; it was hard going for the weary men.

Williams put his horsemen in front to hurry the pace of the infantry. Then, suddenly, they came in sight of a line of fires—campfires. It was Greene's camp beyond a doubt! He had not got away, and the enemy were close upon him! When this thought flashed through their minds, they were heartbroken. All their struggles, all their hardships had been for naught. Now there was only one thing to do; they must face their pursuers and fight to give the main army a chance to get away.

But Williams had had a dispatch from Greene: "It is very evident that the enemy intend to push us over the river. . . . I sent off the baggage and

stores with orders to cross as fast as they got to the river. The North Carolina militia have all deserted us, except about 80 men. . . . You have the
flower of the army, don't expose the men too much, lest our situation grow
more critical."

The date of the dispatch, February 13, and the place from which it was
sent made him sure that Greene would, by this time, be farther on the way.
He reassured his men and led them on to find that the fires were burning
where Greene had camped two days before. Friendly hands had kept them
alight for the benefit of the light troops.

But they could not stop to enjoy them. They kept on until news arrived
from the rear that the British had halted. Then they paused for two or
three hours, still a long distance from the river.

At midnight they were again afoot. In the morning came another dispatch
from Greene, sent the same day as the last: "4 o'clock. Follow our route. I
have not slept four hours since you left me, so great has been my solicitude
to prepare for the worst."

They halted for an hour's rest and a hasty meal, started again, slogged
through the mud, the enemy at their heels, and were still doggedly pushing
on at noon when a courier met them, found Williams, gave him a note dated
the night before: "Irwin's ferry, 12 past 5 o'clock. All our troops are over
and the stage is clear. . . . I am ready to receive you and give you a
hearty welcome." [16]

Williams gave out the news. The word ran back through the column, and
cheer after cheer followed it. They shouted so loud that O'Hara's van heard
them and knew that the game was up.

The reaction among the men was instantaneous. Their hearts were lifted,
their strength renewed. For three hours more they hurried forward. They
were now within fourteen miles of the river. Williams again detached Lee's
cavalry to delay the enemy, while he took the rest of his command on to
Irwin's Ferry. They got there before sunset, found the boats, and were
ferried across. They had marched forty of the hardest miles that ever man
traveled in about sixteen hours.

At dark, Lee's horsemen started after the others. Between eight and nine
o'clock they got to the ferry, just as the boats returned from transporting
Williams's troops. The men took to the boats; the horses swam. By midnight
they were all across. They had hardly landed when the British van arrived at
the river.[17]

Cornwallis got the news in the course of the evening. The river was too
high to cross without boats, and every boat was on the farther shore.
Greene had won the race.

CHAPTER 72

Greene Returns to North Carolina

Cornwallis had lost the race, but he had chased Greene out of the Carolinas. From Virginia to Florida there was no organized American army in the field; the southern states were possessed by the King. So much he had accomplished, and it seemed to be a great deal. But what was he to do next? He could not follow the American army into Virginia; he had no boats to cross the Dan, nor the Roanoke, if he moved eastward. He dared not try the upper fords, for Greene could anticipate the attempt and be there to oppose the crossing. Even if he should get across, Greene could again retreat to join Steuben, who had been enlisting Continentals in Virginia, and he would then be outnumbered: he had lost 250 men by sickness and desertion on this march. There was no feasible way to go forward.

Yet he could not stay where he was, for his base was two hundred and thirty miles behind; he could not get fresh supplies to replace those so rashly destroyed at Ramsour's Mills. The depredations of his army had aroused the country about him in enmity; supplies were not to be looked for there. Pickens, with 700 newly raised militia, was threatening his left flank. Caswell had a force not too far away on his right. To turn back would be to confess the failure of his expedition and would dishearten the Tory population, which had been encouraged by his pursuit of Greene. But there was no practicable alternative. He rested his army one day, then by easy marches took it back to Hillsboro.[1]

There he put the best face he could on his situation. He erected the royal standard and issued a proclamation:

"Whereas it has pleased the Divine Providence to prosper the operations of His Majesty's arms, in driving the rebel army out of this province; and whereas it is His Majesty's most gracious wish to rescue his faithful and loyal subjects from the cruel tyranny under which they have groaned for many years," he invited all the oppressed to repair "with their arms and ten days provisions to the royal standard." [2]

Greene's strategy in plan and in execution had been masterly. He had saved his army and rejoiced the hearts of the patriots throughout America. So much he had done, and it was not little. But after all it was a retreat; though armies may be saved, campaigns are not often won by retreating. Behind him lay the south, still completely dominated by the enemy. He had dragged Cornwallis away from his base and worn down his army. He could turn on him now and destroy him—if only he had the expected recruits from Virginia. But they had not come—not a man had come to him. And most of his militia, their time expired, had left him.

Greene still hoped for reenforcements, expected them in fact. He knew that both North Carolina and Virginia were arousing their militia again, though they were being sent anywhere else than to him. Steuben, who had been enlisting Continentals in Virginia, and was supposed to be on the way to him, had not yet come; he was days, maybe weeks, away. And now, right now, was the time for action. The Dan was falling rapidly; there were many fords near him. Cornwallis might cross and attack him in his weakness, or might slip away, and the chance he had worked for, to catch his enemy in a weakened condition, would be lost. When he got news of the withdrawal of the British, he knew the chance was lost. Now he must make new plans, and they must involve a return to North Carolina. They were soon made and soon in operation. [3]

Greene's first care was for the safety of his heavy baggage. He sent 345 Maryland and Delaware Continentals with it to Halifax Court House. They marched on February 15 and returned on the 17th. [4]

On February 18 he dispatched Lee's Legion and two companies of Marylanders under Captain Oldham, all under command of Pickens (who had by this time joined the army with a body of South Carolina militia) across the river again, with orders to approach Cornwallis as nearly as possible, cut off his foraging parties, annoy him generally, and suppress Tory uprisings. [5] With this force Pickens attempted to surprise Tarleton, who was out on one of his usual troublesome expeditions. Failing to come up with him, Pickens heard of a company of 400 Tory mounted infantry under Colonel John Pyle who were on the way to join Tarleton. They were now on the same road as his own detachment, and not far ahead. Two countrymen whom the Americans picked up thought Lee was Tarleton, since both his and Lee's horsemen wore short green coats. Lee sent one of them ahead to Pyle, with Colonel Tarleton's compliments. Would he kindly draw up his men in a line along the road, so that Colonel Tarleton's men might pass with ease and expedition?

Colonel Pyle readily complied and himself took his post at the right of his line, farthest from the advancing force. Lee's cavalry, with drawn swords, came on in single file past the Tory line, the Maryland foot soldiers in the rear following on and being more or less concealed by the thick woods through which the road ran. When Lee at the head of his men came up to Pyle he halted his troop to shake hands with the other commander. According to his own story, he intended to undeceive Pyle as to his own identity, advise him to disband his men and send them home, and promise that no harm would come to them if they took his advice; but, just as he was about to deliver the message, some of Pyle's men at the far end of the line descried Pickens and his infantry in the rear and fired on them.

Immediately Lee's troops wheeled their horses to the right to face Pyle's men and fell upon them. Sabers slashed them; pistols blazed in their faces. The Tories had only rifles and fowling pieces carried over their shoulders, and the lines were too close for them to use those weapons even if they had had a chance. There was no fight; it was simply a massacre. Of the 400 Tories, 90 were killed, and most of the rest wounded; those fled who could. Not a man in Lee's troop was injured.[6]

Greene and his main army might have stayed in safety north of the Dan until Steuben's Continental recruits and other reenforcements joined him and so strengthened him that he could seek out Cornwallis and attack him. Besides the considerations already mentioned as moving him to return to North Carolina, there was the fact that an abject acceptance of his having been pushed out of that state would inspirit the Tories there to join the British army and make it stronger than it now was. Also, the terms of enlistment of his own militia were short. It was necessary to display belligerent activity.

He had few men, perhaps no more than 1,500. The weather was cold, his thinly clad soldiers were suffering severely; a full quarter of the Maryland line were sick in hospital. His Delaware Continentals were "the admiration of the army and their leader, Kirkwood, was the American Diomed. Like the Marylanders, they had enlisted for the war and, like the veterans of that brigade, were not excelled by any troops in America, perhaps in the world." [7] But, though valiant, they were few. Nevertheless, Greene had to go forward again and without delay.

He sent Otho Williams, with the same light troops that he had led in the retreat, back across the Dan on February 20, instructing him to approach the enemy, watch their movements, retard them as much as possible, and attack them on the march if they withdrew towards Wilmington, but always to keep his force between the British and the main army of the Americans.[8] Three days later, having been reenforced by General Edward Stevens and 600 Virginia riflemen, Greene himself crossed the Dan. His plan now was to wear down Cornwallis's troops by desultory minor actions and to discourage Tory accretions, while his own army was built up by the expected reenforcements. For this service he relied chiefly upon the light troops. His main army he directed towards Hillsboro, Cornwallis's camp.[9]

At that place Cornwallis was in an uncomfortable position. The country round about had been nearly exhausted of provisions. Beef cattle could not be found. Although he had promised the farmers that their draft oxen would be spared, his commissary found it necessary to kill some. This aroused ill feeling among the owners. It was increased by house-to-house forcible requisitions of foodstuffs, which greatly distressed the people.[10] The activities of Lee's Legion, especially in the affair with Pyle, and of Williams's light infantry had chilled the ardor of the Tories, who had been flocking to the King's standard; recruiting suddenly ceased, and many who were on their way to join turned about and went home.[11] At Hillsboro, Cornwallis was, as he wrote to Germain in London, "amongst timid friends and adjoining to inveterate rebels," [12] the friends growing fewer, the rebels increasing day by day. He decided to move to more salubrious quarters.

On February 27 he marched southwest, across the Haw River, and encamped in a favorable position on the south side of Alamance Creek, a tributary, at the junction of roads leading east to Hillsboro, west to Guilford and Salisbury, and downriver to Cross Creek and Wilmington, this last being an avenue of escape, if needed.[13] On the same day Williams gathered to himself Pickens's corps, including Lee's Legion, William Washington's cavalry, and a corps of 300 mountaineer riflemen under Colonel William Preston of Virginia, which had lately joined Pickens.[14] They crossed the Haw that night and took up a position on the north side of the Alamance, within a few miles of Cornwallis's camp on the south side. Greene and Huger came along the next morning, crossed the Haw above Buffalo Creek and encamped between Troublesome Creek, the northernmost tributary of the Haw, and Reedy Fork farther down the river. This camp was about fifteen miles above the British on the Alamance. The American headquarters were alternatively at Speedwell Ironworks on Reedy and Boyd's Mill on Trouble-some.[15]

The American position was not especially advantageous, nor was it long held. During the next ten days Greene was constantly on the move, shifting his camp from one place to another, now nearer Cornwallis, now farther away, his design being to keep the British general guessing as to his where-abouts and his purposes and so to lessen the chances of a sudden attack while his reenforcements were assembling.[16] Williams with the light troops was equally restless. Within a little more than two weeks after recrossing the Dan, they marched two hundred and thirty miles, making sixty miles in one period of two days.[17] Tarleton was moving about in much the same way for similar purposes.

Tired of profitless inactivity and annoyed by the restlessness of the American light troops, Cornwallis made a sudden hostile move at three o'clock in the morning of March 6. He crossed the Alamance under cover of a heavy fog and pushed on towards High Rock Ford on Reedy Fork. Williams's corps lay on another road also leading to that ford. Cornwallis intended to surprise him and, if possible, draw Greene to his aid, thus bringing on a general engagement while Greene's army was still few in num-bers.[18] But the surprise did not come off.

It happened that late in the night of the 5th Williams had sent a small party under cover of the same fog to carry off another small party of the enemy from a mill about a mile from the main British camp. Arriving there, it learned that Cornwallis had marched. When this news reached Williams the British were within two miles of the left of his corps—the Virginia militia under Colonel William Campbell, who had recently joined Lee, relieving General Pickens. Williams sent Lee and Washington to support Campbell, while the rest of the corps retreated towards the ford across Reedy Fork at Wetzell's Mills. Lee, Washington, and Campbell slowed the advance of the British somewhat, but there was an exciting race between Williams and Cornwallis's advance, led by Tarleton's cavalry and Colonel Webster's light infantry, on parallel roads to the ford at the mills. Both parties traveled at their utmost speed, patrols and scouts from each side watching the progress of the other and reporting it. Williams got there first, just as the enemy appeared on rising ground in his rear, and threw out a covering party of Virginia militia riflemen under Colonel William Preston to protect the crossing. He got his men over safely and was joined by Lee, Washington, and Campbell, closely pursued by the British van.

Several near-by fords above and below exposed him to a flank attack. Having decided to retreat, he ordered Lee, Washington, and Campbell to hold the pass as long as possible, without hazarding serious injury, and withdrew the rest of his men. Lee posted a company of Preston's Virginians at the ford by the mill and drew up the rest of his infantry in a line along the stream. Campbell's and the rest of Preston's riflemen were concealed in a thick copse on the right. The cavalry was placed in the rear.

Having arrived at the stream, Cornwallis ordered Webster's brigade—composed of the Royal Welch Fusiliers, the 33rd British Regiment, and Fraser's Highlanders, with a light company of the Guards and the Hessian jägers—to form a line and attack while the rest of his army remained in column. Webster's detachment started for the ford, the Guards in the lead. As they entered the water they were met by a heavy and well directed fire, and fell back in disorder. Webster, disgusted by their hesitancy, rode up, called them to account, and plunged into the stream. His men followed.

When they gained the opposite shore, which lay under a high bank, the flanks of the American line drew in and formed behind the cavalry in the rear, while the center kept up a fire upon Webster's men clambering up from the water's edge; but there was no stopping them. The Americans retreated under heavy fire, and rear-guard action continued for about five miles until the pursuit ceased. Williams then encamped, and Cornwallis returned to his former ground on the Alamance. Greene, having had news of the advance of his enemy, had withdrawn from Reedy Fork and encamped at the ironworks on Troublesome. In the affair at Wetzell's Mill, the Americans lost about twenty killed or wounded. Tarleton admits a loss of twenty-one on his side.

A strange fact of this engagement was Webster's escape from death. Lee had posted twenty-five expert riflemen in a little log schoolhouse at the right of the ford. They all had participated in the King's Mountain affair and were reputed to be dead shots, and they had orders to concentrate their fire on the enemy's officers. Every one of them drew a bead on Webster, conspicuous as he was, and fired. Eight or nine of them tried a second shot, yet not a bullet touched him.[19]

Both armies rested for the next ten days, the British at Bell's Mills on Deep River, Greene at the ironworks on Troublesome. Meanwhile, Greene was considerably strengthened. Steuben in Virginia had raised 2,600 militia and 400 new Continentals and started them south; but, having been informed that Cornwallis was retreating to Wilmington and Greene was pursuing him with a superior force, he halted the militia and sent forward only the Continentals under Colonel Richard Campbell. From North Carolina came two brigades of militia, numbering 1,060, under Brigadier General John Butler and Colonel Pinketham Eaton. Virginia militia, 1,693 of them, also arrived and, with those already in camp, were organized in two brigades under Brigadiers Robert Lawson and Edward Stevens.[20]

Williams' light troops having rejoined the main army, that corps was dissolved "with the highest and best merited encomiums on the spirit and ability with which it had discharged its laborious and important duties."[21] Its various elements were returned to their respective regiments, except that Captain Kirkwood's Delaware company and Colonel Charles Lynch's Virginia riflemen were ordered to join William Washington's cavalry and thus form a legion.[22]

Greene was as strong as he could expect to be. From now on, the lapse of time would only waste his strength, through the usual depletion caused by sickness and desertion and by the expiration of the terms of service of the militia enlisted for no more than six weeks. Also he had just about exhausted the food supplies of the country in which he had been maneuvering for the last two weeks. Now was the time to fight, if he was going to fight at all. Cornwallis was ready, had been for some time. All that was needed was to choose his ground and make a stand on it.

Greene knew where it was; he had studied it six weeks before, on his way north. On April 14 he went into camp near Guilford Court House.

CHAPTER 73

Guilford Court House

On the day that Greene's army went into camp near Guilford Court House, it was composed of the following elements: Otho Williams's brigade of the 1st and 5th Maryland regiments, including the Delaware Continental infantry, commanded by Colonels John Gunby and Benjamin Ford, having 630 rank and file present and fit for duty; Brigadier General Isaac Huger's 4th and 5th Virginia Continental regiments commanded by Colonels John Green and Samuel Hawes, comprising 778 present and fit; the infantry of Lee's Legion, 82 men, and Kirkwood's light infantry company, making a total of about 1,600 regular infantry. There were four brigades of militia: two of about 500 men each from North Carolina under Brigadier Generals Pinketham Eaton and John Butler; two of about 600 Virginians each, commanded by Brigadier Generals Robert Lawson and Edward Stevens. There were two corps of riflemen, 200 in each, under Colonels Charles Lynch and Richard Campbell. These militia and volunteer infantry numbered in all 2,600. Of cavalry, Greene had the 75 horsemen of Lee's Legion and 86 of William Washington's light dragoons. His artillery consisted of four 6-pounders, served by 60 artillerists and matrosses under Captains Anthony Singleton and Samuel Finley.[1] The grand total was, therefore, over 4,400 rank and file.

Although 1,490 of the infantry were rated as of the Continental line, only those 630 weather-beaten, travel-toughened, war-hardened veterans of Maryland and Delaware had ever before been in battle. It was impossible to predict how the untried Virginia Continentals would stand the test of bullet and bayonet. Of the militia, those from Virginia were regarded as good; not much confidence was placed in the North Carolinians. The 400 riflemen of Lynch and Campbell were all volunteers; bound for no stated time, they could leave at a moment's notice.[2] Still, it was as large as any American army ever assembled in the south up to this time, and it greatly outnumbered Cornwallis's army. Although there has been some controversy as to the number of his force, different reckonings varying by two or three hundred, it is probable that 1,900 is about correct.[3]

The battleground chosen by Greene was approachable from the west along a road through a narrow defile shouldered by rising ground on both sides and lined with dense copses. The undulating ground towards the east, beyond the defile, spread out about half a mile on both sides of the road, which ran a little north of east and was the spine of the formation of each army. The whole area, except two cleared portions to be described, was well wooded. Passing north of east from the defile through an enclosed clearing about a quarter-mile square, the road held its course through an oak woods for half a mile to a considerable area of high cleared ground above a rather steep slope. On this height stood the courthouse. There was a wooded elevation about a quarter-mile to the right, or south, of the road midway between the defile and the courthouse. This was the highest point of the field and had the steepest approach.[4]

When Greene marched to Guilford, Cornwallis lay at New Garden, also known as Quaker Meeting House, not more than twelve miles to the southwest. Greene's move amounted to throwing a hat into the ring—a challenge Cornwallis could neither ignore nor refuse. In fact, it gave him the chance he had been so ardently seeking for two months. To be sure, he was not so avid for battle as he had been before his losses at Cowpens and on that hard march to the Dan. On the other hand, scarcity of supplies now compelled him either to fight or to retreat toward the seacoast; and as between those alternatives he had no hesitation.

In the evening of March 14 Cornwallis sent off what was left of his heavy baggage with the sick and wounded under guard of Hamilton's Tory regiment, 100 regular infantrymen, and 20 of Tarleton's horse to Bell's Mills on Deep River. At dawn of the 15th, without pausing to give his men a breakfast, he started for Guilford.[5]

Greene had sent Lee's Legion, horse and foot, with a detachment of riflemen under Campbell along the road to New Garden to observe the enemy. Three or four miles from Guilford, Lee met Tarleton leading the British van—the cavalry, the Hessian jägers, and the light infantry of the

'Guards. He drew back, Tarleton pressing on him, until, in an embanked, narrow lane, his horsemen whirled about and charged, overthrowing Tarleton's first section and driving back the rest. They were pursued until the Americans came upon the head of the main British army. Here there was a hot skirmish for some little time before Lee "retired precipitately" to notify Greene of the coming of the enemy.[6]

Not long before, Morgan had written to Greene about the next battle and the "great number of militia" on the American side: "If they fight, you beat Cornwallis, if not, he will beat you." He advised flanking the lines of militia with riflemen under enterprising officers. "Put the . . . militia in the centre with some picked troops in their rear to shoot down the first man that runs." [7]

Greene followed this advice. His first line, composed of Butler's and Eaton's North Carolina militia, was established across the main road along the edge of the enclosed clearing and behind a zigzag rail fence, so that the enemy emerging from the defile would have to cross five hundred yards of open ground in order to reach the fence and the militia. This line was supported on its right flank by the infantry of Washington's Legion—that is to say, by Kirkwood's light infantry and Lynch's Virginia riflemen—formed at an obtuse angle so that their fire would enfilade the attacking ranks when they came near the fence. Washington's cavalry was in their rear on the far right. The left wing was similarly supported by Lee's Legion infantry, Campbell's riflemen, and Lee's cavalry.

About three hundred yards behind the first line was the second, Virginia militia under Stevens and Lawson. Sentinels were posted behind this at intervals for the purpose suggested in Morgan's letter. It was altogether in the forest and stretched an equal distance on each side of the road.

The third and principal line was drawn up in a curve along the brow of the courthouse hill and about five hundred and fifty yards behind the second. The main road, on which the first and second lines were posted, swerved slightly to the right, or southeast, so that this hill was on its left or north side. This line was, therefore, out of alignment with the others. An enemy force would have to swing to the left from the road in order to make a frontal attack on the third line.

From right to left, as this line faced, it was made up of the two regiments of Virginia Continentals and the two Maryland regiments, including Captain Jaquett's Delaware company. Two guns were in the center of the first line, under Singleton, and two under Finley were in the center of the third. During the battle Greene was with the Continentals. His first line was a full half-mile away and. because of the woods, that and the second were out of his sight. There was no reserve whatever; the entire army was in the lines.[8]

About midday the Americans, looking down the narrow avenue from the battlefield, saw the head of the British column approaching. It was a cold, cloudless spring day, and, though the nearest of the enemy were yet a mile away, the color of their uniforms and the reflection of the sun from their well burnished arms were plainly visible.[9]

As soon as the van was within range, Singleton opened on it with his pair of 6-pounders. Lieutenant MacLeod of the British pushed three guns forward along the road and replied. This duel was kept up, with little effect on either side, for about half an hour while the British were emerging from the defile, company after company at the double, and very smartly deploying right and left into a line facing the American first line at the distance of about a quarter-mile, that is to say a little short of the clearing in front of the Americans.

The right of the British line, under General Leslie, consisted of the Hessian Regiment von Bose and Fraser's Highlanders, with the 1st battalion of the Guards in support. Colonel Webster commanded the 23rd (Welch Fusiliers) and 33rd regiments in the left wing, with the grenadiers and 2nd battalion of the Guards under O'Hara in support. The guns were in the center, a small force of jägers and the light infantry being stationed beside them and behind the left wing. Tarleton's dragoons were held in column in the rear.[10]

When Greene had formed his troops, he walked along the front of the North Carolina militia in the first line asking as Morgan had asked his first line at Cowpens, for just two rounds of fire before they quit the battle. "Two rounds, my boys, and then you may fall back." [11]

About half-past one the battle began with the advance of the British center into the clearing in front of the North Carolinians, the enemy's wings being in the woods to the right and left. Singleton had withdrawn his guns to the second line; those of the British were necessarily silent. There was no martial sound, except the beating of the drums and the squealing of the fifes, as that broad, red line marched forward as if on parade, crossed the first fence, and traversed more than two-thirds of the open space. Then a thousand rifles spoke. Men fell all along the red line; there were gaps in it; but it came steadily forward.

Within musket shot of the zigzag fence the line halted, and delivered a volley; then at the command of Colonel Webster it charged. But it halted again in a straggling line fifty yards from the fence because, says Sergeant

Lamb of the Welch Fusiliers, it was perceived that the Americans' "whole force had their arms presented and resting on a rail-fence . . . they were taking aim with nice precision. . . . At this awful period, a general pause took place, both parties surveyed each other a moment with anxious suspense. Colonel Webster then rode forward in front of the 23rd regiment and said, with more than his usual commanding voice . . . 'Come on, my brave Fusiliers.' These words operated like an inspiring voice. They rushed forward amidst the enemy's fire. Dreadful was the havoc on both sides." [12]

The North Carolinians had now delivered their two fires as ordered. There was no time to reload, even if they had the inclination to do so. Without a moment's hesitation they turned and ran, pell-mell, helter-skelter, back through the woods, through the second line and so to safety.[13] After all, they had done everything they had been asked to do, and they had Greene's permission to leave the field.

The British were now up to the second fence with no opponent visible. But there was a steady and "most destructive fire" [14] upon both their flanks, enfilading their line, so that, if a bullet missed the nearest man, it had an excellent chance to hit another down the line. This fire came from Kirkwood's company and Lynch's riflemen on the British left, and from Lee's infantry and Campbell's riflemen on the right. They still held their ground, although the line they supported had vanished. These oblique lines had to be met by the attackers face to face. On the British left the jägers and the 33rd Regiment wheeled to the left to front Kirkwood and Lynch; on the other end the Regiment von Bose and the Highlanders swung to the right to meet Lee's and Campbell's troops. To fill the gap opened in the center by these maneuvers, the grenadiers and 2nd battalion of the Guards came up from their position in support of the left wing.

The cleared ground was left behind; it was woods fighting now. The Americans on both wings took cover, retired from tree to tree. Lynch and Kirkwood, covered by Washington's cavalry, at last took an oblique position on the right of the second line, the Virginia militia, and held it. On the American left, Campbell and Lee had been joined by one company of North Carolinians, under Captain Forbes, which had not fled the field. It had been Campbell's intention to fall back, as Kirkwood and Lynch had done, and take a position on the left of the Virginia line; but he was delayed by having to engage the 1st battalion of Guards, while the Regiment von Bose struck across his front and cut him off from the Virginians. Now he and Lee and Forbes were being forced farther and farther to their left, away from the rest of the Americans and finally up on to the height of ground already mentioned as being to the south of the main battlefield. The

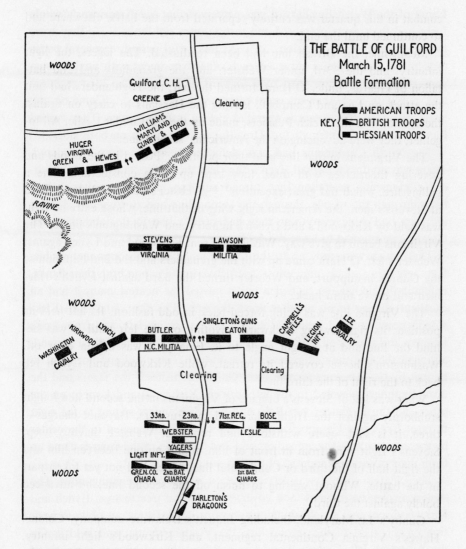

THE BATTLE OF GUILFORD
March 15, 1781
Battle Formation

KEY {
AMERICAN TROOPS
BRITISH TROOPS
HESSIAN TROOPS
}

WOODS

Guilford C. H.

GREENE

Clearing

WILLIAMS
MARYLAND
GUNBY & FORD

HUGER
VIRGINIA
GREEN & HEWES

RAVINE

WOODS

STEVENS
VIRGINIA

LAWSON
MILITIA

WOODS

WOODS

KIRKWOOD

LYNCH

BUTLER

SINGLETON'S GUNS
EATON

CAMPBELL'S
RIFLES

LEE
CAVALRY

WASHINGTON
CAVALRY

N.C. MILITIA

LEGION
INFY.

Clearing

Clearing

WOODS

33RD.

23RD.

WEBSTER

71ST. REG.

BOSE

LESLIE

YAGERS

WOODS

LIGHT INFY.

GREN. CO.
O'HARA

2ND. BAT.
GUARDS

1ST. BAT.
GUARDS

TARLETON'S
DRAGOONS

WOODS

combat in this quarter was entirely separated from the battle elsewhere and so continued until the end.

Meanwhile, the British line had been readjusted. The jägers, the light infantry, and the 33rd, under Webster, and the grenadiers and 2nd battalion of Guards, under O'Hara, formed the left; the Highlanders had quit the attack on Lee and Campbell, leaving the Hessians to carry on against them, and, with the Welch Fusiliers, made up the right under Leslie. All together, they were advancing on the Americans' second line.

The Virginians in that line held their position. "Posted in the woods and covering themselves with trees, they kept up for a considerable time a galling fire, which did great execution." [15] Webster's command struck hard at Stevens's men, the American right wing of that line, whose extreme right was held by Kirkwood's and Lynch's infantry and Washington's horse. The Virginians began to give way. Washington sent Kirkwood and Lynch against Webster's left. O'Hara came up with the grenadiers and the 2nd battalion of the Guards in support, and Webster turned the 33rd against Lynch's riflemen and drove them back.

The Virginia line was being forced back in odd fashion. Its left held its position; its right swung backward, pivoting on the left until it was behind the line and at a right angle to it. Finally, it was driven clear off. Washington's horse covered its retreat, while Kirkwood and Lynch fell back to the right of the third line.

What was left of Stevens's brigade of Virginians in the second line fought stubbornly against the Highlanders and the Fusiliers. Bayonet charges—three, it is said—were withstood and repulsed. Webster, having swept Stevens's right wing from in front of him, found no one between him and the right half of the third or Continental line, which had not yet taken part in the battle. Without waiting to finish off the second line, he advanced boldly against the third.

Gunby's 1st Maryland, including Jaquett's Delaware company, Colonel Hawes's Virginia Continental regiment, and Kirkwood's light infantry, faced Webster at a distance of two hundred yards. Against them he sent the jägers, his light infantry, and the 33rd in a bayonet charge. The Americans waited until the oncoming enemy were within a hundred feet and then loosed a withering blast of fire that brought the enemy to a standstill. Immediately Gunby called for the bayonets. His 1st Maryland and Kirkwood's company sprang forward and drove the British back, down into a ravine and up the farther side in great disorder.[16]

Now was the critical moment of the battle. The Hessians were still engaged with Campbell's riflemen and Lee's Legion on the wooded height far to the south of the main battle. Stevens's Virginians were still holding Leslie's Fusiliers and Highlanders, now drawing back from the bayonet, now advancing from tree to tree to fire. And Webster's troops were beaten and confused. If the cavalry of Washington and Lee had been thrown on the disordered ranks of the enemy, and the whole line of Continentals had charged upon Leslie and O'Hara, as they had charged at Cowpens, the battle might have ended in the destruction of Cornwallis's army. But that was not in accordance with Greene's plans. Morgan had been able to risk his whole detachment in such an all-out attack—even if he should be defeated, Greene would still have the main force. But on this day such a move would risk the entire army; a defeat would mean the loss of the south. So Web-ster had time to recover while Gunby and Kirkwood returned to their former positions.

While a restoration of the lines was being effected O'Hara, who had been wounded, turned over his command of the grenadiers and the 2nd battalion of the Guards to Lieutenant Colonel Stuart. As the resistance of the Virginians in the second line was weakening, Leslie drew off the Welch Fusiliers and the Highlanders, leaving only the 1st battalion of the Guards to care for the Virginians. The Hessians were still struggling with Campbell and Lee in the woods. But for those two contingents so engaged, the whole British army was now free to give its attention to the Continentals in the third line.

Colonel Gunby having been unhorsed, Lieutenant Colonel Howard was leading the 1st Maryland and Kirkwood back to their old position in the line when Stuart, with his grenadiers and Guards, swept around the curve of the courthouse hill and attacked the 5th Maryland in its position supported by two guns. It was largely a new regiment, made up of recruits now in their first battle. The sight of the scarlet and steel was too much for their nerves. Without firing a shot, they turned and ran. Stuart followed, taking the guns as he went. Washington, witnessing this inglorious retreat, called on two small troops of volunteer cavalry to join his horse. All together, they dashed upon the rear of the Guards and rode right through them, slashing right and left. Stuart was killed in this encounter.

Meanwhile Howard had wheeled the 1st Maryland and Kirkwood's company to the right. Washington had just swept clear of the Guards when Howard charged them full in their left flank. But the Guards and the grenadiers were soldiers of the first order. O'Hara, in spite of his wound, rallied them; the Fusiliers and Highlanders came up on their flanks. They stood their ground. So did the Americans, and the fighting was close and bloody.

The British were getting the worst of it when Cornwallis resorted to a desperate remedy. He ordered MacLeod to open fire with grapeshot over the heads of the British between, and full upon the melee of Americans, Guards, and grenadiers. Grape cannot be fired with the accuracy of a rifle bullet, and it is no respecter of persons. The effect of such fire on the British in the fight, as well as on the Americans, was bound to be deadly. It is said that O'Hara, lying on the roadside by the guns, begged Cornwallis not to shoot down his own men. But Cornwallis persisted with bloody results to both armies. The effect was, however, that the Americans withdrew to their former line, and the British had a chance to re-form.

Webster, on the left, was the first to get his men in order. He recrossed the ravine beyond which he had been driven, and charged upon all that was left of the Americans' third line, the 1st Maryland, Huger's two Virginia Continental regiments, Kirkwood's light infantry, and Lynch's riflemen. There was no "give" to that line; it stood fast and, with a concentrated fire, drove Webster back.

Now there was a pause while both sides licked their wounds and prepared to renew the fight. The American militia was gone, the 5th Maryland irretrievably broken. Stevens's Virginia militia in the second line, their colonel wounded, had given way and fled to the woods. Away off to the left of the Americans, out of sight, Campbell's riflemen and Lee's infantry were still engaged with the Regiment von Bose in backwoods fashion. Only that remnant of the third line still held the field. If Greene had known how badly Cornwallis was crippled he might have won a victory in a fight to a finish; but, true to his resolution not to risk destruction of his whole army, he decided at half-past three to retreat.

He had first to stop the fight still going on between the American Continentals and Webster on his right. He ordered the Americans to withdraw, throwing in behind them Colonel John Green's Virginia Continental regiment, which had been held out of the fighting for that purpose. So the retreat began and was soon under way all along the line. Under heavy fire Green's regiment stood firm until all the rest of the American had left the field; then it too retired. "A general retreat took place; but it was conducted with order and regularity," says Stedman, the English historian, who was in the battle. The artillery horses having been killed, the Americans had to abandon their guns. The Welch Fusiliers and Highlanders, with some cavalry, started to follow, but were soon recalled. Greene halted after crossing Reedy Fork about three miles from Guilford, to collect his stragglers, and then went on to his old ground at the ironworks on Troublesome, marching all night.

After Greene had drawn off his men the bush-fighting between Lee and Campbell and the Hessians ceased—but not until Tarleton had been sent in to bring out the Hessians by chasing away the riflemen, with a charge on their flank and rear.

Cornwallis held the field. He had a victory to write home about, but he had paid a price for it. Of about 1,900 men who went into the battle on the British side, more than a fourth were casualties: 93 dead and 439 wounded, many of them mortally. The Guards were sadly reduced: 19 officers, 11 were killed or wounded; among 462 rank and file there were 206 casualties. In all, 29 British and Hessian officers were killed or wounded. General O'Hara and General Howard had suffered injuries; Lieutenant Colonel Webster was mortally wounded.

Not counting the militia who ran clear away and were returned "missing," Greene's casualties were 78 killed and 183 wounded.[17]

In this battle, on both sides the most admirable military qualities were displayed. Of the Americans, the 1st Maryland, Stevens's Virginia militia, and Kirkwood's light infantry bore the palm; but Lynch's riflemen, the Virginia Continentals, Campbell's riflemen, Lee's Legion infantry, and Washington's horse all gave proof of a high degree of valor and steadfastness.

On the whole, however, the laurels for military achievement must be awarded to the British. Starting hungry, they marched twelve hard miles, immediately went into battle against an enemy of greater numbers (even disregarding the North Carolina militia, it was more than 3,000 Americans against 1,900 British) who had been refreshed by a night's sleep and a breakfast. That enemy force was so posted as to have every advantage of its skill in woodcraft and marksmanship and of the superiority of the rifle over the musket. But the British faltered not at all in advancing across a quarter-mile of open ground against two rifle volleys precisely aimed. When the 33rd and the Guards were shattered—the Guards, indeed, torn to pieces —they rallied, re-formed, and attacked with no less vigor for their punishment. Fortescue, the historian of the British army, surveying its whole history from Crecy and Agincourt to the middle of the nineteenth century, says, "Never, perhaps, has the prowess of the British soldier been seen to greater advantage than in this obstinate and bloody combat." The merits and achievements of the Americans in this battle are enhanced, in the judgment of history, in proportion to the military ability of these opponents.

General Francis Vinton Greene estimates the importance and results of Greene's southern campaign up to this time in the following words: "The retreat to the Dan and the battle of Guilford were to the South what the retreat across New Jersey and the battles of Trenton and Princeton were to the North. They turned the tide; and each attracted equal attention in Europe. Greene lost the battle, but he won the campaign, and the first step towards Yorktown was taken."

Henry Lee refers to Cornwallis's superiority in disciplined veteran troops: "General Greene's veteran infantry being only the 1st Regiment of Maryland, the company of Delaware under Kirkwood (to whom none could be superior) and the Legion infantry, altogether making on that day not more than five hundred rank and file."

CHAPTER 74

Cornwallis Abandons the Carolinas

The battlefield at Guilford Court House on the night of March 15 was a sad place. The firing had hardly ceased when the weather broke, and rain began to fall in torrents. The night was unusually dark. The wounded lay scattered about over a wide area. The search for them was prosecuted as best it could be by the tired, hungry British soldiers, but not very successfully, for when day broke 50 men whose wounds were not in themselves mortal were found dead. Those that were gathered up suffered hardly less, for there were no proper surgical stores to meet their needs. There was not even any food. From the time they had their suppers in the evening of March 14, the British troops were entirely without food for forty-eight hours. What each man, sick, wounded, or well, got at the end of that starvation period was four ounces of flour and four ounces of lean beef.[1]

These facts alone are enough to prove that all the military sagacity exercised by the leaders, all the soldierly valor and endurance of hardship displayed by the men of the British army in the last six months had been exercised and displayed in vain. After all that and after the battle just won, Cornwallis found himself almost completely destitute of supplies. His nearest magazine of food was at Wilmington, two hundred miles away. As for securing provision from the country around him, his army was, in effect, the garrison of a besieged town. No foraging party could safely go abroad. No provisions could come unmolested by road or river. He had lost the campaign, and there was no hope of recovery; his army was too weak to fight another battle. If it should try and should lose as many men as in this last one, the patriot countrymen would rise and tear the rest of it to pieces

All he could hope for now was a swift, safe retreat to a place of refuge and a store of food.

Cornwallis stayed at Guilford, resting his men, for two days. During that time the wounded of both armies were given equal attention by the British surgeons and by American army surgeons who had been sent back to the field by Greene under a flag of truce. Cornwallis left about seventy of his own worst wounded men at the Quaker Meeting House at New Garden, with a request that the American general do what he could for them.[2]

Greene, having retired to his old ground on Troublesome Creek, detached Lee's Legion and a corps of riflemen under Campbell to hang on the rear of the British army, now in full retreat, but more particularly to show the countryside that the American army had not been put out of action and to discourage any inclination to join Cornwallis.[3] With the rest of his army, he followed on the 20th.

At Ramsey's Mill on the Deep River where it joins with the Haw to form the Cape Fear River, Cornwallis built a bridge while his army was momentarily resting to facilitate his retreat. Greene sent Lee by a roundabout way to destroy the bridge; but it was found to be too strongly guarded, and the project was abandoned. Greene came up to that point on the 28th, to find that the British army had just crossed the bridge and was on its way down the Cape Fear.[4]

Cornwallis was making for Cross Creek, the settlement of loyal Scottish Highlanders, on the Cape Fear River. He hoped for a plentiful supply of provisions and for the care and refreshment of his sick and wounded in that friendly place. He expected also to arrange for the shipment of supplies up the river from Wilmington. In these hopes and expectations he was disappointed. Provisions for both man and beast were scarce at Cross Creek. The narrow river ran, for a part of its course, through hostile country, and no boats could be got through to him. The Cross Creek settlers did what they could for him, but he could not stay there. He had to push a hundred miles farther to Wilmington.[5]

It was to Cornwallis a distressing march in every respect. His soldierly pride was wounded by this lame-dog finish to his campaign, and he had to stop more than once to bury by the roadside some valued officer who had died of his wounds. Colonel Webster, lamented by the whole army, an officer who "united all the virtues of civil life to the gallantry and professional knowledge of a soldier," [6] was one of these. Two captains of the Guards and two officers of the Regiment von Bose were others. General O'Hara, General Howard, and several other officers of lesser rank, so badly wounded that they could not ride their horses, endured the painful journey in horse litters. On April 7 the melancholy procession reached Wilmington.[7]

After resting and refitting his army, now reduced to 1,435 fit rank and file, Cornwallis had to plan his next move. It was a difficult job. He could not be idle in Wilmington, simply maintain a garrison there; such supine conduct would emphasize to the Carolinians that he had been driven out of the rest of their state and would indicate that he was unable to recover the lost ground. Patriot uprisings throughout the state would be many, and their results bloody. He could not go back to meet Greene again, with any reasonable hope of overcoming him, which would be the only real solution of his problem.

While Cornwallis was studying the problem he got news that added to his perplexity. Greene had marched south from Ramsey's Mill. It seemed evident that he was bound for South Carolina to try conclusions with Rawdon at Camden. Rawdon might need help, but could Cornwallis get it to him in time? He saw obstacles: Camden was a long way off; the intervening country was too poor to support his army on the march; crossing the Pee Dee, if opposed by the enemy, would be hazardous, perhaps fatal; he might be caught between two great rivers and forced to fight without an avenue of retreat; if he were as badly used as at Guilford, it would be all up with his whole army. It was altogether too dangerous an experiment. He decided that he could not get to Camden before Greene; that if Rawdon were already defeated he could do nothing to help him, and that if Greene were defeated he would not be needed. But what should be his active purpose? [8]

Cornwallis concluded that, if Britain was to keep what she had already gained in the South, "a serious attempt upon Virginia would be the most solid plan, because successful operations might not only be attended with important consequences there, but would tend to the security of South Carolina and ultimately to the submission of North Carolina." He therefore "resolved to take advantage of General Greene's having left the back part of Virginia open and march immediately into the province, to attempt a junction with General Phillips." [9] There could be no more eloquent, no more convincing evidence of the complete success of Greene's campaign against Cornwallis than that sentence. The picture of His Majesty's army bottled up in Wilmington until Greene drew off his forces, and then scuttling in haste to enter Virginia by the back door is pathetic in its ignominy.

As early as March 29, the day following his arrival at Ramsey's Mill, Greene had written to General Washington, "I am determined to carry the war immediately into South Carolina." [10] There was plenty to be done in that state and in Georgia. Besides their main positions in Charleston and Savannah, the enemy had outposts, with garrisons of from 120 to 630 each, in South Carolina at Ninety-six, Fort Granby, Orangeburg, Fort Motte, Fort Watson, and Georgetown, a chain that must be broken up if the state was to be redeemed. In the two states the British forces totaled about 8,000.[11]

To Greene there were available scattered commands that might be either drawn upon or reenforced to act independently. Sumter was on the Broad River in western North Carolina, recruiting. Pickens was in western South Carolina, his familiar ground. Marion was hiding in the swamps along the Pee Dee, awaiting his opportunity. Greene sent messengers to them, telling of his intended activities and asking their help. He then proposed to move southward.

First, he had to deal with his North Carolina and Virginia militia. They had been enlisted for only six weeks—a short-term engagement that began for each man when he signed up and ended when he got home again, travel both ways being counted as part of his term. So, though they had been with the army only twenty-three days, their time was up; he had to let them go. His army then consisted of the 1st and 5th Maryland Continental regiments (the 1st including Jaquett's Delaware company), the 1st and 2nd Virginia Continentals, Lee's Legion of horse and foot, Kirkwood's light infantry, and William Washington's dragoons, perhaps 1,400 in all. By a resolution of the "Council Extraordinary" of North Carolina it was provided after Guilford that "every man who abandoned his post in the late action should be enrolled in the Continental army for twelve months." A few hundred such men were eventually rounded up and sent to Greene; they are said to have behaved well.[12]

In the Carolinas and at Augusta, Georgia, Lieutenant Colonel Francis Rawdon, known by the courtesy title of Lord Rawdon, had been in general command since Cornwallis had gone north in pursuit of Greene. He was a young man, but an able soldier. He had entered the British army at the age of seventeen and had been in the American war from its beginning at Lexington. At Bunker's Hill, as a lieutenant, he had greatly distinguished himself by leading the grenadiers of his company after his captain had fallen. Burgoyne said he had that day "stamped his fame for life." He had seen active service in the principal battles in the north from Long Island to Monmouth and in the south from the siege of Charleston to Camden. In person he was tall and dark, and was said to be "the ugliest man in England"; but his bearing was stately and dignified. His manner was genial, and it was said of him that "no man possessed in a higher degree the happy, but rare, faculty of attracting to him all who came within the sphere of his influence." [13] Now, at the age of twenty-six, he was to meet in battle a man twelve years his senior, as fully experienced as he in warfare, with a growing reputation as the wisest strategist in the American army, who would, at the time of their meeting, have 1,400 men to his 900.

On April 6 Greene detached Lee's Legion and Captain Oldham's company of Maryland Continentals with one gun to join Marion on the Pee Dee. He directed them first, however, to proceed down the Cape Fear River towards Cross Creek, to mislead the enemy into thinking that the destination of the whole army was Wilmington. Lee's objective after joining Marion was to be Fort Watson on the Santee below Camden.[14]

Word was sent to Pickens suggesting that he invest Ninety-six if he felt able, or, at all events, that he prevent a reenforcement of Camden from that post. To Sumter, Greene sent a request for a junction of their two forces at Camden. On April 7 he broke camp at Ramsey's Mill and took the road down the Cape Fear, as if intending for Wilmington. The next day he changed his course to the west, across the Little River, the Yadkin, the Rocky River, and so on, the days' marches averaging about eighteen miles. His men had plenty of food now and of rum; it was late spring, instead of midwinter, and they suffered a minimum of hardship.

On the 17th they were in camp on Lynch's Creek. The invalids, spare arms, and heavy baggage were sent off to Salisbury under guard. Orders were given that "the women who have children and all those unable to march on foot must also be sent off, as none will be permitted to ride on wagons or horses, on any pretext whatever." [15]

While Greene was on the march, Lee found Marion. Together they proceeded against Fort Watson. It was a small but stout stockade, surrounded by three rows of abatis and perched upon an ancient tumulus about thirty feet high, which stood upon a bare level plain. It was held by 80 regulars and 40 Tory militiamen commanded by Lieutenant McKay.[16] Lee and Marion invested this little fortress on April 14. They had no artillery, no entrenching tools. Colonel Watson, a British regular officer, who had originally held that post, was on his way to find and fight Marion and might return at any time, so that there was no time for a protracted siege.

Colonel Hezekiah Maham of South Carolina had a plan to meet the situation. In the near-by woods trees were felled, trimmed into logs, and notched to suit their purpose; this took five days. On the night of the 22nd these timbers were carried within rifle shot of the fort and there erected to

form a rectangular structure high enough to overlook the stockade. A rough
platform was laid on top, with a low parapet of logs. At dawn, from this
height, a company of riflemen opened fire upon the fort; their bullets
searched every part of the stockade. At the same time two parties attacked
the abatis. The men in the garrison were unable to repel them without exposing themselves to the marksmen on the tower. They promptly surrendered. With a loss of 2 killed and 6 wounded, Marion and Lee took 114
prisoners. This made the first gap in Rawdon's communications with
Charleston. The device used in the siege was given the name "Maham
Tower" and was subsequently used in similar cases.[17]

Greene had hoped—overoptimistically, it would seem—that he might surprise Rawdon. But news of the American army's approach reached Camden
long before April 19, when he actually arrived in the neighborhood. Halting
for the night four miles from the town, Greene sent Kirkwood's light infantry
ahead to try for possession of Logtown, a group of six or eight cabins in
a rather extensive clearing on a slight elevation less than a mile north of the
town.

Kirkwood marched at eight o'clock in the evening and arrived at Logtown
between nine and ten. He had a smart fight with a picket guard posted there.
By midnight he had driven it out and established his own men in the little
village. Through the night there were desultory attacks, and at sunrise a
smart skirmish; but the Americans held the place until an hour or two
later, when Greene's advance came up. The American force took possession,
and Greene considered his next move.[18]

The town of Camden occupied a strong military position. It was covered
on the south and southwest by the Wateree River, which curved around it
at a distance of less than a mile, and on the east by Pine Tree Creek, a considerable tributary. The north and west were protected by a series of five or
six independent redoubts strung around the central fortification, which was
a strong stockade.[19] The garrison, numbering about 900 in all, consisted of
the 63rd Regiment of regulars and three bodies of Tory troops—the New
York Volunteers, the King's American Regiment (also called Fanning's,
from the man who had raised it in New York in 1776), and the Volunteers
of Ireland, Rawdon's own regiment. There were also 60 Provincial
dragoons and a small party of militia. Colonel Watson had taken 500 other
Tory troops to look for Marion.[20]

Greene realized that his force was not sufficient to take the town by
assault. He hoped that Sumter would soon bring him a substantial addition,
and he expected Lee and Marion to join him as soon as they had reduced

Fort Watson. Meanwhile, he decided to withdraw to Hobkirk's Hill about a mile in his rear, which offered a good position.[21]

The next day, he sent Colonel Washington's horse and Kirkwood's light troops on a foraging expedition. They "went Westerly round Camden, Burn't a House in one of the Enemy's Redoubts . . . took 40 horses and 50 Head of cattle & returned to Camp." [22]

On the 21st, tidings were brought to Greene of the imminent arrival of Colonel Watson and his party of 500 and of their intention to enter Camden, reenforcing Rawdon. To intercept the party, it was thought best to take a position on the east side of the town, Watson being expected from that quarter. This made it necessary to cross Pine Tree Creek and its deep and difficult swampy borders, impassable by artillery and baggage wagons. The impedimenta were sent back twenty miles to Lynch's Creek, and the army shifted its position. But after one night on the new ground more reassuring information as to Watson's movements was received, and Greene moved back to Hobkirk's Hill and sent for the artillery and the baggage.[23]

Up to this time Greene seems to have had no plan except to wait for Sumter, Marion, and Lee; and it may be said at once that Sumter, with his usual rather arrogant independence, had no intention of coming and never did, while the others were too busy trying to catch Watson in the Santee country to give a thought to Greene's predicament.

A deserting drummer of the Maryland line brought Rawdon news about the condition of Greene's force, told him that the artillery had been sent away, and gave him a correct description of the disposition of the troops on the hill. Rawdon promptly relieved Greene of the necessity of making a plan by making one of his own.[24]

Hobkirk's Hill

Hobkirk's Hill was a narrow, sandy ridge of no great height about a mile and a half north of Camden, extending from east to west. It was covered by a dense pine forest. At its eastern end it sloped gradually down to meet the edge of a wide and deep swamp bordering Pine Tree Creek and extending south past the defensive works of Camden. At its southern base the plain was covered by thickets which extended to a space of cleared ground north of the Logtown hill. South of Logtown an extensive clearing reached down to Camden. The main road from that town to the Waxhaws ran almost due north through Logtown and across the middle of Hobkirk's Hill. Because of the forest and of the shape of the hill, there was no clear view from the summit of the approaches.[1]

Greene's troops were encamped in a curved line around the eastern and southeastern end of the top of the hill, in positions corresponding to those the different regiments would take in order of battle, if attacked from that quarter. To guard against surprise, the southern and western sides of the hill were patrolled. On the plain below the southeast side two strong picket guards under Captain Perry Benson of Maryland and Captain Simon Morgan of Virginia were posted, supported by Kirkwood's light troops a little distance in their rear.[2]

Early in the morning of April 25, Colonel Carrington, Greene's quartermaster, arrived in the camp bringing "a comfortable supply of provisions" anticipated in the orders of the day before, which had promised two days' rations of food and a gill of rum to each man. On their arrival, just after the morning drill at daybreak, the men's arms were stacked and the desired distribution was made. Although the rum had not yet come, the provisions were eagerly received, and the men made haste to cook them. Those who had eaten first repaired to a brook running down the northeast side of the hill to wash their clothes. This was the peaceful scene upon which broke, at about ten o'clock, the report of a musket and then another and then many more. As the startled men sprang from their various occupations, the drums in the camp beat to arms.[3]

The attack had come on the picket guards, against whom Rawdon's van pressed forward, his whole force following. The pickets answered this first fire and fell back slowly. "Meanwhile, Kirkwood had hastened to the support of the pickets, and the quick, sharp volleys from the woods told how bravely he was bearing up against the weight of the British army." [4]

The pickets and the light infantry put up a stubborn resistance. Retreating slowly from tree to tree, they obstinately contested Rawdon's advance and so delayed it that the lines on the hill had time to form and even to obey an order to "ease their joints," which meant to sit down, while this preliminary skirmish was being fought in their hearing but out of their sight.[5] "The beautiful example . . . exhibited by Kirkwood, as he deliberately retired firing . . contributed to produce upon the army an effect from which everything was to be hoped for." [6] Not until Rawdon had brought upon them the weight of his whole force did the light infantry and the pickets retreat to the army awaiting them on the hill.

The American line was disposed in a curve following the contours of the hill. The 4th Virginia Continental Regiment, under Lieutenant Colonel Richard Campbell, was on the extreme right of the first line; next was the 5th Virginia under Lieutenant Colonel Samuel Hawes. This wing was commanded by General Huger. Towards the left was Colonel John Gunby's 1st Maryland, and then Lieutenant Colonel Benjamin Ford's 5th Maryland. Colonel Otho Williams commanded that wing. The North Carolina militia, about 250 under Colonel Jesse Read, formed the second, or reserve, line; thus the formation was the reverse of those at Cowpens and Guilford, where the militia were in the first lines. William Washington's cavalry was also held in reserve behind the left wing, with whom presumably Kirkwood's light infantry took their place on their retirement from the front, since they had been lately attached to Washington's dragoons. The artillery, which had just come back from Lynch's Creek, three 6-pounders under Colonel Charles Harrison of Virginia, was posted in the center on the road running over the hill and behind the first line; it was thus concealed from the enemy. There were about 250 men in the militia reserve, 1,174 Continentals, 87 in Washington's cavalry, but only 56 of them mounted, and 40 in the artillery contingent.[7]

Rawdon had made his way to the field of action by a wide detour from Camden towards the east and close to the edge of the Pine Tree Creek swamps, so as to approach the hill on its southeast side, where the ascent was easier. When he had driven in the pickets and their support, he deployed in line of battle: the New York Volunteers in the center, the 63rd British Regiment and the King's American Regiment right and left, the Volunteers of Ireland in support of the right wing, and a corps of "convalescents" under Captain Robertson behind the left. The South Carolina Provincial Regiment and the New York Dragoons were held in reserve, while picked Tory riflemen were sprinkled in the woods on the right and left to snipe at American officers.[8]

Greene watched the display of the enemy and saw that it presented a narrow front, much less extensive than his own line. In this discrepancy he saw his chance. Instead of awaiting an assault by Rawdon's force, now advancing steadily and in good order, he would attack in such manner as to secure a quick and crushing victory. He gave orders accordingly.

Preceded by a discharge of the artillery, the whole first line of the patriots was to charge down the hill upon the advancing foe. While the 5th Virginia under Hawes and Gunby's 1st Maryland crashed into Rawdon's front with the bayonet and without firing, the American right and left wings, Campbell's 4th Virginia and Ford's 5th Maryland, were to wheel upon the enemy's flanks, thus folding their whole line in a deadly embrace. At the same time Washington's dragoons would start on a swift circuit of the combat and fall upon the British rear.

The battle began when the American center stepped a few paces to right and left, disclosing the guns, which at once opened fire with grape and threw the surprised enemy into momentary confusion. Then the Americans started down the slope.

But Rawdon was quick to see the error of his formation and as quick to correct it. He called his supports into his front line, the volunteers of Ireland on the right and Robertson's corps on the left. This extended his front so that it outflanked the Americans and would subject them to an enfilading fire. Nevertheless, they hurried on to the conflict.

At first, despite the alteration of the British line, the attack seemed to be successful. The American right, led by Greene and Huger, gained ground. Hawes's Virginians and Gunby's Marylanders were coming on gallantly with the bayonet. The flanking regiments were hotly engaged. The artillery was still firing grape, and Washington's horse were sweeping around to get at the British rear. Then came the first break in the plan.

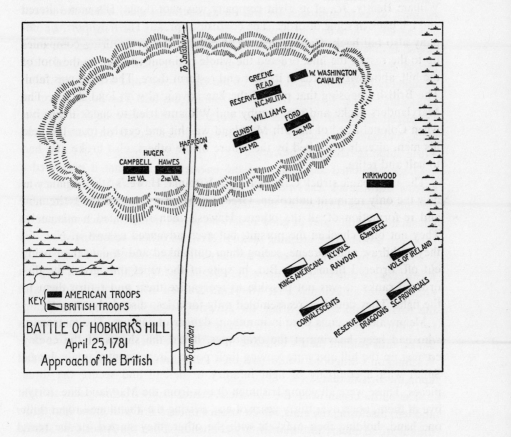

Gunby's 1st Maryland, instead of pushing on with the bayonet without firing, paused to fire a volley. It started again; but, as it did so, Captain William Beatty, Jr., of its right company was shot down. His men faltered and fell back in some disorder. The confusion spread. The neighboring company also fell back. Gunby, instead of rallying the two retiring companies up to the rest of the line, ordered the whole regiment to retire to the foot of the hill, about sixty yards in its rear and re-form there. The effect was fatal. The British opposing that part of the line advanced with loud shouts. The Marylanders broke and ran. Gunby and Williams tried to check them; but when Colonel Ford of the 5th Maryland was hit and carried from the field his men, already disturbed by the failure of the others, also broke and had to halt and retire.

The same panic struck Campbell's 4th Virginia. Hawes's 5th Virginia was now the only regiment unbroken. Greene ordered it to cover the retirement and re-formation of all the others. Hawes's men responded handsomely. They not only checked the pursuit, but even advanced against it. Nor did they withdraw until Greene, seeing them outflanked and in danger of being cut off, ordered them back. But, in spite of the relief thus given the disordered ranks, it was not possible to reorganize them and return them to the fight. They could be reassembled only for a less disorderly retreat.

Meanwhile the guns were in imminent danger of capture. The matrosses, who had been heaving at the dragropes, heard the shouts of the enemy coming up the hill and were leaving their posts. Greene sent Captain James Smith with a company of light infantry to defend and secure the three pieces. These were all young Irishmen drawn from the Maryland line, forty-five of them, none over thirty years of age. Seizing the abandoned ropes with one hand, holding their muskets with the other, they started for the rear; but the British dragoons led by Captain Coffin came galloping up the road. Smith's men dropped the ropes and made ready to receive the charge. Their fire was deadly. The dragoons wheeled and retired, but rallied, came on again, only to be driven back once more. So they fought, back and forth, while the British infantry was coming up through the woods. A sharp fire burst upon the little corps. Smith was wounded, all but fourteen of his men were shot down. Then Coffin made a final charge and not a man escaped; every one was either killed or captured.

Meanwhile Greene himself had rallied the matrosses, and they were drawing off the guns. He dismounted, held his bridle with one hand, and tugged with the other at the ropes. But when Smith's gallant band had been destroyed, the guns seemed hopelessly lost. They would have been, if just then Washington's dragoons had not returned from their errand of encirclement. They charged the enemy impetuously, dispersing them. Horses were hitched to the guns, and they were got away.

But what had Washington been doing all the time? The answer to this question discovers one of the several causes of the defeat. He had made a grand circuit of the field as had been ordered. The thick undergrowth and the tangle of trees, felled to clear the space between Logtown and the hill, had compelled such a long detour that he had emerged in the open far behind the enemy's fighting line. There he came upon a horde of noncombatants, surgeons, commissaries, quartermasters, "all the loose trumpery of the army," who had come out of Camden to watch the battle. Instead of disregarding them and galloping on to strike the rear of the fighting men, he began to take prisoners right and left. He had assembled two hundred when he heard of the American retreat. He mounted fifty of them behind his men and hastily took the parole of the officers he had to leave. Encumbered by reluctant passengers, his men could not fight; and so the intended attack on the enemy's rear was abandoned, and they swung around the circuit again on their way back to the hill. Having arrived, Washington heard the firing in the fight for the guns, dumped his captives by the roadside, and charged.

Greene assembled his men, his wagons, his guns, and the fifty prisoners and retreated in good order. He was followed for two or three miles, but his rear guard effectively discouraged the pursuit. When the enemy desisted from it, he halted to rest his men and await the stragglers.

Washington's dragoons and Kirkwood's light infantry were sent back to the field of action to bring off the wounded, collect stragglers, and pick up prisoners. There they again met Coffin's horsemen, attacked them, and drove them clear off. The rest of Rawdon's army had withdrawn into the town; Washington and Kirkwood had a clear field and were able to gather up all the wounded Americans and take them back to the army. Care of the wounded is much thought of by the survivors of any battle, who can picture the sufferings they themselves would have to undergo, if left helpless in the field. The recovery of these injured men was consoling to all the others. From their temporary halting place, the army marched on to Sanders Creek, the scene of Gates's disastrous defeat.

The American casualties, as reported by the adjutant-general, were one officer and 18 men killed, 7 officers and 108 men wounded, 136 men missing. Tarleton figured the British losses in killed, wounded, and missing at 258, of whom 38 were killed, including one officer; 13 officers were wounded.

Greene was sadly disappointed by the outcome of the battle. The signal failure of the 1st Maryland, the pride of his eye, to meet the test of the first encounter, followed by its inability to recover and return to the fight, was shocking to him. However, he blamed the men less than he did their commander. He felt that, when the first two companies had broken, Gunby should have rallied them to the rest of the regiment in the still advancing line, instead of ordering the whole regiment to the rear to re-form, thus precipitating a general withdrawal and finally a panic. He wrote to Joseph Reed, "We should have had Lord Rawdon and his whole command prisoners in three minutes, if Colonel Gunby had not ordered his regiment to retire, the greatest part of which were advancing rapidly at the time they were ordered off. I was almost frantic with vexation at the disappointment." [9]

A court of inquiry held at Gunby's request confirmed this opinion. Though it found his "spirit and activity unexceptionable," it also found that "his order for the regiment to retire, which broke the line, was extremely improper and unmilitary and, in all probability, the only cause why we did not obtain a complete victory." [10]

Rawdon won the day; but the price he paid was, like that of Cornwallis at Guilford, too high to profit him, as will appear. Greene expressed the sentiments of himself and his men when he wrote to the French envoy, the Chevalier de La Luzerne, "We fight, get beat, rise and fight again."

CHAPTER 7 6

Mopping Up the Carolinas

Greene and his army lay at Sanders Creek until the second day after the battle and then marched up to Rugeley's Mills, where he thought there was a better chance of "recruiting the cattle," that is to say refreshing the horses.[1] Marion and Lee were operating in the vicinity of the confluence of the Congaree and the Wateree in an effort to intercept Watson's force on its way to join Rawdon in Camden. Greene decided to assist them. He broke camp at Rugeley's on May 3, marched to the Wateree, crossed it, and established his army in a naturally strong position behind Twenty-five Mile Creek where it would interfere with Watson's getting into Camden from the south.[2] He believed that if Watson succeeded Rawdon would promptly attempt to engage the Americans. On May 7, having eluded Marion and Lee, Watson did get into Camden; and that same night Rawdon acted as Greene had foreseen. He crossed the Wateree at Camden Ferry, proposing "to turn the flank and attack the rear of Greene's army." [3]

Greene, however, had heard of Watson's arrival and had withdrawn on the same day five miles up the river to Sandy's—or Sawney's—Creek and then four miles farther to a better position on Colonel's Creek, leaving Washington's horse and Kirkwood's light troops as a corps of observation at Sandy's.[4] Rawdon mistook this corps for a picket guard of the main army, which he supposed lay in force close behind this outpost. As he afterward reported to Cornwallis, he found the situation too strong to be forced "without suffering such loss as would have crippled my force for any future enterprize." He returned to Camden. Washington and Kirkwood then marched to rejoin the army.[5]

For a long time Greene had been calling for reenforcements. He had counted on 1,500 to 2,000 men from Virginia and on the 1,000 Carolinians under Sumter. With these additions he could have taken the field, blockaded Rawdon in Camden until hunger compelled surrender, mastered the posts on the Santee and the Congaree, and opened the way to take Ninety-six and Augusta; in a word, he would have certainly reconquered most of the south.[6] Although he had sent several appeals to Sumter, that independent gentleman preferred to act alone, to carry on "rambling, predatory excursions unconnected with the operations of the army." [7] So the 1,000 Carolinians did not come to Greene's aid. Nor did the others. "The 2,000 Virginia militia I have been expecting to join us," he wrote to the Congress on May 5, "have not come out, nor can I learn that they will. . . . Maryland has neglected us altogether; not a man has joined us from that State since I have been in this department. Delaware has not answered my letters. . . . North Carolina has got next to no men in the field and few militia and those the worst in the world." [8]

The troops Greene had were too few for a regular battle. "You see," he said to Colonel William Davie of North Carolina, on his staff, "that we must again resume the partisan war. . . . You observe our dangerous and critical situation. The regular troops are now reduced to a handful and I am without militia to perform the convoy or detachment service. . . . Congress seems to have lost sight of the Southern States and have abandoned them to their fate, so much so that I am even as much distressed for ammunition as for men." He expected Rawdon to resume active operations and "push the Americans back to the mountains." [9]

Yet, in spite of the discouraging outlook after Hobkirk's Hill, Greene was now on the eve of sweeping the enemy from every foothold in the Carolinas, excepting only Charleston, for Rawdon was in worse case than he. Though not visibly beleaguered, Rawdon was cut off from food and forage by the activity of the partisan bands. Also mutiny was brewing among his men, for a rather odd reason.

Among the prisoners taken by the Americans at Hobkirk's Hill, were several deserters from the American army who had joined the British. On May 1, five were executed by hanging.[10] This incident disturbed the minds of many of the men in the Camden garrison, "which was composed very much of deserters" from the American army. The outlook for them, in case of capture by the Americans, was not pleasant; hence the growing unrest.

Under these conditions, Rawdon made up his mind to the drastic step of evacuating Camden and abandoning two other important posts. Immediately after his return on May 8 from the unsuccessful attempt to force Greene to fight, he sent orders to Lieutenant Colonel Cruger to leave Ninety-six and join Browne at Augusta, and to Major Maxwell to abandon Fort Granby and fall back on Orangeburg; both dispatches were intercepted, though Rawdon did not know it. He prepared for the evacuation of Camden, and his preparation was thorough, though hurried. On May 9 he burned the jail, the mills, and several private houses, leaving the town "little better than a heap of rubbish," [11] and destroyed all the stores he could not carry away. The next day he departed, taking with him four or five hundred Negro slaves and "all the most obnoxious loyalists." [12] He left behind 31 American privates and 3 British officers and 58 men, all of whom were too badly wounded to be moved.

Picking up on his route "all the well-affected neighbours . . . together with the wives, children, Negroes and baggage of almost all of them," Rawdon reached Nelson's Ferry on the Santee on the 13th. He had hoped to be in time to relieve Fort Motte, besieged by Marion and Lee, but was too late, as will appear. He had been joined by Major McArthur with about 380 dragoons, and failing succor for Fort Motte he designed to attack Greene, then on his way south, at McCord's Ferry on the Congaree. But Greene had already crossed, and so he finally came to rest at Monck's Corner on the Cooper Run, about forty miles north of Charleston.[13] There we may allow him to remain while we review the activities of Greene's army and the American partisan forces.

Kirkwood's light infantry, a detachment from the Maryland line, and a party of Washington's horse had been sent out from Greene's camp on Colonel's Creek in the evening of May 10, for the night surprise of a party of Tories. They marched eighteen miles without finding their quarry, but did discover that Rawdon had left Camden. Whereupon they turned that way and made eleven miles more by morning, when they entered the town.[14] Greene immediately brought down the rest of his army and destroyed the works, but tarried only one day. Correctly surmising that Rawdon's next move would be to relieve Fort Motte, he set out at once to interpose his force between Rawdon and the besiegers of Motte.[15]

The process of mopping up the Carolinas had begun before the evacuation of Camden. After the fall of that town, the successive steps occurred with almost bewildering rapidity. The first step had been taken by Sumter. Refusing to join Greene, he had been conducting an independent operation, which included a demonstration against Fort Granby (on the site later occupied by the town of Columbia). Finding it too strong to take, he withdrew and marched against Orangeburg, fifty miles to the south on the North Edisto River. Although its garrison was small, consisting of 15 British regulars and 70 Tory militia, it was a strong post. However, "by his address . . . in the disposition of his artillery and troops," he induced a prompt surrender on May 11 without the loss of a man and secured "great quantities of provision and some other stores." [16]

On May 8 Marion and Lee had approached Fort Motte, the principal depot of convoys from Charleston to Camden, on the southern bank of the Congaree a little above its confluence with the Wateree. It was a large and handsome mansion owned by Mrs. Rebecca Motte, who occupied a farmhouse near by since the British had ousted her from it. It had been strongly fortified with a stockade, a deep ditch, and an abatis, and was garrisoned by 150 infantry under Lieutenant McPherson, and a small detachment of cavalry. The Americans invested it and began approaches by parallels. But after two days of that work there appeared "beacon-fires on the distant hills," signals of Rawdon's coming to relieve the beleaguered garrison. It was plain that there would be no time to carry on regular siege operations before his arrival with a force greatly outnumbering the besiegers. With great regret, because the owner and all her family were stanch patriots, it was resolved to burn the fort, if it could be ignited.

When this resolution was made known to Mrs. Motte, she received it with "a smile of complacency," and herself furnished the means of setting it afire, a bow and arrows to be tipped with "combustible matter." Two days later the approaches had been dug to within bowshot of the house. The first arrow, launched by one of Marion's men with the appropriate name of Savage, struck the roof and ignited the shingles; two others were equally well aimed. The garrison started to knock off the shingles, but a few shots from a fieldpiece raked the attic and drove the soldiers from it. A white flag soon appeared, and the garrison surrendered. The British officers were paroled and invited, along with the American officers, to sit down to "a sumptuous dinner" provided by Mrs. Motte, whose "deportment and demeanor" as she conversed with "ease, vivacity and good sense" gave "a zest to the pleasures of the table." [17] It is pleasant to know that the fire was put out, and the house saved from destruction.

Greene, with a small escort, had hurried ahead of the army. He reached Motte shortly after the surrender, and, having ordered the prisoners to a place of security, directed Marion to proceed against Georgetown and Lee against Fort Granby, to which the army was also to march. The paroled British officers were allowed to join Rawdon, then engaged in crossing the

Santee at Nelson's Ferry, as has been stated. Receiving news of the fall of Motte, Rawdon ordered the post at that ferry abandoned.[18]

On May 13 Lee started for Granby, at Friday's Ferry on the Congaree, which he reached the next day. It was held by Major Maxwell, a Maryland Tory, with 352 men, chiefly Tory militia. The "fort" was a strongly built, two-story frame building, surrounded by a parapet with bastions mounting guns, a ditch, and the usual abatis—a strong post not to be taken without difficulty. But what force would have been slow to accomplish, guile quickly effected.

Lee had been told that Maxwell was ruled by cupidity, and that he and his men had gathered a considerable quantity of plunder. After two or three discharges of artillery and a brave show of infantry, he sent a flag to Maxwell and offered to allow all the private property on the premises to be taken away by its possessors, without inquiry as to their title to it, and carried to Charleston, to which place all the garrison were to go as prisoners of war until exchanged. The surrender was promptly arranged on those terms, Maxwell being allowed two wagons to transport his personal plunder. A considerable quantity of ammunition, some salt and liquor, the fort's guns, the garrison's weapons, and a number of horses were thus secured.[19]

Meanwhile Greene's army had been marching steadily southward. On the day Fort Granby surrendered, it was but a few miles distant. As usual, he was on the spot himself and viewed the work of Lee with satisfaction. Exactly twenty days had elapsed since his defeat at Hobkirk's Hill. In that short time, the enemy's imposing chain of posts in the Carolinas was broken by the loss of Camden, Watson, Motte, Granby, Nelson's Ferry, and Orangeburg. Besides Charleston and Savannah, only Georgetown and Ninety-six in South Carolina and Augusta in Georgia remained to the British. Greene had been beaten in every battle; he had barely saved his battered army from annihilation in the grueling retreat to the Dan; it had been reduced in numbers to an apparently almost negligible force; yet now he had swept two states, covering an enormous territory, almost clear of the enemy—almost, but not quite. There was more still to be done.

Georgetown had been assigned to Marion. Lee's Legion with some North Carolina militia under Major Pinketham Eaton was now to help Pickens in an attack on Augusta, while Greene with his army went on to Ninety-six.

Georgetown was no trouble at all: on the night after Marion's men had begun to break ground for approaches to it, the garrison evacuated the works and retreated to Charleston.[20] Lee moved against Augusta with his customary speed. He started from Granby a few hours after its surrender and made thirteen miles that evening. Haste was desirable because Greene was apprehensive that Cruger, hearing of Rawdon's retreat, might withdraw his garrison from Ninety-six and join Browne at Augusta, as indeed Rawdon's intercepted message from Camden had desired him to do. However, Lee learned on his march that Cruger was busily strengthening his fortifications to stand a siege.

The rapidity of Lee's march was made possible by his practice of occasionally dismounting his dragoons and mounting his foot-weary infantry on their horses. By this means, he was nearing Augusta on the third day when he learned that the annual King's present to his loyal Indians, a mass of material not to be overlooked or disregarded, had been temporarily deposited at Fort Galphin (Dreadnought), twelve miles below Augusta. Leaving Eaton with his militia and the artillery to follow on, he mounted his own infantry behind his dragoons for a forced march to the place of deposit.

In the next morning, May 21, he reached the little fort, a stockaded farmhouse garrisoned by two companies of Tory militia. There he detached a part of his force, which had been reenforced by parts of two regiments of Georgia and South Carolina militia, to make a sham attack on one side of the fort. At sight of these men, the major part of the garrison made a sortie. The attackers ran and the garrison pursued, while the main body of the Legion with its auxiliaries rushed the fort with little opposition. A considerable store of blankets, clothing, small arms, ammunition, rum, salt, medicines, and other articles, all most useful to the Americans, was taken. Lee then reassembled his troops and joined Pickens at Augusta.

In the center of that town was a strong fortification, Fort Cornwallis, held by the Tory Lieutenant Colonel Thomas Browne with 250 Tory militia and 300 Creek Indians. About half a mile distant there was another, smaller work, Fort Grierson, held by a Tory colonel of that name with 80 Georgia militia and two pieces of artillery.

The first attack was made on the smaller fort. Pickens and Lieutenant Colonel Elijah Clark of Georgia with their militia were posted on its north and west sides, Major Eaton and his North Carolinians on the south. Lee's infantry and artillery were also on the south side in support of Eaton. Major Joseph Egleston with Lee's cavalry was interposed between the two forts. The three detachments of infantry advanced against the fort simultaneously. There was little resistance. Without formally surrendering, the garrison attempted to escape to the other fort, but Clarke's force intercepted them, fell upon them with the ferocity habitual in those southern conflicts between rebel and Tory, and killed 30. All the rest were captured, including Grierson, who was shot while a prisoner by one of the Georgians, to whom he was "greatly obnoxious" because of the outrages he had visited upon them. The Americans lost a few, but one of them was Major Eaton, who was killed.

Fort Cornwallis was not so easily overcome. It was invested, and the usual approaches by parallels were begun, but were carried on with difficulty because of Browne's vigilance and activity. Twice a heavy detachment of the garrison sallied out and, after driving the men from the trenches in fierce, hand-to-hand fighting in which the bayonet was freely employed, was itself driven back to the fort.

The besiegers then began to erect a Maham tower. Browne turned two of his heaviest guns upon it; but it was completed, and the fire from it dismounted the two enemy guns and raked almost every part of the fort. Again there were sorties from the fort, two of them, and bitter fighting with the bayonet ensued. A pretended deserter from the fort, sent out to burn the tower, was discovered and taken prisoner.

A wooden house near the fort seemed to offer a vantage point for a party of riflemen to cover the proposed assault. They were about to occupy it when a violent explosion blew it to pieces. Browne had left it standing for a trap, had run a sap under it and mined it, but the mine had been prematurely set off.

In the morning of June 4 the besiegers were arrayed in columns ready for the assault, when it was decided again to summon the fort. The offered terms were accepted and on the 6th the garrison marched out and piled their arms. Browne was closely guarded to prevent assassination by the revengeful Georgians. The loss of the Americans in this affair was about 40 men killed or wounded. Except as to the 300 taken prisoners, the enemy's casualties are unknown. The day after the surrender, Lee set out to join Greene at Ninety-six, the only one of all the posts in the interior of Georgia and the Carolinas now held by the enemy.[21]

Ninety-six

When Greene left Camden on May 12 his thought was to interpose his army between the troops commanded by Marion and Lee, attacking Fort Motte, and Rawdon, who, he feared, might go to the relief of that post. The news of its surrender on the day he had left Camden relieved him of that apprehension; he turned west and was within a few miles of Granby when that post fell on the 15th. The way was now clear for him to proceed to his grand objective, Ninety-six. The army crossed the Broad River on the 18th, the Saluda on the 21st at Island Ford.

Ninety-six was so called because it was believed to be that number of miles from the old frontier fort of Prince George on the Keowee River. It was an important link in the chain of posts by which the British had held the Carolinas, because it served to protect the Tory element in its neighborhood, to hold in check the patriots in the settlements to the west of it, and to maintain communication with the Indian tribes that favored the British.[1]

For many years it had been stockaded. But that was insufficient defense against attack by a fully equipped army, and it was now much more strongly fortified. Since the fall of Camden and the other British posts the threat of an attack by Greene had caused still further elaboration and strengthening of its defenses.

The rectangular stockade surrounding the village was now protected by a deep ditch with an abatis, the earth from its excavation having been thrown up to form a high bank on the outside. At the easterly corner of the stockade, connected with it but lying wholly outside that enclosure, was a strong redoubt, the Star, of considerable size, roughly circular but with sixteen salient and reentering angles. This was also ditched about and abatised.

West of the main stockade was a large spring from which a rivulet ran down a little ravine. This was the only water supply for the villagers and the garrison. To protect it, the jail, which was within the stockade near the western corner, had been fortified; and upon the western bank of the ravine a small but strong palisaded fort containing two blockhouses had been built. This seems to have been called Holmes's Fort. A covered way led from the main stockade to the stream. The new works had been planned by Lieutenant Haldane, an engineer officer of the British army.[2]

The garrison of the fort was composed entirely of Tory troops. There were 150 of the 2nd battalion of the Loyalists of New York, a brigade raised by General Oliver De Lancey, a gentleman of wealth and high social position, 200 of the 2nd battalion of the New Jersey Volunteers, and 200 South Carolina Tory militia. Lieutenant Colonel John Harris Cruger, De Lancey's son-in-law, was in command of the whole. Cruger was a gentleman of spirit and courage, able and energetic far beyond the usual run of Tory leaders, and his men, "constantly employed in active service since the year 1776," were now "perhaps equal to any troops." He had also a considerable number of Tory civilians, who had taken refuge in the fort, and a noncombatant force of many Negro slaves, a sort of labor battalion.[3] Although he was well furnished with provisions his only artillery was three 3-pounder pieces mounted on wheel-carriages.[4]

Against this fortress Greene led fewer than a thousand regular troops and a few raw militia. Specifically, his army consisted of the two regiments of Maryland and Delaware Continentals—427 rank and file fit for duty—the Virginia brigade numbering 431, a North Carolina battalion of 66, and Kirkwood's 60 light infantry.[5]

Greene's advance arrived at Ninety-six on May 21, the main army coming the next day. The patriots made four camps in the woods, at the corners of an imaginary rectangle enclosing the fort, all within cannon shot of the stockade. Then Greene surveyed the situation. He saw "a very respectable work . . . so well furnished that our success is very doubtful." His force was not strong enough to invest the place completely, and he had no battering cannon. He decided that he must operate against it in the classic manner, by parallel approaches, and that they should be directed against the Star redoubt, since it commanded the main stockade.[6]

Without delay, without even first summoning the garrison to surrender, Kosciuszko, the chief engineer, began operations within two hundred feet of the Star, which was most discourteous as well as indiscreet. "Had he been acting against a raw and undisciplined militia, his temerity might have been excusable"—his impoliteness in omitting the usual preliminary formal summons might not even have been recognized as such, nor might the beginning of the approaches so rashly near the fort have been regarded as an insult. "But both the British commander and his garrison had seen too much service not to take advantage of so rash a proceeding and to teach him to his cost to shew them a little more respect." "Stung with this indignity," Cruger acted promptly. He mounted his three guns on a platform in the salient of the Star nearest the approach begun by the insolent besiegers. Under cover of a brisk fire from these guns and from some riflemen, a party of 30 under Lieutenant Roney sallied out, attacked the working party, put them all to the bayonet, destroyed their work, "loaded several Negroes with the intrenching tools," and returned to the fort before a rescue party from the American camp could reach the scene. Roney was the only casualty in the attacking force; he was mortally wounded.[7]

Having been taught this salutary lesson, Kosciuszko began again at a respectful distance, twelve hundred feet from the Star. The work was interrupted by frequent sallies from the fort but was pushed so expeditiously that the second parallel was complete by June 3. Then the previously omitted formality was gone through: the garrison was summoned. Cruger made the customary reply denying the request.[8]

From the nearest point in the approaches Greene then directed his artillery in a heavy cross fire, which enfiladed the enemy's works. Under cover of this, the digging was continued energetically night and day, and a sap was pushed forward. Meanwhile the timbers for a Maham tower were prepared. On the completion of the third parallel it was erected to a height of forty feet, within thirty-five yards of the abatis around the Star. It so overtopped that redoubt that the riflemen on its summit silenced the guns in the Star. Cruger answered by piling sandbags to raise the parapet, with loopholes which allowed his riflemen to reply effectively. He also tried to burn the tower by firing hot shot into it, but, lacking the proper furnaces, could not heat the balls sufficiently to ignite the timbers. Greene replied by trying to repeat the incendiarism that had been so successful at Fort Motte. Arrows whose butts were wrapped to fit closely in a musket barrel had points tipped with blazing tow, and then were fired at the barrack roofs. Cruger had the roofs torn off all the buildings, whereby the garrison was exposed "to all the pernicious effects of the night air." [9]

Lee and his Legion arrived on June 8, and Pickens with his militia came soon after. Lee immediately suggested that the approaches had been begun on the wrong side of the fort, the strongest side, while its most vulnerable

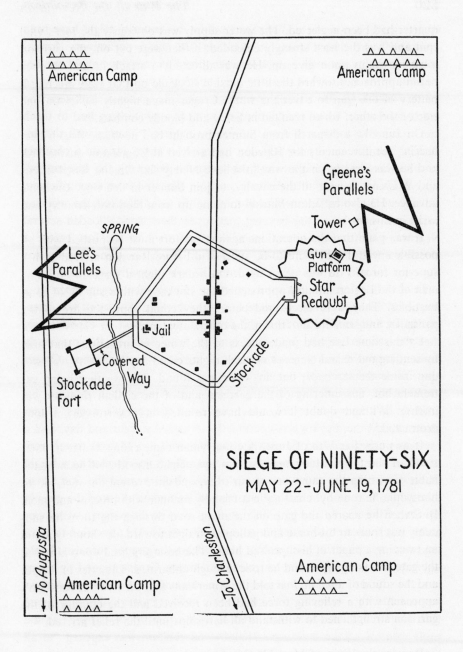

quarter had been neglected. The water supply was obviously the fort's vital spot and was the least strongly defended; if that were cut off, the garrison must inevitably soon give up. He was directed to attack it, and at once began approaches toward the little outside stockade on that side, erecting a battery of one gun to cover the work. Cruger made nightly sallies on one side or the other, which resulted in fierce and bloody combats.[10]

On June 11 a dispatch from Sumter brought bad news. A British fleet bearing reenforcements for Rawdon had arrived at Charleston on the 3rd, and he was already on the way to relieve Ninety-six. Greene sent Pickens and Washington with all the cavalry, to join Sumter in delaying Rawdon's advance. He also called on Marion to come up from the lower country and assist in this work.

It was plain that the operations against the fort must be pushed with all possible speed if they were to be successful before Rawdon arrived with a superior force. Fire was again tried. On a dark night a sergeant and nine men of the Legion infantry approached the stockade with a supply of combustibles. They were discovered before they could apply the fire to the palisades, and six were shot down, the others escaping.[11]

By this time Lee had made access to the water so precarious that only by sending out naked Negroes on dark nights could any be got. A well was dug inside the stockade, but no water was found. The weather being extremely hot, the suffering of the garrison and of the civilian refugees was intense. Without doubt it would have resulted in a surrender, if long protracted.[12]

It was now the 17th of June. A countryman came riding along the lines south of the town. Many people from the neighborhood had been in the habit of visiting the camp out of curiosity, and little attention was paid to him while he rode by, chatting in a friendly manner with officers and men. But when he neared the gate on the main road through the town he suddenly put spurs to his horse and galloped straight towards it, shouting aloud and waving a paper in his upraised hand. The besiegers fired upon him, but the gate was flung open, and he rode through unharmed. The cries of delight and the sound of a *feu de joie* told the Americans that the news of Rawdon's approach with a relieving force had been received and the courage of the garrison strengthened to withstand all hardships until the relief arrived.[13]

Rawdon had lain at Monck's Corner no more than ten days when, on June 3, he got word of the arrival of the fleet from Cork with his longed-for reenforcements. He hastened to Charleston and arranged for the expedition to succor Ninety-six. By the 7th he was on the way with a column made up of flank companies—light infantry and grenadiers—of the 3rd, 19th, and 30th British regiments. At Monck's Corner he picked up his own troops. He had now a force of 2,000 experienced men, including 150 horsemen.[14]

In spite of the excessive heat the rescue force proceeded by forced marches on its journey of nearly two hundred miles to the beleaguered fort. By swinging wide to the right, Rawdon avoided Sumter and the others that had been sent to delay him. At the time when the artful messenger got the good news into the fort the relief force was not more than thirty miles away.

Now there was not even a shadow of doubt that Greene must immediately make his choice among three possible courses of action: march to meet and fight Rawdon before he got to Ninety-six and then return to take the town; storm the fort before Rawdon arrived; give over the siege and retire. He was somewhat inclined to follow the example of Julius Caesar at Alesia and adopt the first course; but, as his force of regulars was only a little more than half Rawdon's, he decided to storm the fort.[15]

His plan for the attack called for two simultaneous assaults—one on the east side, one on the west. Lieutenant Colonel Campbell of the 1st Virginia Regiment with a detachment of the Maryland and Virginia Continentals was charged with the attack on the easterly side, of which the Star was a part. The third parallel of the approaches on that side had been completed, and two trenches had almost reached the ditch around the fort. Fascines were to be ready to fill the ditch, also long poles with iron hooks on their ends to pull the sandbags down from the parapet. A forlorn hope was chosen and was put under command of Lieutenants Duval of Maryland and Seldon of Virginia. The van of this contingent was to be composed of axmen who would cut through the abatis. The hookmen were to follow, and then the main assaulting force for that quarter was to come out of the trenches and swarm over the stockade.

On the west side, the smaller stockade—Holmes's Fort—which guarded the water supply, was to be the first objective. This was assigned to Lee's Legion infantry and Kirkwood's light troops. Captain Rudolph of the Legion was to lead the forlorn hope in that quarter.[16]

The firing of a second gun at noon on the 18th was the signal for the onslaught. On the west, Rudulph led his men swiftly against their objective. They gained the ditch, with the rest of the column close on their heels, and soon opened their "way into the fort from which the enemy, giving their last fire, precipitately retreated." Having so established themselves, Lee's detachment awaited news of the progress of the assault on the other side before following up the blow by passing the rivulet, entering the town, and forcing the fortified prison, which they intended to use as a base for operations that would divide Cruger's efforts to defend his post.[17]

Meanwhile, on the side of the Star, there was a bitter and bloody conflict. At the signal, Greene's little battery began a sustained bombardment of the fort, while the infantry fired by platoons, and the riflemen on the tower opened a continuous fire at the parapet of the Star. At the same moment the forlorn hopes led by Duval and Seldon leapt from the third parallel and ran to attack the abatis at two different points. The axmen soon cut their way through and entered the ditch. The hook men were close after them. The parapet bristled with pikes and bayonets; but they could not reach the men in the ditch, nor could the defenders fire down on them, without exposing themselves to the deadly aim of the riflemen on the tower.

The hook men went to work on the sandbags, pulling them down into the ditch. If the parapet could be stripped of them for a space, Campbell's men could clamber over and fight it out hand to hand. Major Green of De Lancey's regiment commanded the 150 men in the Star. He watched the bags falling into the ditch and saw that the garrison could not rely on musket fire to stop this breach in the defenses. Immediate and direct action was necessary. He issued the orders.

Two parties of 30 men each, led by Captain French of De Lancey's and Captain Campbell of the Jerseymen, issued from a sallyport in the rear of the Star, turned in opposite directions, and rushed upon the axmen and the hook men with the bayonet. There was hard fighting in little space and "the carnage was great"; [18] but when both Duval and Seldon were struck down their surviving men fell back to their support in the approaches.

The attempt had failed, and the failure had been costly. There was little hope of success in another effort, nor was there time to organize another; Rawdon was too near. Greene ordered a withdrawal and sent a flag to Cruger proposing a truce for the purpose of burying the dead. Cruger refused it, reserving that honor for the victor, whoever it might be. Greene then prepared to leave. The retreat began on the 20th, and Rawdon arrived on the 21st. The American losses were 57 killed, 70 wounded, and 20 missing. Cruger lost 27 killed and 58 wounded.[19]

Eutaw Springs

Greene's destination now was Charlotte, North Carolina; his course, therefore, was northeastward. He crossed the Saluda on his first day's march, picking up the baggage and the invalids he had sent off the day before the attack on Ninety-six. He organized a rear guard, consisting of all his cavalry, the infantry of Lee's Legion, and Kirkwood's company, and pushed on, expecting pursuit by Rawdon, who had started after him on the evening of his arrival at Ninety-six. The British van was within sight of the American rear guard before it reached the next river, the Enoree. The Americans retired slowly and crossed the river without being attacked. Rawdon's long and rapid march in the midsummer heat had told heavily upon his troops, and he lay overnight to rest them and then turned about and retraced his steps to Ninety-six.

Greene went on, crossing the Tiger River and the Broad on June 24. Then, finding he was no longer pursued, he detached his rear guard and sent it to watch the enemy and keep the main army informed of their movements.

Rawdon, meanwhile, had regained the fort and ordered its evacuation. He sent orders to Lieutenant Colonel Stuart at Charleston to proceed with his regiment to Friday's Ferry to a meeting on the Congaree. Then he divided his force, leaving a part of it with Cruger to protect the retreat of the garrison and the loyal refugees from the fort, by a more southerly route to Orangeburg.

With 800 infantry and 60 cavalry, Rawdon marched to meet Stuart. The heavy woolen clothing of the British troops burdened them excessively. They could hardly endure the scorching sun and the heavy humidity; 50

died of sunstroke or exhaustion on the march. Tarleton describes their hardships: "During a renewed succession of forced marches under the rage of a burning sun, and in a climate, at this season peculiarly inimical to man, they were frequently, when sinking under the most excessive fatigue, not only destitute of every comfort, but almost of every necessary which seems essential to his existence. During the greater part of the time, they were totally destitute of bread, and the country afforded no vegetables for a substitute. Salt, at length, failed; and their only resources were water and the wild cattle which they found in the woods." [1]

Greene had supposed that the division of Rawdon's force meant that the part left behind was, with Cruger's men, intended to hold Ninety-six. But he was soon informed of the preparations for evacuation. He halted his northward march and turned south towards the Congaree.

Stuart had marched from Charleston to Friday's Ferry in accordance with instructions, but was recalled to Charleston. Greene, learning of this, directed Lee and Kirkwood to try to gain Rawdon's front at that ferry and to join with Sumter and Marion, whom also he ordered to that point. They crossed the Congaree and encamped a mile in front of Rawdon to await Marion and Sumter.

Rawdon, disappointed by Stuart's recall, decided to move south to Orangeburg, and pushed back Lee and Kirkwood. He did not halt until nine o'clock in the evening. Lee and Kirkwood bedded their men a few miles in front of him, only to have them disturbed at dawn by the renewed advance of the British. All that day, they fell back, and Rawdon came on. They crossed Beaver Creek with Rawdon close behind them. Then they gave up trying to keep in front of that fast-moving column, turned aside, and left Rawdon a clear road to Orangeburg.

Sumter, Marion, and Washington's horse at last came up, and on July 10, Greene's whole force was reassembled near Beaver Creek.

Rawdon arrived at Orangeburg and was joined by Stuart and the 3rd Regiment, the famous Buffs. He had then about 1,600 infantry and artillery. A reconnaissance of the British position by Greene and several of his officers convinced them of its strength; there were several buildings in the town that would serve as citadels. The Americans had a strong force of cavalry; the British, none; but the ground was such that this arm could not operate. Cruger was on the way with about 1,400 men. So Greene decided not to attack, though his troops outnumbered Rawdon's.

The Americans, as well as the British, had suffered much from the extreme heat, the incessant marching, and the lack of food. Kirkwood's journal shows that the light troops, from the time they left Ninety-six until they came to Orangeburg, had covered 323 miles in twenty-two days, marching every day with no intervals for rest. Their food had been miserably scanty: "Rice furnished our substitute for bread. . . . Of meat we had literally none. . . . Frogs abounded . . . and on them chiefly did the light troops subsist. Even alligator was used by a few." They were sadly debilitated.[2]

The High Hills of Santee are a long, irregular chain on the east bank of the Wateree about twenty miles north of its confluence with the Congaree. Huge masses of sand and clay, twenty-four miles long, they rise two hundred feet above the river bank to plateaus one to five miles wide and fruitful in cotton and grain. They offered the Americans a salubrious campsite, free from the malaria so prevalent in the country in which they had been operating. On them Greene established his army, and there it remained for six weeks while the wounded recovered, the sick were restored to health, and everyone was invigorated by the pure air, the clear water, and the friendly hospitality of the inhabitants.[3]

Not all the American troops were so favored, however. Rawdon left Stuart in command at Orangeburg, and with 500 men set out for Charleston. Marion, Sumter, and Lee's cavalry were ordered to move in that direction, break up a post at Dorchester, and dislodge the 9th Regiment from Monck's Corner. Although not wholly successful, the American detachment forced the evacuation of Monck's Corner, took 150 prisoners, and captured 200 horses and a number of wagons before Lee rejoined the army on the High Hills, while Sumter held Friday's Ferry and Marion held Nelson's.[4]

Kirkwood's corps was also kept in motion. With Washington's horse it operated two weeks more along the Congaree, but without noteworthy result. On August 5 this detachment joined the army on the High Hills for a period of rest.

Rawdon, broken in health by the hardships of the campaign, sailed for home; but his ship was taken by the French fleet under Admiral de Grasse and he was carried to Brest a prisoner of war. Soon afterwards he was exchanged and returned to England.[5]

By the end of the third week of August, the American army was recuperated sufficiently to permit a renewal of active operations. During the interval reenforcements from various sources had been promised to Greene; but, as usual, few of them arrived. His command was, however, built up to about 2,000 men; with these he decided to move.

Stuart, now in command of the British forces in active operation in the

Carolinas, had taken a position on the west side of the Congaree near the point where it merges with the Wateree to make the Santee. He was but sixteen miles from Greene's camp; but the two great rivers between them were now so flooded as to appear to be lakes, and all the lowlands were under water, so that there was no possibility of a direct movement against Stuart. A wide circuit was necessary.[6]

On August 22 the Americans broke camp and marched twenty miles up the east side of the Wateree. The next day they traveled eighteen miles farther, to Camden, where they crossed the river. Following a southerly course, they crossed the Congaree and, on September 7, were within seven miles of Eutaw Springs, where Stuart and his army were encamped. On that day Marion and his men joined them. Brigadier General Jethro Sumner with a brigade of North Carolina Continentals had joined Greene at the High Hills. Pickens with his militia, and Lieutenant Colonel John Henderson with a small body of South Carolina state infantry, had come up with the main army at the crossing of the Congaree.[7]

Greene's army now consisted of 1,256 Continentals, 73 South Carolina state infantry, 72 state cavalry, 150 North Carolina militia, 307 South Carolinians under Sumter and Pickens, Marion's 40 horse and 200 foot, and about 300 of Lee's and Washington's horse—a total of 2,400. Of these, 200 were withdrawn to guard the baggage, which had been left behind at Howell's Ferry on the Congaree, only two wagons of ammunition, hospital stores and rum having been brought along. Greene's artillery comprised two 4-pounders and two 6's.[8]

Stuart seems to have had the battalion companies of the 3rd British regiment, the six flank companies, grenadiers and light infantry, of the 3rd, the 19th, and the 30th regiments, commanded by Major Marjoribanks of the 19th, the remains of the 63rd and 64th regiments, much reduced by their long service throughout the war, and the garrison of Ninety-six—that is to say a battalion of De Lancey's Loyalists of New York, a battalion of the New Jersey Volunteers, and one of the New York Volunteers. He had also a cavalry regiment of South Carolinians under Major John Coffin, a Boston Tory. The total number of Stuart's men was about 2,000. He had also three fieldpieces—two 6-pounders and a 4.[9]

It will be observed that, unlike the forces of Ferguson at King's Mountain, Tarleton at Cowpens, and Cruger at Ninety-six, which had been composed entirely of American Tories, Stuart's army was largely composed of British regulars. It should also be noted that a large proportion of his Tory troops were deserters from American Continental regiments, of whom it has been said that British discipline had been added to their American training as marksmen, making them, in action, the equals of the Continental troops. On the American side, many of the Continentals were deserters from the British army. To such an extent had this interchange of men taken place that Greene was wont to say: "At the close of the war, we fought the enemy with British soldiers; and they fought us with those of America." [10] There was little to choose between the two armies in the quality and experience of their men; and in numbers they were about equal. Perhaps in no other battle of the war were the two opposing forces so fairly matched.

Stuart had moved from Center Swamp to Eutaw Springs in order to meet a convoy of provisions coming up from Charleston. Otherwise he would have had to detach at least 400 men to meet and guard it, "which, at the time," he wrote later, "I could ill afford, the army being much weakened by sickness." [11]

The two Eutaw springs were really the first and second appearances above ground of a subterranean stream of considerable volume. From the lower of the two basins the water flowed in a winding stream, Eutaw Creek, between steep, heavily thicketed banks to the Santee. Close by the head of the creek, between it and the main highway, which ran east and west and sent off a branch road to Charleston, there was a large brick mansion of two stories and a garret. In front of it was a cleared area, an oblong of about eight acres surrounded by a palisade and divided into halves by the main road. On the side towards the creek and close beside the house was a palisaded garden. All about was a rather sparse woods. In the enclosed clearing the British camp was pitched.[12]

Stuart was comfortably established there, but he was unfortunate in one respect. "Notwithstanding every exertion being made to gain intelligence of the enemy's situation," he wrote to Cornwallis after the battle, "they rendered it impossible, by waylaying the bye-paths and passes through the different swamps." [13] So secure from immediate attack was he, in his own mind, that he sent out at daybreak of September 8, on the very road by which Greene was then advancing, a party of 100 unarmed men attended only by a small guard, a "rooting party" to gather sweet potatoes. At six o'clock two deserters from the North Carolina troops came to tell him that Greene was already on the march. He refused to believe them and ordered them confined. He did, however, dispatch Major Coffin with 140 foot and 50 horse to scout along the road.[14]

Greene had bivouacked on the night of the 7th at Burdell's plantation, seven miles from Stuart's camp. At dawn his army marched in four successive columns. The first was led by Lieutenant Colonel Henderson; it consisted of Lee's Legion and the South Carolina state infantry. Marion commanded the second, made up of the North Carolina militia under Colonel the Marquis de Malmedy and the South Carolina militia under Pickens. The third column was composed of the Continentals under General Jethro Sumner. The rear was closed by Washington's horse and Kirkwood's light troops. This arrangement was made to conform to the proposed deployment into line of battle. The army moved slowly and cautiously in the hope of surprising pickets and patrols of the enemy.[15]

The Americans were within four miles of Stuart's camp about eight o'clock, when Major John Armstrong, who had been reconnoitering ahead with a party of North Carolinians, fell back with the news that he had sighted a body of the enemy. That was Coffin's detachment. Henderson halted his column and drew it up across the road with Lee's Legion in the woods on the right, the South Carolina state troops in the woods on the left.

Hot on Armstrong's heels came Coffin. "With a degree of recklessness which indicated either his ignorance of its strength and the presence of the main body or his contempt for the service," Coffin charged on the American van. He met a shower of bullets. Major Egleston with the Legion cavalry circled around to Coffin's rear, while the infantry of the Legion charged with the bayonet. Coffin's infantry was "destroyed, several killed and about 40 taken with their captain." [16] His cavalry escaped by precipitate flight. The sound of the firing drew the rooting party to the scene, and they were all captured.

Stuart was apprised of Greene's advance by the fleeing cavalrymen. He sent a detachment of infantry down the road to delay the Americans and gain time for him to form his line. Greene had regaled his men with a ration of rum and was about a mile from the enemy's camp when this new opposition was met. It opened on Lee's Legion with one gun. Otho Williams sent Captain William Gaines of Virginia up from the third column at full gallop with two guns to return the fire, while Lee and Henderson on the right and left fired obliquely upon the enemy and drove them back.[17]

Meanwhile, Stuart was arranging his line of battle. He drew his troops out of their camp into the woods in front and formed them in a single line obliquely across the road along which the Americans were advancing. The 3rd Regiment was on the right of the line, its flank resting on the steep bank of Eutaw Creek. On that side it was supported by the six companies of grenadiers and light infantry—about 300 men—under Major Marjoribanks placed at some little distance, somewhat in advance and at an

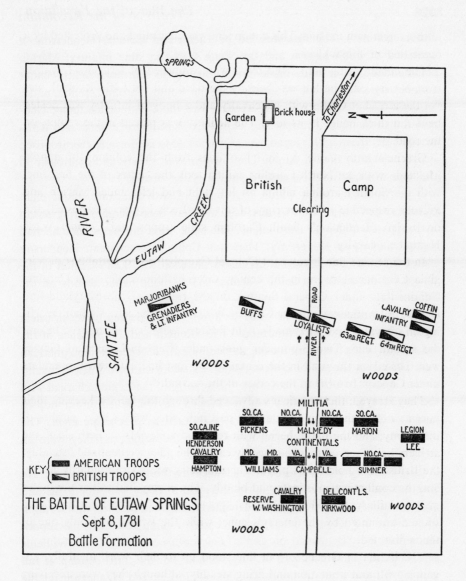

SPRINGS

Garden Brick house

To Charleston →

N

British   Camp

Clearing

RIVER

EUTAW CREEK

SANTEE

ROAD

RIVER

MARJORIBANKS
GRENADIERS & LT. INFANTRY

BUFFS

LOYALISTS

CAVALRY   COFFIN
INFANTRY

63RD. REGT.   64TH. REGT.

WOODS

WOODS

MILITIA

SO.CA.
PICKENS

NO.CA.

NO.CA.
MALMEDY

SO.CA.
MARION

LEGION
LEE

SO.CA.INF.
HENDERSON
CAVALRY
HAMPTON

CONTINENTALS

MD.   MD.   VA.   VA.   NO.CA.
WILLIAMS   CAMPBELL   SUMNER

KEY {
AMERICAN TROOPS
BRITISH TROOPS

CAVALRY
RESERVE
W. WASHINGTON

DEL.CONT'LS.
KIRKWOOD

WOODS

THE BATTLE OF EUTAW SPRINGS
Sept. 8, 1781
Battle Formation

WOODS

obtuse angle with the line. This contingent was concealed and protected by a dense thicket of blackjack.

The center, lying across the road, was composed of Cruger's Loyalists from Ninety-six. The left was held by the 63rd and the 64th. Its flank was "in the air," but Coffin with his cavalry and a body of infantry was posted behind a thick hedge in its rear. The artillery was placed in the center, on the road.[18]

Greene's army came up into two lines from the columns of march. Malmedy with the North Carolina militia took the center of the first line, with the South Carolina militia on his right and left, under Marion and Pickens respectively. On the right of this line Lee's Legion was posted, and on its left Henderson's South Carolina state troops and Colonel Wade Hampton's cavalry.

In the second line Lieutenant Colonel Campbell's two battalions of Virginia Continentals were in the center, three battalions of North Carolina Continentals under General Sumner on the right, and the Maryland and Delaware Continentals under Colonel Williams on the left. William Washington's cavalry and Kirkwood's light infantry were held in reserve behind the second line. Two 3-pounder guns under Captain-Lieutenant Gaines were posted on the road in the center of the first line, and two 6-pounders under Captain Browne in the center of the second.[19]

Thus arrayed, the Americans advanced through the woods, keeping their lines as well as they could. At a little past nine, they were within gunshot of the enemy, and the battle began with repeated volleys from both sides, the artillery being served to advantage by each. The advance continued steadily, the British line holding its place. The musketry was extraordinarily heavy, and the conflict was obstinate and bloody. The enemy had rather the better of it in artillery, both the Americans' "grasshoppers" in the front line being soon dismounted by the enemy's guns, while the British had only one of theirs disabled.

The militia in Greene's front line stood up to their work manfully, advancing without hesitation and firing steadily, although they were receiving the fire of the whole British line, double their number. Greene said their "conduct would have graced the veterans of the great King of Prussia." [20] They fired seventeen rounds before they showed any sign of weakening. At that time Lee's Legion, in an effort to outflank the British left, was hotly engaged with the 63rd Regiment. Stuart sent the 64th and Cruger's Loyalists forward against the American center, Malmedy's North Carolina militia. The attack was sudden, unexpected, and heavy. The North Carolinians broke. Pickens's and Marion's men on the flanks of the broken center gave way. The whole American front line was gone, except its two extremities, Lee's Legion on the right, Henderson's infantry and Hampton's cavalry on the left. They were now fighting separate battles with the 63rd and the 3rd.

Greene acted promptly. He swung Sumner's North Carolina Continentals into the first-line center. They came up with alacrity and precision and reestablished the line. They not only withstood a renewed attack but even drove the enemy back to his first position, and the battle raged as furiously as before.

Signs of weakness now appeared in the British line; it was drawing back before the American attack. Stuart brought up on his left the detachment of infantry and Coffin's cavalry, which had been held in reserve behind his left flank. About the same time Henderson was wounded, and his South Carolina state troops, on the American left, faltered; but Hampton rallied them, and they stood fast against the fire of Marjoribanks's corps in the thicket on the British right.

The situation of the two armies was extraordinary in that, although the battle had been under way for so long and was so bitterly contested, with the whole British army active, the strongest elements of the American army had not been engaged: the Maryland, Delaware, and Virginia Continentals, Kirkwood's light infantry, and Washington's cavalry were mere spectators. But their time for action was at hand.

Sumner's North Carolina Continentals, bearing the brunt of the battle, now heavier than ever by the weight of the reenforced enemy line, could not stand the strain; they gave way and retreated. The British, shouting their triumph, rushed forward with disordered ranks. It was Greene's moment. He ordered the Continentals of the second line to charge. Williams and Campbell led them. At a distance of forty yards they fired a volley, and then, trailing their muskets and shouting defiantly, they sprang forward to a bayonet charge, while Captain Michael Rudulph with Lee's infantry wheeled upon the British left and poured in an enfilading fire. Howard, leading a part of the Marylanders, met the British right, the Buffs, in such close combat that the officers fought with their swords and men on both sides fell mutually transfixed by each other's bayonets.

It was too much for the British line. "Assailed on front and flank," it was driven back "in utter confusion"—first the left, then the center, and finally the right—the Buffs, though a recently raised regiment, holding out longest. The whole line, except Marjoribanks's detachment, "fell back in disorder into the clearing where the camp stood." [21]

Stuart called on Marjoribanks, and Greene countered with his reserve. Washington, attempting a charge upon Marjoribanks, found that his horses

could not penetrate the blackjack thicket. He saw an open space in his
enemy's rear. Wheeling by sections to gain that opening, his corps rode
right across Marjoribanks's murderous fire. Men and horses rolled on the
ground. Washington's own horse was shot down. He became entangled in
the stirrups, received a bayonet wound, and was captured. His second in
command and two of his lieutenants fell. A third was wounded and dismounted, and not a single man of his section escaped death or wounds. A
full half of Washington's whole corps were killed or wounded. Hampton
and his horsemen had come up. With the aid of Lieutenant John Gordon
and Cornet Simmons, both of Washington's cavalry, Hampton rallied the
survivors of that corps and led another charge upon Marjoribanks, without
success.

But Kirkwood's troops were coming on at the double to succor their
companions in the cavalry. Wasting no time in firing, they charged into the
thicket, and "rushed furiously" upon Marjoribanks with the bayonet.[22]
Backward, down into a ravine, they drove their opponents and up the
farther bank; but in a strong position there Marjoribanks stood and held
his ground, forming a new line with his rear to the creek, his left against the
palisaded garden.

Meanwhile the rest of the British were in full retreat through their own
camp and along the Charleston road, the Americans after them. In this rout
300 prisoners and two guns were taken. There was nothing left for the
Americans to do but consolidate their gains, sweep away Marjoribanks and
go after Stuart, who was trying to rally his soldiers on the Charleston road,
and then cut off Major Sheridan of Cruger's force, who was making for the
brick house. But in that moment of almost complete victory the discipline
of the Maryland and Virginia Continentals blew up and vanished. They and
the militia halted in the British camp and fell upon the spoils of a victory
not yet fully achieved. In utter disorder, complete confusion, they looted
the stores, ate the food they found, and drank the liquor until many were
drunk. No efforts of their officers sufficed to bring them back to their duty.

Sheridan had gained the brick house and was firing from it upon the disorderly rabble in the camp. Others were flocking to join him. Only the
infantry of Lee's Legion, a part of the Marylanders under Howard, and
Kirkwood's troops held themselves free from the disorder in the camp.
Though fatigued by their former exertions and "far spent for want of
water," they still fought for the prize of complete victory. Lee's infantry and
Kirkwood's struggled for entrance at the very door of the house and were
saved from Sheridan's fire only by grabbing prisoners and holding them as
shields while they retired. Greene ordered up his guns to breach the wall of

the house, but with swivel guns and muskets its garrison shot down the gunners.

Coffin's cavalry were still in the field. Greene, strangely unaware of the disorder in the camp, ordered Lee's horse to attack him. Egleston, leading the Legion horsemen, turned the head of the ravine, across which Kirkwood had driven Marjoribanks, swept across the field, and charged on Coffin, but was repulsed. Hampton then tried; there was a sharp fight at close quarters, and Coffin was driven back. But, in following him, Hampton exposed his own men to a close fire from Marjoribanks. It was so severe that Colonel Thomas Polk of Hampton's horse "thought every man was killed but himself."

The gallant Marjoribanks then added to his laurels of that day, his last on earth. Abandoning his protected position, he sallied out into the field, captured the American guns brought up to batter the house, and drew them back under its walls. Howard, with Oldham's Maryland company, met Marjoribanks, was wounded, and his troops fell back. Marjoribanks went on, swept down upon the rabble in the camp, and drove them into the woods.

Meanwhile, Stuart had rallied his men. He brought them back to the house. But by this time, after three hours of this grueling battle in the heat of a Carolina summer, both armies had had enough.[23]

Greene's battalions were in confusion, his cavalry was shattered, his guns lost, and many of his best officers wounded; only two of his Continental regimental commanders, Lee and Williams, had come through unscathed. One-fourth of his men were killed or wounded, and the rest were physically exhausted. Stuart's losses, including the prisoners taken by the Americans, amounted to more than two-fifths of his strength. There was no more fight left in either army. Greene drew his men back into the shelter of the woods and collected his wounded, all but those too near the house still in possession of the enemy. Stuart held the field that night, but retired towards Monck's Corner the next day, having destroyed a quantity of stores and left 70 of his more seriously wounded men to the care of the Americans. Marjoribanks, the hero of the day on the British side, had been badly wounded in the last encounter of the battle. He died on the way and was buried by the roadside.

Kirkwood's men and a party of Virginia Continentals under Colonel Thomas Edmunds were not only the last to leave the field but also the only ones to capture and carry off one of the British guns. "Major Edmund of the Virginians, with a Small party of men joined me in the British Encampment," Kirkwood wrote in his journal, "keeping up the fire for A small space of time. Found our army had withdrawn from the Field, made it necessary for us Likewise to withdraw. We brought off one of the Enemy's three Pounders, which with much difficulty was performed through a thick wood for near four miles without the assistance of but one Horse." [24]

"So ended the very bloody and desperate action of Eutaw Springs." [25] "Such was the heat of the action that officers on each side fought hand to hand and sword to sword." [26] Greene said it was by far the most obstinate fight he ever saw. In proportion to the numbers engaged, the losses on both sides were very great. The American casualties as published by the Congress amounted to 522 of all ranks: 139 killed, including 17 officers, 375 wounded, including 43 officers, and 8 missing.[27] The British losses were even more severe, 866 in all, more than two-fifths of the force: 85 killed, 351 wounded, and 430 missing.[28]

Both sides claimed the victory. As the British held the field, it was technically theirs. But the inability of both sides to carry on the fight after the Americans withdrew into the woods gives it the appearance of a drawn battle. As in all Greene's battles in the South, the results were distinctly favorable to his side, though he failed to gain a victory. This one drove the enemy back to the vicinity of Charleston. Except in and about that town and Savannah, the British held no territory in the South. The state governments in Georgia and the Carolinas were reestablished and were able to function without molestation to the end of the war. There was no serious fighting in any of the three states after Eutaw Springs.[29]

The Congress voiced the feeling of the American people when, on October 29, it thanked Greene for obtaining a most signal victory and "the Maryland and Virginia brigades and Delaware battalion of continental troops for the unparalleled bravery and heroism by them displayed in advancing to the enemy through an incessant fire and charging them with an impetuosity and ardor that could not be resisted." A British standard and a gold medal were presented to Greene.[30]

After Eutaw Springs

When Greene withdrew his troops from the field of battle at Eutaw Springs he expected to remain close to Stuart until he could refresh them, and then to attack once more. But there was one bodily need that mere cessation of activity could not supply: the need for water. More than three hours of battle in the excessive heat of that day had generated a thirst that could not be denied. The men's lips were black, their mouths foul from the bitten cartridges, their tongues parched, their whole bodies drained of moisture. "The cry for water was universal." Every canteen had long since been emptied, and there was neither a spring nor a rivulet near them that was not in the possession of the enemy.[1] They had to retire to their position of the night before, Burdell's plantation, leaving Hampton and a strong picket guard to watch the enemy. But Greene did not abandon his intentions against Stuart.

The next day, September 9, he sent Marion and Lee to turn the enemy's left and to take a position between Eutaw Springs and Charleston, so as to hold Stuart where he was and to intercept any reenforcements from his base. But Stuart had hurried his preparations, and McArthur was already on the march from Charleston. Their junction was imminent by the time Marion and Lee gained the desired position, and the American troops were too few to fight the combined enemy forces. The junction of Stuart and McArthur was effected, and together they retired to Monck's Corner.[2]

Greene had hurried, too. Having arranged to send his wounded to the High Hills, he had taken the road after Stuart on the 10th. But the continued intense heat slowed his army; Stuart had a long start, and Greene could not catch him. Twelve miles from Monck's Corner, he halted and encamped. After one day he marched back to Eutaw and did what he could to ease the wounded of both armies left there because they were too severely injured to be moved. Then, by easy stages, the army returned to the High Hills.[3]

Recuperation of the patriots was imperative. Their exertions in the heat and the sultry humidity of the day and their exposure to the chill of the heavy dew at night had exhausted them. "Never," says Henry Lee, "had we experienced so much sickness at any one time as we did now." It "affected every corps, even those most inured to military life, and most accustomed to the climate. Nearly one-half of the army was disabled by wounds or fever." The High Hills offered rest, good air, pure water, accommodation for the wounded, restoration for the sick, and "a plentiful supply of wholesome provision"—but, as before, not for all of them.

The country along the southern bank of the Congaree was open to predatory excursions. On the way back from their pursuit of Stuart, Kirkwood's troops were detached from the main army and sent towards that district. On the fourth day after that, September 19, they came up with their old companions in arms, Washington's cavalry. It does not appear that they encountered any of the enemy; but they were constantly on the move looking for them, and they were in poor health. Kirkwood himself "took the Ague and fever" and was obliged to rest at a friendly plantation for nearly a month. His men were so debilitated that at times there were "scarce men enough to mount two small guards." [4]

In the salubrious camp of the main force, conditions were not much better. The army dwindled. Pickens, Marion, and Hampton were detached to cover various districts. Almost all the militia left; only 100 of North Carolina remained, and their time was nearly up. The camp was simply a hospital, where 350 American and 250 British wounded men, who had been brought in boats up the Santee and the Wateree, had to be cared for by the few sound Continentals and militia. Malaria was prevalent. Ten days after the battle, Greene had not a thousand men fit for duty.[5] On October 25 he wrote to General Washington, "Our troops have been exceedingly sickly, and our distress and difficulties have been not a little increased for want of medicines and hospital stores. . . . We can attempt nothing further except in the partisan way. . . . I look forward with pain to December, when the whole Virginia line will leave us. I hope measures will be taken before that period to reinforce us." [6] At that time, he wrote of his troubles to Colonel William Davie also: "An army which has received no pay for more than two years, distressed for want of clothes, subsisted without spirits, and often short in the usual allowances of meat and bread, will mutiny, if we fail in the article of salt." [7] And mutiny they did, or came so near it that the use of the word is a minor exaggeration.

Unrest spread through the Maryland Continentals. They petitioned Greene several times, complaining of lack of clothing; they called attention to the fact that there were but 200 survivors of the seven regiments. They "left off their usual sports" and gathered in sullen groups discussing their grievances. In the evening of October 21 a number of them "went privately out of camp with their arms." The officers were alarmed and ordered a roll call. The defection was only an experiment to see what would happen; the seceders crept back secretly and answered to their names. But the situation was definitely threatening. While the rolls were being called, Timothy Griffin, of the only South Carolina company still remaining in the camp, came on the parade drunk. Some of the officers were admonishing their men for their irregularities. Timothy cried out: "Stand to it, boys! Damn my blood if I would give an inch!" Captain Samuel McPherson of the Marylands knocked him down. He was arrested, court-martialed for encouraging mutiny and desertion, convicted, and shot the next afternoon, in the presence of the whole army. "No example was ever more effectual." [8]

On October 19 Cornwallis surrendered his army at Yorktown. Historians usually regard that surrender as the end of the war; but at the time it was not generally so regarded. Lord North may have taken the news "as he would have taken a ball in the breast" and exclaimed, "Oh God! It is all over!" as Lord George Germain said he did; [9] but that was not known in America. In fact, the capitulation at Yorktown was the surrender of only one of the three British armies in America, and that the weakest. New York was still held as strongly as ever; Wilmington in North Carolina and Savannah in Georgia were still in British hands, and Charleston, the capital city of the south and its most important strategic position. Yorktown was not everything.[10] In fact, peace was yet more than a year away; and during that time, though no important battle was fought, the troops in the south had to continue their exertions and undergo much hardship.

Although men were released by the fall of Yorktown to reenforce Greene and were soon on their way to him, two months elapsed before they arrived. Meanwhile, Stuart, incapacitated by a wound at Eutaw, had turned over his command to Major John Doyle, who had resumed hostilities. Hector McNeill, an active and daring Tory, with 300 men had marched from Wilmington to Hillsboro, North Carolina, the rebel capital, captured Governor Thomas Burke, some members of his Council, and every Continental and militia officer in the town, and carried them back to Wilmington.[11]

This exploit aroused the Tories throughout the state; especially along the Pee Dee River, they renewed their activities in harassing the patriots and ravaging their homes. Though Greene was weak it was incumbent upon him to quell these new uprisings.

On November 8 the American army struck the tents in the High Hills camp and went down into the South Carolina low country. It had been strengthened by a body of mountaineer riflemen under Colonel John Sevier of North Carolina and Colonel Isaac Shelby of Virginia. Greene had sent them to Marion to help in holding back Doyle, but he got word on the march that the freeborn mountaineers had gone home. Fortunately, as his little army advanced, Doyle fell back to Goose Creek Bridge, and no conflict with him was necessary. This evidence of a disinclination on Doyle's part to meet him, induced Greene to try to push him farther back.

Within fifteen miles of the chief British position at Charleston lay the village of Dorchester, held by 850 of the enemy. Greene decided to try to cut them off. He took 200 of Lee's, Washington's, and Sumter's cavalry and an equal number of Maryland and Virginia Continental infantry. Leaving the rest of his army under command of Otho Williams, he led that detachment against Dorchester. There were skirmishes between his advance and a reconnoitering party from the town, and between the opposing cavalry forces; but, Greene himself being recognized, the town's commander thought the whole American army was upon him. He destroyed his stores, threw his guns into the Ashley River, and fled to a post within five miles of Charleston, where Stuart, who now returned to the field, joined him. The British in South Carolina now held only Charleston and its immediate vicinity; they had 3,300 men in the garrison of the town besides a considerable body of Loyalists. There was "wild alarm" throughout the town, caused by rumors exaggerating Greene's strength, and "the most active Negroes were called to arms and enrolled." [12]

In the meantime, Williams had marched the rest of the army from the High Hills to the singularly named Round O, between the Edisto and the Ashepoo River and about forty miles from Charleston, and encamped there. Greene joined him on December 9. It was a pleasant place at that season of the year. Rice was abundant and, although not so palatable as cornmeal or wheat flour to the troops from the more northerly states, it was food. Game was plentiful in the woods and swamps, fish in the waters, and wild fowl on them. [13]

General Arthur St. Clair with 2,000 Pennsylvania, Maryland, and Delaware Continentals, including Anthony Wayne, painfully made the long and toilsome southward march from Yorktown. Rains were frequent; the roads were alternately frozen and "sloppy." For subsistence his men drove a herd of 400 beef cattle, which did not increase their speed. There were streams to be forded, and, though "the frogs in the swamps sang very sweetly," the swamps had to be crossed in "mud up to our knees." Yet they traveled about fifteen miles a day and arrived at Round O on January 4, 1782.[14]

Kirkwood and his fellow officers of the Delaware Continentals were relieved from duty after six years' continuous service and went home. The two Delaware companies, including new recruits, were then attached to Washington's cavalry to constitute the infantry section of his Legion. Soon afterward they participated in an attempt upon Johns Island, an extensive piece of land close to Charleston, on which cattle for the support of the British army were pastured. On the approach of St. Clair's force from the north, Major Craig in command of the British garrison in Wilmington had prudently evacuated that town and taken his men down to Charleston. With some additional infantry and cavalry, he was now occupying Johns Island.[15]

Lee and Marion had been working down the opposite side of the Ashley. They were now encamped near Charleston. Greene had brought the main army down from Round O and posted it at Ponpon on the Stono River, across from Johns Island. Lee had reconnoitered the island and concluded that an attack was feasible. The project was committed to him and Colonel John Laurens. To make up the necessary force, certain detachments from the Pennsylvania, Maryland, and Virginia Continentals were joined to Lee's Legion and the Delaware companies; this force amounted to about 700 men.[16]

The water separating the island from the mainland was passable only at low tide. Lee evolved an elaborate plan, the success of which depended upon crossing at night, at dead low water, in two columns. The first, led by Lee, passed over safely. The second, under Major James Hamilton, lost its way in the darkness and arrived too late to cross. Those who had crossed had to be recalled, as the tide was rising; they got back with difficulty through breast-deep water. The attempt was abandoned.[17]

The day after that, Greene moved to a position between Charleston and Jacksonboro, where the South Carolina legislature sat under protection of the army. Meanwhile Anthony Wayne had been sent into Georgia with 100 of Moylan's dragoons, commanded by Colonel Anthony White of New Jersey, and a detachment of field artillery. He crossed the Savannah River on January 12 and was soon joined by Colonel Wade Hampton with 300 of Sumter's mounted infantry and by 170 of Jackson's and McCoy's Georgia volunteers. The purpose was "to reinstate as far as might be possible the authority of the Union within the limits of Georgia." [18]

Wayne actively and successfully suppressed Tory partisan bands, prevented Indian reenforcement of the garrison in Savannah, and invested that town so far as to cut off its supplies. Among his encounters with the enemy was one hot fight with a strong band of Creek Indians and a detachment of British soldiers that attacked his camp; he succeeded in routing them. He continued his work until July 11, when the British evacuated Savannah, and he took possession of the town. Then he returned and rejoined Greene in South Carolina. Now, in all the three southern states only Charleston was held by the enemy.[19]

During these months there was little activity in South Carolina, except by Washington's and Lee's legions, who were "constantly kept on the alert, never stationary," continually "marching and countermarching, seldom, if ever, remaining two nights on the same ground, making frequent excursions on the British lines, often falling in with the enemy, when skirmishing would frequently ensue." Little of importance was accomplished, but the incessant activity was fatiguing. Seymour records a total of 117 miles of marching in one period of six days. This was kept up from February until the middle of June.[20]

The men were enduring great hardships. In March, Greene wrote to Washington that he had 600 men "so naked as to be unfit for duty. . . . Not a rag of clothing has arrived to us this Winter. It is true we get meat and rice, but no rum or spirits. Men and officers without pay cannot be kept in temper long." And he wrote later: "For upwards of two months, more than a third of our men were entirely naked, with nothing but a breech-cloth about them, and never came out of their tents; and the rest were as ragged as wolves." Their food was bad, too; the beef was simply carrion. By July he succeeded in procuring "materials for a check shirt, a pair of overalls and a coatee" for each of his men.[21]

Presumably these hardships excused a plot for a mutinous uprising, which was brewing in the camp in April. It began among the Pennsylvania troops, whose mutiny in Washington's camp at Morristown eighteen months before had secured for them the arrears of pay that they demanded. But this new plot, says Lee, "was grounded on the breach of allegiance and reared in the foulness of perfidy. Greene himself was to be seized and delivered to the enemy." It was discovered in time; the ringleader, a Pennsylvania sergeant, was convicted of the crime and executed.[22]

Charleston, the only post in all the South still held by the British, was surrounded on the land side. No supplies could be had for its garrison without penetrating the American lines, and they were tight. Major General

Leslie proposed to Greene a cessation of hostilities and an arrangement permitting the British to buy food and take it through the American lines. Greene referred the proposal to the Congress and refused to enter into such an engagement meanwhile. Leslie thereupon gave notice that he would resume hostile incursions into the surrounding country to take provisions by force.[23]

Greene then organized a force to combat the expected British operations. It was composed of infantry of Lee's Legion, the Delaware troops, 100 infantrymen from the other Continental regiments, and the dismounted dragoons of the 3rd Virginia, all under command of Colonel John Laurens; also the cavalry of Lee's Legion and of the 3rd and 4th Virginia regiments, under Colonel George Baylor of that state. General Mordecai Gist of Maryland was put in command of this light brigade.[24]

This corps took a position at Stono Bridge, in advance of the main army, to oppose Leslie's foraging fleet of small vessels on the Combahee River. They lay there for a month with little activity except foraging, but with no advantage to the health of the soldiers. "At this time," says Seymour, "the men were taken sick very fast, so that there were scarce any left to mount the necessary guards about the camp." On August 23 they were ordered to Combahee Ferry to oppose an enemy force that lay on the other side of the river and had a fleet of "two row-gallies, some topsail schooners and other small craft, the whole amounting to eighteen sail and three hundred regular troops and two hundred refugees [Tories]." [25] Gist dug an entrenchment and mounted a howitzer with a few artillerymen under Captain Smith at Cheraw Point about twelve miles below the ferry, to cut off the retreat of the vessels. The British force had found little rice on the south side of the river, and Gist prevented them from foraging on the north side. They therefore decided to withdraw, dropping down the river at night. Gist was informed of their intention and ordered Laurens, with the Delaware battalion, to hasten to the entrenchments at the Point and reenforce the few artillerymen there; the rest of the brigade was to follow.

Laurens pushed ahead with speed, but the British had landed three hundred men on the north side above the Point and placed them in ambush in the tall grass. The Americans were met by a sudden unexpected volley. Laurens was killed, and a number of his men were also shot down. The rest fell back upon Gist's advancing corps. The enemy followed and drew up in line in a wood. Gist tried to dislodge them, but they were too well protected by piles of logs and thickets of brush for the cavalry to get at them, and they were too strong for the infantry alone to attack them. They got away without loss. Besides Laurens, the Americans lost one man killed and nineteen wounded. Captain Smith, his artillerymen, and their howitzer were captured and carried off.[26]

The enemy continued their foraging activities, penetrating the Broad River country and carrying off provisions and cattle to Beaufort. To oppose them Gist got more men and a 6-pounder, crossed the Combahee, and pushed down to Port Royal Ferry, where were two armed galleys. There was a brisk encounter, in which one of the galleys was captured, the other driven off. Gist's corps then rejoined the main army.[27]

These minor operations are noteworthy chiefly because they resulted in the death of Colonel John Laurens, one of the bravest and most gallant of the American officers. He was the son of Henry Laurens, President of the Continental Congress during a most important and eventful period of its existence. Born in 1755, John Laurens was educated in Geneva and in London. At the age of twenty-two he entered the Continental service and became an aide to Washington. At the Battle of Germantown, as has been said, he distinguished himself by a feat of daring. At Monmouth his services were notable, as also in Rhode Island, in the siege of Savannah, and in the defense of Charleston. He became a lieutenant colonel at the age of twenty-three. The Congress sent him on a special mission to France when he was twenty-five. On his return he again distinguished himself as an aide to Washington in the Yorktown siege, and represented the American army in the discussion of the terms of capitulation. After the surrender, he hastened back to his native state, joined Greene's army, and lost his life at the age of twenty-seven in an insignificant skirmish—an untimely end of a career of brilliant performance and of the greatest promise.[28]

There were a number of unimportant skirmishes arising out of foraging expeditions before it became certain that the enemy was preparing to give up his last hold on South Carolina by evacuating Charleston. During this interval the American army's condition was most miserable. Half naked, ill fed, sick with dysentery (which was often fatal), it barely survived as an army until the British fleet arrived on September 6 to carry away the Charleston garrison. Even then it had to hang on for three months more before, on December 14, the embarkation of the enemy was accomplished, three hundred ships sailing out of the harbor with the British troops, a horde of 3,800 Loyalists, and more than 5,000 of their Negro slaves. And so ended the war in the south.

The campaigns of Greene and his army in the south, which brought about the overthrow of British power in Georgia and the Carolinas, have been ably summarized and brilliantly characterized by three historians of note—one an American, the other two Englishmen. Major General Francis Vinton Greene writes:*

The eleven months campaign—January to December, 1781, from the Catawba to the Dan and from the Dan back to Charleston and Augusta—received at the time the enthusiastic commendation of Washington and his comrades on the one hand and of Tarleton and Stedman on the other. It has always been considered one of the most brilliant in American annals, and it has been quite as much praised by English as by American writers. Though the numbers on each side were small, yet from the military standpoint it is full of interest and instruction and well repays examination in all its details. The marches, the manoeuvres, the sieges, the raids and scouting by both Lee and Tarleton, the improvised pontoon-trains, the proper use of the topography of the country for defence and offence—were all admirable. There was but little artillery on either side, but it was well handled. The four battles were fiercely contested and the percentage of loss on both sides was large. The British had the advantage of well-trained and well-armed troops, but this was more than counter-balanced by the superiority of American generalship. In only one respect can Greene be criticised, and whether the criticism is just or unjust it is hard to say. He lost every battle. Morgan, under similar circumstances, gained a great victory. If Greene had possessed the same temperament as Morgan or Wayne [or, it may be said, as Benedict Arnold] he would probably, both at Guilford and at Eutaw, have made one more effort and risked everything on the result of it. If unsuccessful, he would have been destroyed; if successful, he would have hastened by a few months what he finally accomplished. The general opinion is, and it is probably well founded, that the circumstances did not justify the risk, and that his prudence—in saving his little army while there was yet time and after he had, in each case, inflicted such loss on his adversary as to compel the adversary's retreat—was not the least of the many exhibitions of good judgment which characterized the whole campaign.[29]

Sir George Otto Trevelyan in his history of the Revolution presents this appreciation of Greene's services and the services of his men:

Nathanael Greene, while he was securing those great and decisive results, had depended mainly on his own resources, and had taken all his measures entirely on his own responsibility. So far as any combined action between the Northern and Southern armies was concerned, they might just as well have been operating in two different hemispheres. The intervening spaces were so enormous, and the obstacles to free and rapid communication so formidable, that news of victory or defeat did not arrive at Washington's headquarters in New Jersey until three or four weeks after a battle had been fought in South Carolina; and Washington's letters of advice and criticism, even if he had been unwise enough to write them, would have taken as long, and longer still, to find Greene in one of his shifting bivouacs on the banks of the Santee or the Catawba.

* *The Revolutionary War and the Military Policy of the United States* by Francis Vinton Greene. Copyright, 1911, by Charles Scribner's Sons. Used by permission.

Greene's handful of Continental troops had performed wonders. . . . Between April, 1780, and April, 1781, they had marched above two thousand six hundred miles, besides being engaged in many skirmishes and two pitched battles. They had passed through, or over, a score of streams many of which . . . would have been reckoned large rivers in any other country in the world. Shoeless and in rags, and laden with their heavy firelocks, they plodded through the wilderness for month after month of a never-ending campaign without showing any perceptible diminution of their martial ardor. After a lost battle—which was a familiar experience to them—they almost instantaneously recovered their self-confidence and their self-complacency, with the invariable elasticity of the American soldier. . . .

At Eutaw Springs many of the Continental infantry, the cloth of whose coats had long ago rotted off them in fragments, "fought with pieces of [Spanish] moss tied on the shoulder and flank to keep the musket and the cartridge-box from galling." They sometimes got nothing for ten or twelve days running except half a pound of flour and a morsel of beef "so miserably poor that scarce any mortal could make use of it" and were fain to live upon green corn and unripe apples and peaches. During the pursuit of Cornwallis, after Guilford Court House, many of them fainted on the road for lack of food.[30]

Of Greene himself, Sir John Fortescue has this to say:

Greene's reputation stands firmly on his campaign in the Carolinas, his luring Cornwallis into a false position, and his prompt return upon Camden after the retreat of Cornwallis to Wilmington. His keen insight into the heart of Cornwallis's blunders and his skilful use of his guerilla troops are the most notable features of his work, and stamp him as a general of patience, resolution and profound common sense, qualities which go far towards making a great general. One gift he seems to have lacked, namely, the faculty of leadership, to which, as well as to bad luck must be ascribed the fact that he was never victorious in a general action. . . . Saving this one small matter, Greene, who was a very noble character, seems to me to stand little if at all lower than Washington as a general in the field.[31]

C H A P T E R   8 0

The Dunmore Raids

John Murray, Earl of Dunmore in the peerage of Scotland, was the royal governor of Virginia at the beginning of the War of Independence. An evil-tempered man, rapacious, irascible, tyrannical, and violent, he took a strong stand against the rising spirit of resistance to the encroachments upon the economic freedom of the colonies. When in March, 1775, the Convention of Virginia resolved to put the colony in "a posture of defence" by embodying and arming a force of militia, he countered, on April 21, by sending a body of marines to seize the province's store of powder at Williamsburg.[1] The town rose, drums were beaten, the militia company assembled in arms and demanded the return of the powder. In a passionate outburst, Dunmore swore, "By the living God, if any insult is offered to me, or those who have obeyed my orders, I will declare freedom to the slaves and lay the town in ashes!" All Virginia was aroused; there were threats from every quarter to assemble the militia and march against him. He declared that if they did he would "consider the whole country in rebellion" and would "not hesitate at reducing houses to ashes and spreading devastation wherever I can reach." To the British government he wrote that he could raise "such a force from among Indians, negroes and other persons, as would reduce the refractory people of this colony to obedience." [2]

But the Virginians, stirred by the news from Lexington and Concord, were refractory beyond his expectations. Patrick Henry assembled the militia company of Hanover on May 2 and marched, gathering many adherents on the way. Dunmore was alarmed. He issued a proclamation declaring that he had seized the powder because he apprehended an insur rection of the slaves, "who had been seen in large numbers in the night time about the Magazine," and calling on "all His Majesty's liege subjects" to suppress the spirit of faction and obey the laws. Henry's march was not stayed until May 4, when a messenger from Dunmore paid the insurgents £330, the estimated value of the powder, whereupon he took his men back home.[3]

Emboldened by the withdrawal of the threatening troops, Dunmore issued another proclamation on May 6, stating that whereas he had "been informed from undoubted authority that a certain Patrick Henry and a number of deluded followers" had "put themselves in a posture of war . . . to the great terror of all His Majesty's faithful subjects" and had extorted from the Receiver General £330, he, the governor, now charged all persons not "to aid, abet or give countenance to the said Patrick Henry" and his companions, but to oppose them, lest the colony be involved "in the most direful calamity, as they will call for the vengeance of offended majesty and the insulted laws." In spite of this direful fulmination, various Virginia counties voted thanks to the insurgents, and the resistance was in no way lessened.[4]

It was Dunmore himself, and not the Virginians, that first took fright. He had heard from Gage that Samuel Adams and John Hancock would be excepted from the general offer of pardon to be issued on June 12. Fearing that he might be seized and held as a hostage for these proscribed men, Dunmore left his house secretly in the night of June 8 and took refuge on the *Fowey* man-of-war at Yorktown, while Virginia went on with her warlike preparations.[5] The governor himself also began to gather strength.

At Hampton in October, an armed British sloop was driven ashore in a gale. The colonists seized it, looted it, and set it afire. Dunmore, who had three warships and various other craft, blockaded the town. Its inhabitants called to their aid a company of Virginia regulars, another of minutemen, and a body of the militia. The noble Dunmore had but one answer: burn the town. A landing party attempting this on October 26 was driven off. Another the next day was answered by the accurate fire of a company of Culpeper riflemen, and several in the boats were killed or wounded. One of the tenders with seven sailors was captured without loss of any Virginian.[6]

Dartmouth had written on August 2 to Dunmore approving his purpose of raising "among the Indians, negroes and other persons, a force sufficient, if not to subdue rebellion, at least to defend Government." Dunmore issued another proclamation on November 7 declaring martial law throughout the colony, and requiring "every person capable of bearing arms to resort to

His Majesty's standard or be looked upon as traitors," subject to "forfeiture of life, confiscation of lands, &C., &C.," also declaring all the rebels' indented servants and slaves, "that are able and willing to bear arms," free upon their joining His Majesty's troops.[7]

The tidewater planters had many Negro slaves and many indentured servants, chiefly convicts serving terms of years. Dunmore hoped to alarm the rebellious Virginians by this call for an uprising of the subject peoples, and send them back to their homes to safeguard their families and property. He also called for a small detachment of British regulars stationed in the Illinois country, and authorized John Connolly to raise a regiment in the backwoods of Pennsylvania and Virginia, and one McKee to raise a force of Indians, all of them to march to Alexandria. He himself undertook to raise a regiment of whites, to be called "the Queen's Own Loyal Virginians," and another of Negroes, under the name of "Lord Dunmore's Ethiopians." [8]

Connolly went to Gage in Boston and received authority to engage Indians from about Detroit, with whom he was to take Fort Pitt and then march to Alexandria and join Dunmore. He came back to the south in November and started up the Potomac with two companions, Allan Cameron and Dr. John Smith. The Virginians sent men into the Indian country who arrested the three near Hagerstown with written plans including a letter from Dunmore to the Indian chief White Eyes. At the order of the Continental Congress they were taken to Philadelphia and confined in jail. McKee seems to have faded out of history without achieving any results.[9]

Dunmore got together two or three hundred Ethiopians and a number of candidates for the Queen's Own making a total, with his small force of regulars, of about 1,200 men. Against this mongrel force at Norfolk, Colonel William Woodford marched one of Virginia's two regular regiments (with John Marshall, afterwards chief justice of the United States, as a lieutenant of minutemen) and about 200 volunteer riflemen.

Dunmore sent a detachment to hold Great Bridge, about nine miles south of Norfolk and in Woodford's way. The bridge, crossing the Elizabeth River, was of considerable length, extending from one marshy shore across two islands to the other shore. It was approached at each end by a causeway. On the eastern side, Dunmore's men erected a substantial fortification with seven guns. Woodford's men threw up a semicircular breastwork on the other side, posted a guard of 25 men in it, and encamped in a near-by church. There for several days they faced each other.[10]

At length, to induce an attack on his fortification, Woodford arranged with a Negro to "desert" and inform Dunmore that there were only 300 "shirtmen" (riflemen) opposing him, and that they had but little ammunition. On December 8 the governor sent against Woodford Captain Samuel Leslie of the 14th Regiment with 200 regulars, a party of marines and sailors, a company of the Queen's Own, and enough Ethiopians to make up 600 men. Two fieldpieces accompanied them.[11]

At reveille on the 9th the artillery opened fire with a few shots. Then the regulars, including 60 grenadiers under Captain Fordyce, marched to the attack in column along the narrow causeway, six abreast. Lieutenant Edward Travis, commanding the guard in the breastwork, now reenforced to a total of 90 men, held his fire until the enemy were within fifty yards, when a withering blast struck down the van. Fordyce, with admirable bravery, urged on his men. They rallied "like true-born Englishmen," but a second fire blighted the attempt. Fordyce fell dead, with fourteen bullets in his body; many of his grenadiers were slain; his lieutenant and many others were wounded. The rest fled across the bridge.[12]

Leslie had held 230 of his Loyalists and Ethiopians in his works. He now rallied the remnant of his regulars and reopened fire with his guns. But Woodford had brought his main force down from the church. Colonel Edward Stevens with the Culpeper battalion crossed the bridge, flanked the enemy, and drove all of them into their fort, which they evacuated that night, returning to Norfolk. Leslie's force had lost 60 killed or wounded. He left on the field 12 dead and 17 wounded, three being lieutenants. The only casualty among the Americans was one man slightly injured by a grapeshot. Five days later, Woodford entered Norfolk, and took possession. Colonel Robert Howe with a North Carolina regiment joined him, and assumed command of all the American troops there.[13]

Norfolk, with 6,000 inhabitants, was one of the principal Virginia seaports and did a heavy trade in tobacco. Its business was largely in the hands of Scottish merchants of Glasgow. Their resident factors and clerks, also Scots, were the principal inhabitants, Loyalists almost to a man. The arrival of the dreaded riflemen created consternation among them, and they fled with their families to the ships in the harbor. Among these were the frigate *Eilbeck* with Dunmore aboard, the *Liverpool*, 28 guns, the *Otter*, 16 guns, the *Kingfisher*, 18 guns, an 8-gun sloop, and six or seven small tenders.[14]

Crowded with their crews, the soldiers, the Norfolk refugees, the Queen's Own, and such of the Ethiopians as had not been left to their fate ashore, the ships were not a comfortable refuge. Food was scarce. Dunmore asked for regular supplies of fresh provision, which were refused. Foraging parties, sent ashore, were cut off or driven back under fire. Hunger and disease took toll of the crowded ships, and bodies were thrown overboard daily. The undisciplined riflemen made targets of the vessels. Dunmore gave notice that, on the first day of January, he would burn the town.[15]

At four o'clock in the morning of New Year's Day, 1776, the bombardment began. Red-hot shot and carcasses from sixty guns rained on the town for seven hours without intermission. Landing parties fired buildings on the waterside. The riflemen joined in the sport by making sure that buildings known to belong to refugee Tories did not escape. The conflagration raged for two days and until four-fifths of the town "lay in ashes"—Dunmore's favorite phrase. Some weeks later, on order of the American military authorities, the rest of the houses were valued for compensation to their owners and destroyed to prevent them from sheltering the enemy. The most flourishing town in Virginia was reduced to a mere name on a map.[16]

Dunmore, having left Norfolk in February, lingered in Virginia waters until "the closeness and filth of the small vessels, in which the fugitives were crowded, the badness and scarcity of water and provisions, produced the pestilential fever, which made great havock, especially among the negroes, many of whom were swept away." He had to burn several of the smaller vessels. The rest, between forty and fifty, with the refugees aboard, he sent to Florida and the West Indies, where "a great number of negroes" were sold into slavery. He himself joined the British fleet off Staten Island in August. He soon after returned to England, where he was rewarded for his eminent services in America by being appointed governor of the Bahamas.[17]

The burning of Norfolk failed to intimidate the colonists; instead, it gave an impetus to the growing demand for complete independence, felt by Washington. "A few more such flaming arguments, as were exhibited at Falmouth and Norfolk . . . will not leave numbers at a loss to decide upon the propriety of a separation," he wrote to Joseph Reed on January 21.[18]

George Rogers Clark and the West

Although there was no fighting in the old settled parts of Virginia after the departure of Lord Dunmore and his bobtail forces until the closing period of the war, there was much and bitter fighting upon lands west of the Appalachians owned, or at least claimed, by the Old Dominion. At this point, therefore, a brief account of the war in the Ohio valley will break the narrative of the closing years of the Revolution in the south.

The British asked the assistance of the Indian nations between the Ohio River and the Great Lakes as they sought help from the Iroquois, Cherokees, and Creeks—with some success. From the British post at Detroit they carried on a ceaseless propaganda campaign among the tribes of the Old Northwest to inspire attacks upon the border settlements of Pennsylvania and Virginia (including, of course, Kentucky). They also freely supplied weapons, ammunition, and liquor. Many of the savages responded readily, for they had old grudges against the American frontiersmen, and British officials before the war had been their friends and protectors against exploitation. The thousands of Shawnee, Delaware, Miami, and Ottawa warriors therefore became a menace to the American cause.

Although Dunmore's plan for an attack upon Virginia from the West was not executed, the frontiersmen in the region of Pittsburgh continued to fear assaults by Indians and Tories. Rumors of savages advancing from the Ohio country led on several occasions to almost complete evacuation of western Pennsylvania by backwoods families who retreated to the older settlements. Lieutenant Colonel Henry Hamilton, the well known British agent at Detroit, vigorously attempted to mount a large-scale offensive in the upper Ohio valley that never quite came to pass. However, small parties of red men with muskets and tomahawks quite frequently moved in the direction of Pittsburgh from Detroit, and from other posts under British control north of the Beautiful River. The Indians in the Ohio region, urged by American emissaries to remain neutral, often promised to keep bright the chain of friendship with their backwoods neighbors. But they did not always keep their pledges, and indeed were sometimes provoked by American attacks.

The frontier about Pittsburgh was troubled, but the settlers of Kentucky suffered far more. The first settlers began to occupy the Dark and Bloody Ground immediately before the outbreak of Anglo-American hostilities. Their coming deeply angered the Cherokees and Shawnees, who claimed at least parts of Kentucky as hunting ground. Nor were the tribes appeased because the whites had purchased and extorted from them their claims to the territory. Moreover, other Indian nations, angered by the continuing westward advance of the pioneers, sympathized with the Shawnees and Cherokees. The settlers in Kentucky were under attack even before the shooting at Lexington and Concord; and the breaking out of the Anglo-American war merely intensified the assaults of the Indians. The years 1775, 1776, and 1777 were dark ones for the whites living below the Ohio. The tomahawk and the scalping knife were busy at their ugly work. All the horrors of Indian warfare were heaped upon the Long Knives, who fought back stubbornly and clung desperately to their homes in what seemed to many of them a new Eden surrounded by devils. Fortunately for the Kentuckians, Virginia soon effectively asserted its dominion over the region and sent men and ammunition. Kentucky staggered under the weight of continued Indian forays from the north; but the American grip upon it was only shaken, and the riflemen exacted a heavy toll from their red tormenters. George Rogers Clark, one of their leaders, depicts in miniature the sufferings of the Kentuckians in diary entries made in June, 1777:

5 Harrod & Elliott went to meet Col. Bowman & Co
Glen & Laird arr^d from Cumb^d Danl Lyons who parted with them on Green River we suppose was killed going into Logans Fort
Jno Peters & Elisha Bathy we expect were killed coming home from Cumb^d
13 Burr Harrison died of his wounds rec^d the 30th of May
22 Ben. Linn & Saml Moore arr^d from Illenois
Barney Stagner sen^r killed beheaded $\frac{1}{2}$ Mile from the Fort
a few Guns fired at Boon[e]s[borough] [1]

The situation in Kentucky, and on the upper Ohio, too, seemed grave in 1777 for the Americans. There was a sure remedy for it, the capture of

Detroit, which would deprive many of the Indians of weapons, ammunition, and rum. Very early in the war astute American observers began to urge an expedition against that place. But nothing had been done either by the Continental Congress or by the states to execute such a project. George Morgan, a veteran in Indian affairs who served for a time as the American agent for such matters in the Ohio valley and who ardently championed it, finally resigned his office in disgust. In the spring of 1777 the Congress did send Brigadier General Edward Hand to assume command at Fort Pitt and to lead a punitive expedition into the Ohio country. However, the simultaneous murder by American troops of Cornstalk, chief of the Shawnees, a hostage, goaded the Shawnees to savage reprisal. Hundreds of Indians swept down to and across the Ohio. Hand was unable to take the aggressive for many months. In August and September the Indians defeated several parties of frontiersmen on the south shore of the river in the vicinity of Fort Henry, near the mouth of Wheeling Creek. More than forty whites were slain in skirmishes about that post. In February, 1778, after receiving orders from Congress permitting him to take the offensive if opportunity offered, even against Detroit, Hand set out with 500 men, mostly militia, to attack Sandusky, a forward British base. But melting snow and rain swelled the rivers and forced him to abandon his march. The failure of this expedition, commonly known as the "Squaw Campaign," discouraged the general, although he was not at fault, and he resigned his command.

In 1778 the Continental Congress again planned offensive operations from Pittsburgh, with Detroit as the ultimate objective, sending the southern general Lachlan McIntosh, 500 Continentals, and money for the purpose. McIntosh advanced nearly a hundred miles from Pittsburgh, but lack of supplies and expiration of the enlistment period of some militia who accompanied him forced him to halt. He accomplished relatively little and was relieved at his own request, being succeeded early in 1779 by General Daniel Brodhead, an experienced frontier fighter. Brodhead promptly began to prepare for offensive action. Before he could move, however, the military situation in the Ohio valley was greatly altered in favor of the Americans—and in a most unexpected way. The doughty George Rogers Clark had entered upon his major role in history.

George Rogers Clark, older brother of the almost equally famous William of the Lewis and Clark expedition, was born near Charlottesville, Virginia, in 1752. His formal education was somewhat limited, partly perhaps because of an aversion to academic learning. Like Washington he became a surveyor as a very young man. A lover of Nature and her keen student, he soon appeared as a frontier fighter, serving under Dunmore against the

Shawnees in 1774 and in Kentucky in the early part of the War of Independence. One of his biographers states that he had sandy hair and blue eyes; another, possibly more reliable, declares that he had red hair and black eyes.[2] They agree that he was tall, sturdy, shrewd, courageous, and bold, a born leader of men. He was, like Ulysses S. Grant, fond of liquor; like Grant, he did not let his drinking interfere with military business. He was Virginia's military commander in Kentucky throughout the war.

Doing his share of the fighting in Kentucky in 1777, Clark had an idea—to strike at the British in the Illinois country. This region, lying between the Wabash and Miami rivers on the east, the Mississippi on the west, the Ohio on the south, and the Illinois River on the north, was under British control, and was largely guarded by militia and Indian allies of the crown. From it came some of the attacks upon Kentucky. Clark concluded that the region could be subdued. Such a conquest would relieve the pressure upon Kentucky and would loosen the hold of the British everywhere north of the Ohio. He was particularly hopeful because the white inhabitants of the area, a few hundred families, were overwhelmingly of French origin. Most of these lived at Kaskaskia, near the mouth of the river of the same name, at Prairie du Rocher, about seventeen miles to the north, at Cahokia, some forty-odd miles farther north on the bank of the Mississippi, and at Vincennes, located on the east bank of the Wabash about one hundred and fifty miles from its mouth. Clark saw these Frenchmen as potential allies.

Clark received favorable reports from Benjamin Linn and Samuel Moore, whom he sent as spies into the Illinois territory in the spring of 1777. He was told that Kaskaskia actually had no garrison. In the summer or early fall he wrote to Patrick Henry, then governor of Virginia, urging an attack upon that town. Its capture would establish American control of the Ohio, open up a communication with the Spanish across the Mississippi, block the British upon the great river, give a valuable fur trade to the Americans, cut off an occasional source of food for Detroit, and frighten the Indians of the Wabash valley into neutrality or submission. Clark was ready to lead an expedition against the town; he needed help.[3] To get that help he made his way back to Virginia in the fall of 1777.

There were many reasons why Virginia should not support Clark's seemingly rash proposal. But she claimed the Old Northwest as her own; and Clark's venture, if successful, would bring vast benefits to her and to the United States. Thomas Jefferson, George Mason, and Richard Henry Lee gave their approval, and they persuaded Governor Henry to support the scheme. These men also persuaded the Virginia assembly to authorize Clark to march, without telling most of the members *where* he intended to go. Clark received £ 1,200 for expenses, permission to draw for further funds upon somebody or other, and authority to procure boats, ammunition, and other supplies at Pittsburgh. He was authorized to raise seven companies of troops. According to public instructions, which he was to exhibit, he was to use these men in defending Kentucky. In secret orders he was commanded to attack Kaskaskia and, if feasible, Detroit.[4]

Clark moved rapidly. He hurried off Major W. P. Smith to the Holston River settlements to enlist riflemen with orders to meet him at the Falls of the Ohio (the site of Louisville). Early in 1778 he himself proceeded to Pittsburgh. En route he appointed as captains Joseph Bowman, Leonard Helm, and William Harrod. He and his aides were able to persuade only 150 frontiersmen to accompany them down the Ohio in May—perhaps he would not have started without Major Smith's assurance of the services of 200 men, or four companies, from the Holston. Reaching the Falls on May 27, Clark was joined not by four companies of Holston riflemen, but by a part of a company. A few recruits from Kentucky also were obtained. In addition he secured the services of a fourth captain, John Montgomery.

Establishing his camp on an island in the rapids so as to discourage desertion, Clark now told his men of the real purpose of his expedition. The news that France was about to enter the war had reached the camp. Aid from the French inhabitants in the Illinois region could therefore be expected with some assurance. Clark's proposals were nevertheless seemingly rash. Some of the Holston men promptly deserted, several being recaptured and forced to serve. But most of Clark's men, responding to his magnetic personality, promised their loyal support. Leaving a few of his troops to defend supplies in a blockhouse on the island, he set out for Kaskaskia with about 175 men on June 26 in a flotilla of flatboats. Shooting the rapids while the sun was in total eclipse—a happy augury, as Clark saw it—the little army floated and rowed down to old Fort Massac, about ten miles below the mouth of the Tennessee River. There, instead of proceeding by water, Clark hid his boats. He knew surprise was impossible if he went up the Mississippi. He therefore set out overland for Kaskaskia, about 120 miles distant.

Across level prairies and through trackless forests, with their commissariat on their backs, Clark and his men moved rapidly toward Kaskaskia. Their chief guide, John Saunders, lost his way. He found it again, after he was threatened with death. In the evening of July 4 they reached the Kaskaskia River three miles above the town. They had not eaten for two days, but they were determined to take the town or die in the attempt. About dusk they quietly marched down the river to a point about a mile above

Kaskaskia and on the opposite side of the river. At a farmhouse they learned that the Chevalier de Rocheblave, a veteran French officer who had entered British service, and who commanded at Kaskaskia, had had a report of their coming. He had called the local militia to arms and had sent out spies to confirm the report; but they had failed to find any trace of Clark. He had therefore disbanded the militia. Taking advantage of this happy circumstance, Clark procured boats and quickly crossed the river. He sent one division of his troops to surround the town; another, he led through an open fort gate. He himself marched to Rocheblave's house. The townsmen and the commander were completely surprised. Rocheblave promptly surrendered. Not a shot was fired, and Kaskaskia was in American hands in fifteen minutes. Captain Bowman was immediately sent with thirty men to demand the surrender of Prairie du Rocher and Cahokia, and these towns also quickly submitted to American rule without resistance.

Vincennes likewise came under American control without the firing of a shot. Clark treated the French inhabitants generously, in particular assuring them of religious freedom. However, he sent off Rocheblave, who assumed a defiant attitude, as a prisoner of war to Virginia. His generosity and his determination impressed the Frenchmen, and many of them enthusiastically promised their support to the American cause. Indeed, Father Pierre Gibault of Kaskaskia undertook to secure the surrender of Vincennes and its stronghold, Fort Sackville. Gibault and other Frenchmen left Kaskaskia for Vincennes on July 14, carrying letters to the French inhabitants of Vincennes. There were no British regulars in Vincennes. The letters and the persuasion of Gibault and his companions had the desired effect. Early in August the embassy returned home, announcing that Vincennes and its fort could be entered without resistance. A detachment led by Captain Helm promptly marched. Helm occupied the town and fort, and assumed command of the French militia.

In complete control of the French towns in the Illinois region Clark's position remained desperate. There was grave danger that the Indians in the Old Northwest would come against him in force. But Clark, like his younger brother William, was a master of the arts of Indian diplomacy. In conferences at Cahokia in August and September with the Chippewas, Ottawas, Miamis, Foxes, and other tribesmen—conferences attended by thousands of chiefs and warriors—he flattered, cajoled, and threatened the savages into promises of good behavior, pledges which were kept for many months. Another sore problem was the need for supplies. He solved it largely by calling upon Oliver Pollock for help. Pollock, an American merchant at New Orleans, responded wholeheartedly. Straining his personal credit to the utmost, he sent up the Mississippi the supplies which enabled Clark to keep the field.

The greatest danger for Clark was a British counterattack from Detroit, and the British soon moved. Lieutenant Colonel Hamilton learned early in August of Clark's impudent advance across the Ohio and quickly laid plans to deal with him. There is some dispute whether Hamilton, called the Hair Buyer by American frontiersmen, really bought American scalps from Britain's Indian allies. If he did, the fact is hardly surprising, for the British, French, and Americans all had long been accustomed to paying their red allies for such trophies.[5] The use of Indian allies inevitably brought forth this barbarity and others far more cruel and revolting. In any case, Hamilton was not without courage and enterprise. He realized that Clark's presence in the Illinois country imperiled even the British hold on Detroit. Gathering about 175 white troops, mostly Frenchmen, and 60 Indians, he set out for Vincennes on October 7. Traveling by boat, the force moved along the Maumee-Wabash portage route. Winter came, but Hamilton pushed on, acquiring additional Indian allies as he went until he had at least 500 men under his command. Captain Helm, hearing rumors of his approach, sent out a reconnoitering party. But Hamilton captured this party and another sent to warn Clark. On December 17 he marched into Vincennes. The French militia refused to fight, leaving Helm with one American soldier to defend Fort Sackville. Called upon to surrender the post, he bowed to the inevitable. The French inhabitants of Vincennes immediately resumed their allegiance to Britain.

Hamilton had great plans for dealing with Clark; but he did not move forward from Vincennes at once, probably in large part because of a lack of supplies. Had he done so, Clark would have been in the direst straits: expiration of enlistments had reduced him to about a hundred riflemen, and the French at Kaskaskia and Cahokia were panic-stricken. But Hamilton did not advance. The intrepid Virginian moved instead. With the help of Father Gibault he restored the enthusiasm of the French and mounted an offensive against Vincennes. On February 5 he sent the *Willing*, an armed row-galley with two 4-pounders, four swivel guns, and a crew of forty up the Ohio and the Wabash to cut off any retreat by the British to the Mississippi. Lieutenant John Rogers commanded this craft. On February 6, leading an army of 127 men, nearly half of whom were French, Clark began a bold march overland to Vincennes.

Vincennes was approximately 180 miles by trail from Kaskaskia. To attempt this march in midwinter with the idea of attacking Hamilton in Fort Sackville now seems extraordinarily rash. But the very audacity of

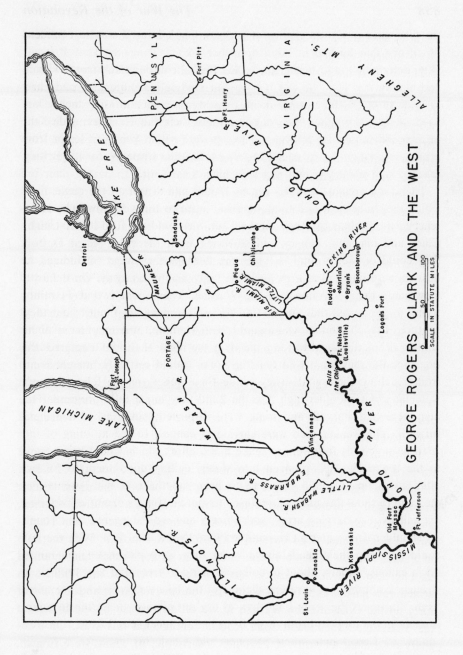

GEORGE ROGERS CLARK AND THE WEST

SCALE IN STATUTE MILES

0   50   100

the plan gave it a good chance of success. Clark himself was so confident of victory that he had in mind a further advance—against Detroit itself. Gay, determined, and masterful, he led his men through swampy lowlands and muddy prairies. The weather was fortunately mild, but they often had to wade through water inches deep. Feasting on game, amusing themselves by dancing and singing, the Americans and their French allies made light of their difficulties. By February 13 they were within twenty miles of Vincennes. Two days were needed to ferry across the Little Wabash, but they reached high and dry ground in the evening of the 15th.

Then their greatest troubles began. Floods had driven off the game upon which they subsisted, and food supplies began to run very low. The army reached the Embarrass River on the 17th, but could not ford it. That night Clark and his men, hungry and shivering from the cold, rested as best they could on wet ground in a drizzle. Perhaps they were encouraged to hear the morning gun at Fort Sackville, only nine miles away. On the 18th they made their way down to the Wabash. They spent two days vainly trying to get across that stream and to still the pangs of hunger; but they captured French hunters who assured them Hamilton was unaware of their coming. They managed to ferry the river the night of the 20th and pushed on, although they were told that the floods would certainly prevent them from reaching their goal. They made three miles on the 21st, through water at times shoulder-high. On the 22nd they made little progress. The men were half starved, and some were dispirited; but Clark drove them forward. The weaker men were carried in canoes. In the morning of the 23rd he urged his followers to make a last effort which would bring them to the town. He then plunged into water, calling upon them to follow, after instructing Captain Bowman to bring up the rear with twenty-five men and to shoot any man who refused to march. Clark's example inspirited his half-frozen, starving army, and officers and men staggered on through icy shoulder-deep water on Horseshoe Plain, then a lake. When the weariest could not keep their heads above water they were picked up and borne on in canoes. Others, about to collapse, clung to trees and logs until their stronger comrades could rescue them. But the lake was crossed. Two miles from Vincennes the army built fires to dry out clothes and received nourishment in the form of broth made from buffalo meat seized from a passing squaw. A Frenchman taken prisoner told Clark his presence was still unknown in the town. He also asserted that 200 Indians had just joined Hamilton.

There could be no turning back, even though the army had exhausted almost all its ammunition. Fortunately, Clark seemed to thrive upon disaster. He had carefully concealed the scanty number of his force from his French informant. Deciding to attempt to frighten into surrender an enemy he could not expect to subdue, he sent the Frenchman into town with a message to his fellow citizens: He intended to capture the fort that night; he did not wish to surprise the townsmen; those who were friends to the United States should go to their homes and remain in them; and those who desired to assist the British should join Hamilton in the fort! At sunset Clark ordered his men forward into the town in two major divisions, marching them to and fro in such a fashion as to give the impression that he had a thousand men. His message and his tactics quickly brought results. The townsmen, some of them secretly and stoutly pro-American, failed to join the British. The Indian allies of the British fled to the woods, after one of their chiefs had vainly offered the services of one hundred warriors to Clark. Some townsmen brought forth ammunition which they had secreted from Hamilton and presented it to the American army as it made its way into the town. With drums beating and the inhabitants cheering, Clark's force paraded up the main street and promptly began an attack on the fort. Not until a number of shots were fired did Hamilton realize that the American army was in Vincennes.

Fort Sackville was a solidly constructed wooden fort near the bank of the Wabash. Its walls, enclosing a space of about three acres, were eleven feet high. At each corner a bastion extended twelve feet above the wall, and there were three pieces of artillery on every bastion. The fort was well stocked with ammunition; and there was food within the walls. It might have been held indefinitely, although the garrison under Hamilton numbered fewer than 100 men—luckily for Clark, the British commander had sent part of his force up the Wabash to hurry in additional supplies.

The Americans and their French allies quickly put Hamilton to the test. During the night they threw up an intrenchment two hundred yards from the main gate. Using the cover of houses and hurriedly built breastworks they even penetrated within thirty yards of the fort. The British responded with cannon and small arms, but the cannon shot flew harmlessly over the heads of the attackers, who responded with rifle fire aimed at the portholes. So accurate was the aim of the Long Rifles that many British gunners were killed and wounded and the cannon silenced by early morning. Sometime after dawn one man in the American army was wounded.

About nine o'clock in the morning on the 24th, while his men were having their first decent meal in several days, Clark sent Hamilton a demand for his surrender. The British commander answered that the garrison was "not disposed to be awed into action unworthy of British subjects." [6] The shooting resumed; but the garrison ceased firing about eleven o'clock, and Hamilton sent out Captain Helm with an offer to surrender upon honorable terms. Clark asked complete surrender within thirty minutes. He told Hamilton he could hardly restrain his men from storming the fort. The British commander then suggested a three-day truce. Clark flatly refused and insisted upon unconditional surrender, but agreed to confer with Hamilton:

Colonel Clarks Compliments to M[r]. Hamilton and begs leave to inform him that Col. Clark will not agree to any other terms than that of M[r]. Hamilton's Surrendering himself and Garrison, Prisoners at Discretion————

If M[r]. Hamilton is Desirous of a Conferance with Col. Clark he will meet him at the Church with Capt[n] Helm[7]

To punctuate this demand Clark dealt sternly with five Indians who had been surprised and captured as they entered Vincennes carrying American scalps. They were tomahawked in sight of the garrison.

At last Hamilton, his subordinate Major Hay, Clark, Helm, and Captain Bowman met at the French church. Hamilton tried to persuade the American leader to moderate his terms but met with a flat refusal. Before nightfall he signed a capitulation by which he and his men became prisoners and the fort and all its contents became American property. The following morning Hamilton and his 79 men formally turned over the fort and gave up their arms. Shortly afterward Clark's victory was augmented by Captain Helm, who moved up the Wabash and captured the detachment of 40 men that had been sent out to bring up supplies. The two captures brought rich prizes in the form of goods used in the trade with the Indians. These were largely distributed among Clark's men as a reward for their devotion.

Clark was embarrassed by the number of his prisoners, almost as great as his own force. He sent Hamilton and others under guard to Virginia. Hamilton was held as a prisoner in the Old Dominion for many months, since Thomas Jefferson, Henry's successor as governor, firmly refused to permit his exchange and ordered him closely confined. No doubt he was fortunate not to lose his life.

Clark now had complete control of the Illinois country—control maintained to the end of the war; but he was not satisfied with his magnificent achievement. He began to plan an advance against Detroit, garrisoned by only 100 men under Captain Richard Lernoult, he was informed. His "very soul was wrapt" in this plan, he later declared.[8] To further it he released all the Frenchmen who had served under Hamilton upon their promise of neutrality for the future. He even gave them arms, food, and boats so that they could return to their homes. He assured some of them going to Detroit that he would be at that place almost as soon as they would. Thus he secured friends and even spies at Detroit. And he wrote to Captain Lernoult, "I learn . . . that you were very busy making new works, I am glad to hear it, as it saves the Americans some expences in building." [9]

The capture of Fort Sackville and Clark's confident and menacing attitude cast fear among the British and their Indian allies alike. Captain Lernoult was alarmed for the safety of Detroit. But at the moment Clark did not have either the men or the supplies to move against the main British base in the Old Northwest. He therefore laid plans for an expedition against that place in 1779. The government of Virginia promised him 500 men, and he hoped to obtain several hundred additional riflemen from Kentucky. His plans could not, however, be carried out. Virginia sent only 150 men under Colonel John Montgomery. Moreover, the Kentucky riflemen, after engaging in a fruitless expedition against the Shawnee town of Chillicothe, displayed no eagerness for an attack on Detroit; only 30 joined Clark. With no more than 350 troops the American commander was again forced to postpone his great project. He accomplished little in 1779. An American force under Daniel Brodhead advanced from Pittsburgh into the country of the Senecas and wrought great destruction among their towns. This success was counterbalanced in part by an exploit of the notorious Simon Girty. As Colonel David Rogers with 70 Americans was moving up the Ohio in October with blankets and munitions obtained at New Orleans, Girty and a band of Indians made a surprise attack. It was extraordinarily successful, only 13 Americans escaping slaughter.

Clark planned a march against Detroit for 1780 also, but was unable to carry it into effect, although the American position on the Ohio was strengthened by the entrance of Spain into the war. But the British were pouring money and goods into Detroit to strengthen their Indian alliances, and their efforts had an effect. They were even able to mount an assault in May against the Spanish post at St. Louis. Fortunately for both the Spanish and the Americans, they were beaten off. They were also able to send out of Detroit the redoubtable partisan leader Colonel Henry Bird with 150 whites and 1,000 Indians toward the upper Ohio. Bird assailed and captured two small American stockaded posts, Ruddle's and Martin's, in the Licking River valley. He carried away more than a hundred prisoners, many of whom were tomahawked on the journey to Detroit, in spite of his efforts to restrain his brutal allies. Clark promptly countered by leading nearly a thousand Kentucky riflemen toward the towns of the Shawnees and Delawares, the bitterest enemies of the American frontiersman. In

August this expedition destroyed Chillicothe, the Shawnee "capital," and moved forward against Piqua, another important Shawnee town on the Big Miami River. At Piqua the Shawnees and other Ohio tribesmen gathered to meet him. Simon Girty assisted them. There was fierce fighting near and in the town. An attempt to surround the Indians failed, but they suffered heavy losses and were finally driven into the woods. Small cannon transported on horseback by the Americans had an important part in this American victory. Piqua was given to the torch. Although it was not possible to move on into the country of the Delawares, Clark had won another important campaign. Meanwhile Fort Jefferson, which he had established as an American base at the mouth of the Ohio, was besieged for six days by British-led Chickasaws and Choctaws; but its defenders beat off all assaults.

The campaign of 1781 west of the Alleghenies began, oddly enough, with a surprise attack upon the British Fort St. Joseph in southwestern Michigan by a Spanish force of about 60 militia and 60 Indians led by Captain Eugenio Pourré. Pourré managed to reach the fort from St. Louis in midwinter and also to catch the British unprepared. The garrison promptly surrendered, in January, 1781. Pourré's feat was strikingly like Clark's capture of Fort Sackville. However, the Spanish commander evacuated Fort St. Joseph within twenty-four hours, remaining only long enough to permit Spain to claim the valleys of the St. Joseph and Illinois rivers at the end of the war—by right of conquest![10] The Spanish were far more active in 1781 on the shores of the Gulf of Mexico. Bernardo de Gálvez, the energetic governor of Louisiana, had laid plans to capture Pensacola, Mobile, and other smaller British posts on the Gulf coast; and he executed his plans with complete success.

For 1781 the American goal was still the capture of Detroit. Clark made his way to Richmond before the end of 1780 to consult Thomas Jefferson, then governor of Virginia. Arrangements were made to send him with 2,000 men against the British stronghold early in the spring. Jefferson hoped that "an extensive and fertile country" could thus be added to the "Empire of Liberty." The expedition was to be largely a Virginia affair, but was to be supported by Congress. Clark was made brigadier general by Jefferson early in 1781 and promptly set to work. But he encountered mountainous difficulties in securing both supplies and men. Finally, after resorting to a draft, he collected 400 men at Pittsburgh and moved down the Ohio, in August. But he had already modified his plans, for it had become apparent that a march on Detroit could hardly succeed. The British and their Indian allies were once more moving toward the Ohio, and Clark was compelled to deal with them. He decided to attack the Indians, then, if possible, to move against Detroit. His decision was confirmed by an exploit of Captain Joseph Brant. A force of 107 Pennsylvania militia under Colonel Archibald Lochay going down the Ohio to join Clark was surprised by Brant and 100 Tories and Indians near the mouth of the Big Miami River and was wiped out, a third being slain immediately. The rest were led off to captivity or a crueler fate. Brant then joined Captain Andrew Thompson and Alexander McKee, who were leading 100 British rangers and 300 Indians toward the Ohio in the hope of waylaying Clark himself. The combined British-Indian forces followed Clark to the Falls of the Ohio, but the Indians refused to join in an assault upon him. Nor were the rangers eager for a fight with Clark. They hurried back to Detroit.

Nevertheless, the situation on the lower Ohio and in the Illinois country was ugly for the Americans. It had been found necessary to evacuate Fort Jefferson in June, and dozens of Kentucky pioneers had fallen victims of Indian rage in preceding months. Fortunately, Fort Nelson, erected at the Falls of the Ohio as the result of Clark's orders, had been completed, a truly commanding position. To restore the situation Clark proposed to march up the Wabash with all available men and to engage the northwestern Indians in a fight to the finish. A victory might still open the way to Detroit. But civil officials of Kentucky and settlers alike urged a defensive policy, and he was again forced to postpone his dream of conquest.

The news of Yorktown did not end the war west of the mountains. Indeed, the British and their Indian allies south of the Great Lakes were more active than ever, partly because of an American massacre of 90 peaceful Delaware Indians of the Moravian towns in Ohio. The Indians, especially the Delaware tribe, sought vengeance, and they obtained it. When Colonel William Crawford, an old friend of Washington, led over 300 troops from Fort Pitt in an attempt to surprise the Wyandots and Shawnees on the upper Sandusky River, he met disaster. His plan was known before he marched, and Colonel Arent S. De Peyster, commandant at Detroit, sent reenforcements to his own allies. On June 4 Captain William Caldwell, a British officer, with 100 whites and 200 Indians encountered Crawford and his men in Sandusky valley. A battle began early in the afternoon and was continued the following day, when 140 Shawnees came to Caldwell's assistance. The Americans then decided to retreat. They cut their way through their encircling enemies. Hotly pursued, they fled helter-skelter for five miles. Reorganized by their officers, they then withstood a final attack and were able to continue their retreat without further molestation. But they had had 50 killed, and several, including Colonel Crawford and

Dr. Knight, a surgeon, were taken prisoner. Most of the prisoners were promptly slaughtered by the Indians. Crawford was tortured horribly and vainly begged Simon Girty to shoot him in order to end his sufferings. Knight, reserved for similar torments at the next town, was guarded en route by only one Indian. The Indian ordered him to gather wood for a fire. Knight found a "chunk," felled his guard, and escaped, finally reaching Fort Pitt with his sad tale.

The Crawford disaster led the raging savages to ravages of the frontier even to the east of Pittsburgh. General William Irvine began to organize a second force at Pittsburgh, hoping to make a more successful attack upon the Sandusky towns. He was never able to move.

Meanwhile 1,100 Indians, no doubt the greatest number ever collected in one body in the war, moved toward Wheeling in July. Luckily, most of these soon returned home for fear of Clark; but 300, with a few Loyalists under Caldwell, McKee, and Girty, crossed the Ohio and appeared at Bryan's Station, a small palisaded fort near Lexington, Kentucky, on the night of August 15. There were in the post forty cabins, occupied by 90 men, women, and children. Males in the garrison numbered 44. An attempt to surprise the fort failed. Irregular firing continued throughout the 17th. An American relieving force of forty-odd men led by Colonel Levi Todd was driven off, but 17 of Todd's men, who were mounted, were able to join the garrison. The garrison refused to surrender. In the morning of the 18th the British and Indians withdrew, moving deliberately and without any effort to hide their march. Girty and his gang hoped to gain an advantage over militia sure to pursue them, and they did.

The Kentucky frontiersmen soon began to gather, over 200 being ready to pursue the marauders within a few hours after the end of the siege of Bryan's. More were on the march, but the officers of the 200, refusing to listen to Daniel Boone's advice to wait for reenforcements, insisted upon an immediate advance. The morning of August 19 brought the opposing forces together on the Lower Blue Licks. Prudent American leaders counseled against fighting, but Major Hugh McGary stampeded the riflemen into battle, calling upon all those who were not cowards to follow him into battle. Colonel Boone, on the left wing of the Americans, drove back the Indians and their allies, but the enemy outflanked the American right wing and center. In five minutes the riflemen fled in a mad panic. Crossing the river in retreat they suffered heavy losses, many being tomahawked as they swam. More lives would have been lost, had it not been for the courage and leadership of Benjamin Netherland. One of the first across the stream, he rallied a covering party which finally forced the red men and their white friends to withdraw and enabled the surviving riflemen to get away. About 70 Kentuckians were slain, and 20 more were captured or badly wounded. Only 7 of the Girty gang were killed, and 10 wounded, and they retreated northward without further hindrance.

The disaster on the Little Blue Licks was followed by other savage forays on the Kentucky frontier. Clark was bitterly criticized as a result, since he was still in command for Virginia beyond the mountains. His response was to the point. He arranged with Irvine for a simultaneous attack upon the Ohio Indians, Irvine to march into the Sandusky valley while Clark struck again at the Shawnees. Irvine did not actually move, for he was informed by Washington that hostilities between Britain and America had ceased; but fear of his forces prevented the Indians from collecting all their forces to deal with Clark. On November 4 Clark led 1,050 mounted riflemen from the mouth of the Licking River toward Chillicothe. He also had some artillery. Six days later the Americans approached Chillicothe. They had hoped for a surprise, but the Shawnee townsmen learned of their approach and fled. Only 10 were killed and 10 wounded. However, Clark burnt Chillicothe and five other Shawnee towns, and destroyed large quantities of corn and other provisions belonging to the Indians. He dealt a blow which the Shawnees would not soon forget.

Clark's punitive expedition against the Shawnees was one of the last actions of the war. Already the diplomats of the United States and Britain had come to an agreement upon peace terms. These included recognition by Britain of American boundaries which gave not only Kentucky but also the whole of the Old Northwest to the United States. To what extent the acquisition of this magnificent domain was due to George Rogers Clark is disputed. At the end of the War of Independence the Americans did not hold Detroit. But they still controlled the Illinois country; and the region between the Illinois country, the Ohio, and Lake Erie was not firmly under the military control of the British. Clark's name may not have been mentioned by the diplomats, but his exploits can hardly be said to have weakened American claims. He was assuredly one of the greatest American frontier figures, an architect of the United States.

CHAPTER 82

The Ravaging of Virginia

During the fall of 1780, the succeeding winter, and the spring of 1781, while Greene was waging an apparently unsuccessful war in the south, the rest of the country was depressed almost to the point of giving up the struggle for independence. For two years, because of its small numbers and its inability to obtain proper supplies, Washington's army had perforce lain idle in the Highlands of the Hudson. On October 5, 1780, he wrote to General John Cadwalader: "We have been half our time without provision and are like to continue so. We have no Magazines, nor money to form them and in a little time we shall have no men [even] if we had money to pay them. We have lived upon expedients till we can live no longer." In December he had not even enough money to pay an express rider for a journey of a few miles, "neither money nor credit adequate to the purchase of a few boards for Doors for our Log huts." [1]

It was with difficulty that the main American army was maintained in strength sufficient to hold its positions in and about Peekskill. The Continental currency had depreciated to the vanishing point. The Virginia Assembly passed a law in April, 1781, fixing the price of cavalry horses, worth $150 in hard money, at $150,000 Continental; and they could not be bought even at that price. [2] The Congress was bankrupt. The people generally began to believe that the war was about over. Washington wrote: "We seem to be verging so fast on destruction that I am filled with sensations to which I have been a stranger till within these three months." And yet the war had already begun to blaze afresh in a new field where, within ten months, the American cause would be finally and lastingly triumphant. That field was the state of Virginia.

For the three years that followed the burning of Norfolk on January 1, 1776, the Old Dominion east of the mountains was unvexed by war; but Virginia and her stores of wealth were a prize too valuable to be forever disregarded by the British. The vast quantities of tobacco she raised strongly supported the credit of the Congress among foreign nations, and the salt provisions she produced helped feed the American army. It would have been well for the British to occupy the state permanently. Clinton did not feel strong enough to detach from New York a force sufficient to do that. In 1779, however, he was able to strike a blow toward destroying its usefulness to the Americans; he organized a large-scale raid.

On May 5, 1779, twenty-two transports heavily convoyed by war vessels under Vice Admiral Sir George Collier sailed from Sandy Hook with the grenadiers and light infantry of the Guards, the 42nd Regiment, the Hessian Regiment Prince Charles, the Tory Royal Volunteers of Ireland, and a detachment of artillery—1,800 men in all, commanded by Major General Matthews. On May 10 they landed at Portsmouth and took possession of that unfortified town without opposition. Detachments pushed on and captured Suffolk, Gosport, and other small towns, also without opposition except in Gosport, where a garrison of 100 in a rather strong little redoubt, Fort Nelson, resisted with a brief and ineffectual cannonade before abandoning the works. In Gosport there were a shipyard, ropewalks, and a very considerable store of ship timbers and naval stores. The Americans burned a nearly completed war vessel on the ways, also two French ships loaded with tobacco and other merchandise; the British did the rest. They sacked and burned all the towns, looted the neighboring plantations, destroyed or carried off 130 vessels and 3,000 hogsheads of tobacco, inflicting a loss estimated at £2,000,000, and sailed away, loaded with plunder of every sort, without the loss of a single man.[3]

Cornwallis was convinced that the conquest of Virginia would be followed by the control of all America. He even proposed the abandonment of New York and the concentration of all the royal forces in the Chesapeake to effect this great result.[4] Clinton would not consent to such a drastic change in the disposition of his army. He did, however, send a large detachment under Benedict Arnold to Virginia in 1780 and order all his subordinates there to cooperate with Cornwallis when that general had begun his march thither from Wilmington in April, 1781.[5]

Benedict Arnold, as a part of his purchase price, had received the rank of brigadier general in the British army. Lacking confidence in Arnold's stability, Clinton attached to his force two experienced and reliable officers, Colonels Dundas and Simcoe, "by whose advice he was to be guided in every important measure." [6] The corps under Arnold consisted of the 18th British regiment, Simcoe's Queen's Rangers, a detachment of New York Volunteers under Colonel Althouse, and Captain Thomas's Pennsylvania Volunteers from Bucks County, about 1,600 in all. [7] The principal purposes of the expedition were the destruction of military stores in Virginia, the prevention of reenforcements for Greene from that state, and the rallying of the Tories.

The expedition sailed from Sandy Hook on December 20 but was scattered by a violent gale on the 26th and 27th. One war vessel and three transports, carrying 400 men, failed to rejoin it when it reassembled off the Chesapeake capes. [8] The rest reached Hampton Roads on the 30th. There the 1,200 remaining troops were transferred to small vessels taken from the Americans. Convoyed by the armed vessels *Hope* and *Swift*, they sailed up the James River, arriving in the evening of January 3 at Hood's Point, where about 50 militia manned a battery of three 18-pounders, one 24, and a brass howitzer. [9] The Americans opened fire, but did no damage to the invaders. The vessels passed the battery; and, about a mile above it, Arnold put Simcoe's Rangers and the light infantry and grenadiers of the 18th Regiment ashore the next morning to attack it from the rear. The defenders had, however, evacuated the battery during the night. The guns were spiked, the howitzer carried off as a prize, and the expedition proceeded up the river to Westover, about twenty-five miles below Richmond, where the men were disembarked. [10]

Although Washington had written several times to Governor Jefferson of the probable invasion of his state, [11] adequate preparations had not been made for its defense when the enemy fleet was sighted off the Chesapeake capes. Then Jefferson sent General Thomas Nelson, Jr., of the Virginia state troops down to the coastal region ("the lower country") to call up the militia in that quarter, "but waited further intelligence before we would call for militia from the middle or upper country." [12] The response to the call was feeble. Years of freedom from attack had resulted in an apathy in Virginia which even the presence of invaders, at the very threshold of her capital, could not dispel. The only force in being was about 200 Continentals newly recruited by Steuben, and it was employed in removing military stores from Petersburg beyond the reach of the enemy.

Henry Lee explains this apathy partly by Matthews's devastation of the towns in 1779, and by the fact that the efforts of Virginia to support

Greene's army in the Carolinas had further exhausted her resources. "Yet," he says, "she possessed enough, more than enough, to have sustained the struggle for their restoration and to have crushed any predatory adventure like that conducted by Arnold." He lays the blame for the supineness of the state upon the government headed by Thomas Jefferson, "a gentleman . . . highly respected for his literary accomplishments and as highly esteemed for his amiability and modesty," who failed to heed Washington's warning and to make any preparations to meet the invasion, with the result that he had left "the archives of the State, its reputation and all the military stores deposited in the magazines of the metropolis at the mercy of a small corps conduced by a traitor." [13] To be sure, Light-Horse Harry and Jefferson were enemies, and the cavalryman could hardly be expected to lavish praise upon the governor. Perhaps Jefferson did all that he could.

Arnold marched his men from Westover, entirely unopposed, against Richmond and entered that town on January 5. About 200 militia under Colonel John Nicholas occupied the heights of Richmond Hill. Simcoe's Rangers were ordered to dislodge them; they fled without firing a shot. A small body of cavalry near the capitol also departed without resistance. The town was thus bloodlessly taken.[14] Arnold then sent Simcoe with his Rangers and the flank companies of the 18th Regiment six miles up the river to Westham, where there was an iron foundry, a "laboratory" (powder factory), and machine shops. These were destroyed with their contents, including five or six tons of gunpowder.[15]

He sent a letter to Jefferson offering to spare the capital if the British vessels were permitted to come up the river unopposed and carry away the tobacco from the warehouses. Although it seems that no effective opposition to the approach of the vessels could have been offered, Jefferson refused to make the bargain.[16] The work of destruction was then begun; buildings, public and private, were burned; other public and private property was destroyed, including state papers. Weapons of various sorts and military stores were carried off on the return march to Portsmouth on the 6th, which was accomplished without a whiff of gunpowder.[17] At Portsmouth, Arnold entrenched and encamped for the winter.

Meanwhile he had sent a scouting party of forty-two of the Queen's Rangers, horsemen, under Simcoe towards Long Bridge. Hearing of the presence of a body of one hundred and fifty of Nelson's militia under Colonel Dudley at Charles City Court House, Simcoe resolved to attack them. He sent his buglers to the right to sound a charge while the rest of his small party advanced on the left. Then, in a loud voice, he ordered his light infantry—of which he had none—to charge. Believing themselves about to

be caught in the jaws of a pincers attack, the militia took fright, gave a confused and scattering fire, and started to disperse. Simcoe's horsemen drove
into their bewildered opponents, killed twenty, and captured eight. He then
returned to join Arnold at Westover, having lost one man killed and three
wounded.[18]

Washington had his eye on Arnold in his isolated position in Virginia. To
capture that traitor and bring him to a deserved end was worth an effort. It
would be, he wrote, "an event particularly agreeable to this country." He
solicited the aid of the French fleet and army at Newport in Rhode Island,
blockaded by a stronger British fleet.[19] At the same time he ordered Lafayette with three regiments of light infantry—1,200 rank and file, drawn from
the New England and New Jersey Continental regiments—to march southward and cooperate with the expected French force. These regiments were
commanded by Colonel Joseph Vose of Massachusetts, Lieutenant Colonel
de Gimat, a French officer, and Lieutenant Colonel Francis Barber of New
Jersey.[20]

A timely storm struck the British blockaders off Rhode Island on January
22, 1781, wrecking several of the largest ships and so scattering the fleet that
Admiral Destouches was able to send out the 64-gun ship *Eveille* and two
frigates under command of Le Bardeur de Tilly to destroy Arnold's vessels
and leave him without naval support. Arnold had, however, withdrawn his
vessels up the Elizabeth River to Portsmouth, to which place Tilly's larger
ships were unable to follow them. The French vessels therefore returned
to Newport on February 24.[21]

Lieutenant General de Rochambeau, in command of the French army,
and Admiral Destouches then agreed to send the whole French fleet and
1,200 soldiers to operate with Lafayette against Arnold. Lafayette promptly
marched from Peekskill and arrived on March 3 at the Head of Elk, where
he embarked his men in small vessels that carried them to Annapolis. On
March 8 Destouches, with eight ships of the line and three frigates carrying
the promised 1,200 troops, set sail from Newport. The British Admiral
Arbuthnot, with an almost exactly equal force, put to sea from Gardiner's
Bay on the 10th and overtook the Frenchmen at the entrance of the Chesapeake on the 16th. In the ensuing encounter Destouches was worsted and
forced to return to Newport.[22] Lafayette's little army was thus left with little
support to face not only Arnold's larger force but also Major General
William Phillips, who had been sent by Clinton with 2,600 men to join
Arnold and supersede him in command, and who had arrived at Portsmouth
on March 26. [23] To assist Lafayette, there were only Steuben's small newly

enlisted force of Virginia Continentals and such untrained militia as Generals Muhlenberg, Weedon, and Nelson were able to raise.

Arnold made the first move. On April 18, while Lafayette was on his southward march from Baltimore, the light infantry of the 76th and 80th British regiments, the Queen's Rangers, the American Legion, and a detachment of Hessian jägers, about 2,500 in all, embarked at Portsmouth under Arnold's command, sailed down to Hampton Roads and thence up the James, landing at various points and destroying whatever they came upon. On the 24th the whole force disembarked at City Point and marched towards Petersburg, where great supplies of tobacco and military stores were guarded by General Muhlenberg with about a thousand militia. The town was unfortified, and its approaches were merely picketed by small bodies. Muhlenberg's men were drawn up on an elevation east of Blandford, a village about a mile east of Petersburg. Arnold divided his force into two columns, sending the main body under Lieutenant Colonel Abercrombie directly towards his enemy, and the Queen's Rangers with one battalion of light infantry on a circuitous route around Muhlenberg's right flank. The American guns, firing grapeshot, were brought to bear on Abercrombie's column and for a considerable length of time held it off. But Abercrombie brought up four fieldpieces to a hill on the American right and so battered it that Muhlenberg decided to withdraw across the Appomattox by a neighboring bridge. The withdrawal was accomplished in good order, and the bridge was destroyed. Thence the retreat was continued to Chesterfield Court House, and Petersburg was left open to the enemy. Four thousand hogsheads of tobacco and several small vessels were burned, but the buildings seem to have escaped destruction.[24]

The success of these marauding expeditions and the lack of effective opposition encouraged Phillips to continue them. He repaired the bridge and marched on April 27, with the light infantry and detachments of jägers and of the Queen's Rangers horsemen, to Chesterfield Court House, where he burned a great range of barracks and 300 barrels of flour, with other stores. No defense was offered by the Virginians. At the same time Arnold, with the 76th and 80th British regiments, the American Legion, and some of the jägers and of the Queen's Rangers, set out for Osborne's, a small village on the James about fifteen miles below Richmond. There the Americans had assembled a considerable naval force, intended for cooperation with the French fleet in an enterprise against Portsmouth. Arnold used every precaution for surprise and succeeded in coming upon the ships without their crews' being aware of his approach. He sent a flag of truce with an offer to leave half of the cargoes unmolested, if they would surrender the other half. The offer was refused. He then brought to bear on the *Tempest*, a 20-gun frigate, two 3-pounders and two 6's. He also sent up a party of the jägers to fire on the crew. The *Tempest*, the *Renown*, 26 guns, and the 14-gun *Jefferson*, as well as a body of militia on the northern bank of the river, replied. But the *Tempest*'s cable having been cut by a shot, she swung around and exposed herself to a raking fire from Arnold's artillery, whereupon her crew took to their boats and escaped under musket fire from the jägers. The incident produced a panic in the other vessels, and the crews gave up the fight, scuttling some of the vessels, setting fire to others, and fleeing from them all.

The result was the burning or sinking of four ships, five brigs, and several smaller vessels, and the capture of two ships, three brigantines, two schooners, and five sloops, all laden with tobacco, flour, naval stores, and other merchandise. More than 2,000 hogsheads of tobacco and the rest of their cargoes were burned. The British suffered no losses. The casualties among the Americans are unknown.[25]

The two British forces, having joined, marched to Manchester and took and burned 1,200 hogsheads of tobacco. At Warwick they destroyed 500 barrels of flour, the flouring mills, several warehouses, more tobacco, and five vessels. Thence, by various stages, between April 30 and May 10, they proceeded to Petersburg, where they surprised and captured ten American officers.

Lafayette with his 1,200 Continentals arrived at Richmond on April 29 to defend that city.[26] Phillips was then on the opposite side of the James, but he made no attempt against this American army, which his own greatly outnumbered. He fell down the river to Jamestown Island with the intention of meeting Cornwallis on his expected arrival at Petersburg. On May 20 Cornwallis arrived with a brigade of the Guards, the 22nd, 33rd, and 71st British regiments, the light infantry of the 82nd, the Hessian Regiment von Bose, Tarleton's Legion, and Hamilton's Tories—about 1,500 men in all [27] —and the two British forces were united. A few days later another force of 1,500 sent by Clinton—two new British regiments and two battalions of Anspachers—brought the British army's numbers up to 7,200 rank and file. Meanwhile Lafayette had received additions to his original force of 2,000 Virginia militia and 40 dragoons, the relics of Armand's Legion. He had now about 3,000 men to oppose the 7,200 British.[28] He could not hope to meet his enemy in the field. "Were I to fight a battle," he wrote to Washington on May 24, "I should be cut to pieces, the militia dispersed and the arms lost. Were I to decline fighting, the country would think itself given up. I am therefore determined to skirmish, but not to engage too far, and particularly to take care against their immense and excellent body of horse, whom the militia fear as they would so many wild beasts. . . . Were I anyways equal to the enemy, I should be extremely happy in my present command, but I am not strong enough even to get beaten." [29]

Cornwallis, on the other hand, was confident of his strength. He wrote to Clinton on May 26, "I shall now proceed to dislodge LaFayette from Richmond, and with my light troops to destroy any magazines or stores in the neighbourhood." He would then move to the Neck at Williamsburg and keep himself disengaged from operations that might interfere with the plan for the campaign, until he heard from Clinton. "The boy cannot escape me," he is said also to have written. [30]

Cornwallis marched from Petersburg on the 24th of May, crossed the James to Westover, and encamped on June 1 at Hanover Junction, whence he sent Tarleton's and Simcoe's corps to scout the position of Lafayette's force, which had been encamped at Winston's Bridge eight miles north of Richmond.

Lafayette had left on May 28, retreating rapidly westward to Dandridge's on the South Anna River to wait the arrival of Steuben's Continentals and of Wayne's detachment of 800 men drawn from the Pennsylvania Continentals. This had been ordered south by Washington in February, but difficulties in organization and in procurement of supplies had prevented it from marching from York, Pennsylvania, until May 20. [31] Meanwhile Lafayette's plan was to keep his force intact and to avoid any engagement with the enemy.

With this in view and to prevent Cornwallis's interposing his army between him and the oncoming force of Wayne, he conducted his men by a series of rapid marches northward to Ely's Ford on the Rapidan twenty miles above Fredericksburg. Cornwallis followed as far as the North Anna River, but could not get between him and Wayne, nor even come up with him and force him to fight. So the British general turned to other objectives.

On June 1 Cornwallis sent Simcoe with his Rangers and the 2nd battalion of the 71st Regiment, 500 men, to Point of Fork, where the Fluvanna and Rivanna rivers join to form the James, and where Steuben with his now five or six hundred Continental recruits was guarding the main depot of American military stores. Simcoe found that Steuben had withdrawn his stores across the Fluvanna and was following them with his whole force. He captured a lingering group of thirty of Steuben's men, but could not pursue the main body for lack of boats. [32] He then employed an artifice. Displaying his small force widely along the river bank, he lighted many campfires and thus produced an appearance of such great numbers that Steuben believed that it was the advance of the whole British army and abandoned his stores and retreated rapidly southward to Cole's Ferry. Simcoe sent some men across the river in canoes and destroyed the stores.[33]

On June 4 Cornwallis dispatched Tarleton with 180 of the Legion's cavalry and 70 mounted infantry against Charlottesville, where the Virginia legislature was in session. On the way Tarleton fell in with a train of twelve wagons carrying much-needed clothing for Greene's army, took it, and burned it. At Charlottesville the legislature, notified of his coming, had adjourned; but he captured several of their number. Governor Jefferson had a narrow escape, avoiding capture by a flight to the mountains. A quantity of powder and of tobacco, a thousand muskets, and some clothing intended for Greene's army were taken and destroyed. Tarleton and Simcoe then rejoined Cornwallis.[34] About this time Arnold was recalled to New York and appeared no more on the southern scene of action. He had rendered genuine service to the British in Virginia, and he might have been useful to Cornwallis.

On June 10 Wayne, with three Pennsylvania regiments under Colonels Richard Butler, Walter Stewart, and Richard Humpton, and the 4th Continental Artillery under Lieutenant Colonel Thomas Forrest—about 800 men in all and six guns—joined Lafayette.[35] Lafayette now felt strong enough to make some effort to protect the remaining American magazines from destruction. He marched south towards the enemy. At Mechunk Creek on the 13th, he was further reinforced by 600 back country riflemen under General William Campbell of Virginia.[36]

Two days later Cornwallis broke his camp at Elk Hill a few miles below Point of Fork, where he had lain since June 7, and took the road towards Richmond. This retrograde movement encouraged the Americans, who regarded it as a confession of inability to continue the destruction of the American magazines and as a sign of a disinclination to engage Lafayette's increased army; but Cornwallis was merely shifting his ground towards the Chesapeake to get in closer relations with his superior, Clinton in New York.

Lafayette followed him at a distance of about twenty miles. When Cornwallis entered Richmond on June 16, the Americans were at Dandridge's on the South Anna. On the 20th Cornwallis resumed his eastward march, Lafayette still hanging on his rear. At that time the American army was composed of Lafayette's original force of light infantry, 800 men and Wayne's 750 Pennsylvanians, all seasoned Continental troops; three Virginia militia brigades under Generals Edward Stevens, Robert Lawson, and William Campbell, 2,100 in all; the 425 new Virginia Continentals raised by Steuben and now commanded by Colonel Christian Febiger; 200 of the 2nd and 4th Continental Artillery regiments with eight or ten guns; 60 regular cavalrymen; and as many volunteer dragoons. The total was about 4,500 rank and file.[37] He scattered these forces on different roads; they encamped separately, but sufficiently near one another to concentrate rapidly. Thus he created an impression of greater numbers than he actually had and made it more difficult for spies and deserters to convey certain intelligence of his numbers to Cornwallis. On June 26 he had his first encounter with the enemy.

Simcoe's Rangers and a party of jägers had been sent on the 23rd to forage and to destroy American stores on the Chickahominy River west of Williamsburg, where the British army was in camp. Lafayette detached Colonel Richard Butler with his Pennsylvania regiment, Majors Call and Willis with a corps of riflemen, and Major William McPherson with 120 horsemen to intercept Simcoe on his return to Williamsburg. They marched all night of the 25th and in the morning came upon the British refreshing themselves at Spencer's Ordinary. McPherson charged upon Simcoe's jägers and threw them into confusion; but the Rangers quickly deployed and came to their comrades' assistance, charging upon McPherson and driving him back. Call and Willis brought up their riflemen and there was a sharp conflict between them and Simcoe's infantry, before the Rangers' horsemen fell upon their flank and pushed them back upon Butler's Continentals. A confused fight ensued, in which Simcoe's men had the advantage. But as soon as he was sufficiently free of his assailants Simcoe, leaving his wounded in the tavern, drew off his force on the road to Williamsburg. He was not pursued, because of the dangerous propinquity of Cornwallis's main force.

Lafayette claimed a success in this fight, asserting that the enemy had lost 60 killed and 100 wounded; but Cornwallis acknowledged only 33 casualties. The American losses were 9 killed, 14 wounded, 14 missing.[38] During the following week there was little activity on either side. Cornwallis remained in his camp at Williamsburg. Lafayette hovered in the neighborhood of the British, changing his position almost daily, the various sections of his army encamping separately as before. His enemy's intentions were unfathomable to him; he could only await their disclosure. The next movement of the British was dictated by Clinton.

New York was threatened by the armies of Washington and Rochambeau. Clinton called on Cornwallis for 3,000 of his men. They had to embark at Portsmouth, and Cornwallis on July 4 started from Williamsburg for that port. In this movement Lafayette thought he saw his opportunity. He would strike while the British were crossing the James, fall upon their rear while the river divided them.

The crossing began at Jamestown Ford on July 5. On the 6th Lafayette detached Wayne with Stewart's Pennsylvania Continental regiment, certain other small parties under Mercer, McPherson, Galvan, Call, and Willis, 500 in all, to march to Greenspring Farm within half a mile of the British outposts; the rest of the army, exclusive of the militia, who were left under Steuben's command at Bird's Tavern, twelve miles in the rear, was held in reserve. At that time Lafayette and Wayne believed that the major part of the enemy had crossed the river, and that only the rear guard was left for them to engage. But Cornwallis had shrewdly calculated that just such an attack would be made and had sent across only Simcoe's Rangers and the army's baggage. The main body of his army lay in wait.

Wayne's contingent advanced across a broad morass, with Armand's and Mercer's cavalry in front, supported by the riflemen on both flanks, and Stewart's Pennsylvanians in reserve. They first met and engaged the patrols of Tarleton's Legion, which was thrown out in front of the main body of the British. Under a hot fire from the Americans, the Legion fell back into a wood, as ordered by Cornwallis to make the Americans believe that they had to contend with his rear guard only. Supported by a part of the 76th Regiment, Tarleton's men stood fast in the wood and stoutly resisted the Americans' advance, while screening from them the British army immediately behind the wood. In this part of the fight, the American riflemen took heavy toll of the British officers.

Wayne, ignorant of the proximity of the whole British army, had no idea of the hazard of his position. On the other hand, Cornwallis was uncertain as to what support the Americans then engaged had in their immediate rear. He could easily have beaten Wayne, but preferred to wait until he could be sure that the rest of Lafayette's army was at hand to offer him a prize worth taking.

About five o'clock Lafayette brought up his original force of light infantry and the rest of the Pennsylvania Continentals, his whole army except the militia who had been left under Steuben's command at Bird's Tavern. Having some doubt as to what part of Cornwallis's army was yet on the near side of the river, he sent across the morass to Wayne only the rest of the Pennsylvanians and a battalion of light infantry, under Major John Wyllys of Connecticut, with two fieldpieces. The fire of these two guns seems to have convinced Cornwallis that the whole American army was at last before him. He ordered an attack.

Cornwallis's army was formed in two lines, the light infantry on the right of the front line, the 43rd, 76th, and 80th regiments on the left. In the second line were the Guards, the 23rd, 33rd, and 71st regiments, the Hessian Regiment von Bose, and Tarleton's Legion. Wayne with his reenforcements was then also preparing to attack. In the center of his line were Stewart's Pennsylvanians, with Butler's and Humpton's on the right and left, Wyllys's Connecticut light infantry extending the line to the right. The American riflemen were holding a ditch behind a rail fence, which they had occupied in the first encounter. Against Wayne's line of 900 men the whole British army advanced. The riflemen bore the first attack with considerable fortitude, maintaining their fire for a short time before they were driven from their post. Wyllys's light infantry, somewhat in advance, were also forced to retire to the American line. Wayne, perceiving that he had taken on the whole British army, and that his small force was in peril of being outflanked on both sides, might well have ordered a retreat, but feared to do so lest it develop into a rout. If he could first check the British advance, he might have a chance to withdraw in order. He therefore ordered a charge with the bayonet upon the British left wing, its right being engaged in driving back Wyllys's troops and the riflemen.

Wayne's troops responded nobly, springing forward under a strong fire of grapeshot and musketry, but, within two hundred feet of the enemy they were brought to a stand. For a quarter of an hour, at this close range, the battle was sharply and destructively contested. But the British right, having beaten back Wyllys and the riflemen, now threatened to swing in upon and envelop the American left. The pressure of overwhelming numbers on Wayne's men was also too heavy to bear. He ordered a retreat. It was successfully accomplished without pursuit, though with the loss of the two guns, and the army was reassembled at Greenspring. The Americans lost in killed and wounded 133, besides 12 missing; the British casualties were 75.[39]

Cornwallis's failure to follow up his success saved Lafayette's army from destruction, but there was some excuse for the failure in that a very dark night had fallen by the time the Americans retreated. "One hour more of daylight must have produced the most disastrous conclusion," says Henry Lee. Cornwallis himself wrote to Clinton that half an hour more of light "would have probably given us the greatest part of the [American] corps." [40] As it was, he resumed his march, crossed the river, and went on his way to Suffolk and thence to Portsmouth. Tarleton was then dispatched to destroy American stores in Bedford County. Wayne and Morgan were sent by Lafayette to counteract his efforts. He accomplished little, except burning more tobacco, and rejoined Cornwallis at Suffolk after an exhausting tour of 400 miles in fifteen days. From Suffolk, Cornwallis sent to Portsmouth the 3,000 men called for by Clinton. Lafayette held his men in camp on Malvern Hill, between Richmond and Westover, awaiting developments.

Throughout this whole campaign, Cornwallis had been harassed by the conduct of his superiors, Germain in London and Clinton in New York. Germain, who has been harshly described as "probably the most incompetent official that ever held an important post at a critical moment," [41] as Secretary of State for the Colonies was charged with the general conduct of the war. He tried to direct it in some detail by letters that took four weeks to three months to reach his generals in America, by which time in most cases the circumstances on which he based his directions had entirely changed.

Clinton was in command of all the King's forces in America. His correspondence with Cornwallis, back and forth, took eight days or more to reach its destination. His directions therefore arrived often too late to be of use. Moreover, he did not quite give Cornwallis a free hand nor give him positive orders. As the two had conflicting views as to the proper conduct of the war, and as the orders Clinton gave usually had a saving clause to the effect that if Cornwallis had other plans he should disregard them, the result was a complete confusion of the intentions and purposes of both parties and discontent in Clinton with what Cornwallis did, expressed in almost every letter. This condition was to have a most important bearing on the outcome of the campaign. It was exemplified in orders Cornwallis received on July 8 to send the 3,000 troops to Philadelphia instead of to New York, on January 12 to dispatch them immediately to New York, then on July 20 and later not to send them at all but to hold them and occupy Old Point Comfort, also Yorktown if possible.[42]

Cornwallis visited Old Point with a corps of engineers and concluded that it was not suitable as a defensive point to command a harbor for the King's ships, which was Clinton's purpose. He thereupon seized Yorktown, and Gloucester across the York River, and proceeded to fortify them. Clinton tacitly acquiesced in this arrangement.[43]

Washington Resumes Operations

While the war was raging in the Carolinas and the minor operations were carried on in Virginia, Washington's army in the north was inactive. But on May 22, 1781, he learned that the French were sending Admiral de Grasse with a new fleet to the West Indies and thence to the American coast to cooperate under his direction with Rochambeau's army (in Newport), and it seemed to be time for the American army to resume offensive operations.[1]

It was indeed time that something should be done in the north lest the American cause die of inanition. The people were tired of the war. Its long continuance had bred apathy as to its outcome. Few men could be induced to enlist for its duration or even for any definitely long term of service. The farmers wanted to be on their farms in seedtime and harvest time. The town dwellers were convinced that somehow or other, without much further effort on their part, a peace would be achieved. There was no capable central authority. The Congress had little real power beyond persuasion of the states to follow its guidance. The financial system was a wreck.

In the army itself there was little coherence, and no prospect of combined operation. At and about West Point, Washington had scarcely 3,500 Continentals, chiefly from New England. The regiments from New York were scattered along its western frontier. New Jersey was guarding its own territory. The best of the Pennsylvanians were in Virginia with Wayne and Lafayette. The Continentals of the more southerly states were with

Greene in the Carolinas. The allied French, about 4,000, were at Newport, Rhode Island, under Rochambeau.

For any of these, for all of these, except the French, there was little better prospect than practical destitution. The few and scattered magazines contained small supplies. The military chests were empty, and the credit of the army was exhausted. The impressment of food had soured the temper of the people.[2] "Instead of having the prospect of a glorious offensive campaign before us," wrote Washington in his journal on May 1, 1781, "we have a bewildered and gloomy defensive one, unless we receive a powerful aid of ships, land troops and money from our generous allies."

In contrast to this was the condition of the invaders. Besides Cornwallis's army of more than 5,000 well supplied veterans in Virginia, Clinton had 14,500 equally well or better supplied in New York. Yet it was against that post that Washington and his generals, upon hearing of the coming of Grasse, in a meeting at Wethersfield, Connecticut, concerted with Rochambeau for an attack.[3] A part of the French fleet, with 700 recruits for the French army in Newport, had arrived with word that more would come in July or August. But it was not until the first week in July that Rochambeau with four regiments of infantry, a battalion of artillery, and the Duc de Lauzan's Legion of horse and foot joined Washington on the Hudson. Meanwhile, Washington had been preparing his army, brigading it anew, drilling his men, calling in outlying detachments to his camp at Peekskill, and in general getting ready for the adventure.[4]

The enterprise against New York was to begin with an attempt against the British forts on the north end of Manhattan Island by General Benjamin Lincoln, commanding two regiments of light infantry and a detachment of artillery, 800 in all, brought down in the night of July 1 from Peekskill in boats and landed secretly on the New York shore under the height on which stood Fort Knyphausen—formerly Fort Washington. The plan was no less ambitious than an effort to take by surprise Fort Knyphausen, Fort Tryon, Fort George on Laurel Hill, the works on Cox Hill at the mouth of Spuyten Duyvil, and those at Kingsbridge. Washington was to arrive early the next day with the main army at Valentine's Hill, four miles above Kingsbridge. There was also a secondary purpose to be effected in case circumstances prevented fulfillment of the first: cooperation with a force led by the Duc de Lauzun in the capture or at least the defeat of De Lancey's corps of Tory horse and foot, then at Morrisania. According to the alternative plan Lincoln was to land above Spuyten Duyvil, march to the high ground in front of Kingsbridge, lie concealed until the beginning of Lauzun's attack, and then prevent De Lancey from turning Lauzun's right while he was cutting off the escape of the Tories over the bridge. It was all very prettily planned, but it did not work.[5]

Lincoln, viewing the ground from Fort Lee on the opposite shore, found it occupied by a considerable British force just returned from foraging in New Jersey. Also, a ship of war lay in the river between. He abandoned the principal attempt and landed his troops above Spuyten Duyvil for the secondary effort. This also failed. He was discovered by another British foraging party stronger than his own and was attacked. Lauzun with his Legion, Sheldon's dragoons, and a detachment of Connecticut state troops under General David Waterbury arrived after a hot and fatiguing forced march, only to find the intended surprise of De Lancey impossible. He gave support to Lincoln, and Washington hastened down from Valentine's Hill. The British took to their boats and escaped.[6] Washington spent the rest of the day in reconnoitering the ground about Kingsbridge, with a view to later operations. The next day his army fell back to Dobbs Ferry, where on the 6th the French army joined it in camp.[7]

Having still in mind an attack on New York, he prepared for a thorough reconnaissance in force. During the four days from the 21st to the 24th of July, screened by 5,000 troops interposed between them and the enemy, and guarded by 150 Continentals, he, Rochambeau, and two other French generals made a thorough examination of the British positions. They seem to have agreed that an attack upon them could not succeed—which, indeed, was undoubtedly true.

Rochambeau had four regiments, the Bourbonnois, Soissonois, Saintonge, and Royal Deux-Ponts, having now an effective strength of perhaps 930 each, besides Lauzun's Legion, the artillery, and engineers. This entire force numbered 4,796.[8] Washington had about as many. Clinton with 14,000 good troops held fortified lines that could not be reached without crossing one river or another held by British war vessels. The situation seems to have been too plain for argument. The wonder is that an attack should have been seriously considered.

Washington now turned his thoughts toward the south. It might be that Clinton would feel obliged to reenforce Cornwallis in Virginia and so weaken his New York garrison. Or he might call on Cornwallis for part of his troops—as he actually did, although he countermanded the order. In such an event, however, Washington might march south to help Lafayette clean up the weakened British force. Or he might go still farther, join Greene in South Carolina, and besiege Charleston.[9] While he was considering these cloudy matters, a letter from Grasse came to Rochambeau—a clear, concise, and definite letter that cleared the air, resolved all doubts, and determined the course of the war.

Grasse would embark the regiments Gatinois, Agenois, and Touraine, 3,000 in all, 100 dragoons, 100 artillerists, 10 field pieces, and a number of siege cannon and mortars, in twenty-five to twenty-nine war vessels. He would sail on August 13 from Santo Domingo directly to the Chesapeake, where he would remain until October 15 and then return with his troops to the West Indies.[10]

That was a time table explicit and definite, of which the Americans were wise to take notice. Washington did so without delay. Grasse's letter was received on August 14. On the 15th Washington wrote to Lafayette directing him so to dispose his troops as to prevent Cornwallis from retreating to North Carolina; to Heath on the 19th to take command of about half of the American army to be left in the Highlands—seventeen thin battalions of New England troops, Sheldon's horse, and some others.[11] He sent General Duportail, on the 17th, to Grasse with a letter saying that Rochambeau's French army and as large a part of the American army as could be spared would meet him in the Chesapeake, suggesting alternative plans for their combined operations according to circumstances, either in Virginia or at Charleston, and asking that frigates and transports be sent up to the Head of Elk to carry the troops down the Chesapeake.[12]

On the 21st the allied armies were started southward. The problem was to conduct their march in such a fashion that Clinton might be left in ignorance of their intentions. This was accomplished by crossing the Hudson by King's Ferry to Stony Point, then marching behind the Palisades and so through Newark and New Brunswick. In New Jersey they paused, established an extensive and apparently permanent encampment as if intended as a base from which to attack Staten Island, thus allowing Clinton to believe that the purpose was still against New York.[13] The true intent had been kept a secret even from the troops. James Thacher, a surgeon in the American army, wrote in his journal on the 15th, "The real object of the allied armies [in] the present campaign has become a subject of much speculation. Ostensibly an investment of the city of New York is in contemplation." From the circumstances of the encampment in New Jersey "we are left to conclude that a part of our besieging force is to occupy that ground. But," he sagely observed, "General Washington possesses a capacious mind, full of resource, and he resolves and matures his great plans and designs under an impenetrable secrecy, and, while we repose the fullest confidence in our chief, our own opinions must be founded only on doubtful conjectures."[14]

Secrecy was of vital importance, for this grand movement southward was a hazardous enterprise which had been, in a measure, forced upon Washington by Grasse's very definite plans. There was danger of an attack while the army was on the march. Moreover, Heath with half of the Americans, perhaps fewer than 2,500, was being left to hold the Hudson Highlands. Clinton, who had just been reenforced by 2,500 Hessians, had nearly 17,000 men in and about New York.[15] A swift attack on Heath would have ruined that half of the American army and left the British in control of the Hudson; and, in the event of failure of the Virginia expedition, New England would have been hopelessly cut off from the south. Then, whatever happened in the Carolinas and Georgia, the Revolution might have collapsed.

Yet the plan was definitely as wise as it was necessary. Unless some great advantage were achieved by the Americans somewhere, the cause might possibly have died of inanition; and nowhere else than in Virginia was there hope of such advantage. As was the case when Washington hazarded all on the daring attack at Trenton, this was a time when audacity would serve; and again Washington was equal to the occasion, although his hand was in some degree forced by Grasse. After three years of dreary inactivity he was ready and able to seize his opportunity and act with the boldness of high courage and the skill of a great captain.

This essential secrecy had been maintained in the most important quarter. It was not until September 2 that Clinton could say, "By intelligence which I have this day received, it would seem that Mr. Washington is moving an army to the southward, with an appearance of haste and gives out that he expects the co-operation of a considerable French armament." [16] By that time the allied armies, having lingered in the camp near Staten Island but a day or two, had passed through Princeton and Trenton, crossed the Delaware, and, for the most part, had reached Philadelphia, at which point concealment of its ultimate destination was neither useful nor possible.

The American army on this march was not a strong force. It comprised two New Jersey Continental regiments, Colonel Alexander Scammell's Continental light infantry, the Rhode Island Regiment, Hazen's "Canadian Regiment," otherwise called "Congress's Own," two regiments of New York Continentals, certain detachments of light infantry drawn from Connecticut and New York State troops, Colonel John Lamb's artillery regiment, and a small corps of engineers, sappers, and miners—about 2,000 in all.[17] Nor can it be said that it was a contented or even a willing army. "The soldiers being mostly from the eastern and middle States, marched with reluctance to the southward, and showed strong symptoms of discontent when they passed through Philadelphia." [18] They wanted a month's pay in hard money. Washington called on Robert Morris, the American superintendent of finance. Morris's only recourse was to Rochambeau's military chest, from which he borrowed $20,000 in specie to satisfy the men's demand.[19]

Philadelphia, always ready to welcome such visitors, British or American, whichever was at the moment in the ascendant, greeted the American soldiers with universal acclaim, although "the streets being extremely dirty and the weather warm and dry, we raised a dust like a smothering snowstorm." Even more gratifying to the populace was the sight of the French army, which followed the others, "dressed in complete uniforms of white broadcloth, faced with green, and . . . furnished with a complete band of music," a contrast to the Continentals' meager array of drums and fifes. The Congress reviewed these elegant allies, and one of their regiments "went through the exercise of fire-arms" before twenty thousand spectators, who were "surprised and enraptured by the rapidity of military evolutions, the soldierly appearance of the troops . . . and the exactness of their motions." They were particularly pleased by the French runners employed to carry orders from one command to another. Dressed in "his short, tight-bodied coat, his rich waistcoat, with a silver fringe, his rose-colored shoes, his cap adorned with a coat-of-arms and his cane with an enormous head," such a fellow was taken by "the common people" to be no less than a general and admired accordingly.[20]

But there was no delay. The armies pushed on to Head of Elk, where the Americans arrived on the 6th, having covered the two hundred miles from their starting point in fifteen days; the French came up two days later. There had been a period of uncertainty as to Grasse's arrival with the French fleet, no news having come since the admiral's letter from Santo Domingo dated July 8. But at Chester, on September 4, a letter from General Gist gave news of the arrival of the fleet in the Chesapeake. By September 18 the allies were all embarked—their advance in light transports at Head of Elk, the main body in frigates at Baltimore and Annapolis —and headed down the bay for landings on the James near Williamsburg, where, by the 26th, all were put ashore.

Meanwhile Lafayette had disposed his forces to prevent Cornwallis from escaping into North Carolina. He had moved his own division from its camp on the Pamunkey to a position near Williamsburg in Cornwallis's rear, while Wayne's force was posted at Cabin Point on the James.[21]

Grasse with a fleet of 24 ships of the line and six frigates had arrived outside Hampton Roads on August 30. His flagship, the *Ville de Paris,* 110 guns, was the greatest warship afloat on all the seas. The others ranged from 64 to 80 guns, most of them 74's.[22] Admiral de Barras, who had succeeded Destouches in command, had sailed from Newport with eight ships of the line. The British admirals Hood and Graves (the senior), with a combined fleet including nineteen ships of the line and seven frigates, left New York for the Chesapeake with intent to intercept Barras's smaller fleet and prevent its junction with Grasse, or at least to block Grasse's entrance into the bay, not being aware of the greater strength of the French fleet. They arrived too late to defend the bay. Grasse not only had entered it, but on September 5, the day the British fleet arrived off the Chesapeake, had disembarked his 3,000 troops under the Marquis Saint-Simon and added them to Lafayette's force.[23]

The British admirals discovered Grasse's fleet at anchor inside the mouth of the bay, off Cape Henry. At sight of his enemy, Grasse slipped his cables and stood out to meet them. The opposing forces were ill matched. Grasse had twenty-four great ships, carrying 1,700 guns and manned by 19,000 seamen, against the British nineteen sail, 1,400 guns and 13,000 men. The action, which began about four o'clock in the afternoon and lasted more than two hours, was inconclusive. The British had the advantage in their position to windward, but their ships seem to have been handled by Graves rather confusedly and the heavier metal of the French so greatly damaged five of them that, when Grasse hauled off at half past six, Hood and Graves were in no condition to renew the action. They maneuvered off the capes for several days, while Grasse reentered the bay. Barras having succeeded in joining him, the French strength was too great to allow the British any hope in further combat. They sailed back to New York, leaving Cornwallis to his doom,[24] because for one reason and another the British fleet could not be brought back to Chesapeake Bay in force and in time to rescue him.

The Siege of Yorktown

The allied forces that marched from Williamsburg presented an impressive appearance of military strength. The American wing, under Washington's command, was composed of Lamb's 2nd Continental Artillery Regiment, with two companies of the 1st and 5th, 310 in all; Moylan's 4th Dragoons and Armand's horse, 100 men; Lafayette's light infantry, two brigades under General Muhlenberg and General Hazen, chiefly New England and New York troops, but including Hazen's "Canadian Regiment," about 1,500 rank and file; General Lincoln's Continental infantry division, two brigades, the first consisting of the 1st and 2nd New York under General James Clinton, the second of the combined 1st and 2nd New Jersey and the Rhode Island Regiment, under Colonel Elias Dayton, numbering 1,725 in all; Steuben's division of two brigades, the first Wayne's 1st and 2nd Pennsylvania battalions and one from Virginia, a total of 900, the second under General Mordecai Gist comprising the 3rd and 4th Maryland regiments, 1,000 men; General Thomas Nelson's three brigades of Virginia militia, under Generals Weedon, Lawson, and Stevens, 3,000 men; 200 of the Virginia state regiment under Lieutenant Colonel Charles Dabney and, finally, a corps of 110 sappers and miners, making a grand total of 8,845 rank and file.[1]

The French wing, commanded by Lieutenant General de Rochambeau, comprised 600 artillery, 600 of Lauzun's cavalry, the Brigade Bourbonnois consisting of the Regiments Bourbonnois and Royal Deux-Ponts under Colonel de Laval and Colonel de Deux-Ponts, 1,800 men; the Brigade Soissonois, two regiments under Colonel de St. Maime and Colonel de

Castine, 1,800 men; and the Brigade Agenois of three regiments under Colonel d'Audechamp, Colonel de Rostaing, and Colonel de Pondeux, 3,000 men. The French had a grand total of 7,800 rank and file, somewhat fewer than the Americans. They were certainly far better equipped, armed, and disciplined than the 3,000 militia that made up more than a third of the American force.[2]

To defend Yorktown, Cornwallis had 193 of the Royal Artillery; Simcoe's and Tarleton's 440 horse; a brigade of the Guards, 467 rank and file under General O'Hara; Abercrombie's 600 light infantry; Yorke's brigade of infantry, comprising the 17th, 23rd, 33rd, and 71st British regiments, about 900 men; Dundas's brigade, composed of the 43rd, 76th, and 80th British regiments, about 1,500; the two Anspach regiments of Colonel de Voit and de Seybothen, 950 men; the Hessian regiments Prince Hereditaire and von Bose, 700 men; 68 jägers; Lieutenant Colonel John Hamilton's 114 North Carolina Tories; and 33 pioneers. The grand total was about 6,000.[3]

At daybreak on September 28, a fine, clear day, the allied troops set out from Williamsburg in light marching order, with various detachments on parallel course. They encountered no opposition until close to Yorktown, where they came upon Abercrombie's light infantry pickets covering the British right, and Tarleton's Legion on the left. A few cannon shot caused these outposts to withdraw at sunset. The allies then formed a camp that extended from the York River above the town in a great curve through woods and fields to the Wormley Creek below, a line over six miles long interrupted only about its middle where the branches of Beaverdam Creek and the bordering marshes intervened and rendered occupation impossible and unnecessary. The French held the left above the creek, the Americans the right, below it. That night they lay on their arms.[4]

Yorktown was on a bluff on the south side of the York River about eleven miles from its mouth. The river in its main course was about two miles wide; but, opposite the town, the point of land projecting from the opposite side on which was the village of Gloucester narrowed it to about half a mile. In its rear, the town was almost encircled by two deep ravines which nearly met at their heads. For a long time after its founding in 1705 it vied with Williamsburg as the capital city of the province and therefore contained several public buildings besides about sixty dwelling houses.[5]

The fortifications erected by the British army extended in a curve around the town and consisted of seven redoubts and six batteries connected by intrenchments. There was also a line of batteries on the river side, one of which, the Grand Battery, mounted eleven heavy guns commanding the narrows between the town and Gloucester Point. These main fortifications were supported by certain outworks, three small redoubts along the edge of the ravine southwest of the town, two on the east side near the river, another, the Fusiliers' Redoubt, on the extreme northwest, also close to the river, and a battery to the eastward beside the road to Hampton. Gloucester was defended by a line of intrenchments drawn across the Point in the rear of the village. In the river off the town lay two frigates, the *Charon* and the *Guadeloupe,* 44 guns each, and three large transports.[6]

Cornwallis had garrisoned Gloucester with 700 men under Lieutenant Colonel Dundas, and Tarleton's Legion. To immobilize that force Lauzun's Legion, 800 marines from Barras's ships, and Weedon's brigade of 1,500 Virginia militia, all under command of General de Choisy, had been sent to take a position beyond the fortified line.

On the morning of September 30 the allies had a pleasant surprise. During the night Cornwallis had quietly abandoned the outlying redoubts southwest of the town and the battery by the Hampton road, drawing their garrisons into the town, but still holding the Fusiliers' Redoubt and the two close to the river on the east side of the town.

The surrender was thought by the American and French officers to be an unmilitary act, as the outlying positions could have been held for some time, delaying the close investment of the town. Clinton afterwards criticized it. But Cornwallis had a reason. He had received from Clinton, the day before, a dispatch dated September 24 saying, "It is determined that above five thousand men, rank and file, shall be embarked on board the King's ships and the joint exertions of the navy and army made in a few days to relieve you." [7] Expecting this succor, he felt that he could best hold out by concentrating his force within the main works and so notified Clinton.

As all these abandoned works except the battery were enclosed, they were immediately useful against the town and were promptly occupied by the allies. The battery was worked upon that night to turn it into an enclosure; and a new redoubt in line with the others was begun. In the same morning the French light infantry attacked the pickets in front of the Fusiliers' Redoubt and drove them in; but the redoubt was held. The Americans suffered a signal loss that day in the fall of Colonel Alexander Scammell, a brave and much loved officer. He and a small party were reconnoitering the abandoned works, when they met a detachment of Tarleton's Legionaries and were forced to surrender. After they were taken captive, it is said, Scammell was shot in the back by one of Tarleton's troopers and mortally wounded.

The abandoned redoubts were subjected to a heavy fire from the guns in the main fortifications; but the work of transforming the battery and constructing the new redoubt was carried on without interruption and with few casualties.

The first week of October was devoted by the allies to preparations for the advancement of the siege. Twelve hundred Americans were detailed to make thousands of stakes, also fascines, gabions, and saucissons—various forms of wicker basketwork needed for the intended approaches by parallels. Bringing up the heavy siege guns from the landing on the James, six miles distant, was difficult because of lack of horses; but the task was finally accomplished. In the meantime there was some excitement on the Gloucester side of the river.

On October 3 Choisy started to move his force nearer to the British fortification. That morning Dundas with nearly all his men came out of the works on a grand forage. The wagons loaded with corn were on their way back, covered by Simcoe's Rangers and Tarleton's Legion, when Choisy's van, entering one end of a lane, came upon this rear guard leaving the other end. Tarleton turned back to meet them. Lauzun's dragoons charged upon him, and there was a hot little encounter in which Tarleton and Lauzun came near meeting hand to hand. Just before they met, Tarleton's horse was overthrown. The rest of the British horse came up, and in the confusion, Tarleton secured another mount, sounded a retreat, and re-formed his men behind a company of infantry. The French pushed on, and a company of Virginia militia under Lieutenant Colonel John Mercer opened fire on the enemy, checking an attempt by Tarleton to renew the combat. The British retired to their lines with the loss of twelve men and one officer. Choisy established his camp close to the lines and held that position until the end of the siege.

By the evening of October 6 the preparations for the siege were completed; the heavy guns were at hand, and the first parallel was begun at six hundred yards' distance. Because of the ravine in front of the upper end of the town, the approaches were directed against the lower end. Fifteen hundred men were at work with the digging, while twenty-eight hundred guarded them. They worked all night, and the trenches were dug sufficiently deep by morning, with an embankment on the side toward the town, to cover the men from the enemy's fire. During the night the French

Regiment Touraine carried out a diversion against the Fusiliers' Redoubt. The redoubt was defended with "uncommon gallantry," as Cornwallis reported, and the French lost fifteen or twenty men.

The digging was continued without cessation, though under constant fire. To protect the approaches against sorties, four palisaded redoubts and five batteries were erected at intervals along the first parallel. There was considerable illness, the French especially suffering from ague. Similar disorders attacked the British, who were equally busy strengthening their defenses, as many as a thousand of them being reported on the sick list. Steuben, one of the few American officers who had had experience in sieges, was busy with advice as to the best methods of defending the approaches against sorties. Henry Knox, commanding the American artillery, was busily engaged in placing his guns and instructing his artillerists. By the 9th a sufficient number of batteries were in place to begin an effective bombardment of the town. The first to fire was the French battery on the extreme left opposite the Fusiliers' Redoubt. Four 12-pounders and six howitzers and mortars drove the frigate *Guadeloupe* from its station to the Gloucester side. An American battery on the extreme right brought six 18- and 24-pounders, four mortars, and two howitzers to bear on the works at the end, Washington himself firing the first shot.

On the 10th two other batteries opened; the Grand French Battery at the end of the approaches, with ten heavy guns and two mortars, and an American battery of four 18-pounders and two mortars. A red-hot ball fired by the French set the *Charon* on fire and in a vast sheet of flame it burned to the water's edge. Two transports were similarly destroyed. The next day, the first parallel having been extended to two thousand yards' length, the second was opened at three hundred yards from the defenses. Fifty-two guns were now in play, and the fire from the town was nearly silenced. At this time, Cornwallis wrote to Clinton, "We have lost about seventy of our men and many of our works are considerably damaged; with such works on disadvantageous ground, against so powerful an attack we cannot hope to make a very long resistance. P.S. 5 P.M. Since my letter was written (at 12 M.) we have lost thirty men. . . . We continue to lose men very fast." [8]

During the night of the 11th, seven hundred fifty yards of the new parallel were completed, a ditch three and a half feet deep and seven feet wide, a work of "amazing rapidity," in spite of "very heavy fire of the enemy's shot and shell going over our heads in a continual blaze the whole night. The sight was beautifully tremendous," wrote one of the officers in his journal.[9]

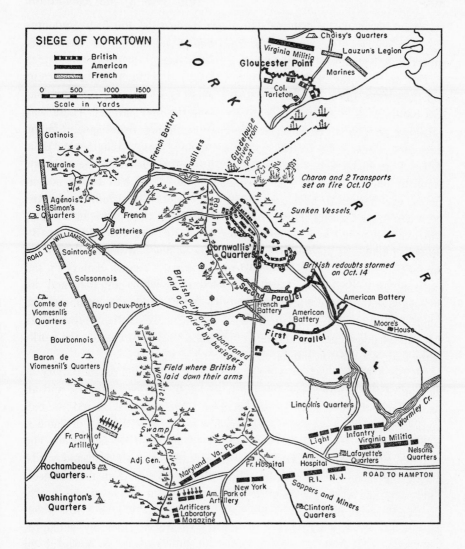

SIEGE OF YORKTOWN

British
American
French

0   500   1000   1500
Scale in Yards

YORK RIVER

Choisy's Quarters
Lauzun's Legion
Virginia Militia
Gloucester Point
Marines
Col. Tarleton

Gatinois
Touraine
Agénois
St. Simon's Quarters
French Battery
Fusiliers
Guadeloupe driven from post
Charon and 2 Transports set on fire Oct.10
Sunken Vessels
French Batteries
Cornwallis' Quarters
British redoubts stormed on Oct.14
ROAD TO WILLIAMSBURG
Saintonge
Soissonnois
Comte de Viomesnil's Quarters
Royal Deux-Ponts
British outworks abandoned and occupied by besiegers
Second Parallel
French Battery
American Battery
American Battery
Moore's House
Bourbonnois
Baron de Viomesnil's Quarters
Field where British laid down their arms
First Parallel
Warwick River
Swamp
Lincoln's Quarters
Wormley Cr.
Fr. Park of Artillery
Adj Gen.
Maryland Va. Pa.
Fr. Hospital
Light Infantry
Virginia Militia
Lafayette's Quarters
Nelson's Quarters
Rochambeau's Quarters
Am. Hospital
R.I. N.J.
ROAD TO HAMPTON
Washington's Quarters
Am. Park of Artillery
New York
Sappers and Miners
Artificers
Laboratory
Magazine
Clinton's Quarters

So far the fight had been carried on by the artillery alone; but now the infantry had its part. The two British redoubts close to the river on the east side of the town prevented the carrying of the second parallel to the river's edge, and so they had to be taken. On the night of the 14th the task was given to two corps—the American light infantry to attack the redoubt on the right by the river bank, the French chasseurs and grenadiers the one on the left, about a quarter of a mile from it. The Gatinois and Royal Deux-Ponts regiments furnished 400 men under Colonel de Deux-Ponts. The American force was made up of men drawn from Lieutenant Colonel de Gimat's battalion of Connecticut, Massachusetts, and Rhode Island troops, Lieutenant Colonel Alexander Hamilton's New York and Connecticut men, and Lieutenant Colonel John Laurens's from New Hampshire, Massachusetts, and Connecticut men, 400 in all, with an added corps of sappers and miners, Hamilton in general command. Substantial reserves were provided for both detachments.

At eight o'clock the French advanced in columns by platoons, 58 chasseurs, carrying scaling ladders and fascines to fill the ditches in the van. Three or four hundred feet from their objective, they were challenged by a Hessian sentinel with, *"Wer da?"*—Who goes there? No reply was made, and the enemy opened fire. A strong abatis had to be forced, and a number of men fell before the pioneers cut through it. Then the chasseurs dashed upon the redoubt and began mounting the parapet under a heavy fire from the garrison of 120 British and Hessians under Lieutenant McPherson. A charge by the defenders was met by a volley from the French and a countercharge. The Hessians threw down their arms, the French shouting *"Vive le Roi!"* The fort was won in less than half an hour of fighting. The attackers lost 15 killed and 77 wounded; the enemy, 18 killed and 50 sound or wounded men taken prisoners.

The American attack on the other redoubt was begun at the same time. This work, the smaller of the two, was held by 70 men under Major Campbell. The Americans advanced with unloaded muskets and fixed bayonets. Led by a forlorn hope of 20 men of the 4th Connecticut under Lieutenant John Mansfield, they crashed through the abatis without waiting for the sappers to cut it away, crossed the ditch, and swarmed over the parapets in spite of the bayonets of the garrison. In ten minutes they overcame all resistance, with a loss of 9 killed and 31 wounded, including Gimat and several other officers.

Immediately upon the taking of the two redoubts fatigue parties set to work extending the second parallel. By morning they had pushed it on to include the captured works. The next day Cornwallis wrote to Clinton:

"My situation now becomes very critical; we dare not show a gun to their old batteries, and I expect that their new ones will open to-morrow morning. . . . The safety of the place is, therefore, so precarious that I cannot recommend that the fleet and army should run great risque in endeavouring to save us." [10]

Cornwallis was facing the inevitable end, but was not yet ready to give up. He organized a sortie to cripple the two new batteries in the second parallel, "against the fire of which, it was foreseen that the British works on the left, already half ruined, could not stand many hours." [11] Lieutenant Colonel Abercrombie was to lead 350 men in two parties: one made up of men from the Guards with a company of grenadiers commanded by Lieutenant Colonel Lake of the Guards; the other, of light infantry under Major Armstrong. Just before daybreak of the 16th, they gallantly dashed upon the batteries, drove off the French guards in one of them, and spiked four guns by driving bayonet points into their touchholes and breaking them off. The other battery, held by Americans, was also forced, and its three guns similarly disabled. But the Comte de Noailles brought up his grenadiers and attacked the intruders, killing 8 and taking 12 prisoners, with a loss of 20 of the French. The rest of the British retreated to their works. It was a brave effort, but it was without any good result. Even the disabled guns were in service again within a few hours.

Still Cornwallis would not give up. There was a bare possibility of saving his army by a retreat, such as Washington had so successfully made after the Battle of Long Island. If he could get his men across the river to Gloucester, pick up the part of his army there, and overcome Choisy's small force holding that position, he might proceed by forced marches through Maryland, Pennsylvania, and New Jersey, where there were no substantial organized American forces to oppose him, and reach Clinton in New York. The Americans and French on the south side of the river would be put to it to cross in time to overtake him. He counted on taking the 600 horses of Lauzun's Legion in Choisy's command and picking up others on the way to mount as many as possible of his infantry. Traveling without baggage, his progress would be swift. "Undoubtedly," says Stedman, "the attempt was beyond calculation hazardous, and the issue totally precarious; but, if it afforded even a glimpse of hope, it was preferable to an immediate surrender."

Before midnight of the 16th Cornwallis embarked the greater part of the Guards, the light infantry, and part of the 23rd Regiment in small boats and landed them on the Gloucester side. But a violent storm arose and not only prevented a return of the boats, but also drove them a long way down the river. That ended all chance of escape. The boats did return the next day and brought back the troops that had been carried across, but that availed nothing.

In the morning the allies opened on the doomed town with all their guns. "By the force of the enemy's cannonade," says Stedman, "the British works were tumbling into ruin; not a gun could be fired from them." Anyhow, their ammunition was exhausted. So, in the morning of the 17th a red-coated drummer mounted the parapet and began to beat a parley. No one could hear him in the din of the cannonading; but he was seen, and his message was understood. The fire of the American guns ceased. An officer bearing a white handkerchief advanced from the town. He was blindfolded and led to the rear of the allies. Being presented to Washington, he asked for a twenty-four-hour armistice and the appointment of commissioners to discuss terms of surrender. Washington allowed two hours within which to receive proposals in writing. Within that time Cornwallis submitted his terms, which included a condition that his troops be returned to England on parole not to serve against France or America during the war or until exchanged. Washington refused and demanded a complete surrender of the enemy as prisoners of war. To this Cornwallis perforce agreed.

On the 18th commissioners from both sides met and drew up the articles, which were signed the next day. At two in the afternoon, the garrison marched out, spick-and-span in new uniforms, their colors cased and their bands playing an old British march entitled "The World Turned Upside Down." The allies were paraded in two lines. The French, resplendent in their white broadcloth uniforms, "displayed a martial and noble appearance. . . . The Americans, though not all in uniform, nor their dress so neat, yet exhibited an erect, soldierly air and every countenance beamed satisfaction." [12]

Between these lines the defeated army passed. Cornwallis did not march. Excusing himself on account of illness, he left the command to General O'Hara, who tendered Cornwallis's sword to the American general. Washington referred him to General Lincoln who accepted the token of surrender and immediately returned it to O'Hara.

In a field behind the approaches a squadron of French hussars formed a circle into which the British and Hessian regiments successively marched, piling their arms. The defeated troops at Gloucester were surrendered to Choisy by Tarleton, who had succeeded in Dundas in command. Tarleton, having in mind his evil reputation, had told Choisy that he feared for his life if he were left to the mercies of the American militia. Choisy therefore had only Lauzun's Legion and Mercer's Virginians drawn up for the ceremony, keeping the rest in the camp. No violence was offered to Tarleton.

The main body of prisoners was marched off to prison camps in Virginia and Maryland, under guard of militia. Cornwallis and his principal officers were paroled and allowed to go to New York, after being dined for several days at the tables of Washington, Rochambeau, and other American and French officers.

The prisoners taken by the allies numbered 7,247 of all ranks and 840 seamen. Eighteen German regimental standards and six British were captured, as well as 244 pieces of artillery, thousands of small arms, and considerable quantities of military stores and equipment. The casualties on both sides during the siege were comparatively light, the Americans losing 20 killed and 56 wounded, the French 52 killed and 134 wounded, the British 156 killed and 326 wounded.

Although Cornwallis's position had been hopeless from the first, the outcome of the siege was a near thing after all, for by October 5 Clinton had actually assembled 7,000 troops in New York to go to his aid. The fleet, twenty-five ships of the line, two of 50 guns, and eight frigates, did not sail until October 19, the day of the surrender. It arrived off the Chesapeake capes on the 24th. Its arrival a week sooner might have saved the British army.

News of the event was carried to the Congress by Lieutenant Colonel Tench Tilghman. Riding posthaste, he reached Philadelphia at three o'clock in the morning of the 22nd and delivered the glad tidings to President Thomas McKean. A watchman who conducted Tilghman to McKean's house then began to cry through the streets, "Past three o'clock and Cornwallis is taken!" On receipt of Washington's official dispatches two days later the Congress went in procession to the Lutheran church for services of thanksgiving. As it spread throughout the country, the news was hailed with rejoicing and celebrations, in the well grounded belief that the war was about over.

It was received in England on November 25. Lord George Germain communicated it to Lord North, who received it "as he would have taken a ball in his breast," crying out wildly as he paced to and fro, "Oh God! It is all over!" which he "repeated many times, under emotions of the deepest agitation and distress." [13] The King was also shocked, but he soon after expressed himself as determined to carry on the war "though the mode of it may require alterations." [14] But opinion in Parliament did not uphold this view, and early in 1782 the Commons voted to authorize the King to make peace with America, declaring on March 4 that it "would consider as enemies to his Majesty and the Country all those who should advise or by any means attempt the further prosecution of offensive war on the Continent of North America, for the purpose of reducing the revolted Colonies to obedience by force."

Commissioners were appointed by both sides. On November 30, 1782, they signed provisional articles, but not until September 3, 1783, was the definitive treaty acknowledging the independence of the United States of America formally signed.

Notes

CHAPTER 38

There is a dearth of original material for an account of the Siege of Fort Stanwix and the Battle of Oriskany. The chief sources are Marinus Willett's report to Governor Trumbull, his *Narrative,* published in 1831, and St. Leger's report to Burgoyne, both appearing in Dawson, I, 250–252. For detailed secondary accounts recourse may be had to Nickerson, Lossing, and Dawson, among others. Stone's *The Campaign of Lieut. Gen. John Burgoyne and the Expedition of Lieut. Col. Barry St. Leger* contains the fullest story and perhaps the best. These are the principal sources of the narrative.

1. Stone, *B,* I, 37.
2. The uniforms of the Rangers consisted of green coats and waistcoats, faced and lined with scarlet, and either buckskin Indian leggings reaching from the ankle to the waist, or leather overalls. They wore skullcaps of black leather, with a brass plate in front marked "G R" and "Butler's Rangers." Buff leather cross-belts were similarly marked on a brass plate at their intersection.
3. Dawson, I, 237. The fort, renamed Schuyler at the beginning of the Revolution, is often referred to by that name. It is better known by its original name, which is retained in this narrative.
4. Neilson, 18, says 2,000 axmen, certainly a great exaggeration.
5. Nickerson, 197.
6. Nickerson, 203, says the wagon train comprised "four hundred heavy ox-carts." The source of this information is not given. That there were anywhere near so many is incredible. Burgoyne's train, to transport the heavy baggage of 7,500 men on a long journey, was drawn by 500 horses and 50 ox teams. Certainly, 800 shirt-sleeved farmers on a two-day march would require no such preposterous procession as 400 carts. Nickerson, 204, estimates the full length of Herkimer's column, including the oxcarts, at three-quarters of a mile to a mile. With twenty feet for each cart in the train, which would be a nose-to-tailboard crowding, 400 carts alone would extend a mile and a half. Spaced out to give practicable room and allow for the marching men in a close-up formation, the column would have extended at least three miles.
7. It has been claimed that at Stanwix was first displayed in battle the Stars and Stripes. It appears to be quite certain that the homemade flag hoisted on its

ramparts showed thirteen stripes, alternately red and white, but that in its canton
or field (the upper inside corner), it bore the cross of St. George superimposed
on the cross of St. Andrew, instead of the stars of the United States flag
adopted by the Congress in June, 1777. Indeed, it satisfactorily appears that the
Stars and Stripes flag so adopted was not intended for the American army, but
only for ships. Thruston is probably the best authority on the flag. See also
Quaife, 62, on the flag at Fort Stanwix.

8. The conference between St. Leger's and Gansevoort's officers is fully reported in
   Willett's *Narrative,* 55–58.
9. Arnold, 153–154.

CHAPTER 39

1. Fitzpatrick, VII, 352.
2. Stedman, I, 279; Gordon, II, 466; Dawson, I, 212–217.
3. *Journals,* VII, 323, 379.
4. Arnold, 133–138.
5. Fitzpatrick, VIII, 377.
6. Hudleston, 165.
7. Nickerson, 183.
8. Lossing, I, 99 n.
9. Hudleston, 166.
10. Neilson, 78.
11. Van Tyne, 403.
12. Wilkinson, I, 231.
13. Hudleston, 163–164.
14. Fiske, I, 290.
15. Fisher, II, 86.
16. Fitzpatrick, VIII, 430.
17. Trevelyan, III, 148–150.
18. Fiske, I, 290. There is another version of the story of Jane McCrea; namely, that
    she was killed, not by an Indian, but accidentally by a bullet from the musket of
    a member of a party of Americans pursuing her captors. It appears that Mrs.
    McNeil told this to her granddaughter from whom Benson Lossing (I, 97–99)
    got it in 1848. The question has been elaborately discussed, e.g., by Nickerson,
    470–472; but historically it is of little importance whether she was killed in one
    way or the other, of as little importance as it was to the girl herself. The only
    significance to be attached to her death arises out of the effect the story had
    upon the minds of her countrymen in exciting them to join the army. The story
    they heard is the real thing. That the Wyandot Panther shot and scalped Jane
    McCrea is just as certain as that Hamlet stabbed Polonius.
19. *Journals,* VIII, 375.
20. *Journals,* VIII, 604, and IX, 787.
21. *Journals,* II, 97.
22. Patterson, *passim.*
23. Wilkinson, I, 229.
24. Nickerson, 286–288. Stark's conduct at this time seems to have been motivated
    by that spirit of localism, of jealousy between the various colonies that, for so
    long, made them unwilling to cooperate as an united nation. New Hampshire and
    New York had fought over their conflicting claims of jurisdiction over the ter-
    ritory that became Vermont. There was bad blood between them. Stark, with his
    New Hampshire brigade, had defended Vermont at Bennington without help
    from New York. Now he let New York defend itself at Saratoga without calling
    on New Hampshire. That seems to be the explanation of his misbehavior.
25. Hadden, 119.
26. Fonblanque, 274.
27. Fonblanque, 275–276.
28. Wilkinson, I, 233.

29. Lossing, I, 45; Wilkinson, I, 234–238. This description is also derived from maps in Greene, FV, Arnold, Trevelyan, Nickerson, and others.
30. Patterson, 153.

CHAPTER 40

The original authorities for this battle are rather copious. Eelking's *Memoirs of Major General Riedesel*, Lamb's *Memoirs*, Pausch's *Journal*, Hadden's *Journal*, Anburey's *Travels*, and Burgoyne's *State of the Expedition*, present first-hand accounts by participants on the British side. On the American side are Wilkinson's *Memoirs*, interesting, but not very reliable. The secondary sources chiefly studied for this narrative include Lossing's *Pictorial Field Book*, Dawson's well documented *Battles*, Neilson's *Original Account of Burgoyne's Campaign*, Arnold's *Life of Benedict Arnold*, Stone's *Campaign of Lieut. Gen. John Burgoyne*, Fortescue's *History of the British Army*, Nickerson's *Turning Point of the Revolution*, Hudleston's *Gentleman Johnny Burgoyne*, Patterson's *Horatio Gates*, Lowell's *Hessians in the Revolutionary War*, and Irving's *Life of George Washington*.

1. Dawson, I, 305.
2. Dawson, I, 285; Anburey, I, 240–241; Wilkinson, I, 234.
3. Anburey, I, 242.
4. Lamb, 158; Hadden, 155–160; Trevelyan, III, 157; Dawson, I, 285–286; Burgoyne, 69; Anburey, I, 242.
5. Arnold, 170.
6. Riedesel, I, 145.
7. Riedesel, I, 145; Pausch, 133–134; Dawson, I, 305; Wilkinson, I, 435.
8. Dawson, I, 305; Burgoyne, 69.
9. Hale was not present, having been captured at Hubbardton.
10. Lossing, I, 51.
11. Trevelyan, III, 162.
12. Lossing, I, 51; Arnold, 170–171; Trevelyan, III, 162.
13. Nickerson, 307–308; Lossing, I, 51.
14. Arnold, 179.
15. Anburey, I, 242; Lamb, 159.
16. Wilkinson, I, 237.
17. Lamb, 159.
18. Wilkinson, I, 236.
19. Lamb, 159; Burgoyne, Appendix, lxxxvi.
20. Dawson, I, 288; Wilkinson, I, 239.
21. Anburey, I, 243. Fraser's inactivity throughout the battle is hard to understand. He had almost twice as many men as were in the center. He was nearer than Riedesel to the center, with less difficult ground separating him from it. Yet he sent no aid, except this once and then only temporarily. His immobility is not explainable except on the theory that his position on the right was too valuable to be hazarded. But Riedesel hazarded a more important element of the situation, the baggage provisions and supplies, when he went to aid the center.
22. Anburey, I, 245.
23. Trevelyan, III, 165.
24. Hadden, 165.
25. Lamb, 160.
26. Riedesel, I, 149.
27. Hadden, 166.
28. Lamb, 161, says that Burgoyne "behaved with great personal bravery; he shunned no danger; his presence and conduct animated the troops; he delivered his orders with precision and coolness."
29. Lossing, I, 52.
30. Riedesel, I, 149; Lamb, 160.
31. Pausch, 137–138.

32. Fortescue, III, 235–236; Stedman, I, 337; Hadden, 165; Dawson, I, 289; Burgoyne, 104.
33. Dawson, I, 289.
34. The judgments rendered here upon Arnold and Gates may seem too favorable to the former and too harsh toward the latter. Channing, III, 276–277, contends that on the evidence available to him Gates and Morgan deserve credit for the American success, such as it was, in this struggle; and that Arnold's share in the battle has probably been greatly overemphasized. Patterson, 153–155, takes much the same view.

CHAPTER 41

The principal original sources of information concerning Sir Henry Clinton's enterprise against the two forts are the dispatches of General George Clinton and General Putnam to Washington, and the dispatches of Sir Henry Clinton and Commodore Hotham to Howe. These are reprinted in Dawson, I, 341–346. Secondary accounts of value are to be found in Dawson, Carrington, Leake, Stedman, Gordon, and Irving. Nickerson presents an especially detailed account. It has not been thought desirable to make specific references as to particular events, except where direct quotations occur. Stedman and Irving afford excellent maps.

1. Nickerson, 339–346.
2. Fonblanque, 280 n.
3. Nickerson, 320.
4. Anderson, T, 254, 258, 265–266.
5. Wilkin, 72.
6. Stedman, I, 358.
7. Leake, 173.
8. Nickerson, 341.
9. Marshall, I, 245.
10. Dawson, I, 346.
11. Stedman, I, 364.
12. Putnam's failure to offer any resistance to the enemy outraged the feelings of the people of the vicinity.

CHAPTER 42

1. Riedesel, I, 152.
2. See maps in Greene, FV, Walworth, Fonblanque, and Burgoyne.
3. Riedesel, I, 155.
4. Irving, III, 234–235; Wilkinson, I, 253–260; Arnold, 191.
5. Arnold, 194.
6. Arnold, 178.
7. Gordon, III, 546; Nickerson, 323–326.
8. Burgoyne, Appendix, lxxxviii.
9. Burgoyne, 166.
10. Riedesel, I, 159–162.
11. Riedesel, I, 161–163.
12. Riedesel, I, 162.
13. Riedesel, I, 162.
14. Anburey, I, 257.
15. Dawson, I, 292.
16. Trevelyan, III, 177.
17. Dawson, I, 292.
18. Riedesel, I, 163; Burgoyne, Appendix, xc.
19. Anburey, I, 261; Wilkinson, I, 267.
20. Wilkinson, I, 268.
21. Arnold, 204.
22. Arnold, 200.
23. Fortescue, III, 240.

24. Trevelyan, III, 164–165.
25. Stone, W, 66.
26. Trevelyan, III, 163–164. Arnold's enemies said afterwards, accounting for his recklessness, that he was drunk that day. No liquor was needed to intoxicate Arnold while a battle was on. The smell of gunpowder smoke was quite enough. If he was in liquor, Gates might well have asked the question Abraham Lincoln is said to have put when U. S. Grant was accused of drunkenness: "What kind of whisky does he drink? I'd like to get some for my other generals."
27. Wilkinson, Gates's aide, who tells many stories hardly believable, tells a pretty one about his chief. Sir Francis Clarke, Burgoyne's aide-de-camp, having been wounded and captured, was carried to Gates's headquarters and laid upon a bed. Gates engaged in an effort to convince him, by argument, of the merits of the American cause. Clarke, suffering the agonies of a mortal wound, declined to agree. Gates lost his temper and left the room, calling to Wilkinson to come with him. As they went out, Gates testily asked him, "Did you ever hear so impudent a son of a bitch?" Clarke died that night. It should be recalled that Wilkinson became a bitter enemy of Gates, and that his memoirs are not to be trusted.
28. Fortescue, III, 410.

CHAPTER 43

1. Riedesel, I, 166; Burgoyne, 43; Wilkinson, I, 279.
2. Burgoyne, Appendix, xci; Lamb, 165.
3. Burgoyne, 107.
4. Nickerson, 370; Wilkinson, I, 280.
5. Lamb, 165; Anburey, I, 268.
6. Wilkinson, I, 282; Anburey, I, 269. Riedesel, I, 167, says 800 were left in the hospitals.
7. Riedesel, I, 170.
8. Anburey, I, 268; Burgoyne, 73, Appendix, xci.
9. Riedesel, I, 171.
10. Wilkinson, I, 284.
11. Wilkinson, I, 285–289.
12. Wilkinson, I, 287.
13. Riedesel, I, 173.
14. Riedesel, I, 175–178.
15. Riedesel, I, 178.
16. Riedesel, I, 179.
17. Lamb, 166.
18. Riedesel, I, 174.
19. Burgoyne, Appendix, xciii.
20. Riedesel, I, 179–180.
21. Riedesel, I, 181.
22. Burgoyne, Appendix, ciii.
23. Stedman, I, 346–347.
24. Stedman, I, 347; Fonblanque, 307.
25. Stedman, I, 349–350.
26. Riedesel, I, 183.
27. Nickerson, 399.
28. Anburey, II, 2.
29. Pettengill, 110.
30. Dawson, I, 299–300.
31. Fortescue, III, 245–247.
32. Gordon, III, 45.
33. *Journals*, IX, 950.
34. Riedesel, I, 218; Lamb, 191.
35. Heath, 134.
36. Jones, I, 212.

37. Gordon, III, 48.
38. *Journals*, X, 29–34.
39. *Journals*, X, 35.
40. Riedesel, I, 227.
41. Jones, I, 210–214.

CHAPTER 44

1. Gordon, III, 10.
2. Gordon, III, 11–12.
3. Fitzpatrick, X, 195.
4. Gordon, III, 13–14.
5. Lafayette, 35.
6. Waldo, 307.
7. Sparks, *W*, V, 193 n.
8. Fitzpatrick, X, 193.
9. H. E. Wildes, *Valley Forge* (New York, 1938), 179.
10. Duncan, 219–227.
11. Greene, GW, I, 557, 561; Baurmeister, 58; Trevelyan, III, 321.
12. Lee, 18.
13. Hughes, III.
14. Watson, II, 322; Fitzpatrick, VII, 327 n., and X, 97, 117, 118.
15. The principal contemporary sources of material for the narrative of the Quintin's Bridge affair are Simcoe and Stedman. Dawson, I, 379–382, presents a full account, well documented.
16. Simcoe again furnishes a first-hand account of this affair, and Stedman is to be relied upon. Dawson's account, as usual, is full and is well supported by citations.
17. Greene, GW, I, 552.
18. Greene, GW, I, 553–554.
19. Hughes, III, 265–266.
20. Fitzpatrick, XI, 469.
21. Lafayette, 35.
22. Wildes, *op. cit.*, 174–175.
23. Trevelyan, III, 324.
24. Stedman, I, 308, 310.
25. Van Tyne, *L*, 157.
26. Palmer, 31; Fiske, II, 48 (portrait).
27. Palmer, 3–4, 9, 13, 14.
28. Palmer, 124.
29. *Journals*, X, 50.
30. Tower, I, 322.
31. Palmer, 137.
32. Palmer, 140.
33. Palmer, 141.
34. Palmer, 142, 144.
35. Palmer, 145.
36. Palmer, 146.
37. Palmer, 147–148.
38. Palmer, 152.
39. Palmer, 156.
40. Palmer, 156.
41. Fitzpatrick, XI, 233.
42. Palmer, 157.
43. Palmer, 160.
44. Palmer, 164.
45. Fitzpatrick, XI, 360–363.
46. *Journals*, XI, 465.
47. Dawson, I, 388.

CHAPTER 45

There is an excellent brief account of the Barren Hill affair in Gottschalk's *Lafayette Joins the American Army,* 185–193. Gottschalk's biography of Lafayette largely supersedes Tower's work. Nolan's *Lafayette in America Day by Day* is also useful.

1. *Journals*, X, 84.
2. Lafayette, 4, 6.
3. Trevelyan, III, 219–220.
4. Tower, I, 34.
5. Lafayette, 9.
6. Trevelyan, III, 219–220.
7. Lafayette, 14–15. Lafayette was doubtless correct in his assumption that his government did not wish to stop him, but merely to pretend so.
8. Tower, I, 180.
9. Lafayette, 17.
10. Tower, I, 183.
11. Tower, I, 186.
12. *Journals*, VIII, 721–722, 743–744.
13. Tower, I, 188–189.
14. Lafayette, 8.
15. Lafayette, 105.
16. Lafayette, 19.
17. Knollenberg, *passim.*
18. *Journals*, X, 87.
19. Lafayette, 35, 137. Knollenberg, Chap. 8, "Conway and Lafayette."
20. Burnett, 292–293.
21. Tower, I, 272–274.
22. Tower, I, 283–285.
23. Lafayette, 159.
24. *Journals*, X, 217, 253–254.
25. Stedman, I, 379.
26. Fitzpatrick, XI, 418–419.
27. Fitzpatrick, IX, 480.
28. Pontgibaud, 74.
29. Greene, FV, 146, map.
30. Tower, I, 329; Marshall, I, 288; Irving, III, 405–406.
31. Tower, I, 331.
32. Tower, I, 331–332.
33. Lafayette, 47.
34. Marshall, I, 289.
35. Tower, I, 334.
36. Tower, I, 335; Marshall, I, 288–291; Stedman, I, 376–379.
37. Lafayette, 78.
38. Tower, I, 336.
39. Marshall, I, 289 n.
40. Trevelyan, III, 284, 366–367.
41. Serle, 295. For the best account of Galloway's career, see Boyd, *Anglo-American Union.*
42. Trevelyan, III, 358–361; Irving, III, 409–410; Gordon, III, 129; Bancroft, V, 247–248.
43. Trevelyan, III, 365; Irving, III, 413; Van Doren, 95.

CHAPTER 46

1. Fitzpatrick, XI, 435.
2. Fitzpatrick, XI, 445, 448. On British strategy, 1778, see Willcox, S.
3. Fitzpatrick, XI, 465, 471, 483.

4. The map Washington used, which bears many notes in his handwriting, is preserved among the Washington Papers in the Library of Congress. A reproduction appears as Plate 14 in *The George Washington Atlas* (Washington, 1932), edited by Lawrence Martin and issued by the George Washington Bicentennial Commission.

5. There are at least four contemporary accounts of this beginning of the evacuation, all written by men in the British army who were on the ground, and no two of them agree as to the make-up of this first contingent. André, who was adjutant general of the army and should have known, says (p. 74) it comprised the 5th Brigade, the 46th and 55th regiments, Simcoe's Rangers, and Stirn's Hessians. Montresor, who was the army's chief engineer, says (p. 499) the 16th and 17th dragoons, the Hessians, and the Hessian grenadiers went across that day. Lieut. Gen. Archibald Robertson says (p. 173) it was the 5th Brigade and all the Hessians. Maj. Baurmeister says (p. 87) the 16th and 17th dragoons and the artillery. He puts Stirn's and Loos's Hessians over on the 15th, the Hessian grenadiers, Simcoe's corps, and the jägers over on the 17th. It is a matter of the least possible importance, except as showing how little confidence can be placed upon the details in even the apparently most reliable contemporary statements. We really know nothing more than that all those brigades and regiments got across at about that time, which is enough.

6. Frothingham, 251. Fortescue, III, 265, says there were but 15,000 on the march. Possibly some thousands went in the ships.

7. Montresor, 499.

8. André, 74.

9. Marshall, I, 292; Stryker, *M*, 58. Baurmeister, 67, describes this exploit, not naming McLane, of course, and calls the party "one enemy patrol."

10. Stryker, *M*, 64.

11. Stryker, *M*, 58; Fitzpatrick, XII, 82–83.

12. Fitzpatrick, XII, 107.

13. Stryker, *M*, 38, 42.

14. Fitzpatrick, XII, 110; André, 77; *Atlas*, pl. 38.

15. Dawson, I, 396; Stephenson, II, 74; Fitzpatrick, XII, 38, 75 n.

16. Fitzpatrick, XII, 113, 116; Marshall, I, 294.

17. Belcher, I, 324.

18. Greene, FV, 142; Lowell, 142; Irving, III, 420; Fisher, II, 179.

19. André, 77–78; Dawson, I, 415–416; Greene, FV, 143.

20. Lowell, 213.

21. Stephenson, II, 79; Marshall, I, 296; André, 78.

22. Stryker, *M*, 80.

23. Marshall, I, 294; Hughes, III, 348; Irving, III, 422; Stryker, *M*, 80.

24. Quoted in Stryker, *M*, 102.

25. Stryker, *M*, 100–101; Marshall, I, 295.

26. Stryker, *M*, 115–116.

27. Stryker, *M*, 95–98.

CHAPTER 47

This account of the Battle of Monmouth is based chiefly on William S. Stryker's book *The Battle of Monmouth* (edited by William S. Myers), an exhaustive monograph. No attempt is made to describe all the details, the unmeaning marches and countermarches of the various brigades and regiments in the first part of the battle, the shifting here and there of this or that contingent. An attempt is made to present the essential features of the conflict, avoiding unnecessary and confusing detail. Other authorities examined include the contemporary accounts in André, 74–81; Robertson, 177; Stedman; Fitzpatrick, XII, 74–130; Lafayette, 50–53; also the extended studies in Carrington, 412–415, and Dawson, I, 394–417, including Clinton's report; also such descriptions as are given in Greene, FV, 142–148; Hughes, III, 357–381; Tower, I,

347–393; Irving, III, 420–443; Marshall, I, 292–300; Duer, 195–197; Lossing, II, 148–158; and Gottschalk, *Lafayette Joins the American Army*, 204–233.

1. Tower, I, 366.
2. Quoted in Stryker, *M*, 185.
3. Stryker, *M*, 209.
4. Stryker, *M*, 212.
5. Stryker, *M*, 293–294.
6. *Journals*, XVI, 33.

CHAPTER 48

There is ample available documentation of the enterprise against Rhode Island. The diary of Lieutenant Frederick Mackenzie of the Royal Welch Fusiliers tells the story from the British side in the most remarkable detail. On the same side, other contemporary accounts are to be found in Stedman and in Pigot's dispatch to Clinton, quoted in Dawson, I, 442–444. On the American side, the contemporary accounts are in Gordon, Marshall, Fitzpatrick, and in the letters of Sullivan and other American and French officers in Volume II of the *Letters and Papers of Major-General John Sullivan*.

1. Fitzpatrick, XII, 131.
2. Fitzpatrick, XII, 146, 147, 165, 182. On the march from Englishtown many of the men, exhausted by the heat, had to be carried in the wagons (Bolton, 204).
3. Fitzpatrick, XII, 182.
4. Greene, FV, 149.
5. Fitzpatrick, XII, 208; Sparks, *C*, II, 160, 171; Sparks, *W*, VI, 12 n.
6. Fitzpatrick, XII, 184.
7. Fitzpatrick, XII, 195, 202, 204.
8. Marshall, I, 306; Dawson, I, 433.
9. Stedman, II, 28; Dawson, I, 433.
10. James, 102; Mackenzie, II, 330, 340.
11. Gordon, III, 158–159.
12. Marshall, I, 307.
13. Mackenzie, II, 332.
14. Mackenzie, II, 344.
15. Stedman, I, 29.
16. Stedman, II, 29; Mackenzie, II, 332. Mackenzie, II, 341, says there were thirty-five vessels in the British fleet. Mackenzie, II, 342, says there were in the French fleet twelve ships of the line and four frigates. The French fleet was actually the stronger because it was more powerful in ships of the line. Mahan, 71.
17. Mackenzie, II, 342.
18. Mackenzie, II, 346.
19. Mackenzie, II, 345.
20. James, 104; Stedman, II, 30.
21. James, 106.
22. Gordon, III, 161–164; Dawson, I, 435.
23. Dawson, I, 443.
24. Mackenzie, II, 357–360.
25. Marshall, I, 309–310; Gordon, III, 161–164.
26. Amory, 85.
27. Mackenzie, II, 381; Dawson, I, 437.
28. Gordon, III, 166.
29. Mackenzie, II, 383.
30. Gordon, III, 167; Sullivan, II, 283.
31. Amory, 82.
32. Amory, 96.
33. Greene, FV, 154.

34. Mackenzie, II, 389.
35. Gordon, III, 169; Marshall, I, 315–316.
36. Marshall, I, 313.
37. Fitzpatrick, XII, 385.
38. Marshall, I, 315.
39. *Journals*, XII, 1021.
40. Fitzpatrick, XII, 343.
41. Sparks, *W*, V, 548.
42. Hughes, III, 410.
43. Fitzpatrick, XIII, 230.
44. Fitzpatrick, XII, 409.
45. Fitzpatrick, XII, 460.
46. Fitzpatrick, XIII, 53, 78, 82, 173, and XIV, 184.
47. Greene, FV, 155–156.
48. Thacher, 158, 161.
49. Fitzpatrick, XIII, 352, 489, 466.
50. Fitzpatrick, XIII, 437.

CHAPTER 49

The fullest account of the taking of Stony Point is to be found in Henry P. Johnston's *The Storming of Stony Point,* a completely documented monograph. Where not otherwise specifically noted, reference is made to that work. The official reports of Wayne and Clinton are printed in Dawson, I, 524–527. Other contemporary accounts are in Stedman, Gordon, *The Literary Diary of Ezra Stiles,* II, 364, and the "authorities" reprinted in Johnston's book.

1. Kemble, I, 179; Robertson, 193–194; Fitzpatrick, XV, 223, 234–235.
2. Fitzpatrick, XV, 176, 195, 202, 210, 213, 221, 225.
3. Stedman, II, 141; Robertson, 194.
4. Thacher, 164.
5. Irving, III, 497; Fitzpatrick, XV, 243; Johnston, *S,* 41.
6. Irving, III, 502; Johnston, *S,* 83–84; Marshall, I, 363; Greene, FV, 158, map.
7. Johnston, *S,* 64.
8. Fitzpatrick, XV, 260, 261, 280, 292, 313.
9. Fitzpatrick, XV, 339.
10. Fitzpatrick, XV, 297, 345; *Journals,* XIV, 823.
11. Garden, III, 74.
12. Johnston, *S,* 62–63.
13. Johnston, *S,* 69–71.
14. Irving, III, 504.
15. Johnston, *S,* 158–160.
16. Johnston, *S,* 124.
17. Johnston, *S,* 91, 101.
18. *Journals,* XIV, 886, 891. Captain Archer, who carried the news of the victory to the Congress, rode at speed, 46 miles one day, 63 miles the next. "I came into the City with colors flying," he wrote to Wayne, "trumpets sounding and heart elated, drew crowds to the doors and windows and made not a little parade, I assure you. These were Baron Steuben's instructions and I pursued them literally, although I could not help thinking it had a little the appearance of a puppet-show." (Reed, II, 115.)
19. Stedman, II, 145.
20. Johnston, *S,* 131, 135.

CHAPTER 50

Contemporary sources of material for Paulus Hook comprise Lee's report to Washington, a British account in Gaine's New York *Gazette and Weekly Mercury,* both in Dawson, I, 549–553; letters by sundry participants in Reed, II, 125–127; Stedman, II,

153; Gordon, III, 283–284; Marshall, I, 368–370; and the Allen McLane Papers, New-York Historical Society. Dawson's account is full and well documented. W. H. Richardson's monograph *Washington and the Enterprise Against Powle's Hook* gives many details, but is unfortunately not annotated.

1. Irving, III, 513.
2. Irving, III, 515. Hughes, III, 474, citing no authority, attributes to Washington the initiation of the enterprise: "Encouraged perhaps by the public rejoicing over the brief exploit against Sandy Hook, Washington cast about for another dramatic blow. His eyes fell on . . . Paulus Hook. . . . He talked with Major Henry Lee and asked him to look into the matter." Washington's first letter to Lee on the matter, dated August 10, although it begins with an acknowledgment of receipt from Lee of a plan to attack the Hook, refers to "the idea I had of the matter" with respect to the number of men required; and a letter of August 12 to Stirling says, "I have had in contemplation an attempt to surprise the enemy's Post at Powlus Hook." But nothing in either letter necessarily contradicts Irving's statement—concurred in by Greene, FV, 159, and definitely endorsed by Frothingham, 296—that Lee originated the scheme. Marshall, I, 368, definitely attributes the scheme to Lee. Moreover, on July 28 one of Washington's aides wrote to Lee asking him to come to see Washington "on the very subject you mentioned in y^r letter of this date . . . in order that the scheme you propose may be adopted." Lee's letter seems not to be extant; its subject, therefore, is not known, but it is highly probable that the "scheme" was none other than the enterprise against the Hook.
3. Fitzpatrick, XVI, 72.
4. The description has been derived from Dawson, I, 543–544; Irving, III, 513; Richardson, map facing p. 4; Lossing, II, 622 n., with plan; Marshall, I, 368.
5. Richardson, 59.
6. McLane MS. journal in New-York Historical Society.
7. Richardson, 15; Irving, III, 514; Dawson, I, 545.
8. Dawson, I, 545, 549.
9. Reed, II, 127; Dawson, I, 546.
10. Dawson, I, 546, 549.
11. Richardson, 15–16.
12. Dawson, I, 546, 549.
13. Reed, II, 126.
14. Dawson, I, 547, 549. Stedman, II, 153, says that Lee's troops approaching the Hook were mistaken by a sentinel for Van Buskirk's foraging party returning and were "suffered to pass." Robert E. Lee's "Life of General Henry Lee" prefacing Henry Lee's *Memoirs*, says eight or ten soldiers disguised as countrymen carrying provisions for sale "procured the gate to be opened by the sentinel and held it until the rest of the party, concealed near, rushed in." Neither statement is supported by Henry Lee's dispatch, or by any other contemporary account.
15. Dawson, I, 548–549.
16. *Journals*, XV, 1100.
17. Sparks, *W*, V, 543.
18. Fitzpatrick, XVII, 126.
19. Fitzpatrick, XVIII, 198.

CHAPTER 51

1. Fitzpatrick, XVII, 105.
2. Fitzpatrick, XVI, 491, and XVII, 105.
3. Fitzpatrick, XVII, 210.
4. Kapp, 179–180.
5. Thacher, 180.
6. Hughes, III, 495.
7. Thacher, 161.

8. Stephenson, II, 121.
9. Thacher, 185.
10. Kapp, 182–183; Thacher, 190–191.
11. Rodney, C, 344–345.
12. Rodney, C, 334.
13. Fitzpatrick, XVII, 366.
14. Fitzpatrick, XVII, 273.
15. Fitzpatrick, XVII, 449–450.
16. Rodney, C, 338.
17. Kapp, 184.
18. Lossing, I, 319 n.
19. Thacher, 188. Major Patten of the Delaware Regiment was rather scornful of Stirling's adventure. He wrote to Caesar Rodney: "Their Intention was to *sweep* the Island. Why they did not do it I am not at present able to tell you. . . . We hear that they drew up in the face of the Enemy and remain^d there for some Hours without firing a single shot. . . . Rivington's Royal Gazette will no doubt . . . give us a Pompous description of this adventure of his Lordship." (Rodney, C, 334.)

CHAPTER 52

1. *Simcoe's Military Journal*, Marshall's *Washington*, Gordon's and Ramsay's histories, Wayne's letter to Hartley and Cornwallis's dispatch to Clinton, in Dawson, I, 452, 453, and Gaine's New York *Gazette and Weekly Mercury*, of Oct. 5 and 19, 1778, in Dawson, I, 453, present the principal contemporaneous accounts of this affair. Irving, III, 471–473, is a good secondary source.
2. Pulaski's report to the Congress and Ferguson's report to Clinton, in Dawson, I, 459–460, Gaine's New York *Gazette and Weekly Mercury* of Oct. 26, 1778, Stedman, Gordon, and Marshall are the contemporary authorities for this affair.
3. Tarleton's dispatch to Clinton, in Dawson, I, 506, and Heath's *Memoirs* are the principal contemporary sources. Dawson's account is full and well documented.
4. This invasion of Connecticut is well covered by Tryon's report to Clinton and Collier's letter to the Admiralty and an article in the *Connecticut Journal* of July 7, 1778, printed in Dawson, I, 512–514, 516, and by Lamb, Gordon, and Stedman. There are good secondary accounts in Barber and Hinman.
5. Heath's letter to Washington, Feb. 10, 1780, in Sparks, C, II, 395–398, gives a good account of this affair. Heath's *Memoirs* and Thacher's *Military Journal* are other contemporary sources.
6. For the affairs at Connecticut Farms and Springfield reference is made to Marshall, Stedman, Washington's letters to the Congress of closely subsequent dates, Greene's letter to Washington of June 23, 1780, in Sparks, C, III, 6, Gordon, and Johnson's *Greene*, I, 192.
7. A first-hand account of this affair, with a plan of the fort, is in Tallmadge, 59–63.
8. In *Pennsylvania,* II, 632–674, may be found a "Diary of the Revolt of the Pennsylvania Line," giving in full all letters and documents pertaining to the mutiny. Cf. also Van Doren, *M, passim.*
9. Heath, Marshall, Stedman, and Arnold's dispatch of Sept. 8 to Clinton in Arnold, 348–352, contain the chief contemporary accounts of this invasion. Dawson, I, 721–732, presents a detailed narrative, well supported by citations of authorities.
   In this report to Clinton, Arnold attributed the destruction of New London to an explosion of gunpowder in one of the storehouses, which had been fired. This, he said, "communicated the flames to a part of the town, which was, notwithstanding every effort to prevent it, unfortunately destroyed." This does not account for the burning of Groton. The contemporary historian Gordon (IV, 179) rejects the excuse: "The burning of the town was intentional and not accidental." Caulkins's *History of New London* presents a detailed and circumstantial account of the deliberate and systematic application of the torch to one street after another.

CHAPTER 53

1. The chief sources for the Wyoming Valley battle are Stone, *B*, and Dawson's account, appended to which are Zebulon Butler's report to the Board of War and John Butler's relation. Swiggett's *War Out of Niagara* and Chapman's account in an appendix to Campbell's *Annals of Tryon County* have been helpful.

CHAPTER 54

1. Lossing, I, 255.
2. *Pennsylvania*, I, 485.
3. *Pennsylvania*, I, 485.
4. These narratives of the ravishment of German Flats, Unadilla, and Cherry Valley are based on the accounts in Dawson, I, 464–471; Stone, *B*, I, 331–334, 338–345; Lossing, I, 253–255, 268–269, 296–298; and Swiggett, 138–157.
5. The story of Minisink and the succeeding fight is based upon the authorities cited in the preceding note.

CHAPTER 55

The materials for a story of Sullivan's Expedition are full and authentic. Of the officers and men engaged in it no fewer than 28 kept journals or afterward wrote accounts of it. Of the journals 17 are printed in full in the *Journals of the Military Expedition of Maj. Gen. John Sullivan Against the Six Nations of Indians,* published by the State of New York in 1887. These have been supplemented by examination of secondary accounts, Stone, *B*, Campbell, Dawson, Lossing, and other obvious sources.

1. *Journals*, XIII, 252.
2. Fitzpatrick, XIV, 3, 18, 75.
3. Fitzpatrick, XIV, 94, 168, 314.
4. Fitzpatrick, XIV, 180.
5. Patterson, 287.
6. Fitzpatrick, XV, 189.
7. Fitzpatrick, XV, 190.
8. Winsor, VI, 639, 667 n.
9. Sullivan, III, 4.
10. Sullivan, III, 20, 47; Amory, 107; Gordon, III, 308.
11. Stone, *B*, II, 10, 12.
12. Fitzpatrick, XV, 348–349.
13. Sullivan, III, 75.
14. Fitzpatrick, XVI, 1.
15. Sullivan, *J*, 194–195.
16. Sullivan, III, 96.
17. Sullivan, *J*, 260.
18. Sullivan, III, 197; Sullivan, *J*, 229.
19. Sullivan, *J*, 25.
20. Sullivan, *J*, 265.
21. Sullivan, *J*, 44.
22. Sullivan, *J*, 8, 27; Sullivan, III, 111.
23. Sullivan, *J*, 27.
24. Sullivan, *J*, 186.
25. Sullivan, III, 127.
26. Sullivan, III, 126, 128; Sullivan, *J*, 31, 234.
27. Sullivan, III, 131.
28. Sullivan, III, 134.
29. Sullivan, *J*, 13.
30. Sullivan, III, 134; Fitzpatrick, XVI, 437; *Journals*, XV, 1170.

31. Fisher, II, 245; Dawson, I, 541.
32. Stone, *B*, II, 26.
33. Fitzpatrick, XV, 302, 418.
34. Stone, *B*, II, 42–43; *Journals*, XV, 1212; Fitzpatrick, XVI, 485.

CHAPTER 56

The material for this chapter has been gathered chiefly from secondary sources, including Stone, *B*, Campbell, Swiggett, and Lossing. Specific references are deemed unnecessary in most cases.

1. Fitzpatrick, XVI, 492.
2. Swiggett, 214.
3. Lossing, I, 261–262.
4. Stone, *B*, 168.

CHAPTER 57

1. This description of the Carolinas is largely based on Ramsay, *R*, I, 2–3, and Greene, GW, III, 1–10, citing Morse's *American Universal Geography*, edition of 1793.
2. Greene, GW, III, 10–11; Irving, IV, 26, 86; Ramsay, *R*, I, 3–5.
3. McCrady, *R*, I, 33–35.
4. Lee, 174–175.
5. Greene, GW, III, 122; McCrady, *R*, I, 566; A. K. Gregorie, in *Dictionary of American Biography*, XVIII, 221.
6. McCrady, *R*, I, 566.
7. The descriptions of Marion and Sumter are drawn from Greene, GW, III, 122–127, and Irving, IV, 89, 196, and Lee, 174–175.
8. *Dictionary of American Biography*, XIV, 559.
9. Force, 4, IV, 981–982; Bancroft, IV, 320.
10. Force, 4, IV, 982–983; Dawson, I, 129.
11. Dawson, I, 131; Bancroft, IV, 387.
12. Dawson, I, 129; Force, 4, V, 63–65.
13. Dawson, I, 133.
14. Dawson, I, 130–132; Force, 4, V, 59 et seq., 170–171.

CHAPTER 58

The principal original authorities for this first battle of Charleston are John Drayton's *Memoirs of the American Revolution* (Charleston, 1821), William Moultrie's work of the same name, and Force's *American Archives*—a treasure house of contemporary letters and documents. McCrady's *The History of South Carolina in the Revolution, 1775–1780* is a very full and detailed account, based chiefly on Drayton and Moultrie. Gordon's and Stedman's histories are of value as contemporary relations, while Dawson and Carrington give excellent accounts.

1. McCrady, *R*, I, 6.
2. Bancroft, IV, 382.
3. Bancroft, IV, 383.
4. Fitzpatrick, IV, 221, 267, 271, 273.
5. Fitzpatrick, IV, 451.
6. Fitpatrick, IV, 221–223.
7. Trevelyan, Pt. II, Vol. II, 41–49; Bancroft, IV, 232–234, and V, 66–67; Irving, I, 413–419.
8. Force, 4, IV, 812; Bancroft, IV, 484.
9. Gordon, IV, 275.
10. Force, 4, IV, 1153; McCrady, *R*, I, 132–135; Gordon, II, 175.
11. Force, 4, IV, 807, 1062.

12. Force, 4, IV, 830.
13. Force, 4, IV, 1538; *Journals,* IV, 201–204.
14. *Journals,* IV, 157, 206, 174.
15. Force, 4, IV, 1537.
16. Force, 4, IV, 733, and V, 928, 1517.
17. Force, 4, V, 80, 981.
18. James, 430.
19. Dawson, I, 135; Gordon, II, 279; Stedman, I, 183.
20. McCrady, *R,* I, 132, citing *Annual Register,* XIX, 157; Stedman, I, 183; Force, 4, V, 981; Gordon, II, 279.
21. Stedman, I, 184.
22. Force, 4, V, 1220, and VI, 720.
23. Moultrie, I, 141.
24. McCrady, *R,* I, 13, 126–127.
25. Force, 4, VI, 1188.
26. McCrady, *R,* I, 145; Dawson, I, 140; Moultrie, I, 142.
27. Force, 4, VI, 1206; Stedman, I, 186; Bancroft, IV, 405; Carrington, 188.
28. Gordon, II, 280.
29. Gordon, II, 282; Moultrie, I, 174.
30. Force, 4, VI, 1210.
31. Moultrie, I, 178.
32. Force, 4, VI, 1210; Moultrie, I, 175.
33. Bancroft, IV, 403.
34. Force, 4, VI, 1129; Moultrie, I, 176.
35. Force, 4, VI, 206.
36. Gordon, II, 284–286; Ramsay, *R,* I, 147; Dawson, I, 140; McCrady, *R,* I, 159.
37. McCrady, *R,* I, 144; Moultrie, I, 141.
38. Moultrie, I, 142.

CHAPTER 59

1. Sparks, *W,* V, 549.
2. Ramsay, II, 130.
3. Dawson, I, 476.
4. Ramsay, II, 130–131.
5. Dawson, I, 476.
6. Jones, C, II, 323. The best original authority for this Battle of Savannah is Campbell's very fully detailed dispatch to Germain in Dawson, I, 477–479. Dawson, as usual, gives a good account, as also do Ramsay, Jones, C, and Henry Lee.
7. The affair at Beaufort is fully covered by Moultrie's dispatch to Lincoln and a letter from an American officer, in Dawson, I, 482–484.
8. Ramsay, *R,* II, 14.
9. Garden, II, Appendix, xvi. Contemporary accounts of the Kettle Creek encounter are to be found in Stedman, Ramsay, *R,* Marshall, and Garden. Detailed secondary accounts are in McCrady, *R,* I, Jones, C, and Dawson.
10. Contemporary accounts of the action at Briar Creek are to be found in Dawson, I, 492–494, also in Stedman, Lee, Gordon, Lamb, and Ramsay, *R.*
11. Dawson, I, 497.
12. Ramsay, *R,* II, 32. First-hand accounts of this affair may be found in Dawson, I, 501–503. Other contemporary accounts are in Ramsay, *R,* Marshall, Lee, Gordon, Stedman.

CHAPTER 60

1. Jones, C, II, 384. Contemporary accounts of the siege of Savannah are to be found in Stedman, Ramsay, *R,* Marshall, Gordon, Lee, Lincoln's diary, Moultrie's memoirs, and the dispatches of various officers, cited in Dawson, I, 562–569.

CHAPTER 61

Contemporary accounts of the siege of Charleston are to be found in Ramsay, *R,* Tarleton, Lee, Gordon, Stedman, Marshall, Moultrie's memoirs, and the various dispatches cited in Dawson, also in Uhlendorf.

1. McCrady, *R*, I, 431.
2. McCrady, *R*, I, 500.
3. Moultrie's memoirs say that only 1,500 to 1,600 Continentals marched out, 500 being in hospital, but careful calculations in McCrady, *R*, I, 507–510, show that there were 2,650 Continentals in the garrison.

CHAPTER 62

1 Contemporary accounts of the affair at the Waxhaws are in Marshall, Ramsay, *R,* Gordon, Lee, Stedman, Moultrie, Tarleton, and in various letters cited in Dawson. The English Stedman, II, 193, gives Tarleton's troops credit for activity and ardor, but admits that "the virtue of humanity was totally forgot."
2. The best contemporary account of the engagement at Ramsour's Mills was written for Gen. Joseph Graham—first published in the *Catawba Journal,* Charlotte, N.C., in 1825 and reprinted in full in Schenck, 51–62. Other such accounts are in the works cited in note 1.
3. The story of the encounter at Williamson's plantation in Dawson, I, 601–603, differs in details (particularly as to the numbers engaged) from the much fuller account in McCrady, *R*, I, 594–599, which has been followed in this narrative.
4. Gordon, Ramsay, *R*, Stedman, Lee, and Tarleton are the contemporary sources for the skirmish at Rocky Mount.
5. Tarleton, Lee, Gordon, and Stedman furnish contemporary accounts of the Hanging Rock affair. Davie's narrative is copiously cited in Dawson.

CHAPTER 63

1. Fitzpatrick, XVIII, 197–198.
2. Carrington, 491.
3. Kapp, *passim.*
4. Fitzpatrick, XVIII, 226–227, 243, 257–258.
5. Gordon, III, 390; Carrington, 514; Winsor, VI, 475.
6. Kapp, 179, 198.
7. Kirkwood, 9.
8. Kapp, 198–199.
9. Fitzpatrick, XVIII, 265.
10. Kirkwood, 10.
11. Kapp, 200.
12. Kapp, 203; Bancroft, V, 384. North Carolina was "solely occupied with" providing for "her own militia" (Johnson, I, 485).
13. Kirkwood, 10.
14. Moore, II, 310.
15. Kapp, 202; Gordon, III, 390.
16. Kapp, 203; Gordon, III, 391.
17. Fiske, II, 190; Bancroft, V, 384.
18. Kapp, 203; Bancroft, V, 384; *Journals,* XVII, 508.

CHAPTER 64

1. Kapp, 205.
2. Gordon, III, 392; Kapp, 207.
3. Lossing, II, 462.

4. Schneck, 86.
5. Greene, GW, III, 17–18; Fiske, II, 192; McCrady, *R*, I, 658; Johnson, I, 294.
6. McCrady, *R*, I, 659.
7. Greene, GW, III, 18–19; Johnson, I, 294.
8. Kapp, 207–208; Gordon, III, 429–430; Johnson, I, 487.
9. Gordon, III, 430–431; Kapp, 212; Greene, GW, III, 19–20; Johnson, I, 487.
10. Kapp, 209; Irving, III, 92; Johnson, I, 294, 486.
11. Greene, GW, III, 20.
12. Johnson, I, 506; McCrady, *R*, I, 659.
13. McCrady, *R*, I, 657; Greene, GW, III, 21; Gordon, III, 430. The number of men in Porterfield's force is variously stated. McCrady, *R*, I, 520, 837, says 400. Gordon, III, 430, says 100. Lossing, II, 464, says 100. Dawson, I, 613, says there were 800 Virginians in all. This includes Stevens's 700. Colonel Otho Williams calls it "a small detachment" (Johnson, I, 488).
14. Greene, GW, III, 22; Johnson, I, 295, 488.
15. Seymour, 4.
16. Greene, GW, III, 22; Kapp, 215; Gordon, III, 432; Johnson, I, 488.
17. Greene, GW, III, 23; Kapp, 216–217; Gordon, III, 431.
18. Greene, GW, III, 23; Kapp, 217; Winsor, VI, 476; Johnson, I, 489.
19. Though Caswell's force had been figured at 1,200 originally, Dawson computes it at 2,100 at this time, by deducting the strength of the other contingents from the known total strength of Gates's army. There may have been additions bringing up his original number to this figure.
20. Greene, GW, III, 25–26; Kapp, 219; Johnson, I, 491. One finds it difficult to realize that, in the eighteenth century, all armies had their trains of camp followers, even of women and children. Many of the women were wives of the men in the ranks; others had more temporary and more promiscuous attachments. They played their part in the camps, washing the soldiers' clothes, cooking their food, and so on. They were so customary and usual that the historians take them for granted and seldom mention them except on occasions such as this, when they were sent away.
21. Kapp, 219.
22. Kapp, 219–220; Tarleton, 102, comments on this failure of Gates to use his opportunity: "He had not sufficient penetration to conceive that by a forced march up the creek, he could have passed Lord Rawdon's flank and reached Camden which would have been an easy conquest and a fatal blow to the British."
23. Kapp, 220; Gordon, III, 433; Tarleton, 104.
24. Kapp, 220; Greene, GW, III, 25; Gordon, III, 434.

CHAPTER 65

The original sources for the Battle of Camden are Otho Williams's narrative, in Johnson, I, 485–510; Gates's dispatch to the Congress, in Tarleton, 148–151; Tarleton, 107–111; Cornwallis's dispatch to Germain in Tarleton, 132–137; Lamb, 302–305. Other contemporaneous accounts are in Gordon, III, 432–442; Lee, 182–185; and Ramsay, *R*, II, 146–149. Later full descriptions are in Dawson, I, 613–619; Carrington, 514–518; and McCrady, *R*, I, 666–680.

1. Gordon, III, 433; Kapp, 220; Lee, 180; Johnson, I, 492.
2. Kapp, 205.
3. Tarleton, 139.
4. Gordon, III, 436. Carrington, 514, makes the Continentals 1,400, but he evidently overlooked natural wastage of the original number.
5. Johnson, I, 487–493.
6. Johnson, I, 493.
7. Johnson, I, 493. Lee, 182 n., comments on the fact that Armand's corps was

made up chiefly of deserters from the British army. "It was the last corps in the army which ought to have been intrusted with the van post."

8. Greene, GW, III, 26; Kapp, 224. That he actually so boasted is doubtful. His intention seems to have been to advance no farther than Sanders Creek, not to Camden and attack it in the morning.

9. Johnson, I, 495; Kapp, 221; Greene, GW, III, 26–27.

10. Seymour, 5.

11. Johnson, I, 494.

12. Greene, GW, III, 27; Kapp, 226; Lossing, II, 465.

13. Johnson, I, 297, 494; Kapp, 226; Greene, GW, III, 27.

14. Tarleton, 107; Johnson, I, 297, 494.

15. Tarleton, 107; Kapp, 227; Greene, GW, III, 27; Gordon, III, 437; Lee, 182.

16. Heitman, 448.

17. Johnson, I, 494; Kapp, 227.

18. Johnson, I, 495; Greene, GW, III, 27; Kapp, 227.

19. Greene, GW, III, 28; Kapp, 227–228; Gordon, III, 438.

20. Kapp, 226, 229; Carrington, 516.

21. Johnson, I, 495, quoting Otho Williams's narrative. Kapp, 230, says the American artillery was divided, two guns in Gist's right wing, two on the center, and two on the left. But Williams ought to have known.

22. Tarleton, 108–109, 135; Dawson, I, 616.

23. Johnson, I, 495; Greene, GW, III, 28–29; Kapp, 231; Gordon, III, 439.

24. Carrington, 516.

25. Johnson, I, 497; Kapp, 231; Greene, GW, III, 28; Gordon, III, 440; Carrington, 516–517; Dawson, I, 617; Schenck, 89. Colonel Dixon had seen service in the Continental army under Washington. To his experience and firmness Lee, 187, ascribes much of the merit of his regiment. "Yet praise," he says, "is nevertheless due to the troops. Dixon's regiment held its ground for some time, even beat back the enemy, but was swept away before the final debacle."

26. Bancroft, V, 388; Schenck, 88; Greene, GW, III, 20. Gordon, III, 446, writes: "Smallwood had been separated from the first Maryland brigade, after the men had been engaged a while and finding it impractical to rejoin them, as well as apprehending they must be overpowered and could not retreat, rode off for personal safety."

27. Bancroft, V, 388; Dawson, I, 617; Carrington, 517; Kapp, 232; Greene, GW, III, 30; Gordon, III, 440.

28. Lossing, II, 467.

29. Bancroft, V, 388.

30. Dawson, I, 618.

31. Fiske, II, 196.

32. Kapp, 235.

33. Gordon, III, 443; Lee, 186; Lossing, II, 467; Kapp, 234; Dawson, I, 618.

34. Johnson, I, 497; Dawson, I, 618; Tarleton, 111.

35. Gordon, III, 443; Kapp, 236.

36. Moore, 312 n.

CHAPTER 66

1. Marshall, I, 405; Fiske, II, 197.

2. Seymour, 6.

3. Tarleton, 111–112; Johnson, I, 498.

4. Seymour, 7.

5. Johnson, I, 501.

6. Seymour, 7.

7. Schenck, 99.

8. Schenck, 99, 100; Greene, FV, 220.

9. Tarleton, 140–141.

10. Dawson, I, 619.

11. Gordon, III, 442–443.
12. Gordon, III, 459; Seymour, 7; Lee, 208.
13. *Archives,* III, 1343; Bennett, 459.
14. Lee, 208; Schenck, 184.
15. Gibbes, I, 12; Gordon, III, 455.
16. Bancroft, V, 390; Tarleton, 114–119; Gordon, III, 447; Seymour, 7.
17. Gordon, III, 459, 469. Schenck, 183, says Buford brought "the mangled remnant of his regiment and 200 recruits." Gordon, 460, says his regiment was recruited "to about 200 men." The words "cut to pieces" are advisedly used. Bancroft, V, 378, says that Buford and about 100 men "saved themselves by flight. The rest, making no resistance, vainly sued for quarter. . . . A hundred and thirteen were killed on the spot; a hundred and fifty were too badly hacked to be moved; fifty-three only could be brought to Camden as prisoners."
18. Seymour, 8; Kirkwood, 11. Gordon, III, 461, Bancroft, V, 477, and Schenck, 184, say that there were four companies of light infantry, but do not name the commanders. It may be that they regarded the Virginia riflemen as the fourth company.
19. Fiske, II, 260–261; Bancroft, V, 476.
20. *Journals,* XVII, 319, and XVIII, 921.
21. Gordon, III, 459; Greene, GW, III, 32.
22. Bennett, 456. Otho Williams reports (Johnson, I, 501) on the behavior of the Continentals in their difficult situation at Hillsboro: "Absolutely without pay; almost destitute of clothing; often with only a half-ration and never with a whole one . . . not a soldier was heard to murmur after the third or fourth day of their being encamped . . . they filled up the intervals from duty with manly exercises and field-sports." Inducements to desert were offered—rum in particular, of which "most desirable refreshment" they had none—but without effect. On the contrary, they brought "some of the most bold and importunate incendiaries" to their officers for punishment.
23. Johnson, I, 508.

CHAPTER 67

1. Fisher, II, 337–338.
2. Tarleton, 153. Marshall, Stedman, Lee, and Lamb give contemporary accounts of the affair at Wahab's Plantation. McCrady has a good secondary account.
3. Lee, Stedman, Tarleton, and Lamb give contemporary accounts of the affair at Charlotte. Schenck's narrative is full of detail.
4. Irving, IV, 51.
5. Schenck, 119.
6. A good account of Ferguson is in Wilkin, 152–171. Lamb, 308–309, has a sympathetic description.
7. Lee, Marshall, Ramsay, Tarleton, Moultrie, and Gordon give contemporary accounts of King's Mountain, but the very full and authenticated story in Draper supersedes all others.
8. Bancroft, V, 401; Lee, 201–203; Schenck, 178–182.
9. Seymour, 8.
10. Tarleton, Stedman, Marshall, Ramsay, and Gordon have contemporary accounts of this affair. McCrady, *R,* I, 820–823, gives a full account.
11. Contemporary accounts of the affair at Blackstock's may be found in Ramsay, Lee, Tarleton, Stedman, and a more detailed secondary account in McCrady, *R,* I, 824–829.

CHAPTER 68

1. *Journals,* XVIII, 906. The resolution also directed Washington to order a court of inquiry into the conduct of Gates in his late campaign, and the tenure of office of the new general to be appointed was limited in time "until such enquiry

be made." It never was made, and Greene continued to hold his place without special limitation.

2. Fitzpatrick, XX, 181–182; *Journals*, XVIII, 994–996.
3. Greene, GW, III, 35–36.
4. Greene, GW, III, 39–47.
5. Greene, GW, III, 48–64.
6. Johnson, I, 510.
7. Greene, GW, III, 68–70.
8. Reed, II, 344, 346.
9. Sparks, *C*, III, 189; Gordon, IV, 30.
10. Sparks, *C*, III, 189.
11. Gordon, IV, 30; Greene, FV, 226.
12. Fisher, II, 378.
13. Fisher, II, 377.
14. Johnson, I, 346; Lee, 222; Greene, FV, 226.
15. Greene, FV, 226; Fisher, II, 380.
16. Johnson, I, 346.
17. Greene, GW, III, 91.
18. Johnson, I, 50; Gordon, IV, 32.
19. Kirkwood, 13; Seymour, 11–12.
20. Gordon, IV, 31; Schenck, 200.
21. Gordon, IV, 31; Greene, GW, III, 135; Seymour, 12.
22. Lee, 222; Schenck, 199; Greene, GW, III, 133.
23. Lee, 224.
24. Greene, FV, 228; Fortescue, III, 365. There is doubt as to the number of men Leslie brought to Winnsboro. Some accounts give him 3,000 when he left New York, others 2,500. Some historians imply that he brought his whole force to Winnsboro; but this is obviously not so, else Cornwallis would have had more than 4,000 men there. The truth seems to be that he actually added 1,500, leaving the rest at Wilmington. See Greene, GW, III, 137; Stedman, II, 317; McCrady, *R*, II, 17. Tarleton, 216, says 1,530.
25. Tarleton, 214.
26. Fortescue, III, 366; Greene, FV, 228.
27. Fortescue, III, 366; Greene, GW, III, 138.
28. Tarleton, 250, 252.

CHAPTER 69

This account of the Battle of Cowpens is based on contemporary accounts in Tarleton, Lee, Gordon, Stedman, Ramsay, supplemented by McCrady and by Dawson's very full, annotated description.

1. Dawson, I, 647; Greene, GW, III, 138; Gordon, IV, 33; Schenck, 205. The 3-pounders were not mounted on wheeled carriages but propped up on legs, hence the resemblance to a grasshopper. On the march, they were carried on horseback.
2. McCrady, *R*, II, 30–31.
3. McCrady, *R*, II, 23, 32.
4. Stedman, II, 320; McCrady, *R*, II, 30.
5. Fisher, II, 353.
6. McCrady, *R*, II, 35; Dawson, II, 648; Lossing, II, 430.
7. Johnson, I, 576.
8. Lee, 226.
9. Greene, GW, III, 140, 144.
10. Johnson, I, 377; Schenck, 209; Lossing, II, 433–434.
11. Johnson, I, 377–379; Dawson, 649; Marshall, I, 471; Schenck, 211–212; Greene, GW, III, 142.
12. Stedman, II, 320; Dawson, I, 648.

13. The accounts of casualties on both sides are, as usual, conflicting. The numbers stated in the text are taken from Greene, FV, 230, after comparison with the various contemporary narratives.
14. Fortescue, III, 368.
15. Marshall, I, 368.
16. Trevelyan, VI, 154–155.

CHAPTER 70

1. Greene, FV, 231.
2. Johnson, I, 385.
3. Johnson, I, 386–387.
4. Seymour, 15; Kirkwood, 13; Schenck, 228; Johnson, I, 386.
5. Schenck, 227; Fortescue, III, 370.
6. Fortescue, III, 371; Stedman, II, 325; Johnson, I, 387.
7. Fortescue, III, 376; Stedman, II, 325.
8. Fortescue, III, 370; Johnson, I, 388.
9. Seymour, 15.
10. Johnson, I, 389; Stedman, II, 326; Fortescue, III, 371; Trevelyan, VI, 156; Gordon, IV, 37; Schenck, 234; Lee, 232.
11. Schenck, 230.
12. Fortescue, III, 371; Stedman, II, 327; Lee, 233; Sparks, C, III, 225.
13. Gordon, IV, 41–42.
14. Greene, GW, III, 154, 158; Gordon, IV, 38–39; Johnson, I, 404.
15. Gordon, IV, 38–39; Johnson, I, 407.
16. Fortescue, III, 371; Stedman, II, 326; Schenck, 234, 237.
17. Schenck, 236–237.
18. Tarleton, 230; Dawson, I, 655; Stedman, II, 327.
19. Schenck, 238–239.
20. Schenck, 238; Stedman, II, 327–328; Sparks, C, III, 226; Lee, 233–234; Fortescue, III, 371–372; Dawson, I, 655–656; Greene, GW, III, 155–157; Kirkwood, 13; Seymour, 15–16.
21. Schenck, 251. Tarleton, 270, modest as usual, acknowledges that he "with excellent conduct and great spirit attacked" the militia at Tarrant's Tavern "instantly and totally routed them." Against this huddle of militia, whose rifles had been wet by the rain so that few of them would fire, and who had emerged from the tavern wishing only to get away, he "resolved to hazard one charge . . . he desired his soldiers to advance and *remember the Cowpens.* Animated by this reproach, a furious contest ensued. They broke through the centre with irresistible velocity, killing near fifty on the spot, wounded many in the pursuit and dispersed near five hundred of the enemy." According to Irving, IV, 251, there were about a hundred in this party of militia. Greene, GW, III, 157, says three hundred, and a British officer who rode over the ground soon after the attack, saw only ten dead bodies on the ground (Stedman, II, 329 n.).
22. Schenck, 252. Greene, GW, III, 259, tells of a tradition that a portrait of George III hung over the fireplace when General Greene received this gift. He turned its face to the wall and wrote on the back of it, "Hide thy face, George, and blush."

CHAPTER 71

1. Greene, FV, 232.
2. Tarleton, 236.
3. Sparks, C, III, 226.
4. Fortescue, III, 371–372; Stedman, II, 330; Schenck, 253.
5. Johnson, I, 419; Schenck, 253.
6. Stedman, II, 331; Fortescue, III, 372; Tarleton, 271.
7. Kirkwood, 13.

8. Seymour, 16.
9. Johnson, I, 425–426; Stedman, II, 331; Gordon, IV, 42–43; Lee, 236; Marshall, I, 475.
10. Johnson, I, 427, 429; Sparks, *C*, III, 227, 234; Stedman, II, 331; Lee, 236–237.
11. Johnson, I, 429–430.
12. Kirkwood, 13; Seymour, 16; Greene, GW, III, 168.
13. Johnson, I, 430.
14. Greene, GW, III, 165
15. Lee, 248 n.
16. Gordon, IV, 44–45.
17. Lee, 237–247.

CHAPTER 72

1. Greene, FV, 236.
2. Tarleton, 263. Seymour, 17, says: "A vast number of the inhabitants joined them [the British], taking the oath of allegiance, and many more they compelled to do the same, forcing them away from their wives and children."
3. Johnson, I, 433–434.
4. Kirkwood, 13; Johnson, I, 433–434.
5. Lee, 253.
6. Lee, 256–258. Lee's story of his amicable intentions towards Pyle's men is hard to credit; it has too much the air of an afterthought to palliate a piece of strategy fully matured and intentionally executed, whose outcome shocked its author. Stedman, II, 334, says that Pyle's men cried for mercy, "but no quarter was granted; and between two and three hundred were inhumanly butchered, while in the act of begging for mercy. Humanity shudders at the recital of such a massacre." The bloody results of the attack are, in themselves, sufficient proof of its relentless ferocity.
7. Johnson, I, 443.
8. Johnson, I, 449.
9. Gordon, IV, 50; Johnson, I, 444.
10. Stedman, II, 337. Stedman himself was the commissary that slaughtered the oxen and made the requisitions.
11. Gordon, IV, 49; Johnson, I, 448.
12. Tarleton, 273.
13. Fortescue, III, 373.
14. Lee, 259; Gordon, IV, 49.
15. Gordon, IV, 49; Lossing, II, 399; Greene, GW, III, 184–185; Johnson, I, 461.
16. Lee, 264; Lossing, II, 399; Greene, GW, III, 185.
17. Kirkwood, 15–16; Greene, GW, III, 186–187.
18. Lee, 264; Greene, GW, III, 188.
19. Lee, 266–267; Stedman, II, 336; Tarleton, 242–243; Gordon, IV, 51–52; Johnson, I, 463.
20. Johnson, I, 438; Lee, 269; Greene, GW, III, 189.
21. Johnson, I, 472.
22. Kirkwood, 14. Kirkwood says merely "one [company] from Virginia"; but as in the battle at Guilford Court House, Washington's horse, Kirkwood's company, and Lynch's riflemen were posted in one group it seems fairly certain that the identification in the text is correct.

CHAPTER 73

1. Johnson, II, 2–3; Gordon, IV, 54.
2. Johnson, II, 3.
3. Fortescue, III, 374 n.
4. Fortescue, III, 375; Schenck, 316–317. There are maps in Stedman, II, 342; Schenck, 320; Greene, FV, 238.

5. Johnson, II, 4; Schenck, 328; Stedman, II, 337.
6. Lee, 272–275; Stedman, II, 337; Johnson, II, 4; Tarleton, 278.
7. Schenck, 321–322.
8. Schenck, 322–328; Johnson, II, 4–6.
9. Lossing, II, 402.
10. Fortescue, III, 375; Greene, FV, 238; Schenck, 330.
11. Schenck, 335–345.
12. Lamb, 361.
13. They ran because they could not face the enemy bayonets, having none of their own. They had no time to reload their rifles. It took three minutes to do that. They ran fast, because that was the sensible thing to do; in disorder, because they were not trained soldiers, but a mere collection of individuals having no formation.
14. Fortescue, III, 376.
15. Stedman, II, 339. Stedman was in this battle.
16. Seymour, 20–21.
17. This account of the battle is partly based on accounts of participants: Lee, 272–285; Tarleton, 276–286; Stedman, II, 337–347; Lamb, 345–357; and Seymour 20–21. The contemporary account in Marshall, I, 480–487, has been consulted and also later accounts in Johnson, II, 1–15; Schenck, 320–372; Fortescue, III 374–380; Greene, FV, 338–342; and Greene, GW, III, 190–202.

CHAPTER 74

1. Trevelyan, VI, 166.
2. Tarleton, 286; Lee, 286–287; Johnson, II, 26.
3. Lee, 287.
4. Lee, 289; Johnson, II, 27.
5. Stedman, II, 352.
6. Tarleton, 289.
7. Stedman, II, 352.
8. Stedman, II, 354; Tarleton, 291, 334–335, 337–338.
9. Tarleton, 333, 334–335. On Cornwallis's decision to march into Virginia see Willcox, 11–14.
10. Sparks, C, III, 378.
11. Greene, FV, 244.
12. Schenck, 394.
13. Wilkin, 74–83.
14. Greene, GW, III, 233–234; Lee, 325; Schenck, 399.
15. Schenck, 399–400; Lee, 325; Johnson, II, 44; Greene, GW, III, 231–235.
16. Greene, GW, III, 233.
17. Lossing, II, 500; Stedman, II, 360.
18. Lee, 332; Lossing, II, 500; Stedman, II, 360.
19. Kirkwood, 16; Seymour, 24.
20. Greene, GW, III, 271–272.
21. Stedman, II, 356; Fortescue, III, 386; Schenck, 400.
22. Greene, GW, III, 241.
23. Kirkwood, 16. Seymour, 24, says they "brought away 350 horses and cattle."
24. Lee, 334, 335; Greene, GW, III, 242, 243; Seymour, 24.

CHAPTER 75

This account of the battle is largely based on the contemporary and later accounts, in Stedman, II, 355–358; Tarleton, 474–485; Lee, 334–341; Seymour, 24–26; Gordon, IV, 81–85; Ramsay, R, II, 230–231; Greene, GW, III, 243–251; Johnson, II, 76–85; McCrady, R, II, 188–198; Schenck, 400–412.

1. Greene, GW, III, 243; Schenck, 402; Lee, 336.
2. Johnson, II, 77; Schenck, 403; Lee, 336.
3. Lee, 336; Greene, GW, III, 245.
4. Greene, GW, III, 245.
5. Greene, GW, III, 245.
6. Johnson, II, 77.
7. Greene, GW, III, 244; Schenck, 403–404; Greene, FV, 246; Johnson, II, 77.
8. Fortescue, III, 386; Johnson, II, 79; Schenck, 404.
9. Greene, GW, III, 252.
10. Greene, GW, III, 253.

CHAPTER 76

1. Greene, GW, III, 257, 262; Johnson, II, 83; Lee, 342.
2. Lee, 342, 344; Greene, GW, III, 267; Kirkwood, 17; Seymour, 26.
3. Tarleton, 492; Greene, GW, III, 271, 276; Lee, 344; Gordon, IV, 88.
4. Greene, GW, III, 271, 276; Lee, 344; Kirkwood, 17.
5. Tarleton, 492; Lee, 344; Greene, GW, III, 276.
6. Greene, GW, III, 254; Reed, II, 353.
7. Greene, GW, III, 265.
8. Greene, GW, III, 264–265; Gordon, IV, 87–88; Reed, II, 351–353.
9. Greene, GW, III, 265.
10. Gordon, III, 89; Kirkwood, 17; Seymour, 26.
11. Greene, GW, III, 277.
12. Lee, 345.
13. Sparks, C, III, 510; Tarleton, 490–494; Lee, 344–345; Greene, GW, III, 277; Gordon, IV, 89; Lossing, II, 475.
14. Kirkwood, 17; Seymour, 27.
15. Lee, 345.
16. Sparks, C, III, 310.
17. Dawson, I, 689–692; Lossing, II, 683; Lee, 345–349; Gordon, IV, 89–90; Greene, GW, III, 278–279.
18. Lee, 349; Greene, GW, III, 280.
19. Lee, 349–352.
20. Ramsay, II, 318; Schenck, 415.
21. Lee, 353–358, 360–371; Gordon, IV, 91; Dawson, I, 673–679.

CHAPTER 77

1. Lossing, II, 483–484.
2. Dawson, I, 692; Johnson, II, 140; Lossing, II, 485.
3. Stedman, II, 366; Lossing, II, 484; Johnson, II, 139.
4. Johnson, II, 140–141.
5. Lossing, II, 485 n.
6. Johnson, II, 141; Stedman, II, 367.
7. Stedman, II, 367; Dawson, I, 693; Lossing, II, 485.
8. Stedman, II, 368; Dawson, I, 693.
9. Stedman, II, 368, 369.
10. Lee, 371–372.
11. Lee, 373–374; Lossing, II, 486.
12. Stedman, II, 370.
13. Johnson, II, 148; Lossing, II, 486; Lee, 374.
14. Fortescue, III, 388–389; Stedman, II, 371.
15. Lee, 375.
16. Greene, GW, III, 312; Lee, 376; Johnson, II, 149.
17. Lee, 377; Greene, GW, III, 313–314; Kirkwood, 19; Seymour, 28.
18. Lee, 376–378; Johnson, II, 149–150.
19. Stedman, II, 373; Greene, FV, 252.

CHAPTER 78

1. Tarleton, 523.
2. The narrative of the American army's movements after Ninety-six has been derived chiefly from Lee, 377–386; Stedman, II, 374–375; Greene, GW, III, 318–322; Johnson, II, 152–165; Lossing, II, 488–489; McCrady, *R*, II, 300–440. The quotations about food and the condition of the army are from Lee, 385.
3. Greene, III, 334; Lee, 448.
4. Greene, III, 332–334; Lee, 386–394.
5. Wilkin, 86–89.
6. Johnson, II, 208, 216; Greene, GW, III, 385.
7. Lossing, II, 491.
8. Johnson, II, 218; Greene, GW, III, 386. These are Johnson's figures. Greene, FV, 254, gives a total of 2,300, 1,254 being Continentals. Lee, 465, gives a total of 2,300, of which 1,600 were Continentals, horse, foot, and artillery.
9. Johnson, II, 230; Greene, FV, 254. Fortescue, III, 380, allows Stuart "fewer than 1,600 effective men." On the other hand, Lossing, II, 491, states that, when they left the High Hills only 1,600 Americans "were fit for active duty."
10. Johnson, II, 220.
11. Tarleton, 524; Stedman, II, 377.
12. Lossing, II, 492; Johnson, II, 224.
13. Tarleton, 524.
14. Tarleton, 525; Stedman, II, 378; Fortescue, III, 389; Johnson, II, 222; Lee, 466. The number in the rooting party and its fate are left in doubt by the conflicting statements of the authorities. According to Stedman there were 400, and they "fell an easy prey to Greene's army"; "a few straggling horsemen escaped" and brought the news to Stuart. Johnson says there were 100, and they were captured. Lee says there were 200 or 300, and they escaped. Fortescue says there were 100, and all were captured except the cavalry guard. Stuart's report to Cornwallis (quoted in Tarleton, 525) makes the number 400.
15. Dawson, I, 713; Lossing, II, 484; Johnson, II, 220.
16. Lee, 466.
17. Greene, GW, III, 393; Lee, 466; Johnson, II, 222.
18. Lee, 467; Stedman, II, 378; Lossing, II, 495; Fortescue, III, 390; Carrington, 379–381.
19. Lee, 467; Lossing, II, 495; Johnson, II, 223.
20. Johnson, II, 225.
21. Fortescue, III, 390.
22. McCrady, *R*, II, 454.
23. Fortescue, III, 392.
24. Kirkwood, 23. This account of the battle has been derived from Lee, 475–478; Stedman, II, 377–381; Gordon, IV, 167–172; Greene, GW, III, 384–402; Lossing, II, 492–499; Schenck, 444–459; Fortescue, III, 389–392; McCrady, *R*, II, 442–463.
25. Fortescue, III, 392.
26. Gordon, IV, 171.
27. Tarleton, 533.
28. Greene, FV, 257. Stuart reported to Cornwallis 525 casualties, including 247 missing. As the prisoners taken by the Americans numbered well over 400, this report is plainly incorrect.
29. Greene, FV, 257.
30. *Journals*, XXI, 1084–1085.

CHAPTER 79

1. Lee, 474.
2. Lee, 475.
3. Lee, 475; Kirkwood, 25; Seymour, 31–32.

4. Kirkwood, 25–26; Seymour, 25–26, 32.
5. Johnson, II, 242.
6. Sparks, *C*, III, 430.
7. Greene, GW, III, 408.
8. Gordon, IV, 173–174.
9. Wraxall, II, 238.
10. Fisher, II, 504.
11. Stedman, II, 406; McCrady, *R*, II, 465–466.
12. Greene, GW, III, 421; Gordon, IV, 176.
13. Johnson, II, 268; Kirkwood, 27.
14. *Pennsylvania*, II, 703–705.
15. Bennett, 459; Lee, 524–525.
16. Seymour, 33; Lee, 525–526.
17. Lee, 529–536; Seymour, 33; Greene, GW, III, 431.
18. Jones, C, 505.
19. Jones, C, 505–520; Stillé, 286–291.
20. Bennett, 459.
21. Sparks, *C*, III, 490, and IV, 524; Gordon, IV, 292.
22. Lee, 517, 548; Greene, GW, III, 450.
23. Lee, 549, 565.
24. Johnson, II, 329.
25. Seymour, 39; Johnson, II, 339.
26. Johnson, II, 340–341; Seymour, 39–40; Bennett, 461.
27. Johnson, II, 343; Seymour, 40; Bennett, 460.
28. McCrady, *R*, II, 646–649.
29. Greene, FV, 257–258.
30. Trevelyan, VI, 176–178.
31. Fortescue, III, 409.

CHAPTER 80

1. Force, 4, II, 477, 516, 526, 539–541, 711, 1023, 1103, 1191.
2. Bancroft, IV, 146–147.
3. Bancroft, IV, 179; Force, 4, II, 465–466; Gordon, II, 85–91.
4. Force, 4, II, 516.
5. Gordon, II, 85–91; Bancroft, IV, 202, 254.
6. Bancroft, IV, 317.
7. Force, 4, III, 6, 1385.
8. Bancroft, IV, 317–318.
9. Force, 4, III, 1047, 1543, 1660, 1714, and IV, 342, 508, 615, 616 n.; Gordon, II, 114–115; Andrews, 312–313; *Journals*, III, 394, 415, 445.
10. Dawson, I, 122, 346; Force, 4, IV, 349–350; Lossing, II, 329.
11. Gordon, II, 114; Dawson, I, 112.
12. Force, 4, IV, 224, 228 n., 538.
13. Dawson, I, 122–124, 125–126; French, *F*, 576–577; Lossing, II, 329–330; Force, 4, IV, 538–539; Gordon, II, 112–113.
14. Force, 4, III, 1191, and IV, 577; Trevelyan, I, 345–346.
15. Gordon, II, 206; Lossing, II, 333; Force, 4, IV, 293.
16. Force, 4, IV, 53; Gordon, II, 206–207; Dawson, I, 126; Lossing, II, 333–334.
17. Gordon, II, 298–299; Force, 4, IV, 946.
18. Fitzpatrick, IV, 297.

CHAPTER 81

For some unknown reason Mr. Ward's manuscript, when it came to the editor, did not include a description of the war in the Ohio valley. It was thought necessary to insert a brief account of it, emphasizing the George Rogers Clark expedition of 1778–1779.

Writings concerning the war in the region of Beautiful River are too numerous to cite. In the nineteenth century Justin Winsor, Theodore Roosevelt, Consul W. Butterfield, Burke A. Hinsdale, and others made major contributions. Reuben G. Thwaites, Louise Phelps Kellogg, and others have since added greatly. George Rogers Clark has also been a favorite subject. William H. English published a useful account of Clark's exploits in the Old Northwest in 1896, followed seven years later by one written by Thwaites. In 1926 appeared Temple Bodley's biography of Clark. In 1930 James A. James's *Life of George Rogers Clark,* the best biography, was published. His volume is the basis for much of this chapter. Professor James also edited the *George Rogers Clark Papers, 1771–1784,* a very useful and convenient compilation.

1. James, *CP,* 22.
2. Bodley, 8; James, *C,* 114–115.
3. James, *C,* 30–32.
4. James, *CP,* 34, 36, 115–116; James, *C,* 114–115.
5. American colonial assemblies frequently offered handsome rewards for enemy Indian scalps. It has not been shown that, in practice, a distinction was made between a French scalp and that of a hostile Indian.
6. James, *C,* 143–144.
7. There is a facsimile of this message in James, *C,* opp. p. 144.
8. James, *C,* 148.
9. James, *C,* 149.
10. F. J. Teggart, "The Capture of St. Joseph," *Miss. Vall. Hist. Rev.,* XIX (1918), 214–228; Lawrence Kinnaird, "The Spanish Expedition Against Fort St. Joseph in 1781: A New Interpretation," *Miss. Vall. Rev.,* XIX (1932), 173–191.

CHAPTER 82

The best account of Lafayette's maneuvers is to be found in Gottschalk, *Lafayette and the Close of the American Revolution,* 189–306.

1. Fitzpatrick, XX, 122, 458, 473.
2. Sparks, *C,* III, 298.
3. Gordon, III, 260–261; Lee, 135; Jones, I, 295–296; James, 163; Stedman, II, 137–139.
4. Clinton, II, 12.
5. Clinton, II, 58–59.
6. Irving, IV, 289.
7. Dawson, I, 641; Stedman, II, 382.
8. Dawson, I, 642.
9. Dawson, I, 642; Sparks, *C,* III, 200; Simcoe, 159.
10. Simcoe, 160; Sparks, *C,* III, 200; Lee, 299.
11. Fitzpatrick, XX, 31, 147, 190, and XXI, 21; Lee, 298.
12. Sparks, *C,* III, 200.
13. Lee, 298–300.
14. Simcoe, 161–163; Dawson, I, 643.
15. Simcoe, 163; Sparks, *C,* III, 201.
16. Dawson, I, 644.
17. Sparks, *C,* III, 201.
18. Lossing, II, 237–238; Simcoe, 165–167; Dawson, I, 645.
19. Fitzpatrick, XXI, 231, 229.
20. Johnston, *Y,* 34.
21. Tower, II, 222–226.
22. James, 270–275.
23. Wilkin, 66; Gordon, IV, 62.
24. Dawson, I, 684–687; Stedman, II, 383; Simcoe, 189–197.
25. Dawson, I, 687–689; Simcoe, 198; Lee, 200.
26. Tower, II, 293.

27. Clinton, II, 77.
28. Johnston, *Y*, 37.
29. Lafayette, I, 417.
30. Clinton, II, 79–81; Johnston, *Y*, 38.
31. Stillé, 264, 286.
32. Simcoe, 212–219; Palmer, 275.
33. Simcoe, 220; Stedman, II, 389; Palmer, 279.
34. Tarleton, 303–305; Lee, 424.
35. Johnston, *Y*, 45; Stillé, 266.
36. Johnston, *Y*, 52.
37. Johnston, *Y*, 52–55.
38. Dawson, I, 698–700; Lee, 299; Simcoe, 225–237.
39. Dawson, I, 701–704; Gordon, IV, 117; Simcoe, 239; Lee, 301–304; Lamb, 373.
40. Lee, 436; Clinton, II, 132.
41. Greene, FV, 264.
42. Clinton, II, 126, 141, 145, 146, 164.
43. Clinton, II, 174.

CHAPTER 83

On the events and the strategy which led to the siege of Yorktown, the most recent and the best writings are to be found in Gottschalk, *Lafayette and the Close of the American Revolution*, 189–306; Willcox, "The British Road to Yorktown: A Study in Divided Command"; and Adams, "A View of Cornwallis's Surrender at Yorktown." Among the contemporary accounts on the British side, those published in Stevens are of the greatest importance.

1. Fitzpatrick, XXII, 103.
2. Fitzpatrick, XXII, 21.
3. Fitzpatrick, XXII, 103–107.
4. Fitzpatrick, XXII, 136, 325.
5. Fitzpatrick, XXII, 301–304.
6. Johnston, *Y*, 82–83; Fitzpatrick, XXII, 329–330.
7. Fitzpatrick, XXII, 330.
8. Greene, FV, 269.
9. Fitzpatrick, XXII, 429–433.
10. Sparks, *W*, VIII, 522–523.
11. Fitzpatrick, XXII, 501, and XXIII, 20.
12. Fitzpatrick, XXIII, 7.
13. Johnston, *Y*, 88–89.
14. Thacher, 268.
15. Sparks, *W*, V, 545.
16. Clinton, II, 193.
17. Johnston, *Y*, 87–88.
18. Sparks, *L*, I, 366.
19. Fitzpatrick, XXIII, 12; Fisher, II, 489.
20. Thacher, 271–272.
21. Johnston, *Y*, 96.
22. James, 444–445.
23. James, 289.
24. James, 288–294.

CHAPTER 84

This account of the Siege of Yorktown is based upon contemporary sources— Marshall, Fitzpatrick, Gordon, Clinton, Lafayette, Thacher, Lee, Tarleton, and Simcoe—as well as upon the various histories and biographies of the participants. Reliance has been placed upon Henry P. Johnston's able, exhaustive, and well documented monograph, *The Yorktown Campaign*. The account in Gottschalk, *Lafayette and the Close of the American Revolution*, 307–328, is also valuable.

1. Johnston, *Y*, 112–115.
2. Johnston, *Y*, 116–117.
3. Johnston, *Y*, 118–119.
4. Johnston, *Y*, 119–120.
5. Lossing, II, 304.
6. Lossing, II, 304 n.
7. Clinton, II, 198.
8. Clinton, II, 204.
9. Johnston, *Y*, 141 n.
10. Clinton, II, 205.
11. Stedman, II, 48.
12. Thacher, 346.
13. Wraxall, II, 238.
14. Johnston, *Y*, 160.

GLOSSARY OF MILITARY TERMS

Abatis A defense formed by placing felled trees lengthwise, one over another, with the branches toward the enemy's line.

Amuse To occupy or divert the attention of the enemy from the real point of attack.

Banquette A raised step along the inside of a parapet or bottom of a trench, upon which soldiers stand to fire at the enemy.

Bastion A pointed projecting part of a fortification thrust out from the face of the main line or at an angle at its corners.

Battalion A body of soldiers, consisting of several companies and being part of a regiment. In the Revolutionary War a full regiment was often called a battalion.

Battalion companies The companies left in a regiment after the grenadier and light infantry companies had been withdrawn from it.

Berm The narrow space between the ditch and the base of the parapet of a fortification.

Brigade A subdivision of an army composed of two or more regiments.

Canister Small round shot packed in a case fitting the bore of a cannon, which scatter on its discharge.

Carcass An iron shell packed with ignited combustibles and pierced with holes through which the flame blazes, for setting fire to buildings or ships.

Chandelier A wooden frame filled with fascines.

Chevaux-de-frise A framework of heavy timbers fitted with iron spikes on top used to check infantry, and also sunk in a channel to prevent the passage of ships.

Cohorn A small mortar for throwing grenades.

Column A formation of troops narrow laterally and deep from front to rear.

Counterscarp The outer wall or slope of the ditch surrounding a fortification.

Covered way A space about thirty feet broad extending around the counterscarp of the ditch, being covered by the parapet.

Curtain The part of the wall of a fortification connecting its bastions.

Demilune An outwork, like a curved bastion, to protect a bastion or curtain.

Deploy To spread troops out from a column into a line of battle.

Dragoon A mounted infantryman; but often used in the sense of cavalryman.

Embrasure An opening in a parapet to permit the firing of a gun.

Epaulement The shoulder of a bastion where it meets the curtain, or a simple outwork added to a fortification.

927

Fascine　A long, cylindrical bundle of brushwood or the like, firmly bound together, used to fill ditches, construct batteries, etc.

Fieldpiece　A light, portable cannon for use on a field of battle.

Flank　The side of a marching column or the end of a line of battle.

Flank companies　The companies of grenadiers and light infantry drawn from a regiment.

Flèche　A small earthwork, V-shaped and open at the rear.

Forlorn hope　A picked body of soldiers, detached to the front to begin the attack; a storming party.

Fraise　A palisade of pointed timbers planted in an upward slanting position.

Gabion　A cylindrical wicker basket open at both ends, to be filled with earth and used in fortifying a position or erecting a battery.

Glacis　The sloping approach to the parapet of a covered way.

Grapeshot　Small iron balls enclosed in an open frame fitting the bore of a gun, which scatter when the gun is discharged.

Grasshopper　A 3-pound cannon, so called because it was mounted on legs instead of a wheeled carriage.

Gun　Any firearm except a pistol, but usually a cannon of whatever caliber and not a musket or rifle.

Howitzer　A short, light gun to fire a heavy projectile at a high angle of elevation and low velocity.

Invalids　Soldiers disabled for active service.

Linstock　Instrument holding slow matches with which cannon were fired.

Mask　To hinder or hold from activity an enemy fortification or body of troops.

Matross　A soldier next in rank below an artilleryman, assisting with the guns.

Merlon　The part of a parapet between two embrasures.

Mortar　A short piece of ordnance with a large bore having trunnions on its breech to throw shells at high angles.

Ordnance　Heavy guns.

Parallels　Trenches approaching a fortification by a series of zigzags.

Parapet　The wall of a fortification.

Partisans　Irregular troops, guerrillas.

Picket　A small, detached body of troops set out in front of a camp to discover the approach of the enemy.

Platoon　A small body or squad of infantry acting as a unit, as when firing.

Pound　The rating of a gun by the weight of its projectile.

Provincials　Troops raised in the colonies on the side of Great Britain; Tory troops.

Quarter　Exemption from being put to death, granted to vanquished troops.

Rank and file　The common soldiers, privates.

Ravelin　An outwork of two faces forming a salient angle constructed outside the main ditch and in front of the curtain of a fortification.

Redan　A simple form of earthwork, not completely enclosed, with two faces forming a salient angle, like a flèche.

Redoubt　A small independent earthwork, usually square or polygonal, completely enclosed.

Regiment　A body of troops made up of companies and commanded by a colonel.

Royal   A small mortar.

Sally port   An opening in a fortification for the passage of troops.

Sap   A covered trench or tunnel for approaching or undermining a fortification.

Saucisson   A sausage-shaped fascine.

Spontoon   A pike or halberd carried by infantry officers.

Stand of colors   A complete set of colors.

Traverse   A barrier thrown across the approach to a fortification or across its interior to cut off a part.

A P P E N D I X   A

ETHAN ALLEN'S CAPTIVITY

After Ethan Allen's surrender, he was roughly treated by Brigadier General Prescott, whom he had to face in the city, an elegantly dressed soldier who looked with disdain upon this wild man wearing a deerskin jacket, rough breeches, hobnailed cowhide shoes, and a red woolen cap. On learning that this man had taken Ticonderoga, Prescott "put himself into a great fury," brandished his cane, and called him "hard names." Allen shook his fist at the general. "You'd better not cane me. I'm not used to it," he shouted. "Offer to strike and that's the beetle of mortality for you" (by which he probably meant his fist). The other officers interceded, and the general turned upon certain captive Canadians, ordering them to be bayoneted. Allen stepped between them and their captors. "I'm the one to blame," he cried, tearing open his shirt and offering his breast to the bayonets. Prescott was taken aback. After a moment of sullen silence, he said: "I'll not execute you now. But you shall grace a halter at Tyburn, God damn ye!" They handcuffed him, shackled his legs with thirty-pound irons attached to a bar eight feet long. He was confined on shipboard for a month in this uncomfortable equipment, sent to England, and lodged in Pendennis Castle. But the government did not know what to do with him. Reprisals might follow his gracing Tyburn Tree. So they shifted the problem to the other side of the water. He was ordered aboard the *Solebay* frigate to go back to America as a prisoner of war. There was a remarkable demonstration at Cork, when the vessel put in there. Irish sympathizers loaded him with gifts of money, delicate foods, fine clothes, including two silk suits and two beaver hats.

He reached Halifax in June, 1776. In October he was taken to New York and admitted to parole. Captain Alexander Graydon, who saw him there, described him in his *Memoirs* (p. 243):

"His figure was that of a robust, large-framed man, worn down by confinement and hard fare; but he was now recovering his flesh and spirits; and a suit of blue clothes, with a gold-laced hat, that had been presented to him by the gentlemen of Cork, enabled him to make a very passable appearance for a rebel colonel. . . . I have seldom met a man possessing, in my opinion a stronger mind, or whose mode of expression was more vehement and oratorical. His style was a singular compound of local barbarisms, scriptural phrases and oriental wildness; and, though unclassical and sometimes ungrammatical, it was highly animated and forcible. . . . Notwithstanding that Allen might have had something of the insubordinate, lawless, frontier spirit in his composition . . . he appeared to me to be a man of generosity and honor."

The British tried to bribe him, with a colonelcy in a regiment of Tories, a gift of money, and a promise of a large tract of land, to desert the American cause. He told the officer that tempted him that he "viewed the offer of land to be similar to that which the devil offered Jesus Christ . . . when, at the same time, the damned soul had not one foot of land upon earth." That closed the conversation.

His brother brought him money, so that he was able to live in comfort on Long Island until he was arrested and confined in jail in New York, on a charge of breaking parole, which he admitted was "partly true." After eight months there, he was exchanged and started at once for the American army at Valley Forge. Washington received him with kindness, and wrote that he had found "something in him that commands admiration." In the spring Allen returned to his beloved Vermont, just then so named. He never again had an active part in the war.

A P P E N D I X   B

THE CASUALTIES AT LONG ISLAND

It may seem almost incredible that, in a fight lasting four hours, as between Stirling and Grant, during which time the firing on both sides, even though not continuous, was heavy enough to exhaust Grant's ammunition, so few of the Americans were hit. But, when certain facts are considered, the lack of results is easily understood.

First, the distance between the lines appears not to have been much less that 150 yards at the beginning and between 300 and 600 yards for the rest of the fight, until Grant made his final advance. Musketry at that time was utterly ineffective at such distances. The British musket's ultimate range, when fired from the shoulder horizontally, was no more than 125 yards, at which distance the ball fell to the ground.

In the second place, the British soldier, as has been remarked elsewhere, was no marksman. He was never taught to take aim at a single object, or even at the mass of the enemy. His instructions were to throw the gun to the shoulder in a horizontal position, "point it—not sight it—toward the enemy and, at the word of command, to pull the trigger." Its effect was "entirely entrusted to volley shooting at ranges not exceeding 100 yards." As Trevelyan puts it: "He was taught to point his weapon horizontally, brace himself for a vicious recoil and pull a ten-pound trigger till his gun went off: if, indeed, it did go off when the hammer fell."

The British really relied on cold steel, this ineffective volley firing being usually merely a prelude to a charge with the bayonet. Such an attack, carried out by a body of trained men, terrible in their brilliant uniforms, their compactness, their grim courage, was, time and again in this war, enough to put the untrained American militia, most of whom had no bayonets, to flight even before the charge fell upon them.

A third consideration is that Grant's orders were merely to menace Stirling's men, to hold them in their position, until Howe gave the two-gun signal of his presence in their rear. Ambrose Serle says, "Grant had been ordered to advance no further." He therefore kept up an ineffective fire at long range for that purpose. He may even have instructed his gunners to overshoot the enemy, lest too much execution drive them from their position and let them escape to their lines before Howe had them entrapped.

932

In military language it was Grant's duty to "amuse" Stirling's force and "divert its attention" from the flanking movement—though Stirling's men would probably have described the fire from the British muskets and fieldpieces as anything else than "amusing" or "diverting."

Nevertheless, Stirling's men, ignorant of the British strategy and believing that at any minute Grant's force might advance and attack at close quarters, are entitled to the praise they received for their courage and steadfastness.

After the battle, stories of a brutal massacre by the British and Hessians, particularly the Hessians, of unresisting Americans offering to surrender were widespread throughout the colonies. The Americans were so inflamed by them that, when Count Donop fell in the attack on Red Bank on the Delaware on October 22, 1777, his death was hailed as an example of "God's revenge against murder."

Field, who in 1869 wrote a book about the battle, says that "there is no incident of the battle better attested than the massacre." He tells in lurid language of "entire battalions of Hessians" charging on unarmed men and never pausing "while one of them remained alive," of Americans "bayoneted, while lying on the ground and begging for quarter," and states that thus "nearly two thousand Americans were pitilessly put to death"—this in spite of the fact that Washington reported the loss of only about 1,000 in all, including those captured, and that pretty certainly no more than 1,000 Americans were killed, wounded, or captured in the whole battle.

The more modern historians either ignore these reports or, like John Fiske, declare that "the stories of a wholesale butchery by the Hessians, which once were current, have been completely disproved." But this is certainly a too sweeping statement. There can be little doubt that a number of Americans, when surrounded, hesitated to surrender and were bayoneted while practically defenseless.

A P P E N D I X   C

THE FEELING BETWEEN NORTHERN AND SOUTHERN TROOPS

At the outbreak of the Revolution, the inhabitants of the colonies below New York and those above knew little of each other. In spite of a considerable commerce between them, there had been, by and large, few personal contacts. Very few of the rank and file of Pennsylvanians, for instance, had ever wandered so far from home as Boston, and Massachusetts men were equally unfamiliar with Maryland. Even among the upper classes there was a similar lack of acquaintance with their distant fellow countrymen. Philadelphia was new to John Adams when he came down to the Congress of 1774. George Washington had been only briefly in New York and New England.

This common ignorance had bred mutual ill feeling among the troops from the several colonies when in the campaigns of 1776 they were for the first time brought together. The New England Yankees suspected and distrusted the "southern" soldiers. The southerners reciprocated with dislike and even contempt. This was first noticeable in the army in New York and on Long Island, the first contact of these discordant elements.

The better uniformed and equipped Continentals from Pennsylvania, Delaware, and Maryland, with aristocratic disdain, looked down upon the homespun rustics of New England. (Greene, GW, I, 209; Reed, I, 239.) Captain Graydon of Shee's Pennsylvanians, in his *Memoirs* (pp. 147–149), derides the officers of the "Eastern battalions" for trying "to preserve the existing blessing of equality" with their rank and file, excepting, however, the officers of Glover's Marblehead regiment, who "seemed to have mixed with the world, and to understand what belonged to their stations." Of the privates also, he had a low opinion. Even in Glover's regiment, he noted with disgust "a number of negroes, which, to persons unaccustomed to such associations, had a disagreeable, degrading effect."

After the headlong flight of the Connecticut militia from Kip's Bay, on September 15, 1776, this contempt of the Yankees was openly shown. Caesar Rodney wrote to his brother Thomas, "That the New-England men behaved in a most dastardly, cowardly and scandalous manner is most certain." In another letter he quoted a gentleman of his acquaintance as writing to him, "These were not Southern Troops." (Rodney, C, 129, 125.)

In the camps after that, the southern troops, proud of the distinction they

934

had achieved on Long Island, were free with their tongues. Graydon (p. 156) says, "In so contemptible a light were the New England men regarded that it was scarcely held possible to conceive a case which would be construed into a reprehensible disrespect of them."

The Yankees naturally resented being called cowards. The tension grew so great that Colonel John Haslet of Delaware thought it a most serious matter. "Some officers," he wrote, "have poured such contempt upon the Eastern Troops & great Animosity subsists just now among them—'tis true they are not like the Children of the South, this however between Ourselves, 'tis even got among the Soldiers, whose Officers I think much to blame, who have sown the seeds of Discord, & [I] have used my small Influence to discourage it . . . 'tis likely to have most Dangerous Consequences." (Rodney, C, 138.)

Commissary General Joseph Trumbull of Connecticut accused Adjutant General Joseph Reed of Pennsylvania of doing "more to raise and keep up a jealousy between the New England and other troops than all the men in the Army beside . . . his stinking pride . . . has gone so far that I expect every day to hear he is called to account by some officer or other." (Force, 5, III, 1498.)

A like condition existed in Schuyler's Northern Army on Lake Champlain. It has been noted in the text that all the Pennsylvania troops were brigaded together and encamped apart from the rest for the sake of peace. Here there was used, hardly for the first time, an expletive afterwards attached to the Union troops by the Confederates and which is still in general vogue in the South, though now with little malice. Charles Cushing of Massachusetts in a letter refers to the fact that "none of the 'damn'd Yankees' . . . as the Southern troops are pleased to call us," were in the disaster at Trois Rivières. (Force, 5, I, 130.)

A New England brigadier general described the animosity between the northern and southern troops: "It has already risen to such a height that the Pennsylvania and New England troops would as soon fight each other as the enemy. Officers of all ranks are indiscriminately treated in the most contemptible manner, and whole colonies traduced and vilified as cheats, knaves, cowards, poltroons, hypocrites and every term of reproach, for no other reason but because they are situated east of New York." (Jones, CH, 122.)

One of the chief causes of this discord was the objection of the southern officers to the "leveling principle," the extreme democracy, prevalent among their Yankee colleagues in their attitude toward the private soldiers. The southerners felt that this was derogatory to the standing of all of them as officers and gentlemen. When Colonel Asa Whitcomb of Massachusetts detailed one of his sons, a private in his regiment, to act as his servant and allowed another son, also a private, to set up a cobbler's bench in the colonel's quarters, Wayne's Pennsylvanians were highly incensed. They assaulted the colonel's quarters and even his person, threw out the bench and climaxed their protest by firing thirty or forty rounds at his men, driving them from their tents and barracks and wounding several of them. (Jones, CH, 122–123.)

Washington was much concerned about these internecine disorders and entreated Schuyler to use his exertions "to do away the unhappy, pernicious distinctions and jealousies between the troops of the different governments. . . .

I am persuaded, if the officers will but exert themselves, that these animosities and disorders will in a great measure subside."

These ill feelings and consequent disorders did finally subside, after the troops from both sections had marched and camped and fought side by side, had got used to each other, discovered each other's good qualities and made allowance for each other's differences and defects.

A P P E N D I X   D

GENERAL HOWE AND MRS. MURRAY

General Howe has been blamed for allowing the American troops south of Kip's Bay to escape capture after his landing. Trevelyan (Pt. II, Vol. I, 324) writes: "Howe's great chance had come. The garrison of New York—as well as the three brigades of infantry which had been stationed along the bank of the East River, south of the point where the British landed—might all be had for the taking . . . not one of the retreating battalions would ever have reached the American lines in military order, and with half its full numbers, if Howe had promptly pushed his troops athwart the peninsula [island], which here was less than three thousand yards wide." Similar observations have been made by Gordon, F. V. Greene, Fortsecue, T. G. Frothingham, Fisher, Fiske, Botta, and others.

It seems so obvious that the movement across the island would have had fatal results, at least to Putnam's division, if not also to those of Parsons, Wadsworth, and Scott, that one looks for the reason why it was not made. It is found, according to several historians, in a very pretty little story.

The story appeared first in Thacher's *Military Journal* (p. 58) and in Gordon's *History* (Vol. II, p. 328), and it has been rehearsed by later writers countless times. John Fiske's version (Vol. I, p. 225) closely follows the originals, but in somewhat more elegant language: "When Howe had reached the spot known as Murray Hill . . . Mrs. Lindley Murray * . . . well knowing the easy temper of the British commander, sent out a servant to invite him to stop and take luncheon. A general halt was ordered; and while Howe and his officers were gracefully entertained for more than two hours by their accomplished and subtle hostess, Putnam hastily marched his 4,000 men up the shore of the Hudson." Thacher adds the statement, "It has since become almost a common saying among our officers that Mrs. Murray saved this part of the American army."

The legend presents Mrs. Murray, a middle-aged Quaker lady, the mother of twelve children, in the light of a siren, a veritable Circe, "with feminine delaying wiles" (Frothingham, 145) beguiling "the gallant Britons . . . with smiles and pleasant conversation, and a profusion of cakes and wine" (Lossing, II, 611) while they "lingered over their wine, quaffing and laughing, and bantering

* Wrong first name. It was Mrs. Robert Murray.

937

their patriotic hostess about the ludicrous panic and discomfiture of her countrymen" (Irving, II, 355). It has been accepted as a historic fact, by Irving,
Lossing, Johnston, Gordon, Fortescue, Frothingham, Bancroft, Winsor, Trevelyan, Fiske, Bryant, and the *Dictionary of American Biography*, not only that
the "subtle" hostess served her guests cakes and wine, but that she actually
held up the whole British force for those two critical hours, during which, but
for that beguilement, it would have hastened to cut off Putnam and all his
men. General G. W. Cullum, writing about this affair in Winsor's *Narrative
and Critical History* (Vol. VI, p. 284), goes so far as to say, "Howe was in
close pursuit of this rear-guard [Putnam's] . . . but unexpectedly stopped for
nearly two hours" at Mrs. Murray's "to enjoy her old Madeira."

With such a wealth of authority behind it, who shall deny the lady her
heaped-up honors? Yet one must.

Not deny that the cakes and wine were served, no. Howe's first division
moved at once from the landing place to Murray Hill and halted there, at the
very door of Mrs. Murray's mansion. It was an excessively hot day. What
more natural, what more in accord with the polite customs of the time, than an
impulsive invitation from the good lady to Howe and Clinton and Cornwallis
and the other generals to enjoy the cool of her parlor and to refresh themselves
with her "old Madeira," instead of broiling in the sun? So much may be accepted
as probable. But that Howe was bamboozled into forgoing immediate, proper
military activity, that the whole British force was brought to a stand, not only
while but because, Howe and his generals enjoyed Mrs. Murray's hospitality, is
quite unbelievable.

The simple fact is that Howe's tactics, planned beforehand and exactly
carried out, had as their first objective only the possession of the Incleberg
height. On taking that commanding position, the first division was to wait until
the arrival of the rest of his force for any further major movement.

The first division numbered no more than 4,000 men, less than a third
of the whole force which was to come over from Long Island. Washington
had three or four times 4,000 men fit for duty. If Howe had thrown his troops
across the island at once, he would have exposed them to attack on two fronts,
by Putnam, Wadsworth, Parsons and the rest on the south and Washington on
the north, each American force greatly outnumbering the British. Good behavior by the Americans, under such conditions, might easily have resulted in a
complete defeat of Howe's first division long before all his second arrived.

That Howe planned the task of the first division exactly as it was accomplished, and was not diverted from his plans by the excellent Mrs. Murray,
is proved by Clinton's testimony on page 63 of his "Historical Detail" (cf.
Anderson, 177 ff.): "It happened unfortunately too that much time was
lost before the second embarkation landed (it being some hours after the first);
as by our striking immediately across the Island great numbers of the enemy
must have been taken prisoners; but my orders being to secure the Inclenberg,
I do not think myself at liberty to attempt it before Sir William Howe joined
us."

Clinton commanded that first division and led it immediately to the hill.
So say the *Diaries* of General Archibald Robertson (p. 98): "We then went

on to the heights of Inklenberg about a mile in front . . . where we halted. . . . About 2 General Howe came up and after the 2d Embarkation arrived about 4 we moved on." The *Diary* (p. 48) of Lieut. Frederick Mackenzie of the Royal Welch Fusiliers confirms this: "As soon as the troops were formed, they advanced to Murray's hill (or Ingleberg) an advantageous piece of ground . . . the whole of the Troops [the second division] . . . were landed at Kipp's Bay about 5 o'clock in the afternoon. General Howe [then] made a movement with the greatest part of the army towards Haerlem."

It was all according to plan. Whether Howe was too cautious in planning had no more to do with the question about Mrs. Murray's part in the affair than Mrs. Murray's undoubtedly sincere hospitality had to do with the delay at Incleberg—which was exactly nothing.

A P P E N D I X E

THE TREACHERY OF WILLIAM DEMONT

On November 2, 1776, William Demont, an ensign in Magaw's 5th Pennsylvania and the regimental adjutant, deserted and carried to Lord Percy "the plans of Fort Washington." To the receipt of these papers Edward F. De Lancey, in his monograph on the capture of the fort, ascribes a change in Howe's plans—which, before that, he assumes, had intended an immediate crossing to New Jersey and a descent upon Philadelphia.

De Lancey's conclusion, that the attack upon the fort and its capture was attributable to Demont's treachery, seems hardly justifiable. His belief that Howe had planned to cross to New Jersey without first attacking the fort is a pure assumption, based on nothing more than the guess of Colonel Joseph Reed and "a great majority" of the American officers (Reed, I, 248, and De Lancey, 18). There is nothing other than this guess upon which to base such assumption.

The only evident change in Howe's plans was the abandonment of his attempt to get behind the American army and the consequent withdrawal of his forces from in front of the American lines at North Castle on November 4. That his intention then was immediately to withdraw from Manhattan Island leaving Fort Washington intact, and devote all his energies to the capture of Philadelphia, nobody knows, nor can know. Moreover, such an intention is inherently improbable.

That Howe himself regarded the fort as an important factor in his plans is clearly shown by a sentence in his letter of November 30 to George Germain (Force, 5, III, 924): "The importance of this post, which, with Fort Lee on the opposite shore of Jersey, kept the enemy in command of the navigation of the North River, while it barred the communication with York by land, made the possession of its absolutely necessary." That he should have intended to leave it standing, while he marched against Philadelphia, is incredible.

That Demont's plans of the fort disclosed so much not already known to the British as to cause them to undertake the reduction of the fort, which, otherwise they would not have attempted, is equally incredible. Although Graydon, fully conversant with the facts, says that Howe "might have been more thoroughly informed of everything desirable to be known" as to the fort by Demont, yet he might have acquired "a perfect knowledge of the ground we occupied . . . from hundreds in New York" (Graydon, 215). That pretty well disposes of the importance of Demont's treachery.

A P P E N D I X   F

ARNOLD AT FREEMAN'S FARM

James Wilkinson, twenty years of age, was Gates's adjutant at the time of the battle of Freeman's Farm. He wrote on September 21 to St. Clair, "General Arnold was not out of camp during the whole action." In his *Memoirs,* published thirty-nine years later, he said: "It is worthy of remark, that not a single general officer was on the field of battle on the nineteenth of September, until the evening when General Learned was ordered out."

William Gordon, the contemporary historian (II, 551), wrote, "Arnold's division was out in the action, but he himself did not head them; he remained in the camp the whole time."

George Bancroft (V, 184) presumably relied on both Wilkinson and Gordon when he wrote (V, 184) that "on the American side not one" major general was on the field, "nor a brigadier till near its close"—evidently referring to General Learned's futile attack on Fraser's division.

These positive statements by historians deserve respectful consideration and an examination of countervailing evidence, if any there be, before they are disregarded.

There is evidence to the contrary. Colonel Richard Varick wrote on the 22nd to General Schuyler, "Arnold has all the credit of the action"; and after the surrender he wrote, "During Burgoyne's stay here he gave Arnold great credit for his bravery and his military abilities; especially in the action of the 19th" (Arnold, 179, 189).

Colonel Henry Brockholst Livingston, on the 22nd, wrote to Schuyler that some of the officers proposed an address to Arnold "returning thanks for his services and particularly for his conduct during the late action" (Arnold, 178). Again, on the 23rd, he wrote of Arnold, "Believe me, Sir, to him alone is due the honour of our late victory" (Arnold, 180).

Major Cochran wrote to the Vermont Council of Safety on the 21st: "General Arnold, with his division, attacked a division of Burgoyne, in which General Arnold gained the ground" (Arnold, 186).

Varick, Livingston, and Cochran were in the camp on the day of the battle. They offset Wilkinson.

Opposed to Gordon is Charles Stedman (I, 336–337), a contemporary English historian of high repute: "The enemy were led to battle by general Arnold, who distinguished himself in an extraordinary manner."

In 1844 Charles Neilson, whose father's house was within the American lines and who received much information from his parent as well as from surviving "old revolutionary officers and soldiers" of the vicinity, published an account of Burgoyne's campaign which is generally regarded as authoritative. On page 148 of that book he contradicts Wilkinson's statement.

Max von Eelking in his *Memoirs and Letters and Journals of Major General Riedesel* (I, 150), the material for which he derived from Riedesel says that deserters from the American army stated that "they were commanded on this occasion by General Arnold."

So much for the authorities. Considering the known facts of the affair, one might ask, Who directed the movements in that four- or five-hour battle if Arnold did not? Is it conceivable that the ten or more regiments engaged, each led by its own commander, with no general officer over them could have acted in unison and as coherently as they did act—in making that "countermarch" from Fraser's right to Burgoyne's center, for instance? No direction could have been given from the American camp, from which the battelfield was not visible. There must have been a leader on the field, and there has never been a suggestion of anyone in that capacity other than Arnold.

Again, consider the nature of the man, proud, ardent, impatient, brave, always eager for action in the thick of combat. It is not conceivable that he would have remained an idle spectator—not even a spectator, indeed, for from the camp he could not even have seen what was going on—while his own men fought through half a day.

One must conclude that John Marshall, Washington Irving, Botta, Lossing, Fiske, Woodrow Wilson, F. V. Greene, Fonblanque, S. G. Fisher, Hall, Trevelyan, Nickerson, Fortescue, Dawson, and Carrington are right in rejecting the statements of Wilkinson and Gordon and giving Arnold the honor of active participation in the battle as the directing head of the American troops.

Trevelyan (III, 186 n.) says that Wilkinson's "impudent falsehood has been judged worthy of refutation by several excellent historians. . . . One might as well demand evidence to prove that Nelson was in the sea-fight off Cape St. Vincent."

PRINCIPAL AUTHORITIES

WITH KEY WORDS USED IN THE NOTES

Abbatt, *P*	William Abbatt. *The Battle of Pell's Point.* New York, 1901.
Abbott	Wilbur C. Abbott. *New York in the American Revolution.* New York, 1929.
Adams	Randolph G. Adams. "A View of Cornwallis's Surrender at Yorktown," *American Historical Review*, XXXVII (Oct. 1931), 25–49.
Adams, CF	Charles Francis Adams. *Studies Military and Diplomatic, 1775–1865.* New York, 1911.
Adams, *J*	Charles Francis Adams, editor. *Familiar Letters of John Adams.* New York, 1876.
Adams, *L*	*Letters of John Adams, Addressed to His Wife* . . . 2 vols., Boston, 1841.
Alden	John Richard Alden. *General Gage in America.* Baton Rouge, La., 1948.
Allen	*Ethan Allen's Narrative of the Capture of Ticonderoga* . . . Burlington, Vt., 1849.
Allen, GW	Gardner W. Allen. *A Naval History of the American Revolution.* 2 vols., Boston, 1913.
Almon	John Almon, editor. *The Remembrancer.* 17 vols., 1775–1784.
Amory	Thomas C. Amory. *The Military Services and Public Life of Major-General John Sullivan.* Boston, 1868.
Anburey	Thomas Anburey. *Travels Through the Interior Parts of America.* 2 vols., Boston, 1923.
Anderson	Enoch Anderson. *Personal Recollections* . . . (*Papers of the Hist. Soc. of Del.*, No. XVI). Wilmington, 1896.
Anderson, T	Troyer S. Anderson. *The Command of the Howe Brothers During the American Revolution.* New York, 1936.
André	John André. *Major André's Journal* . . . Tarrytown, N.Y., 1930.
Andrews	Matthew P. Andrews. *History of Maryland* . . . New York, 1929.
Archives	*Delaware Archives.* 5 vols., Wilmington, 1911–1916.
Arnold	Isaac N. Arnold. *The Life of Benedict Arnold.* Chicago, 1880.
Ashburn	Percy M. Ashburn. *A History of the Medical Department of the United States Army.* Boston, 1929.
Atlas	Lawrence Martin, editor. *The George Washington Atlas.* United States George Washington Bicentennial Commission. Washington, 1932.
Bancroft	George Bancroft. *History of the United States* . . . 6 vols., New York, 1887.
Barber	John W. Barber. *History and Antiquities of New England* . . . New Haven, Conn., 1870.
Barker	John Barker. *The British in Boston* . . . Cambridge, Mass., 1924.

943

Baurmeister   Bernhard A. Uhlendorf and Edna Vosper, editors. *Letters from Major Baurmeister to Colonel von Jungkenn* . . . Philadelphia, 1937.

Belcher   Henry Belcher. *The First American Civil War* . . . 2 vols., London, 1911.

Benedict   Erastus C. Benedict. *The Battle of Harlem Heights* . . . New York, 1880.

Bennett   Caleb P. Bennett. "Narrative of . . . the Delaware Regiment . . ." *Pa. Mag. of Hist. and Biog.*, IX (1885), 451–462.

Bodley   Temple Bodley. *George Rogers Clark*. Boston, 1926.

Bolton   Charles K. Bolton. *The Private Soldier Under Washington.* New York, 1902.

Botta   Charles Botta. *History of the War of the Independence* . . . Edinburgh, 1844.

Boudinot   Elias Boudinot. *Journal or Historical Recollections* . . . Philadelphia, 1894.

Bowen   John S. Bowen and J. Smith Futhey. "A Sketch of the Battle of Brandywine," *Bulletin of the Hist. Soc. of Pa.*, Vol. I, No. 7 (Sept., 1846), pp. 3–13.

Boyd   Julian P. Boyd. *Anglo-American Union: Joseph Galloway's Plans to Preserve the British Empire, 1774–1788*. Philadelphia, 1941.

Brooks   Noah Brooks. *Henry Knox* . . . New York, 1900.

Bruce   Robert Bruce. *Brandywine* . . . Clinton, N.Y., 1922.

Burgoyne   John Burgoyne. *A State of the Expedition from Canada* . . . London, 1780.

Burgoyne, *OB*   *Orderly Book of Lieut. Gen. John Burgoyne* . . . Albany, N.Y., 1860.

Burnaby   Andrew Burnaby. *Travels Through North America.* New York, 1904.

Burnett   Edmund C. Burnett. *The Continental Congress.* New York, 1941.

Burnett, *L*   Edmund C. Burnett, editor. *Letters of Members of the Continental Congress.* 8 vols., Washington, 1921–1936.

Butcher   H. Borton Butcher. *The Battle of Trenton* . . . Princeton, 1934.

Campbell   William W. Campbell. *Annals of Tryon County* . . . Cherry Valley, N.Y., 1880.

Carrington   H. B. Carrington. *Battles of the American Revolution.* New York, 1888.

Caulkins   Frances M. Caulkins. *History of New London, Conn.* . . . New London, 1860.

Channing   Edward Channing. *History of the United States.* 6 vols., New York, 1905–1925.

Chastellux   Marquis de Chastellux. *Travels in North-America* . . . New York, 1828.

Chittenden   L. E. Chittenden. *The Capture of Ticonderoga.* Rutland, Vt., 1872.

Cincinnati	H. H. Bellas. *A History of the Delaware State Society of the Cincinnati* . . . (*Papers of the Hist. Soc. of Del.*, No. XIII). Wilmington, 1895.
Clarke	John Clarke. *An Impartial and Authentic Narrative of the Battle Fought* . . . *on Bunker's Hill* . . . New York, 1909.
Clinton	Sir Henry Clinton and Earl Cornwallis. I *Narrative of the Campaign in 1781* . . . II *Answer to Sir Henry Clinton's Narrative* . . . III *Observations on Earl Cornwallis' Answer.* Philadelphia, 1865–1866.
Coburn	Frank W. Coburn. *The Battle of April 19, 1775* . . . Lexington, Mass., 1912
Coburn, *B*	Frank W. Coburn. *The Centennial History of the Battle of Bennington* . . . Boston, 1877.
Codman	John Codman. *Arnold's Expedition to Quebec.* New York, 1902.
Coffin	Charles Coffin. *History of the Battle of Breed's Hill* . . . Portland, Me., 1835.
Cooch	Edward W. Cooch. *The Battle of Cooch's Bridge* . . . Wilmington, Del., 1940.
Cowpens	*The Battle of King's Mountain and the Battle of the Cowpens.* Washington, 1928.
Cresswell	*The Journal of Nicholas Cresswell, 1774–1777.* New York, 1924.
Curtis	Edward P. Curtis. *The Organization of the British Army in the Revolution.* New Haven, Conn., 1926.
D.A.B.	*Dictionary of American Biography.* 20 vols. and Index, New York, 1928–1937.
D.A.H.	James Truslow Adams, editor. *Dictionary of American History.* 5 vols. and Index, New York, 1940–1941.
Dawson	Henry B. Dawson. *Battles of the United States* . . . 2 vols., New York, 1858.
Dearborn	*Journal of Captain Henry Dearborn in the Quebec Expedition, 1775.* Cambridge, Mass., 1886.
Dearborn, *J*	*Journals of Henry Dearborn, 1776–1783.* Cambridge, Mass., 1887.
Dearborn, N	Henry Dearborn. "A Narrative of the Saratoga Campaign," *Fort Ticonderoga Museum Bulletin,* Vol. I, No. 5 (Jan., 1929), pp. 3–12.
De Lancey	E. F. De Lancey. *The Capture of Mount Washington* . . . New York, 1877.
Digby	*The British Invasion from the North* . . . *with the Journal of Lieut. William Digby* . . . Albany, N.Y., 1887.
Drake	Samuel A. Drake. *Bunker Hill.* Boston, 1875.
Draper	Lyman C. Draper. *King's Mountain and Its Heroes.* Cincinnati, 1881.
Duer	William A. Duer. *The Life of William Alexander, Earl of Stirling.* New York, 1847.

Dunbar	Seymour Dunbar. *A History of Travel in America.* 4 vols., Indianapolis, 1915.
Duncan	Louis C. Duncan. *Medical Men in the American Revolution, 1775–1783.* Carlisle, Pa., 1931.
Eelking	Max von Eelking. *The German Allied Troops* . . . Albany, N.Y., 1893.
Ellis	George E. Ellis. *History of the Battle of Bunker's (Breed's) Hill.* Boston, 1875.
Evelyn	W. G. Evelyn. *Memoirs and Letters* . . . *1774–1776.* Oxford, 1879.
Fellows	John Fellows. *The Veil Removed.* New York, 1843.
Field	Thomas W. Field. *The Battle of Long Island (Long Island Hist. Soc. Memoirs, Vol. II).* Brooklyn, 1869.
Fisher	Sydney G. Fisher. *The Struggle for American Independence.* 2 vols., Philadelphia, 1908.
Fiske	John Fiske. *The American Reovlution.* 2 vols., Boston, 1901.
Fitzpatrick	John C. Fitzpatrick, editor. *The Writings of George Washington.* 39 vols., Washington, 1931–1944.
Fletcher	Ebenezer Fletcher. *The Narrative of* . . . New York, 1866.
Fobes	Simon Fobes. *Journal of a Member of Arnold's Expedition to Quebec.* Tarrytown, N.Y., 1927.
Fonblanque	E. B. de Fonblanque. *Political and Military Episodes* . . . *Derived from the Life and Correspondence of the Right Hon. J. Burgoyne.* London, 1876.
Force	Peter Force, editor. *American Archives,* Fourth and Fifth Series. 6 vols. and 3 vols., Washington, 1837–1846, 1848–1853.
Fortescue	Sir John W. Fortescue. *A History of the British Army.* 13 vols., London, 1899–1930.
Fraser	Georgia Fraser. *The Stone House at Gowanus.* New York, 1909.
French, *B*	Allen French, editor. *A British Fusilier in Revolutionary Boston,* by Frederick Mackenzie. Cambridge, Mass., 1926.
French, *C*	Allen French. *The Day of Concord and Lexington.* Boston, 1925.
French, *F*	Allen French. *The First Year of the American Revolution.* Boston, 1934.
French, *G*	Allen French. *General Gage's Informers.* Ann Arbor, Mich., 1932.
French, *T*	Allen French. *The Taking of Ticonderoga in 1775.* Cambridge, Mass., 1928.
Frothingham	T. G. Frothingham. *Washington, Commander in Chief.* Boston, 1930.
Frothingham, *A*	Richard Frothingham. *The Alarm on* . . . *April 18, 1775.* Boston, 1876.
Frothingham, *C*	Richard Frothingham. *The Centennial.* Boston, 1875.
Frothingham, *S*	Richard Frothingham. *History of the Siege of Boston.* Boston, 1851.

Frothingham, W Richard Frothingham. *Life and Times of Joseph Warren.* Boston, 1865.

Fuller J. F. C. Fuller. *Decisive Battles of the U.S.A.* New York, 1942.

Ganoe William A. Ganoe. *The History of the United States Army.* New York, 1924.

Garden Alexander Garden. *Anecdotes of the American Revolution.* 3 vols., Brooklyn, 1865.

Gibbes R. W. Gibbes. *Documentary History of the American Revolution.* 3 vols., Columbia, S.C., and New York, 1853–1857.

Gilmore James R. Gilmore. *The Rear-Guard of the Revolution.* New York, 1897.

Goolrick J. T. Goolrick. *The Life of Gen. Hugh Mercer.* New York, 1906.

Gordon William Gordon. *The History . . . of the United States of America.* 4 vols., London, 1788.

Gottschalk Louis R. Gottschalk. *Lafayette Comes to America.* Chicago, 1935. *Lafayette Joins the American Army.* Chicago, 1937. *Lafayette and the Close of the American Revolution.* Chicago, 1942.

Graham James Graham. *Life of General Daniel Morgan.* New York, 1856.

Grahame James Grahame. *The History of the United States . . .* 4 vols., London, 1836.

Graydon Alexander Graydon. *Memoirs of His Own Time.* Philadelphia, 1846.

Greene, FV Francis Vinton Greene. *The Revolutionary War and the Military Policy of the United States.* New York, 1911.

Greene, GW George W. Greene. *The Life of Nathanael Greene.* 3 vols., New York, 1867–1871.

Hadden [James M.] *Hadden's Journal and Orderly Books.* Albany, N.Y., 1884.

Hall Hiland Hall. *The Battle of Bennington.* Milford, Mass., 1877.

Hanger *The Life, Adventures, and Opinions of Col. George Hanger . . .* 2 vols., London, 1801.

Hartley Cecil B. Hartley. *Life of Major General Henry Lee . . .* Philadelphia, 1859.

Hatch Louis C. Hatch. *The Administration of the American Revolutionary Army.* New York, 1904.

Heath *Memoirs of Major-General William Heath . . .* New York, 1901.

Heitman Francis B. Heitman. *Historical Register of Officers of the Continental Army . . .* Washington, 1914.

Henry John J. Henry. *Account of Arnold's Campaign Against Quebec . . .* Albany, N.Y., 1877.

Hildreth Richard Hildreth. *The History of the United States of America.* 6 vols., New York, 1880.

Hinman   Royal R. Hinman. *A Historical Collection, from Official Rec-
                  ords, Files, etc., of the Part Sustained by Connecticut During
                  the War of the Revolution.* Hartford, 1842.
Holbrook   Stewart H. Holbrook. *Ethan Allen.* New York, 1940.
Hollister   *The Journal of Josiah Hollister.* (Chicago, 1928?)
Honyman   *Colonial Panorama, 1775: Dr. Robert Honyman's Journal . . .*
                  San Marino, Calif., 1939.
Hooton   F. C. Hooton. *Battle of Brandywine.* Harrisburg, Pa., 1900.
How   *Diary of David How.* Morrisania, N.Y., 1865.
Howard   George E. Howard. *Preliminaries of the Revolution, 1763–1775.*
                  New York, 1905.
Hudleston   F. J. Hudleston. *Gentleman Johnny Burgoyne.* Indianapolis,
                  1927.
Hufeland   Otto Hufeland. *Westchester County During the American Rev-
                  olution, 1775–1783.* New York, 1926.
Hughes   Rupert Hughes. *George Washington . . .* 3 vols., New York,
                  1926–1930.
Humphrey   *A Journal Kept by William Humphrey . . . on a March to
                  Quebec . . .* Tarrytown, N.Y., 1931.
Humphreys   David Humphreys. *The Life and Heroic Exploits of Israel Put-
                  nam.* Hartford, Conn., 1847.
Huntington   *Letters Written by Ebenezer Huntington During the American
                  Revolution.* New York, 1914.
Hutchinson   *The Diary and Letters of . . . Thomas Hutchinson.* 2 vols.,
                  London, 1883–1886.
Irving   Washington Irving. *Life of George Washington.* 5 vols., New
                  York, 1855–1859.
James   W. M. James. *The British Navy in Adversity.* London, 1926.
James, *C*   James A. James. *The Life of George Rogers Clark.* Chicago,
                  1928.
James, *CP*   James A. James, editor. *George Rogers Clark Papers, 1771–
                  1784 (Colls. of the Ill. State Hist. Lib., Virginia Series, III–IV).*
                  2 vols., Springfield, Ill., 1912–1926.
Johnson   William Johnson. *Sketches of the Life and Correspondence of
                  Nathanael Greene.* 2 vols., Charleston, S.C., 1822.
Johnson, V   Victor L. Johnson. *The Administration of the American Com-
                  missariat During the Revolutionary War.* Philadelphia, 1941.
Johnston, *C*   Henry P. Johnston. *The Campaign of 1776 Around New York
                  and Brooklyn (Long Island Hist. Soc. Memoirs, Vol. III).*
                  Brooklyn, 1878.
Johnston, *H*   Henry P. Johnston. *The Battle of Harlem Heights.* New York,
                  1897.
Johnston, *S*   Henry P. Johnston. *The Storming of Stony Point.* New York,
                  1900.
Johnston, *Y*   Henry P. Johnston. *The Yorktown Campaign.* New York, 1881.
Jones   Thomas Jones. *History of New York During the Revolutionary
                  War . . .* 2 vols., New York, 1879.

Jones, C   Charles C. Jones, Jr. *The History of Georgia.* 2 vols., Boston, 1883.

Jones, CH   C. H. Jones. *History of the Campaign for the Conquest of Canada* . . . Philadelphia, 1882.

Journals   *Journals of the Continental Congress, 1774–1789.* 34 vols., Washington, 1904–1937.

Kapp   Friedrich Kapp. *The Life of John Kalb.* New York, 1884.

Kemble   *The Kemble Papers (New-York Hist. Soc. Collections, 1883–1884.* 2 vols., New York, 1884–1885.

Kirkwood   *The Journal and Order Book of Capt. Robert Kirkwood (Papers of the Historical Society of Delaware,* No. XVI). Wilmington, 1910.

Knollenberg   Bernhard Knollenberg. *Washington and the Revolution.* New York, 1940.

Lafayette   *Memoirs, Correspondence and Manuscripts of Gen. Lafayette.* 3 vols., London, 1837.

Lamb   R. Lamb. *Memoirs of His Own Life* . . . Dublin, 1809.

Landers   H. L. Landers. *The Battle of Camden.* Washington, 1929.

Leake   Isaac Q. Leake. *Memoir* . . . *of General John Lamb.* Albany, N.Y., 1857.

Lecky   W. E. Hartpole Lecky. *The American Revolution, 1763–1783.* New York, 1898.

Lee   Henry Lee. *Memoirs of the War in the Southern Department* . . . New York, 1869.

Lefferts   Charles M. Lefferts. *Uniforms* . . . *in the War of the American Revolution, 1775–1783.* New York, 1926.

Lossing   Benson J. Lossing. *The Pictorial Field Book of the American Revolution.* 2 vols., New York, 1850–1852.

Lossing, S   Benson J. Lossing. *The Life and Times of Philip Schuyler.* New York, 1883.

Lowell   E. J. Lowell. *The Hessians* . . . *in the Revolutionary War.* New York, 1884.

Lundin   Leonard Lundin. *Cockpit of the American Revolution: The War for Independence in New Jersey.* Princeton, 1940.

Lushington   Stephen R. Lushington. *The Life and Services of General Lord Harris* . . . London, 1840.

McCrady, R,I   Edward McCrady. *The History of South Carolina in the Revolution, 1775–1780.* New York, 1901.

McCrady, R,II Edward McCrady. *The History of South Carolina in the Revolution, 1780–1783.* New York, 1902.

McDonald   John M. McDonald. *The McDonald Papers,* Pt. I. White Plains, N.Y., 1926.

MacDonald   William MacDonald. *Documentary Source Book of American History.* New York, 1937.

MacElree   Wilmer W. MacElree. *Along the Western Brandywine.* West Chester, Pa., 1909.

Mackenzie   *Diary of Frederick Mackenzie.* 2 vols., Cambridge, Mass., 1936.

McMichael   "Diary of Lieut. James McMichael . . . 1776–1778," *Pa. Mag. of Hist. and Biog.,* XVI (1892), 129–159.

Mahan   Alfred T. Mahan. *The Major Operations of the Navies in the War of American Independence.* Boston, 1913.

Mahon   Philip H. Stanhope, Lord Mahon. *History of England from the Peace of Utrecht* . . . 7 vols., London, 1858.

Marshall   John Marshall. *The Life of George Washington.* 2 vols., New York, 1930.

Marshall, C   *Extracts from the Diary of Christopher Marshall 1774–1781.* Albany, N.Y., 1877.

Martyn   Charles Martyn. *The Life of Artemas Ward.* New York, 1921.

Mauduit   Israel Mauduit. *Observations upon the Conduct of S—r W—m H—e, at the White Plains.* Tarrytown, N.Y., 1927.

Metzger   Charles H. Metzger. *The Quebec Act.* New York, 1936.

Miller, *O*   John C. Miller. *Origins of the American Revolution.* Boston, 1943.

Miller, *T*   John C. Miller. *Triumph of Freedom, 1775–1783.* Boston, 1948.

Montresor   "Journals of Capt. John Montresor," *New-York Hist. Soc. Colls.,* 1881, pp. 113–520. New York, 1882.

Moore   Frank Moore. *Diary of the American Revolution.* 2 vols., New York, 1863.

Moore, GH   George H. Moore. *"Mr. Lee's Plan—March 29, 1777": The Treason of Charles Lee.* New York, 1860.

Morison   George Morison. *An Interesting Journal of Experience During the Expedition to Quebec* . . . Tarrytown, N.Y., 1916.

Moultrie   William Moultrie. *Memoirs of the American Revolution* . . . 2 vols., New York, 1802.

Muhlenberg   Henry A. Muhlenberg. *The Life of Major-General Peter Muhlenberg.* Philadelphia, 1849.

Murdock   Harold Murdock. *The Nineteenth of April, 1775.* Boston, 1923.

Murdock, *B*   Harold Murdock. *Bunker Hill.* Boston, 1927.

Neilson   Charles Neilson. *An Original* . . . *Account of Burgoyne's Campaign.* Bemis Heights, N.Y., 1926.

Nickerson   Hoffman Nickerson. *The Turning Point of the Revolution.* Boston, 1928.

Niles   H. Niles. *Principles and Acts of the Revolution in America.* Baltimore, 1822.

Nolan   J. Bennett Nolan. *Lafayette in America Day by Day.* Baltimore, 1934.

Ogden   "Journal of Maj. Matthias Ogden," *New Jersey Hist. Soc. Proc.,* New Ser. XIII, 17–30 (Jan., 1928).

Onderdonk   Henry Onderdonk. *Revolutionary Incidents of Suffolk and Kings Counties.* New York, 1849.

Palmer   John M. Palmer. *General von Steuben.* New Haven, Conn., 1937.

Parton   James Parton. *The Life and Times of Aaron Burr.* 2 vols. New York, 1858.

Partridge	Bellamy Partridge. *Sir Billy Howe.* New York, 1932.
Patterson	S. W. Patterson. *Horatio Gates.* New York, 1941.
Pausch	*Journal of Captain Georg Pausch . . .* Albany, N.Y., 1886.
Pell	John Pell. *Ethan Allen.* Boston, 1929.
Pennsylvania	*Pennsylvania in the War of the Revolution.* 2 vols., Harrisburg, 1880.
Pennsylvania Archives	Samuel Hazard, editor. *Pennsylvania Archives,* First Series. 12 vols. Philadelphia, 1852–1856.
Percy	*Letters of Hugh, Earl Percy . . . 1774–1776.* Boston, 1902.
Pettengill	R. W. Pettengill, editor. *Letters from America, 1776–1779.* Boston, 1924.
Phinney	Elias Phinney. *History of the Battle at Lexington.* Boston, 1825.
Pitkin	Timothy Pitkin. *A Political and Civil History of the United States.* 2 vols., New Haven, Conn., 1828.
Pontgibaud	Chevalier de Pontgibaud. *A French Volunteer of the War of Independence.* Transl. from the French. New York, 1898.
Quaife	Milo M. Quaife. *The Flag of the United States.* New York, 1942.
Ramsay	David Ramsay. *The History of the American Revolution.* 2 vols., Trenton, N.J., 1811.
Ramsay, *R*	David Ramsay. *History of the Revolution of South-Carolina.* 2 vols., Trenton, N.J., 1785.
Read	William T. Read. *Life and Correspondence of George Read.* Philadelphia, 1870.
Reed	William B. Reed. *Life and Correspondence of Joseph Reed.* 2 vols., Philadelphia, 1847.
Reynolds	Grindall Reynolds. *The Concord Fight.* Boston, 1875.
Richardson	William H. Richardson. *Washington and "the Enterprise Against Powle's Hook."* Jersey City, 1938.
Riedesel	Max von Eelking. *Memoirs and Letters and Journals of Major General Riedesel During His Residence in America.* 2 vols., Albany, N.Y., 1868.
Riedesel, F	Friederike von Riedesel. *Letters and Journals . . .* Albany, N.Y., 1867.
Ripley	Ezra Ripley. *A History of the Fight at Concord.* Concord, Mass., 1827.
Roberts	Kenneth Roberts, editor. *March to Quebec.* New York, 1940.
Robertson	*Archibald Robertson . . . His Diaries and Sketches in America.* New York, 1930.
Rodney, C	*Letters to and from Caesar Rodney, 1756–1784.* Philadelphia, 1933.
Rodney, T	*Diary of Capt. Thomas Rodney, 1776–1777.* Wilmington, Del., 1888.
Sabine	Lorenzo Sabine. *The American Loyalists.* Boston, 1847.
Sawyer	Charles W. Sawyer. *Firearms in American History,* Vol. I. Boston, 1910.
Schenck	David Schenck. *North Carolina, 1780–81.* Raleigh, 1889.

Senter   *The Journal of Isaac Senter* . . . Philadelphia, 1846.

Serle   *The American Journal of Ambrose Serle.* San Marino, Calif., 1940.

Seymour   William Seymour. *A Journal of the Southern Expedition, 1780–1783 (Hist. and Biog. Papers of the Historical Society of Delaware,* Vol. II). Wilmington, 1896.

Shurtleff   N. B. Shurtleff. *A Topographical and Historical Description of Boston.* 1871.

Simcoe   J. G. Simcoe. *Simcoe's Military Journal* . . . New York, 1844.

Simms   W. Gilmore Simms. *The Life of Francis Marion.* New York, 1857.

Smith   Goldwin Smith. *The United States . . . 1492–1871.* New York, 1893.

Smith, J   Justin H. Smith. *Arnold's March from Cambridge to Quebec.* New York, 1903.

Smith, JH   Justin H. Smith. *Our Struggle for the Fourteenth Colony.* 2 vols., New York, 1907.

Spargo   John Spargo. *The Bennington Battle Monument.* Rutland, Vt., 1925.

Sparks, *C*   Jared Sparks. *Correspondence of the American Revolution* . . . 4 vols., Boston, 1853.

Sparks, *L*   Jared Sparks. *The Life of George Washington.* 2 vols., London, 1839.

Sparks, *W*   Jared Sparks. *The Writings of George Washington.* 12 vols., Boston, 1858.

Squier   "The Diary of Ephraim Squier, of Arnold's Expedition to Quebec," *Mag. of Hist.* Vol. XL (1930), No. 4 (Extra No. 160), pp. 203–214.

Stedman   Charles Stedman. *The History . . . of the American War.* 2 vols., London, 1794.

Stephenson   N. W. Stephenson and W. H. Dunn. *George Washington.* 2 vols., New York, 1940.

Stevens   B. F. Stevens, editor. *The Campaign in Virginia, 1781.* 2 vols., London, 1888.

Stiles   *The Literary Diary of Ezra Stiles.* 3 vols., New York, 1901.

Stillé   C. J. Stillé. *Maj. Gen. Anthony Wayne* . . . Philadelphia, 1893.

Stocking   *An Interesting Journal of Abner Stocking* . . . Tarrytown, N.Y., 1921.

Stone   E. M. Stone. *Life . . . of John Howland.* Providence, R.I., 1837.

Stone, *B*   William L. Stone. *Border Wars of the American Revolution.* 2 vols., New York, 1864.

Stone, *W*   William L. Stone. *The Campaign of Lieut. Gen. John Burgoyne and the Expedition of Lieut. Col. Barry St. Leger.* Albany, N.Y., 1877.

Stryker, *F*   W. S. Stryker. *The Forts on the Delaware.* Trenton, N.J., 1901.

Stryker, *M*   W. S. Stryker. *The Battle of Monmouth.* Princeton, 1927.

Stryker, *TP*   W. S. Stryker. *The Battles of Trenton and Princeton.* Boston, 1898.

Sullivan   *Letters and Papers of Major-General John Sullivan . . .* 3 vols., Concord, N.H., 1930–1939.

Sullivan, *J*   *Journals of the Military Expedition of Maj. Gen. John Sullivan Against the Six Nations of Indians.* Auburn, N.Y., 1887.

Swett   S. Swett. *History of the Bunker Hill Battle.* Boston, 1827.

Swiggett   Howard Swiggett. *War Out of Niagara.* New York, 1933.

Sydney   William C. Sydney. *England and the English in the Eighteenth Century.* 2 vols., London, 1892.

Tallmadge   *Memoir of Colonel Benjamin Tallmadge.* Boston, 1876.

Tarbox   I. N. Tarbox. *Life of Israel Putnam.* Boston, 1876.

Tarleton   Banastre Tarleton. *A History of the Campaigns of 1780 and 1781 . . .* Dublin, 1787.

Thacher   James Thacher. *Military Journal of the American Revolution . . .* Hartford, Conn., 1862.

Thruston   R. C. Ballard Thruston. *The Origin and Evolution of the United States Flag* (U. S. Pub. Docs., 69th Congress, 1st Sess., House Doc. 258). Washington, 1926.

Tower   Charlemagne Tower. *The Marquis de La Fayette in the American Revolution . . .* 2 vols., Philadelphia, 1895.

Townsend   Joseph Townsend. "Some Account of the British Army . . . and of the Battle of Brandywine," *Bulletin of the Hist. Soc. of Pa.,* Vol. I, No. 7 (Sept., 1846), pp. 17–29.

Trevelyan   George O. Trevelyan. *The American Revolution.* 6 vols. (including *George III and Charles Fox,* numbered V and VI), London, 1909–1914.

Tyler   Moses C. Tyler. *The Literary History of the American Revolution, 1763–1783.* 2 vols., New York, 1941.

Uhlendorf   Bernard Uhlendorf, editor. *The Siege of Charleston . . .* Ann Arbor, Mich., 1938.

Van Doren   Carl Van Doren. *Secret History of the American Revolution.* New York, 1941.

Van Doren, *M*   Carl Van Doren. *Mutiny in January.* New York, 1943.

Van Tyne   C. H. Van Tyne. *The War of Independence: American Phase* Boston, 1929.

Van Tyne, *C*   C. H. Van Tyne. *The Causes of the War of Independence.* Boston, 1922.

Van Tyne, *L*   C. H. Van Tyne. *The Loyalists in the American Revolution.* New York, 1902.

Waldo   "Valley Forge, 1777–1778: Diary of Surgeon Albigence Waldo," *Pa. Mag. of Hist. and Biog.,* XXI (1897), 299–323.

Walpole   Mrs. Paget Toynbee, editor. *The Letters of Horace Walpole.* 19 vols., Oxford, 1903–1925.

Walton   Joseph S. Walton. "George Washington in Chester County," *Chester Co. Hist. Soc. Bulletin,* 1899–1900.

Walworth   Ellen H. Walworth. *Battles of Saratoga, 1777.* Albany, N.Y., 1891.

Watson, E   Elkanah Watson. *Men and Times of the Revolution.* New York, 1856.

Watson, J   John F. Watson. *Annals of Philadelphia, and Pennsylvania.* 3 vols., Philadelphia, 1927.

Weelen   Jean-Edmond Weelen. *Rochambeau.* New York, 1936.

Wells   "Journal of Bayze Wells . . ." *Conn. Hist. Soc. Colls.,* VII, 239–296. Hartford, 1899.

Whitton   F. E. Whitton. *The American War of Independence.* New York, 1931.

Wildes   H. E. Wildes. *Anthony Wayne.* New York, 1941.

Wilkin   W. H. Wilkin. *Some British Soldiers in America.* London, 1914.

Wilkinson   James Wilkinson. *Memoirs of My Own Times.* 3 vols., Philadelphia, 1816.

Willcox   William B. Willcox. "The British Road to Yorktown: A Study in Divided Command," *American Historical Review,* LII (Oct., 1946), 1–35.

Willcox, S   William B. Willcox. "British Strategy in America, 1778," *Journal of Modern History,* XIX (June, 1947), 97–121.

Winsor   Justin Winsor. *Narrative and Critical History of America.* 8 vols., Boston, 1884–1889.

Wirt   William Wirt. *Sketches of the Life and Character of Patrick Henry.* Philadelphia, 1818.

Wraxall   *The Historical and the Posthumous Memoirs of Sir Nathaniel W. Wraxall, 1772–1784.* 5 vols., London, 1884.

INDEX